The Call of the Sea

The Call of the Sea

INCLUDING: *The Lost Sea*

NEW YORK

by Jan de Hartog

The Distant Shore AND *A Sailor's Life*

Atheneum

Author's Preface

THE THREE BOOKS IN THIS VOLUME (FOUR, IF THE TWO PARTS OF THE *Distant Shore* are considered separately, as they were in Europe) are the first I wrote in English. Occasionally I have, in a review, been over-flattered by a comparison with Joseph Conrad; in reality, however, my case is more like that of Arthur Koestler, who began to write in Hungarian, then shifted to German, continued in French and ended up writing in English. I had published a dozen books and several plays in Dutch before I changed over to English.

The Lost Sea was the first; I dictated it in Paris in 1949; until then I had written only dialogue in English. It made me discover, for the first time, the joy of writing in this language, which is a musician's joy rather than a poet's or a painter's. It is like a superb Renaissance-built cello of amazing warmth and range; my only trouble was that I could not read music, I had to hum my composition for someone else to write down. I have been asked occasionally why I dictated such a fragile, delicate story, why I did not write it down myself, as I had done with all my previous books. The reason is that, at that time, I did not know how to spell.

The book was published in 1951 by Harper in New York, where my friend Michael Bessie was then Senior Editor; I was to follow him later to his own company, Atheneum, which is now publishing this edition. The press was without exception kind and even enthusiastic; as a matter of fact, never since have I had such a reception. The book was illustrated by Joseph Low and looked so exquisite that it received an award from the A.I.G.A. as one of the best-designed books of the year—the first to receive this distinction among Harper books for several years. Despite all this, its commercial success was slender, to say the least. If there is a moral here, I have been unable to decide which one. It depends on how I feel.

The first part of *The Distant Shore* was written immediately after *The Lost Sea*. It too was dictated and it is also told in the first person singular, which at the time was easier for me after my theatrical experience in English, as, in a sense, a story told by a narrator is a monologue. It has given many people the impression that it is an autobiographical story, like *The Lost Sea* and also *A Sailor's Life*. This is not so; though there are elements in it that are based on my own experience, as there are in all books, it is by and large a fairly accurate rendition of something I witnessed rather than lived through myself. In the Dutch edition, where the first part was published under the title *Stella* and the second as *Thalassa*, I thought it necessary to add this note:

"As the story is based on the experiences of a Dutch sailor, who would give permission to use it only on condition he and his friends could not possibly be recognized, I have in 'OTWA' created a fictional organization which embodies aspects of all Dutch fighting units during the Second World War."

This is a fair description, as I used the mentality and the organization of the Dutch MTB flotilla that operated in the North Sea and the English Channel, the work of the Dutch salvage tugs on the Western Approaches, and the locale of the European Section of the Royal Dutch Airlines, which kept up a virtually suicidal service with unarmed civilian planes on the Bristol-Lisbon-Cairo route. I took pains, however, to keep well within the limits of probability; when eventually Sir Carol Reed made a film of the first part under the title *The Key*, the British Navy gave full cooperation, which it would not have done had the story been a mere flight of fancy.

It is one of the ironies of the writing business that in the rare instances where an author uses a personal experience virtually without "correcting nature" he will usually be reprimanded for stretching the reader's credulity. This happened in the case of the second part of *The Distant Shore*, particularly the section dealing with the deep-sea diving in the Mediterranean. Many people told me that they thought the burlesque schooner with the piano on the aft deck and the crew of fantastic creatures altogether too farfetched. This happens to be the one episode in the whole book that is strictly true. I must confess, however, that I see their point: I didn't believe it myself when it happened to me, and if it weren't for the fact that some members of that crew and I are still good friends and in frequent correspondence, I would have concluded that the whole thing must have been a pink mirage. It was, in more respects than one, among the least sober episodes in my life.

The Distant Shore was published in 1952; later Pocket Books issued a paper edition in two volumes entitled *Stella* and *The Sea;* after the movie was made, the first part was renamed *The Key*. To make matters even more complicated, in southeastern Europe, where the book for some

vi

reason had a much more spectacular success than anywhere else, a one-volume edition of *The Distant Shore* was published under the title *The Convoy Cantata*.

A Sailor's Life has this in common with the two previous books: it deals with a world that has vanished forever. I was not aware of this when, in response to the excessively polite letter of the German youth who wanted to go to sea which is mentioned in its introduction, I set out to write a "Young Sailor's Vade Mecum." Only after I had completed the collection and given it to friends at sea to read was it pointed out to me that the scruffy old freighter I describe, as well as the old rescue tugs and windjammers, were virtually all sunk during the Second World War. Even if the Young Sailor wanted to, he would be unable to find the type of washstand I give him full instructions for, and the last merchant marine vessel to carry a lamp-trimmer was taken out of circulation in 1943. This came rather as a shock to me; I had, so far, only felt old in connection with the Zuiderzee, which changed beyond recognition during my lifetime. Now I suddenly had to recognize the melancholy fact that not only my childhood, but my young manhood as well had taken place in another century: the age of steam in the latter case, sail in the former. I had it brought home to me in several sea stories written by otherwise experienced seamen that they obviously had never known the most distinctive characteristics of the sailing ship: first its motion, which was virtually always perpendicular, though the world was permanently lopsided to either port or starboard, depending what tack you were on; then its sound, made up of creakings and moanings, swishings and sighs, which made the sea outside seem much nearer. When the wind began to blow in its sixes and sevens, a multi-toned hooting, humming and fluting would result that set the whole hull aquiver, as if you were being carried inside a huge, muted French harp. Owing to their cathedrals of canvas exposed to the tremendous pressure of the wind, the old ships rarely rolled the way even the largest modern liners do. Their pitching, too, was less pronounced, as they sliced through the waves with considerably more grace than their motorized successors; a clipper ship running at fourteen knots downhill hardly pulled a stern wave. It was the graceful, almost majestic up-and-down movement as she was lifted and lowered by the long, slow swell that was most characteristic of the windjammer, and I have never felt it quite like that on any other vessel—only, occasionally, in an airplane. It makes me feel very old indeed.

Not that I regret the great birds' passing; I have never before or since been so abjectly sick with fear as when I had to go up and out on a heaving spar to help furl a sail. It still occasionally happens to me in a nightmare that I hear the bosun's voice: "One hand for yourself, one for the company! And *don't* look down!" The voice somehow seems to belong to another species, half man, half bird, to which I never quite belonged. Up there, the suggestion of being carried off by a huge, angry bird became almost an hallucination; only a beetle inadvertently carried aloft by a swan and clinging in breathless panic to the shaft of one of its wing feathers can have shared my terror. But occasionally, at sea, gazing out over the wake at the distant horizon, I still imagine I see one, ghostly wraith between ocean and sky, shadowing us from afar as was their wont. It was another peculiarity that no one seems to have written down and that now has been forgotten completely: the old sailing ships stuck much closer together, not within hailing distance, but within sight. Maybe the wind had something to do with it: each captain tried to make the most of it and so they usually all came up with more or less the same course; but also, as I said before, the sea was so much closer, the ship so much more at the mercy of powers vastly superior to its own strength, man had to take into account so many minute shifts in nature's mood and temper, that one overriding emotion of those centuries at sea was a sense of smallness and utter dependence on the whims of fortune. If, during the last half century, there has been a steady decline in what is commonly called "religion," a large part of it is due to the circumstance that man, at least at sea, has nothing left to fear except his brother, lurking under the surface with enough poised violence to incinerate whole cities. If the old windjammer did not make you religious, it made you an atheist, which, seen from our point in space, amounts to virtually the same thing. The element that is lost in the process of mechanization is man's humility, which may well have been the key to his survival. "Thy sea is so large and my ship is so small" has become a cute little motto to be screwed onto the bulkheads of cabin cruisers, where once it was the only thought, roaming idiotically and with spiraling intensity in the vacant brain of the jelly-kneed apprentice, left alone on the poop while the officer of the watch, gone down to "listen to the leak," seemed to have fallen asleep or overboard. Those were moments of unequaled religious intensity as the deserted young man, quaking on the quarterdeck, frantically promised perpetual chastity to the Almighty God if only He saw to it that the huge, evil hummingbird would remain unaware that all he could come up with in case she were to decide to take off on her own was to burst into tears and bawl for the skipper.

The writing of *A Sailor's Life* was, without doubt, my most enjoyable, most gratifying labor as an author. Once I had found the knack of how

viii

to cope with the congenital garrulity of middle age, when everything begins to remind you of something else, I had a wonderful time reminiscing and philosophizing. The knack was, really, a gimmick which I stumbled upon with the nonchalant guilelessness of a stroller on the beach. Plagued by the inveterate compulsion to string everything together and thus end up inside the Gordian knot of my own knitting yarn, I suddenly hit upon the complete and definitive solution, which I hereby present to all would-be compilers of memoirs, aphorisms or other travelogues of life: I made a list of all the subjects as they came to mind; then I wrote each subject on a separate strip of paper, rolled the strips into little balls, put them all in an empty cookie tin and every morning asked my wife to shake it and pull one for me. That was the subject I would write about, at once, without having had a chance to lie awake the night before, thinking about it and planning. The result was complete peace of mind when not writing, and benign bonhomie while writing, which must sound like the Hereafter to all authors' wives.

The three books in this volume share one characteristic: they all have, besides their major theme, a secondary one, running concurrently, and that is "the handling of ships." *The Lost Sea, The Distant Shore, A Sailor's Life*—part of each is devoted to descriptions of the sheer technical aspect of how to handle a ship. So the title *The Call of the Sea*, under which the three are now united, is an apt one: here are three books that are, each in its own way, at least in part a product of the writer's fascination with ships and the sea. It is, in essence, a mate's fascination; there comes a time when a man, provided he sticks with it, will no longer be fascinated by the sheer technical ability of handling ships for the simple reason that, finally, he has mastered it completely. Captains want to talk about Life, and Death, and God, and the Meaning Of It All, rather than about counterwinds when mooring in the lee of a sea wall, or to which side your arse will swing when churning full astern with the tide. The best example of what it means to be a captain, in all its aspects, is the maneuver I once observed on board a freighter, one of a convoy, obeying the command to scatter and anchor in forty fathoms of water on the luff shore of Bermuda in a fairly strong wind. All other ships worked their way cautiously and somewhat nervously toward the shore, sounding all the time, finally to anchor. The freighter, under the command of an old, overweight master prone to pensiveness, never awoke from its habitual, peaceable snooze. The captain simply told the mate to pay out forty fathoms of chain, stopped the engine and left it to the wind to calmly cradle his slumbering ship, anchor dangling in the deep, toward the shore, knowing that it would bite and hold the moment it reached the forty-fathom line. It took about three quarters of an hour, which he spent explaining to me the technique of natural childbirth, of which his youngest daughter was a devotee. Judging by the results, she was as relaxed as he.

The call of the sea ceases only when it is finally obeyed.

Contents

The Lost Sea

THE TRUE CHARACTER OF A NATION COMES OUT IN ITS CHILDREN'S SONGS. As a ten-year-old, at school in Holland, I sang with the class in triple descant about a little horseman who fell in love with a little maiden and betrayed her. The little maiden went into a nunnery, the little horseman came to take her out with three of his friends; after they had found the nunnery locked and the little maiden had addressed them through a peephole, they dragged up a blunderbuss and razed the nunnery to the ground. When the little maiden came, blackened, out of the ruins and still did not want to marry the little horseman, he shot himself, and his three friends became monks.

We sang this song beautifully, without wondering at its contents. One fell in love, one betrayed, one blew up nunneries and one was overcome by remorse; that seemed to be the way of the world we were about to enter.

A windy world of narrow streets lined with nets drying, leading to the harbor with its forest of masts and its quay silver with the scales of fish. To us ten-year-olds this world was peopled with giants who never seemed to notice us at all. When we were playing on the quay our game was constantly interrupted by huge barrels crashing down from the ships onto the cobbles, scattering us as if we were sparrows. When we were playing at marbles on the sidewalk, and so absorbed in our game that we had momentarily lost our sparrow's alertness, we would suddenly duck with terror as one of the giants stepped right over us on his way to his ship. When we took off our clogs to go into a house or a shop and we looked at them in the row of giants' clogs outside, we felt painfully small.

We would play at being big. We'd strut along the streets with the giants' swagger, and call at each other: "Oi-oi, Dirk!" or "Wind's changing, Karel!" But we could never keep that up for long, for then the mist-gun would boom, or a burst of hammering from the yard would rattle the

3

silence, or a true giant would round the corner like a jammer turning in the wind; and we would scatter, sparrows again, the clatter of our clogs streaking down to the harbor like a gust of hail.

We had many games, but we always played at being grownups. We picked up wooden shoes, thrown away by the giants, and rigged them as ships, numbered with the famous numbers of the fastest botters from our village, for Huizen was famous for the speed of its ships. We would send the clogs fishing in the dead end of the harbor, where the driftwood and the pink corpses of cats were gently rocked by the tide that swirled outside. We would split into two groups, one of Huizers, and the other of Volendammers. The Huizers would lie peacefully fishing among the Brasso tins and the cats, and suddenly the Volendammers would swoop down on them, get caught in their nets, and cause havoc, and tear sails, and we would dance on the quay screaming like sea gulls, and yet there was nothing to see but half a dozen waterlogged old clogs dumbly rocking among the refuse.

Any stranger from beyond the harbor or the tramway station wouldn't have understood at all what we were playing at. To the strangers the Zuider Zee was a picturesque little inland sea which was born in 1302, when the great Elizabeth Flood swept half of Holland, and which would die in 1931 when the big dam thrown across its entrance would be completed, after which the sea would be reclaimed and turn into land again. Occasionally strangers from even further away would pass through the village in big buses, or enter the harbor in motorboats painted white and gold. They would crowd the streets for a while, men with spectacles and women with painted mouths, speaking a funny language and wearing outlandish clothes, pointing cameras at old Henk on his way from the smokery with his arms full of eels, or at mad Barbara who had lost three sons at sea and who was called "Crabby" because her madness made her walk sideways. They would also point their cameras at the giants' ships lying in the harbor; but then a yell would burst from the forest of masts and clogs and stones would be thrown at them, and the voices of the giants would holler: "Get out of here, dirty red lips! Away, ye whores of Babylon!" Then the strangers would be rounded up quickly by their shepherds and herded back on board their motorboat, or to the market where the bus was, pursued by us, crying shrilly: "Get out of here," and "Whores of Babylon," until they were gone.

The tourists came to marvel at the quaint old costumes, the little streets, the baggy trousers and mad Crabby, who after her last son died began showing her bed to strangers for a penny, saying that the Black Skipper

4

had slept in it. The tourists didn't know about the Black Skipper. Like the strangers from nearer home they knew what they were going to see before they got there, and so they never saw the truth. The Zuider Zee was pretty to look at; anyone sailing along its coast in a white motorboat and looking at the little red and green towns in the flamingo-colored haze of the dawn thought it a pity that this wonderful world of sunlight and water should be doomed to turn back into land.

To the people in the villages it was more than a pity, for they were doomed themselves. The Zuider Zee, still the richest fishing ground of northern Europe, where the herring were so thick and sometimes the shoals made the shallow sea boil, would turn brackish with the growing of the dam. The two thousand botters of the little towns along the coast, which had hardly been able to cope with the harvest for six centuries, would find less and less to catch. The result would be poverty, and an even bitterer competition between the local fleets.

Now the most ferocious competition was between the Volendammers and the Huizers. They owned the biggest ships and had been enemies since the great flood, for the Volendammers were Catholics and the Huizers Protestants, and the Volendammers fished before the wind, dragging a single net, whereas the Huizers fished in pairs, drifting cross-seas, dragging their net between them. The two always got in each other's way.

The tourists, photographing a bunch of little boys in quaint costumes, playing with ships made of wooden shoes in the dead end of the harbor, heard our shrill cries and the clatter of our clogs when we danced with excitement, and thought we were just children at play. They had never heard of pairs of Huizer botters quietly fishing at sunrise, their long shallow nets stretched between them, their crews asleep; and then the sudden red cloud of the Volendammers' sails descending upon them out of the dawn. The Volendammers, groaning with sail, would pass between the pairs of sleeping Huizers, dragging their sharp triangular net at great speed, and try to cut the nets of the enemy with the sharp cables of their draggers. But the Huizers' nets were strong; the Volendammers who tried to cut them would be braked by the impact, their topsails would come crashing down, bollards would splinter, burning stoves in the fo'c'sles would topple over, filling the pokey cabins with screams and smoke. Then the crews of the two Huizers and the crew of the Volendammer would scramble aft and start hauling in their nets frantically, trying to be the first to reach the center of the tangle. Whoever reached that first would cut the other man's net; but usually all three would arrive there at the same moment. Then a battle would begin, the ferocity of which was

5

echoed by the sea gull screeches of dancing children on the quays for months to come. The crews would lash out at each other with handspikes and poles, and when they got nearer with hatchets and knives. They would board each other's ship, fighting; the Volendammers would throw burning wads of cotton waste drenched in paraffin on board the Huizers' ships; the Huizers would crowd in on them brandishing the pole with the sharp hook they used for hauling in their nets. They would try to slam that hook in the top of the Volendammer's mainsail just underneath the leech, for if they managed to do that and hung at the pole with their full three men's weight, the sail would be torn down to the bottom, the wind would burst it and blow it right out of the leeches.

If that happened the Volendammer was lost. The mainsail was his heart; once that was cut out, the big evil bird would lie fluttering in the wind, turning aimlessly. Once a Volendammer saw his mainsail go he wept and gave in; then the Huizers would tear the baggy trousers off the vanquished and beat their bare behinds until they howled with pain and humiliation. They would tear all the sails, smash up the cabin, set fire to the beds, cut the net at its roots and leave the smoking wreck to be picked up by its countrymen. The Volendammers' trousers would be stored away until the Huizer fleet sailed home; then, when the ships swung into the harbor one by one, the crowd lining the quay would cheer and wave when they saw on the flag line of the victor the trousers of the slain enemy flapping bulkily in the breeze.

We children of Huizen had seen this several times, and those were the moments in which to be grownup seemed a state of glory. Oh, for the day that we ourselves would sail into the harbor with our ship, and see the quay thick with the white bonnets and the multicolored shawls of the women and the girls, and hear that big sickening roar of glory roll toward us like sunlight driven by a sailing cloud. That was what we played, when we danced at the dead end of the harbor and the tourists pointed their cameras at us and we screamed: "Get out of here, whores of Babylon." That was life, the world that lay ahead of us: the red clouds of the Volendammer sails, the terrible fight among banging beams and billowing smoke, the screams of the wounded, the home-coming in the sunset with all the world shouting: "Hurray! Down with the Catholics! Glory to the Black Skipper! Hurray!" We all wanted to grow up to be the Black Skipper, for the Black Skipper was the only one who always won.

The Black Skipper was the King of Huizen; a blue-eyed giant of incredible age with gold rings in his ears, and a black astrakhan cap on the back of his white-haired head. His ship was the HZ 69, one of the two

6

largest among the hundred that homed at Huizen. The other big one was the HZ 55, sailed by Arie Kos, the Black Skipper's fishing partner. Everybody around the Zuider Zee knew the Black Skipper's name, and the children of Volendam were in terror of him without ever having set eyes on him. When the children of Volendam were naughty, their mothers said: "Go to sleep, or I'll sell you to the Black Skipper!" and there wouldn't be another squeak out of them until dawn.

We children of Huizen knew the Black Skipper well. Wherever he went on the rare occasions that he was home he drew a wake of silence through the streets full of playing kids. We would follow him, a silent body at a distance, to see which bed he would sleep in that night. He would turn around after a while, hearing the rumbling of a hundred tiny clogs behind him, and say: "Go home." The clogs would splatter, with the sound of a barrel thrown into the harbor; and then we would peer round corners and below the hedges of the drying nets, and see him knocking, and hear his voice: "Hello, love," when a woman opened her door. He never said a name, he only said: "Love," and the wise ones among us whispered that this was because he couldn't remember any names. Mad Crabby showed her bed to strangers for a penny, saying that the Black Skipper had slept there as if it was something special. That was because she was mad.

The legend was that there wasn't a spinster or a widow, young or old, sad or gay, in whose bed the Black Skipper had not slept. None but one: the widow of the lighthouse keeper of the Island of Schokland, who had taken over her dead man's job.

One day long ago the Black Skipper had sailed into her lonely port, rattled the door of the lighthouse to ask for water, and she had thrown the water on his head from the top window of her tower. The Black Skipper had been as angry as the little horseman; he had gone back to the HZ 69, taken out an ice bomb used to burst the pack ice in the winter, and blown her door out of its hinges. Out of the blackened hole, after the white smoke had lifted, the woman came with an oar in her hands and pushed him into the harbor. Ever since that day, whenever the HZ 69 passed Schokland's lighthouse, the Black Skipper was said to shake his fist at the white tower and shout: "I'll have you yet one day!"

This was the legend, and there were many legends about the Black Skipper. So many that he moved among us like an aging god, turning the grownups into sparrows like us, because he never noticed them. And that was why the children loved him: in the light of his setting sun even the smallest objects threw long shadows.

WHILE I WAS STILL A LITTLE BOY AMONG THE HUNDREDS, I DREAMED LIKE all of us only of growing up. In school we were told that we were growing up all the time, every day a little bit, and that if we waited long enough, one day we would be giants ourselves. We didn't believe this; we believed in a magic moment somewhere ahead of us, when we would suddenly be admitted into the real world, the world beyond the harbor. To us to be grown up meant to sail.

For the real life of the giants was not lived ashore. They came home every two months or so to sleep, all three hundred of them, and they seemed to be sleeping even when they walked the streets. Every time the women said that the fleet would stay home for a week, and when the giants arrived they contradicted this and said they would stay for a fortnight; but they never stayed longer than three days. One morning, soon after their arrival, we would be woken up by a great sound of anchor chains, and when we shot out of bed and clattered to the harbor, hundreds of breathless little kids, capless, buttoning their coats as they ran, we would find the quay full of angry women and weeping girls. The black birds of the botters would spread their wings and sail out into the pink haze of the sunrise, the sky vast and green above them. They would sail out with hoarse cries and hollered shouts of: "Go home!"; the women would shout back with high, angry voices until the last of the botters had rounded the pier. Then a great chill of loneliness would come out of the empty harbor, there would be a silence which lasted until one woman began to cry: "Good-by," and then the multicolored shawls would start waving at the sunrise, as if all the women on the quay had suddenly become twice their size, and the good-bys would mount in volume and in ardor until they sounded like a chord on a big organ. We children, who didn't know what it was all about, would always catch the sadness and

8

the love of that last chorus, and we would weep with the women because it was beautiful.

The months that the village was a women's village only were dreary and slow. We would play our games and go to school and sing in triple descant behind the steamed windows, but behind our games and behind our songs was always the great longing for that magic moment. We were children waiting to be born.

The law said that no child could sail or work until he was fourteen, but this was not true. The magic moment could come any time between the ages of ten and twelve, for every botter from every port around the Zuider Zee carried, apart from its crew of three or six, two secret people: a cat and a little boy. The cats were occasionally seen when the fleet was home: big ugly monsters the size of dogs, with cauliflower ears and broken tails, covered with patches of tar. The children were never seen; because they were illegal they were kept out of sight, and that was why they were called "sea mice."

Every boy was waiting for the moment when he would be turned from a sparrow into a sea mouse, but nobody could say when that moment would come; it depended on whether there was a vacancy. Sea mice grew up into sea boys or drowned. One day the mother of Kris Muis, who had sung with our class and vanished, was seen weeping in the streets without her bonnet, running with her hair losing its pins; people said that was because her son had been killed by a sea lion. We weren't sad at all that Kris Muis was dead; we weren't even frightened by the sea lion; we were jealous of the one who would take his place and who didn't yet know it himself.

Nobody knew how sea mice were chosen. Some said you had to go and hide on board a ship that had lost its sea mouse; others that if you waited at the dead end of the harbor until the dusk became night, the skipper would come and pick one. We tried to hide as soon as a ship came in that had lost its sea mouse; but there were too many of us, and we were always chased away. When the fleet was in we loitered at the dead end of the harbor and got frightened and cold in the gathering darkness; some of us would go home, the others were rounded up by the women. It was a mystery how the botters got their sea mice, what miracle had happened to the boy whose name would be called in vain at the beginning of school the morning after the fleet left.

I was ten years old when the miracle happened to me. It was a miracle so vast and unbelievable that thinking of it still fills me with pride and wonder, for I became the sea mouse of the Black Skipper.

9

HUIZEN HAD NO ORPHANAGE. WHENEVER THERE WERE CHILDREN WHOSE parents had died, they were taken into the families of relatives.

As everybody in the village was related in some way or other, there was never much difficulty in finding a home for waifs. But through the years it had become the custom to concentrate the waifs around widows.

There were widows who, when their husbands drowned, were left behind with one child, and who within a couple of years found themselves mothering a family of sixteen. Sometimes these families got too large for one woman; it depended on what she could take. Annie Snoek, for instance, had never less than a dozen and yet she was always cheerful, singing all day and laughing, and whenever you passed her house there was a smell of something delicious from the kitchen. Her children were noisy but nice to have as friends; although she hadn't brought them into the world she somehow gave them a bit of her light.

Mother Bout, however, who never had more than three, couldn't cope with them at all, perhaps because she was too thin. She ran her house like a prison. There were times for everything and she stuck to them as if the universe depended upon it. If we were five minutes late for dinner she would breathe through her teeth; if we played on the quay too late at night she'd bring the time home to us with a shiver as we heard her running through the streets screeching like an owl. Originally she must have been a nice woman, otherwise she would never have taken us in; but after we had gone to bed, all three of us in one cupboard bed, and she vanished with her candle through the hatch in the attic floor, hissing: "Say your prayers or I'll smack you!" we prayed to God that he might make Mother Bout break a leg.

She had no favorites among us, but she had scapegoats. The scapegoats changed about every month; one month Bulle Groot would be the cause of anything that went wrong, the next it would be me, the one after that Jaap Bros. The last time it was me was because of an arrow.

We had made a bow of a broken fishing rod, and two arrows of bullrushes with fishing hooks for heads and plumes at their tails. In the courtyard behind the house was an open washing place: a corner screened off by a thin wall of dry rushes. Inside a watering can was suspended from a little gallows, a rope attached to its spout; if you pulled the rope you had a shower. We had painted a bull's eye on the screen around the washing place; the morning it happened two of us pulled the bow taut, Bulle Groot held the arrow and I shouted: "Fire!" The arrow swished off with a zing, pierced the screen, and from behind it came such a bloodcurdling yell of agony that we nearly died on our feet. Before Mother Bout had appeared around the corner of the screen, we were already halfway to the harbor, carrying our clogs to run faster.

When we finally piled up in the dank straw in the hidden corner behind the smokery, three panting bodies shivering with fright, I asked: "Where do you think we hit her?" Jaap Bros said: "In her behind." Bulle said: "She hasn't got one." We were very brave, joking about her and giggling, huddled close together in the straw; but we came home very late. She sat waiting for us in the lamplight, her spectacles on the tip of her nose which gave her a second set of eyes. She looked straight at me and said: "I know who did this." I was sent to bed without dinner; Bulle hid some bread for me under his shirt, and I munched it in the darkness after she had gone down with her candle. Bulle said: "From now on it's you," and I knew he was right.

Two days later the fleet came home. I wasn't allowed to go out, but Bulle and Jaap helped me climb through the attic window. I went to the harbor with a feverish feeling, shouting and running as soon as I was out of her earshot. I did all sorts of crazy things that night; I threw stones at cats, made faces at mad Crabby, chased Jaap along the quay, snatched off his cap and threw it in the harbor.

The moment I had done that I was sorry and frightened; we tried to fish it out but the tide carried it away. We followed it along the pier, throwing stones at it, trying to force it inland; when at last it had got within reach it was nearly sunk. Bulle and Jaap both held my left hand while I bent over as far as possible to grab it; then Bulle slipped, Jaap let go of me, and I fell headlong into the harbor.

I couldn't have been in the water for longer than a few seconds, but it seemed very long. My eyes were wide open and I saw a swaying trunk of air go up from my mouth to the surface of the green glassy water. I don't remember choking or being afraid; I just felt as a man must feel the second after he is beheaded: very surprised, seeing a last vision. I remember seeing a wonderful black botter sailing out, its wings covering the sun, and a man in a red cloak standing at the helm, his arms crossed, steering with the small of his back. The man was me, but not really me; he was the promise inside me which would have been fulfilled one glorious day if I hadn't been drowned in the harbor.

Bulle and Jaap pulled me ashore. The world reeled around me: water turned into sky, the botters in the harbor seemed to stand swaying upside down on their thin masts like toadstools. I felt a choking pressure on my chest, and that was the first moment I struggled; the pressure was Bulle who had sat down on top of me because had been taught at school that was the thing to do with a drowned man, to get the water out of his lungs. No water came out of me, only a shrill cry of pain and fear, and the odd thing about that cry was that I called "Mem!" the name by which Mother Bout insisted we should call her.

As soon as Bulle had got off me I got up and saw the water and the sky drop back into their places. The botters lay upright in the harbor again, their masts pointing at the green evening sky, and from the sea the night came creeping in with the blue haze of the dusk. It was a wonderful world to look at; I felt a rush of happiness and gratitude that I had returned to it.

But reality oozed back into that void of happiness with a feeling of fear that soon grew into panic: the reality of Mem's anger on finding out that I had escaped from my confinement, of the wet clothes and Jaap's lost cap, which could still be seen, a small black dot bobbing peacefully toward the night. If only my clothes hadn't been wet, I might have climbed back through the attic window the way I had come; Jaap could say about the loss of his cap that the wind had blown it away.

We decided, all three of us, that we must dry my clothes quickly; whatever happened, no matter how late we got home, we must dry my clothes. While I started to undress on the seaward side of the pier, where we couldn't be seen from the shore, Bulle and Jaap gathered some driftwood which the high tide had left in the cracks between the huge pieces of basalt which the pier was made of. The wood had lain there for weeks bleaching in the sun, and was quite dry.

We made a fire with Jaap's three matches, put up a stick on either side of it and strung my belt between them. We hung my clothes over the belt, but the wind blew the flames from underneath them; occasionally there was a faint hissing sound like a kettle starting to boil. The waves lapped lazily against the pier, and withdrew with a soft gurgling sound in the cracks. From the harbor came distant shouts and laughter, and the hollow crunch of wood as the tide made the botters rub shoulders. A late sea gull circled gackering overhead, an unnerving gossipy sound, as if after having had a good look at us it would sail in one sweep to Mother Bout's house and tell her what it had seen.

We sat there until it was dark and the sounds from the harbor grew faint. The tide reached its turning point, the waves grew still and gurgled no more in the cracks. The hissing of my wet clothes when touched by the flames grew louder, until it sounded like a steam winch waiting. I grew colder and colder, sitting stark naked on the basalt, my knees drawn up under my chin, my arms around my legs. The numbness of the earth seemed to creep up inside me until I had become part of it: of the water, the stones, the dead seaweed glistening in the night.

In the end it felt as if I was living only with my eyes. The wind stirred my hair that was no longer part of me. I felt it like the pier must have felt the stirring of the frayed bits of old rope hanging from its rusty rings. I was beyond fear and hope, as if I would sit there forever: cast-iron child, with the world playing around it, like the mermaid on the village pump.

In the end Bulle and Jaap decided that they would go home; they would imitate my body in the cupboard bed with a pillow and a mop, and tell Mem I was asleep. I would wait where I was until my clothes were dry; Jaap and Bulle would take turns at keeping awake, and when they heard the soft screech of a sea gull outside they would open the attic window and let me in.

After they had left time came to a stop. Night had descended forever; I would never grow up any more but sit there, motionless, waiting for the dawn of Judgment Day. My eyes went on living, for I remember the warm softness of tears in them, but I never felt them going down my face. A pale half-moon arose on its back from the haze, until it floated in the night like a ship emerged. And then, as I sat there listening in my grave, the miracle happened.

I heard wooden steps approaching, but couldn't look around. The steps didn't bring back any fear or hope; I just listened and waited. The steps paused on the crown of the pier, and I felt someone looking at me. Then they came down, slithering on the seaweed, cracking the twigs of dead reed in the cracks as they crushed them. I saw two gigantic wooden shoes appear in the faint red glow of the dying fire. I saw striped stockings, blue and white, and the bottom of black breeches dissolving into night. Above

13

those there seemed to be a gap, but after looking long and intently I saw, somewhere high up, two gleams. They frightened me, because if they were eyes they were set very far apart.

When in the end I made out what they were it took me a long time to believe it; for this was the miracle. They weren't eyes: what reflected the glow of the fire was two little gold earrings. The giant who looked down on me was the Black Skipper.

I don't know how long it took him to speak, for I had lost all sense of time. When in the end he asked: "What are you doing here?" I couldn't answer. If he had come a few hours earlier, just after Jaap and Bulle had left, I would still have had the strength to flee, as we had done all our lives whenever he addressed us. Now I sat there, motionless, living only with my eyes, a sparrow with a broken wing.

He didn't say any more. After looking at me for a while, his face slowly taking shape in the moonlight, he bent over me and picked me up.

I squeaked for the last time: "Mem!" then I died in his arms. When I woke up I had turned into a sea mouse.

I WAS WOKEN UP BY A VERY ROUGH FEELING, AND THE STRONG SMELL of coffee. It felt as if I was a coffee bean among many being turned and shaken, being slowly sucked down to be crushed in a mill which was turned with a loud grinding noise. I couldn't get out of this nightmare of being a coffee bean; when I finally opened my eyes and squealed in terror, I saw two enormous sweaty faces bent over me, glistening in the oil light as if they had been blown with gold dust.

I recognized the Black Skipper and Krelis, his deckhand; both had black astrakhan caps on the backs of their heads and squatted underneath a wooden ceiling that was very low. They were rubbing me with large horny hands and I screamed in pain. The Black Skipper said: "All right, that'll do," and the words were heavy with the smell of tobacco and fish. They turned away and I followed them with my eyes, and then I saw where the smell of coffee came from.

I was lying in the big bunk in a botter's fo'c'sle. A little stove stood against the mast; on it a black coffee kettle was steaming. Krelis said: "What are we going to do with him?" and the Black Skipper answered: "Keep him." Then he poured coffee into a white mug and said: "It's such a devil of a job to find a mouse that I'm not going to let this one get away now I've got him." Krelis said: "Aye, let's hope he'll last longer than the others." The Black Skipper grunted as he sipped his coffee. "Have you found out yet how the others got away?" he asked. "No," said Krelis. "Somebody must have sneaked on board and let them out."

I hardly listened to the last things they said; it was the first that had made my mouth fall open: "It's such a devil of a job to find a mouse."

I couldn't believe my ears. All the boys of Huizen had wondered how to become a sea mouse, but one thought had never entered their heads: that the skippers should wonder as much how to get one. The secret must have been that we never offered ourselves alone; there were always scores

15

of us trying to sneak on board or offering ourselves in the dusk at the dead end of the harbor. The skippers never got hold of one of us alone, and they daren't choose one from a crowd for fear of being given away.

That realization was so complicated and so enormous, that I was about to fall asleep again from exhaustion, when I felt something heavy on four legs walk across my chest. I was too terrified to sit up. I just opened my eyes wide and saw it was an animal. I couldn't make out at first whether it was a dog or a cat; I saw it stand up on its hind legs, put up one paw toward a ring hanging from the ceiling, and suddenly with a loud bang a trap door fell open just beside me. The animal vanished through the square hole into the darkness beyond, from which came a seaweedy stench of wet ropes and bilge water.

It was a cat.

When I woke up again we were at sea. A dented square of sunlight slid to and fro on the cabin floor. There was a regular rattling, shoving and sloshing sound of the kettle moving on its stove, the lamp swinging, oil skins rubbing against the wall, and the bilge water in the gutter outside the door to the cockpit flowing from starboard to port. I felt as if all my insides had turned into water and were sloshing from port to starboard too. I had never been at sea before, and somehow the thought of being sick had never been connected in my mind with the magic moment.

As I lay there clenching my teeth, trying to keep my insides inside, the sliding patch of sunlight was darkened by a body stooping into the cabin. He was the third member of the crew of the HZ 69: a boy of about fifteen years of age whom I knew well enough by sight to know that he was called Bonk. In my eyes he was a man; he had big red hands and big red ears and very blue eyes wide apart in a freckled face underneath invisible eyebrows. He eyed me as cruelly as a fish, and said: "What are you doing in my bed, you little stinker? Scram where you belong!" He had a high piping voice like Mother Bout's, and I remembered having heard him singing a solo in the church choir last Christmas: "Where sheep may safely graze."

I didn't know where I belonged, and so I asked him. One of his big red hands flew up as if it had an independent life of its own, and he smacked me in the face. "Rat!" he cried as the smack rang out. "Whenever you address me you'll have to call me sir!" I said: "Yes, sir," and I bit my lip to keep it from trembling. He said: "Get your skeleton out of my bunk and go forrard!" I saw no forrard, so I asked: "Where, sir?" "Forrard!" he screamed. "Through the hatch! And hurry or I'll kick you through!" I crawled hastily into the square black hole, that had opened beside me when the cat had pulled the catch of the trap door the night before; as I did so the voice that once so soothingly had assured the sheep that they might safely graze screamed, "Hurry up!" and a big knobby stockinged foot hit me on the tailbone and shoved me down the hole. There was a sharp click of a lock snapping shut and darkness closed over me.

I lay trembling in that darkness for quite a while. It was full of creakings and crunchings and the sound of waves breaking against the bow. Every time the ship hit a wave there would be a hard resounding blow, setting everything aquiver—a sound so hard and loud that every time my heart nearly stopped as I thought we had hit a rock. The blows were accompanied by a metallic clank, as if a hammer hit an anvil. After a quarter of an hour of motionless, terrified listening I realized it was the ring of the anchor, clanking every time the ship reared.

It took me quite a while before I began to discern any shapes in the darkness. The first I saw were two faintly luminous disks very near, occasionally obscured as if something hid them. Then I realized it was the cat, sleepily blinking. When I began to see him more clearly I saw the most horrifying cat I had ever set eyes on.

His size was enormous, the pattern on his forehead so irregular that it made him look as if he squinted. He was, like all botter cats, covered so solidly with patches of tar that it coated him almost completely. Round the small of his back there was a distinct gap and this made him look as if he was wearing an ill-fitting suit. The suggestion of his wearing a suit was enhanced by the fact that he had no tail left at all; it looked as if he was wearing it tucked away inside his trousers. His claws were so dirty and broken and swollen with salt that he couldn't retract them any more; they looked like horrible little black fingers and clicked when he walked on something hard.

The very sight of him squinting at me with that bleary drunken gaze terrified me. When he yawned, opening his jaws wide enough for me to put my fist in, the smell of rotting fish he sent across to me was so overpowering that the seasickness lurched up inside me with a wave of nausea, and I vomited on the floor. The cat got up, arched its back, at which the gap between its coat and its trousers widened to a belt of bare pale skin, knelt down on its elbows and began lapping it up.

I rolled on my back, sicker than before, wishing to be dead. I saw that I was lying in what was called the cable hole: a triangular coffin of about a yard high, crammed with piles of curled-up ropes, disused nets, broken lamps, and frayed rope cushions. The ceiling was thick with glass floats in

17

nets, bunches of hooks strung together, blocks, holed pieces of cork on strings, all of them swaying jerkily with the sickening rise and fall of the bow of the ship. In the center of the biggest pile of rope was a sort of nest: a dog's basket of old clothes and cotton waste.

I dragged myself toward it; and the moment I curled up inside, the cat joined me. I was too sick to defend myself; I let the monster snuggle up against me with his horrible scratchy suit. It took him some time to find a comfortable position and then he began to purr. Never had I heard a cat purring louder. It was a deep roaring noise, like an engine. I tried to sleep again, but every time the ship rose it seemed to rear on its hind legs, to hover for a breath-taking second suspended in the air, after which it crashed headlong into a wave that seemed to consist of gravel. Every time we hit a wave the purring of the cat was interrupted by a hiccup; every time I thought we would never rise again.

It was a sad, despairing hour. In the end I lost all hope of ever seeing the sun again. I lay there gasping in the darkness, in the embrace of a monster, relentlessly being hammered to pulp. But after that hour, a hatch was opened among the rubble swinging at the ceiling, and I saw Krelis' enormous head silhouetted against the most beautiful background I ever saw.

It was the vast hollow expanse of a black triangular sail, reaching up to the sky: the jib of the HZ 69, the fastest botter of the fleet. The jib I had so often seen from afar, sailing into the harbor like a thunderous cloud.

And now the jib was mine. I was a man.

IT TOOK ME FOUR DAYS TO GET OVER MY SEASICKNESS, AND THEY WERE days on the rack. I was dressed in clothes that were too big for me; but Krelis cut off the legs of the breeches and the arms of the coat with a knife, and so they fitted me. I was put to work regardless of my condition, and the work was not helpful to one who constantly felt on the brink of vomiting.

When at night the nets were hauled in, and the silver of the catch poured into the cockpit until I was standing up to the hips in a boiling mass of squiggling, slithering herrings, I was given a little net of my own and told to pick the dinner. We fished for herring, but among the thousands of slender, silver green fish were occasionally found ugly flat flappers, sole or plaice. I was to pick those from the jumping silver while the men poured the herrings by the basketful into the "bun"—a large reservoir inside the ship in which the water was constantly refreshed from outside.

Usually there were about two dozen flappers among the herrings, but while the cockpit was still full it was difficult to catch them as I was immobilized by the squirming mass in which I stood half submerged. Every time I saw one but missed it, Bonk the boy saw it too, and he would never fail to throw a herring at my head. He seldom missed, and so in the end I stood there, shivering, numbed with the cold of the sea, covered with scales, my face dripping with slime and tears, heaving with dry choking sobs as there was nothing left inside me to vomit. Then I would be given a knife and told to prepare the dinner.

It was the most sickening job of all. I was told to get hold of the strong, struggling flappers one by one, press them down on the deck, cut their crunching heads off, slit open their bellies, and take the guts out. Murk, the cat, would sit waiting for me, his pink tongue slightly protruded, panting with anticipation; and the horrible crunching would go on as he chewed their heads with the side of his mouth, squinting up at me with the falseness of the jungle. After I had beheaded and gutted the flappers I had to scrape them, and that was the sound that invariably made me get up and stagger to the rail, which was half as high as I. I would pull myself up with a frantic effort, lift my chin on the gunwale and retch. At those moments the sea would seem to swirl around me until I felt like being sucked down by the whirl of dirty water emptying from a bath. The second time he saw me do this the Black Skipper said to me: "Don't kill yourself, child; be sick in the gutter," the first words he had spoken to me since the moment he took me in his arms.

Once the fish was ready to cook, I took it into the cabin, which would seem pitch-dark after the brilliance of the silver fish reflecting the sun; I would grope my way to the shelf on starboard, finger along the Bible, the candle, the skipper's spectacles, the broken alarm clock until I got to the jam jar in which the sail needles were kept. The needles should on no account get rusty, so they were kept in oil; this oil was used to fry the fish in. I would pour some of it into the frying pan, light the stove and put the pan on the fire. I had to hold on to it with both hands, for the catch was hauled in while we were lying cross-seas, and the ship would roll with colossal swayings. It was quite a job to keep the pan horizontal and prevent the oil from spilling on the stove; before I mastered it the cabin used to get so thick with evil-smelling blue smoke, that I had to dash out several times before the oil was hot enough to put the fish into.

The terrifying thing about frying flappers was that they seemed to come to life again. They would curl up and arch their backs as if in a horrible dream of life, but after a minute or so they would give up, stretch themselves quiveringly in the attitude of death and turn into food. Each of the men would have nearly half a dozen fish for his dinner, the rest of the meal consisted of potatoes. I had brought those to the boil before in a big iron pot, and after the water had boiled for a couple of minutes I put the pot in the hay chest and covered it with a pillow; when I took it out an hour later, the potatoes would be cooked to a turn. The pot was put in the center of the floor and I would pile up three stacks of half a dozen fish each on the bare board; then I'd stick my head out and call: "Skipper! Dinner!" and they would let everything drop and file into the cabin, leaving their clogs outside.

They squatted on the floor, each behind his own pile of fish; I'd hand the skipper the Bible and his spectacles. He'd open the book at random and read exactly ten lines, never mind where they began or where they ended, because it was all God's word. After that he would say: "God, thank you for the catch, guide the winds and keep the rain, and typhus to the Catholic pirates, Amen." After that they would eat silently and with great speed, picking potatoes from the pot with one hand and holding their fish with the other.

They would stack the bones neatly in front of them, while I poured the cooled-off oil back into the jam jar with the needles, put on the coffee kettle and took out the mugs and the tin of babblers. Babblers were square lumps of hard brown sugar; after they had finished their meal and the coffee had been poured into their mugs, they would pass the tin, put a babbler in their mouths, take a sip of coffee and rinse their mouths with it, the babblers clattering against their teeth. One babbler would do for two mugs; after those, they would lie down on their backs and suck the rest of it until it was gone.

Perhaps the lumps of sugar were called babblers because as they sucked them they would begin to talk. The quarter of an hour after dinner, while the three of them were lying on their backs, their hands behind their heads, blinking sleepily at the ceiling, was the time of the stories. They would discuss the catch, the weather, and women; during that quarter of an hour Murk the cat and I were supposed to clean the floor and to remove all traces of the meal. But Murk worked hardest at it, because he couldn't understand the human language; the stories meant nothing to him but the purrings of the big animals in whose nest he lived. I took a very long time wiping the mugs, cleaning and piling up the bones for Murk to take outside, for never in my life had I heard more fascinating stories.

It was a pity that the Black Skipper used to fall asleep so soon after the meal was ended, for his stories were the best of all. They were glimpses of the true giants' world, flashing visions of ferocious battles, of fights with sea lions the size of a man caught in the net on a cold October morning, of sunken villages whose churchbells still could be heard ringing when a gale turned the sea into a raging caldron; of women unlike Mother Bout or even Annie Snoek: so large and gay and pink and generous that a man felt like dying in their arms and understood the gospel in their kisses because they made him love all mankind. When Krelis began to talk about women it was different, but whenever the Black Skipper mumbled about them, the rest of his babbler clattering against his teeth, they seemed to be large pink angels, beyond fear and jealousy and anger, holding in their hands the keys to some promised land, which had to be taken away from them in a big struggle full of laughter and kisses and resounding smacks.

The Black Skipper's stories of women gave me my first wish to love. Somehow the fights with the Catholic pirates and the romps with the pink angels became one: an initiation, a glorious trial of ferocity and tenderness from which one would emerge as a giant at last. When at night the nets were out and we were drifting sideways along with the wind and I had finally curled up in my dog's basket in the cable hole, exhausted like Murk from a heavy day, I dreamed for a while, half awake half asleep, of what life would be like once I had reached the size and the power of the Black Skipper. It seemed a life glowing with memories, and one thing he said I never forgot until this day: "Only memories make for happiness." He said that to go through a thing for the first time was agony, the second time: boredom, but the third time: happiness. I began counting the experiences I went through: waking up in the morning, scrubbing the cabin floor, straightening the bed in which the three men slept like herrings in a cask—Bonk with his head between the feet of the skipper and Krelis; I tried to taste the happiness when I did these things for the third time, but it was very faint; perhaps the experiences were not big enough.

I waited impatiently for the big experiences to come, but they took a long time. Every day seemed to be exactly the same as the one before; the nets were hauled in at dawn, put out again at noon; I peeled the potatoes, boiled them and put them in the hay chest; I got the flappers, killed them, and watched them writhing in the boiling fat; then after the meal was over and the sleepy stories had been told, the nets would be hauled in again and a second day seemed to start before the sun had gone under: the stream of squiggling silver, the coldness of the sea mounting, squirming up to my hips, the herrings thrown in my face by Bonk, the desperate dashes of the jumping flappers in the slithering mass of herrings, slowly sliding from starboard to port with the rolling of the ship.

I never saw the sea for I was not allowed on the foredeck, and the rail was too high for me to look over. All I saw was the sky with the mast, the rigging, and the sails swaying in it. At nightfall when the sky turned green, another mast and another rigging would loom up beside us: the "buyer," the fastest ship of the fleet, carrying three times as much sail as the other botters and manned by six people. They would take over the living fish from all the botters of Huizen, count them by basketsful and store them in their vast hold. Then, when they were full, they would hoist every sail they had and race to the west, to Amsterdam, trying to be there ahead of the buyers of the other fleets, to be the first at the market in the morning and get the highest price.

I was longing to see the buyers racing; in my imagination it became a magnificent sight: more than a dozen ships, their hulks and their rigging hidden by a colored cloud of sail, foaming away toward the sunset, trying to beat each other by putting on more than their masts could carry. I had seen our buyer in the harbor: a colossal ship, its mast sheathed with iron, its stays as thick as my arm; but I never saw it at sea, for I was too small. Never was the agony of my smallness brought home to me more acutely than during those days; just over the edge, just beyond the black wall of the rail lay a wonderful glittering world of sea and ships and clouds and horizon; but whenever I tried to pull myself up to have a look at that promised land, Bonk kicked me or Krelis shouted or the Black Skipper said: "Don't kill yourself, child; be sick in the gutter."

I was jealous of Murk who was allowed to climb the foredeck and sit there, high up, licking himself in a hopeless effort to clean some of the tar away before he curled up and fell asleep, blind to the marvel of the world around him. I grew so jealous of him that I threw things at him when he fell asleep up there, on the very spot where I longed to go more than anywhere else; but then Bonk would smack me and shout: "Rat! What do you mean by pestering dumb animals? I'll teach you!" and he would go on punching me and kicking me in the side with his knee until Krelis smacked him and kicked his behind with a wooden shoe as big as a boat and then the Black Skipper would say: "Stop it."

The Black Skipper standing at the helm, steering with his back, his light blue eyes looking at the things I couldn't see, was a sight I could look at for minutes on end. He was a promise, a goal, a vision of a wonderful future; he seemed to sail with a host of angels behind him, fat angels blowing trumpets, like the gold dolls on top of the organ in church.

I didn't understand at the time why the mere looking at him made me feel as if I was hearing music; only much later did I realize why. He was the first human being I loved.

THE FIRST TIME I SAW THE SEA WAS ON SATURDAY NIGHT TOWARD SUNSET. After the noon catch had been hauled in, the buyer came much earlier than usual. I didn't dare ask, but I understood from the snatches of conversation I overheard that we would be putting into port that night and that was how I realized that it was Saturday.

I knew that every Sunday every botter on the Zuider Zee put into port to go to church. This was seldom their home port; as the fish was bought at sea while they followed the shoals on their circular way along the coast they often found themselves far from home at the end of the week. But as to go to church twice on Sunday was necessary for the soul, two or three ports below the wind got all the botters there were, depending on where the shoals were on Saturday.

Like all the children of Huizen I had heard stories about these fishermen's Sundays, and we had hoped feverishly that one Sunday the whole fleet would sail into our port. But this never happened; not only was Huizen a difficult port to get into, lying right in the prevailing wind, it also was too small.

But the main reason why Huizen was never chosen for a fishermen's Sunday was the size of its church. Our church could hold one thousand people at the utmost, if extra stools were put up in the aisles, and a fishermen's Sunday meant an invasion of anything from four to five thousand fishermen at a time.

Hoorn and Enkhuizen were the favorite Sunday ports. Both had a big harbor and enormous churches that rose from the little towns like ancient battleships; both had a wide-open anchorage, sheltered from the winds and with an easily accessible shore. The reason why we children of Huizen had hoped so fervently for the miracle of our village being chosen for a fishermen's Sunday was the stories we were told about them. It was said that the fishermen went to church twice each Sunday in order to make good the damage to the towns and to their souls they had done on finding themselves together in such a happy number. The stories told about incredible orgies: screaming women chased through the streets, customs shacks set on fire, shops pillaged; one legend said that on a Monday morning long ago Bokke Bas, a famous fisherman from the Island of Urk, had sailed out of Enkhuizen with the head of a statue of Jan Pieterzoon Coen, the hero who discovered the Dutch Indies, covered with the burgomaster's wig.

After that Saturday evening the buyer had left and the net was not put out again. I knew it was one of the golden towns we were sailing to at such great speed. They were called "the golden towns" and in my imagination that was because the steeples of their churches and the roofs of their houses were inlaid with gold.

I had given up trying to look over the rail several days before; but when I realized where we were bound for I couldn't resist the temptation and tried it again. Hardly had I pulled myself halfway up when Bonk kicked me again, Krelis kicked Bonk, and the Black Skipper said: "Stop it." My face must have been very miserable for suddenly I heard him say: "Come here, child."

I approached him fearfully; I thought he was going to punish me for he looked very severe.

"Are you still sick?" he asked.

I whispered: "No, sir."

"Then what were you scrambling up that rail for?"

"I wanted to look, sir," I said.

He looked at me so grimly that I felt the tears welling up in my eyes. "Look at what?" he asked.

I swallowed and whispered: "The sea."

"The sea?" he replied incredulously, knitting his brows in what to me seemed to be divine wrath. Then his face slowly relaxed as the realization of my smallness dawned on him. He didn't smile; I never saw him smile during the months I sailed with him; but the expression on his face at that moment was the nearest I ever saw him get to it.

"Come here," he said, and stretched out his hand. I approached hesitantly, overcoming the resistance of ten years' sparrow's experience; then suddenly he grabbed me by the collar of my coat, flung me in the air like a sack, and caught me in his elbow.

This was so unexpected that during the first half minute or so I saw nothing. I felt a sudden wave of nausea as if I was going to be sick again. Then I heard him say: "All right, look!" and I did.

25

The sight I saw took my breath away. The sea was a sheet of silver under a tremendous dome of a cloudless evening sky, green like weathered brass. On that sea, in line with us and behind us, sailed the biggest fleet I had ever seen. Hundreds and hundreds of botters sailing in formation, town by town. The most impressive thing about that fleet was the colors of the sails. I knew that all the fishing ports around the Zuider Zee had slightly different colored sails; fishermen's sails were never white—they were cured immediately after manufacture to withstand the weather and the salt. The curing was done locally, each town had its own secret process; that was why our sails were black and the Volendammers' red. But only that night, looking around me open-mouthed from the arm of the Black Skipper, did I realize how many ports there were around the Zuider Zee. There were blue sails, green sails, orange sails, black sails; they had been mended by patches of other colors and over them fluttered the town pennants: thin ribbons twelve yards long, stretched taut in the breeze, blue for the west coast, red for the east. Some of the pennants were almost as long as the masts, and I felt a pang of jealousy at the thought that we hadn't got one, but at the same moment I saw Bonk hoisting it. Our pennant was the longest of all: a bright blue ribbon jumping out toward the shore, fluttering nervously in the green sky, reaching for the promised land.

I looked ahead and saw the coast. An orange sunset flamed behind the silhouette of what seemed a miracle city seen from afar. It had at least a dozen steeples and what looked like gold domes glistening in the sun. The haze of the night had begun to rise: a thin white streak on the horizon colored pink by the setting sun, and it made the city look as if it floated on a cloud. I must have thought aloud: "What is that?" for the Black Skipper said with a voice that was curiously proud: "Hoorn the Golden," as if he had created it himself.

I looked away from the city because I heard a rush of water and the singing wind in rigging overtaking us. It was the HZ 55, Arie Kos's botter, our fishing partner whom I hadn't seen all week. I had only heard the shouts passing from ship to ship and known it was there; now I saw it. It was the first botter under full sail I saw from close quarters; at first she seemed nothing but a cloud of black sails riding a white wave. Her pennant was stretched so taut in the wind that it seemed to crackle; the number HZ 55 in her black mainsail was so dazzling white that it seemed to dance in the sunlight. She overtook us and I saw a deckhand waving; Krelis and Bonk waved back and shouted, but at that moment a flash of lightning struck in that dream of color and sails and sea. It was a moment of such unreality that I felt a shiver of fear, like realizing that I was about to wake up from a wonderful miracle world, for at the helm of the HZ 55 stood Skipper Arie Kos, also with a child in his arms. They came so close that I couldn't be mistaken any longer; the child looked at me gravely and I stared back open-mouthed. Then it waved and I waved back; a newly dead arriving on a distant shore.

For the child on Skipper Kos's arm was Kris Muis, our playmate from school who had been killed by a sea lion.

IT SEEMED SO UNBELIEVABLE THAT I COULD THINK OF NOTHING ELSE ANY more. I remembered his mother running through the streets weeping. I remembered the whispered gossip among us as to who would be the successor to our drowned friend. I remembered lying awake at night, with Bulle and Jaap breathing in sleep beside me, imagining what it had been like: the struggle in the water, the sea lion's ferocious teeth, the terrible pain, the blood. The story said that a sea lion, when it caught a boy, ate only his head; I had seen Kris Muis's headless body bobbing lonely in an endless sea, limp like the dead cats in the harbor. And now, for one long hollow minute, I gazed at him, alive, sitting on Skipper Kos's arm, and he waved to me and smiled.

It was such a dark and menacing mystery that I simply had to talk to somebody about it and find out that it was true. After the Black Skipper had put me down, I sidled over to Bonk squatting on the deck, his back against the mast, whitewashing the clogs for the Sunday. It took me a long time before I had worked up enough courage to address him, a thing I had never dared do before. I was still wondering whether I should when I heard myself say: "Sir . . ."

Bonk looked up and stared at me with his fish eyes and grunted.

"Was that Kris Muis?" I asked.

His face changed as if only then he had caught sight of me, an unpleasant sight indeed. "Kris who?" he said, flabbergasted, as if he had been addressed by a cat that could suddenly speak.

I felt a trembling creep up my spine but I went on recklessly: "The mouse on board the 55," I said. "Is that Kris Muis?"

Bonk's mouth sagged open in blank amazement. Then he suddenly snarled, as if at last the realization of the outrage began to ooze into his consciousness. "Jesus Christ!" he said. "Do you think I know the names of mice?! Holy Mother! The cheek of it! Actually sitting there, one thumb high, and asking me the name of a mouse! ME!" Then he pushed a brushful of whitewash in my face, so that I toppled over backward with a stinging pain in my eyes. "Rat!" he screamed. "Scram to your nest in the forehole and write a thousand lines: mice have no names, mice are . . ."

Then a clog as big as a boat nearly skinned my nose as it swung past my face, and Bonk yelped. I heard the Black Skipper's voice say: "Stop it," and I scurried away to the cable hole where I wiped the whitewash off my face with one of the rags on which I slept. Murk was there, asleep; he got up when I pulled the rag from underneath him, arched his back showing the white belt of his tummy, and yawned. Then he sniffed at the white stuff dripping on the ropes, and jumped up toward the square of sky, disgusted.

I didn't actually see us entering the harbor, I heard it. At first there was a great noise of water as the botters of our line converged toward the narrow entrance between the piers. I heard shouts all around and the rattle and rush of jibs swishing down; then the Black Skipper's voice hollered and our own jib dropped from the sky with a terrific sound of heavy sail furling and iron rings screeching down the forestay; the heavy top block hit the deck overhead with a colossal bang and the roar of the water against the bow shrunk to a soft splashing. There was a noise of clogs on decks all around us, the banging of beams, and the flapping of huge sails in the wind like cannon shots. Then all of a sudden the whole cable hole seemed to explode to dust in a terrific collision. There was a noise of iron so loud that it made my throat ache, and I was flung back among the lamps and the glass floats, screaming with terror.

For a minute I seemed to suffocate in a dense red cloud; my lungs stung as if I was breathing pepper. I sat trembling in that corner until the red cloud lifted, then I saw that my bed had been thrown aside and some of the rags sucked into the hawsehole. All that had happened was that the HZ 69 had dropped anchor in the bay of Hoorn the Golden; I had slept on the chain for a week without knowing it.

When, exhausted, I had hoisted myself onto the foredeck through the manhole and stood blinking in the sunset, I heard laughter all around me. The Black Skipper's voice called: "Child, come here," and I was picked up by Krelis and carried to the cockpit. "Wash him," said the skipper. "What on earth has happened to the brat?"

I never saw myself; but when Krelis washed my face with a wad of cotton waste in a pail, I saw the water turn orange and realized that the whitewash and the rust must have got mixed on my face. When I finally stood, clean, in front of the Black Skipper, with the cold drops of water that had run into my collar squiggling down my back, he said to Krelis: "Take him ashore and buy him a suit."

"Aye aye," said Krelis, and he picked me up. "And have his head shaved!" shouted the skipper after us; then I was lowered into a boat.

In the boat I got the proof that the incredible vision was true. Looking up at me with very blue eyes, in a wonderful suit of black baggy breeches and a black vest separated by a red sash, blue and white striped stockings and dazzling white new clogs, sat Kris Muis, an astrakhan cap with an orange top on the back of his shaven head. He lifted his hand lazily, in a very grown-up greeting, and when I had overcome my awe, my first feeling was an intense, deep jealousy. For on the back of his left hand was tattooed a big blue anchor.

THAT FIRST EVENING IN HOORN WAS CRAMMED SO FULL OF WONDROUS THINGS that in the end I accepted everything happening to me in a sort of daze.

I was taken through streets teeming with men in at least a dozen different costumes, past brilliantly lit shop windows piled high with treasures I didn't even begin to know the uses of, until at last we ended up at the tailor: a hunchback in shirt sleeves in an alley of shelves stacked with bundles of clothes. He asked Krelis where we came from and when Krelis said: "Huizen," the hunchback wheeled a ladder to a corner, climbed to the top layer, looked at me with one eye shut and pulled out a bundle. Kris Muis, who had left his clogs outside, sat on the corner of the counter, yawning and chewing, a bored man.

I didn't get a chance to speak to him until we were on our way home, for after the tailor I was taken to the clog-maker, after the clog-maker to the cap-seller, after the cap-seller to the barber and after that my cap didn't fit any more but rested on my ears. The barber tore a strip off a newspaper and tucked it in the band. I decided secretly that every day I would take out one layer of paper to keep the cap fitting.

When we got out of the barber's it was night and my head felt very cold. I wasn't sleepy at all although I had been used to going to bed at sunset, but I had a headache and my feet hurt in the new clogs as I stumbled along, dragged by Krelis who got maddened by the little steps I made. The lights in the streets were on but I couldn't see the shops any more, because by then there were too many men about. I seemed to be dragged through a furrow Krelis plowed in a solid mass of fishermen: Urkers, Elburgers, Stavoreners, Enkhuizers and Bunschoters. Every port around the Zuider Zee had its men there, except Volendam.

Nobody knew where the Catholics went to church and nobody cared. It was wise of them not to show their noses, because there were so many Protestants about that liked to do something together and didn't know what. If a Volendammer had appeared among them, they would have known what; now they were looking for policemen, as the women of Hoorn had got wise long ago and stayed indoors with bread for two days and all their pails full of water, so as not to be forced by thirst to break through the siege.

Kris Muis, who sauntered along beside me as if he was twice my size and could see everything, told me about the policemen on our way back to the bay. I didn't hear half of what he said, because of the noise the thousands of clogs made on the pavement, the bellowing wisps of song, the terrifying gusts of laughter, the murderous back-slapping and the oi-oi-ing going on all around me. I gathered that the only time sea mice could show themselves in the open was on Saturday nights and Sundays in the golden towns, when all the fleet was in. Then there were so many fishermen about in the streets looking for trouble that the policemen packed their bags as soon as the sails of the armada were sighted and went to stay with their aunts in the country. Kris Muis said this was a pity, for that if the fishermen found a constable who had decided to stick it they disarmed him, took off his trousers, slammed his cap so deep over his eyes that it turned into a collar and carried him, singing, to the burgomaster's house, where they threw him through the window into the parlor. The burgomaster, Kris said, had tried shutters of steel, but they hadn't worked for the fishermen had uprooted the iron statue of Her Majesty and used it as a battering ram, after which the policeman had been chucked through the hole, screaming as he sailed.

We passed a large crowd in the market place on our way; they were shouting and singing: "What happened on Baldhead's nuptial night," which Kris Muis said was in honor of the burgomaster. Krelis took me on his shoulders as we crossed the crowd, because the legs stood so thick that I nearly suffocated. I saw the burgomaster's house: a gabled façade with huge windows in gaslight, but not a candle showed inside, and the handles of the big double doors were tied together with a chain and padlock. The crowd went on singing and calling for Baldhead, asking to see his daughter, and shouting questions about the weight of his wife, but nobody showed behind the vast windows; it looked like a deserted palace.

I wasn't feeling happy, swaying on Krelis' shoulders over the shouting heads. I was afraid of losing my new clogs which were too big for me and the wind was very cold on the back of my shaven head. Kris Muis vanished in the crowd on the market place; I shouted in Krelis' ear that he had gone, but Krelis said: "Don't you worry, he'll find his way back all right. And so will you, if you have been around this town once." We passed a tumble of arms and legs of men joyfully fighting; a monster with a flat Urker cap and only two yellow teeth left in his lower jaw leered up at me and shrieked: "There goes my breakfast!" but I held tight on to Krelis' shoulders and we lost him safely in the milling crowd.

We passed another palace with a lion and a unicorn on top of its façade, so big that it looked as if the house itself was peeping between their legs. Krelis said that it was the governor's house, but that he hadn't been in town for centuries because the noise on Saturday nights made it impossible for him to govern. He said that it was going to be turned into a museum, showing the riches of the past and the ruins of tomorrow.

I heard a lot about the ruins of tomorrow, once we got back on board. I was ordered to go to sleep instantly, after the skipper had made me turn around twice in front of him to show what Krelis had got me. The cabin was full of people: Huizers and Elburgers squatting in a thick ring around the coffeepot that sat in a multitude of mugs, like a chicken too small for its eggs. Three tins of babblers stood open on the floor between them, and the tobacco smoke hung so thick under the ceiling that the shadows of the rings around the lamp cut it in slices. I vanished through my hole in the bunk and shut the trap door behind me; but I didn't go to sleep at once. I sat there listening, with Murk purring and yawning in the darkness behind me and finally smacking his lips in his sleep.

All the voices on the other side of the partition talked about was the ruins of tomorrow; the ruins that would be left of their towns and their fleet once the big dam was laid across the mouth of the Zuider Zee. I had never thought much about the big dam, although I had often heard of it. It lay so far ahead in the future that it seemed as unreal as death. That night I heard that the first step had been made; the dam between the mainland and the Island of Wieringen had been completed a week ago. It didn't make much difference yet; the botters had seldom crossed the narrow straits as they were too shallow and the herring never went there. But even so, it was the first step, one-eighth of the total distance across. If the fishermen on the Zuider Zee let that onslaught on their livelihood pass unpunished, the Negroes from below Amsterdam would take courage and go on with their devilish plan. Something had to be done, the voices said; whatever happened, that dam had to be blown so high that the sods of it would hail down on their damned cities, Babylons of sin, homes of the painted mouths, the steam trawlers and the electric frying pans.

Never before had I heard such grim emotion in men's voices, as when I sat listening motionlessly behind that trap door in the darkness. For the first time in my life I overheard the giants talking among themselves and all they talked about was the day the dam would be blown up. I felt very frightened, and yet curiously elated; for now I was a member of a big conspiracy no children or women knew of. I felt the same grim emotion rise inside me; I saw in that darkness a fleet of empty botters under full sail soaring down toward the wicked dam, their fo'c'sles crammed with dynamite. I saw the bursting volcano of the explosion, heard the mounting thunder of the colossal bangs piling on top of each other, until the sky trembled with noise. It seemed like the victory of a fleet of Saint Jorises: a large sluggish dragon made of mud, stretched out in the sea, teeming with Negroes from below Amsterdam, with wide painted mouths, brandishing electric frying pans.

I felt a slight sadness at the same time, because to me the worst enemies in the world had been the Catholic pirates of Volendam, for so long that I had almost begun to like them. It felt like a good-by to a trusted homeland, like entering a new vast space full of frightening emptiness and strange shadows and a new enemy.

I fell asleep where I sat, before the voices stopped, dazed and exhausted, and very much alone.

THE NEXT MORNING WE WENT TO CHURCH, AND THAT WAS THE FIRST TIME
I realized how many sea mice there were hidden in the botters of the
Zuider Zee.

There seemed to be thousands of us, silently trooping down the streets
toward the sound of the big bell tolling. It was like a funereal procession
of dwarfs, for we were separated from the giants the moment we set out
for church. I followed the crowd of boys without knowing which way we
were taking; it was a different way from the giants, for all the way to
church there wasn't a full-sized fisherman in sight. All of us were carrying
a psalm book; Krelis had given me one when I set out.

We met our skippers again at the doors, but they behaved as if they
didn't see us; this caused the curious sensation of being invisible again,
that I had known so well when I was still a child in Huizen. It gave us
an anticipation of the authority of God, as if, even though we were now
being shown in the open, we were still illegal, with God frowning on us
from the skies with a big policeman's cap on.

In church itself we were separated from our skippers also; the giants
sat below with the sea boys, the mice crowded the gallery. We sat down
in the long high benches, leaving our clogs in the alley.

The first few minutes were not boring, because there was slow solemn
organ music and from the ceiling hung scores of little ships, complete with
sails and life boats, turning slowly in the slanting beams of sunlight. The
ships and the tops of the arches were all we could see of the church, for
the benches were so high that we had to look upward all the time. The
church was cold, but there was a warmth of many boys around me and the
thick rich smell of soft soap and baize.

Only when the service started did we become intolerably bored. The
preacher howled in such an unnatural voice that it would have been difficult to understand him anyhow. But apart from that there were so many

35

echoes in the church, that it sounded as if five invisible preachers were hollering at the same time. The deserts of meaningless bawling between the hymns seemed endless; and when the hymns came, only the beginning and the end of them were beautiful, for then the organ played by itself. As soon as the men began to sing it sounded like an angry crowd clamoring for blood. Nobody could keep the tune, because nobody knew what it was; and the song was sung in such a slow tempo that the organ sounded as if it were dragging a thousand wailing voices along, grinding its way mercilessly.

We children sang a song entirely our own; and it wasn't one song, it was a dozen. We had been sitting still, silently, for so long that the chance to make a noise went straight to our heads. Some of us sang about Jesus, others about Baldhead's nuptial night. Toward the end of the hymn it sounded like a screaming battle of music between God and the Devil. The mice of Urk, in the bench next to us, sang a very filthy song very fast, beating time with their fists on the high ledges of their benches; they ended by shooting peas at the little ships with slingshots and dancing on the seats. But punishment swished down on us, with angry shouts and the biting pain of a fishing rod. It was the "dog beater," a man appointed to keep animals out of the church during the services who also made the collection. He spent most of his time prowling behind the benches, looking for mischief among us, at which he would lash out with his fishing rod and hit the instigator on the head. When collection time came he turned the fishing rod around; it had a little black sack attached to it in which we were supposed to put the cents given to us by our skippers before we set out to church. Nobody put a cent in; when the black bag came back to the dog beater it seemed like a garbage sack. Buttons, bits of paper, wet sweets and chewed cigar butts had all got together into a sticky lump which he emptied in the alley, his eyes bloodshot with rage. He shook his fist at us, turned around his rod and slammed it down on the row, regardless. At first I was frightened and tried to hide myself from the blows, but Kris Muis, sitting beside me, nudged me and said: "Scream!" I soon found out that if we screamed loud enough the blows would stop; so we resumed our mischief with a feeling of victory, while the invisible parson resumed his fivefold hollering and the dog beater stood choking in the alley between us, forming words with his lips.

The service lasted three hours, from nine to twelve, and the last hour was the longest. We groaned and writhed with boredom. We made rabbits with our handkerchiefs, put on our caps square-ways, the Urker boys began to undress and put on their clothes inside out. In the end there

36

was nothing left to do to make life last, but to pull faces in unison or to stick out one hundred tongues at the same moment at the dog beater, dying with helpless rage. The dog beater became our only hope of survival; the Urker boys took off their trousers and turned their bare behinds toward him, at which he grabbed his fishing rod like a harpoonist going berserk and lashed out at them with such ferocity that the smacks resounded underneath the arches like pistol shots multiplied a dozenfold. The Urker boys began to scream so sharply that I felt it in my teeth. We all began to scream, and out of that rising spiral of pointless screaming came a chorus: "A-men, a-men, a-men!" and then suddenly we shut up, almost at the same moment, and sat very still and stared piously in front of us.

Five huge skippers had appeared behind the benches; five Urkers of such enormous size and with such terrifying faces that I felt my legs tingle with fear at the mere sight of them. One of the Urkers advanced slowly in the alley, between our benches, noiseless in his stockinged feet. By then the Urker mice were silently praying, but their prayers were of no avail. The giant looked at the benchful of motionless children with a long motionless stare, then his big hand rose in the air, descended in the middle of the second row and grabbed an ear. It pulled out one of the praying boys, who didn't even struggle. The boy was led toward the back, half walking half squatting; we didn't dare look around, the eerie silence hung over us menacingly for minutes on end. Kris Muis whispered: "He's taking off his breeches." Then there was one colossal smack, a yelp as of a rabbit at the moment its neck was wrung, and then silence again, with the shapeless howling of the preacher lapping against the ceiling, multitudinous and monotonous like the surf. The boy came back to his seat with stooped shoulders, whimpering, and he seemed much smaller. The silent guard of Urkers stood glowering at the backs of our heads until our limbs went asleep; then there was a last hopeless, murderous song of the men down below, a last blast from the organ, a last wail from the five invisible parsons, and never had I muttered "Amen" with more sincerity.

When we were out of the church at last and started on our way home we ran, danced, shouted and sang like school children setting out for the year's big holiday. I felt, like all of us, an irresistible urge to do mischief, to break things, and I started shouting filthy words, throwing my clogs at windows, rattling doorknobs and ringing bells like all of us. We were swept to the harbor by a wave of communal emotion, and the emotion was relief, so profound, so inexpressible that I came home with a brass bell knob in my hand. Kris Muis had a black eye and everywhere were boys who limped on one clog or tried to pin up tears in their jackets. Many of us were wet, for when the wave of our relief had washed down the empty streets of Hoorn the Golden, windows had been opened and pails of water had been emptied on our heads: futile protests against the fruits of Christianity.

THE HOUR AFTER SUNDAY LUNCH WAS THE ONLY TIME OFF THE SEA MICE had during the week.

After the bones had been thrown overboard, the potato pot washed, the coffee mugs wiped and the floor cleaned by the cat and the men sank down on their backs, sleepily sucking the remains of their babblers, then we mice slunk out of the cabins, manned the boats and rowed ashore.

The boats had to be back at half-past two, to ferry the fishermen ashore for a second church service that began at three. Between half-past one and half-past two on Sunday the golden towns were handed over to the children.

When Kris Muis, who had told me about this, had hissed and whistled from the boat until all the mice of the two dozen botters lying side by side in the bay piled up in it, we set out for the shore. There was not much room in the boat to row, as we were too many. Kris and a boy called Freek of the HZ 11 took hold of one oar together and paddled from the stern.

When we arrived at the quay it was already full of kids. The harbor itself was jam-packed with botters; they were lying in solid rows, side by side and stem to bow; you could walk right across the harbor by jumping from ship to ship. We, anchored in the bay, were the overflow; if the weather had been rough we would have to go on and put into Enkhuizen. But it was a cloudless week end, with bright sunlight and a gentle breeze, and so the whole fleet had descended on Hoorn. I had no idea of the number of ships, but, according to the number of mice that sprung forth from them during that one hour when the giants lay sleeping, there must have been hundreds for the big quay was teeming with us.

I had thought that we went ashore to play, but I was mistaken. We went ashore to be men. During one glorious hour each week we were giants ourselves; we smoked pipes, put our caps as far on the backs of our heads as possible, and waddled with our legs wide apart, our fists in our pockets, grunting: "Oi-oi" and discussing the dam in little groups, loitering around the bollards. We talked about our ships, our nets, our catch, and when we were tired of grumbling about the price of the herring and the quality of the sails coming from that new factory in Friesland, we waddled along the water's edge and made a tour of the punished.

The punished were the big attraction of the week's hour of manliness. As even mice occasionally did something which made their skippers angry, and as they couldn't be spared to be punished during the week or the hours of the church services, retribution for the week's big sins befell them between half-past one and half-past two on Sundays.

The way of punishment was the same on all botters. Before the giants went to sleep after lunch, they took the mouse who had sinned to the foredeck, tied his hands behind his back, passed the loose end of the rope with which the jib was hoisted under his arms and hauled him halfway up the mast. Then he was left during the hour of rest.

It was a painful punishment, but mainly a humiliating one, for all the mice of the fleet would file past during that hour, and laugh at the wretches, who vainly tried to throw their hanging bodies round so as to hide their faces from the crowd. We would shout and jeer at them, and occasionally pull out a slingshot to have a potshot at them. They looked ludicrous, dangling there at half staff height; some of them were weeping, others were angry and shouted back at us. They were the ones that were shot at.

That afternoon I saw about two dozen hanged, and the preventive effect of that spectacle was very strong. I made up my mind never to do anything that would result in my exposing myself to such utter humiliation, or at least never to get caught at anything. Kris Muis said that he had hung there himself one Sunday and enjoyed it; you had a lovely view of the town from there, but he didn't manage to make the idea attractive.

I told him, in our bored grown-up way, that everybody in our village thought he was dead. He snorted and said: "Pah! Children." I asked him whether his mother knew he was still alive; he shrugged his shoulders and said he had sent her a postcard from Enkhuizen some time ago, telling her to stop worrying. He would not go back ashore, he said, until he had been promoted to sea boy; then he would marry Annie Sluiters and beat the hell out of her, because she had screamed out when she saw him peeping through the hawsehole last time the fleet was in, and he was sure that she had given him away.

I deduced from his conversation that his skipper had the same idea about women as Krelis; he talked about "beating" a lot, and said that he didn't care what his mother thought as she was only married into the family. I tried to talk about women the way the Black Skipper did, but Kris never realized what I discussed. When I began to talk about a green eye opening in a kiss, very close and large, looking as if you saw the Zuider Zee through a porthole on an early autumn morning, he shrugged his shoulders and spat. I was hurt, because I had repeated the phrase word for word as I had heard it from the mouth of the Black Skipper, but I was too impressed by the way he spat to go on about it. He said his sea boy was the best spitter of the fleet; when the nets were out and the breeches folded and skipper and deckhand in their bunk, the sea boy would sit up on his elbows between their legs, take aim, and spit out the candle on the shelf four yards away. He, himself, was not a bad spitter, he said; he tried to demonstrate it on one of the punished, a very small Urker boy hanging very low, but he got no further than a yard or two—his spittle never even reached the ship. I heard it dropping in the water, although he said: "Bullseye," shoved his cap on the back of his head and waddled on.

I began to think that Kris Muis was a bit of a bragger, but as he was my friend I didn't want to believe this until I saw it proved. The spittle was no proof; it might have been the wind. But when we rowed back on board he dropped the oar, snatched it out of the water in the nick of time, and although he did this very deftly he got his arm wet up to the elbow. When we finally reached our ships and the mice scrambled up the gunwales, I saw a sight that filled me with anger and sadness.

The beautiful anchor, tattooed on Kris's left hand, of which I had been so jealous, had turned into a shapeless blot. He had painted it on with ink.

AT A QUARTER TO THREE THE DOUBLE PROCESSION OF MEN AND BOYS again set out toward the sound of the solemn bell calling the faithful.

The second service lasted as long as the first, but somehow it seemed to be over more quickly for we spent most of it asleep. Most of the mice had been listening the night before to the conversation of the giants behind the partition, and so they were sleepy now. Furthermore Kris Muis had warned me that Sunday night was the best night of all, for then stories were told in the cabins by the Liars; so if I wanted to listen I had better take this chance to snatch some sleep.

I had heard about the Liars before, but I had never been very interested in them for they never did anything real; they just sat down in a circle of people and told lies. I had never seen one because for some reason all Liars were Urkers. Kris told me more about them; he said they were very funny because they told impossible stories about mermen ringing at midwives' doors at night to get help for their mermaid-wives who were having a child, about turtles in China so big that whole gardens grew on their backs, about sea monsters with seven heads, and the skinning of Eskimo women. The funny thing about these stories was that the Liars told them as if all this had happened to them personally; they never told a story in the third person, but always began: "One day when I was in Tasmania," although everybody knew that they had never been out of the Zuider Zee. There was only one Liar who was really good, and he was called Bokke Prins. When he told a story you forgot where you were, and he could go on until the dawn without one of his listeners falling asleep. Kris had heard him only once, because he was very expensive; first he had to be given half a bottle of Geneva to drink before he even started, then he drank another half a bottle during his story, and if he wasn't given a second whole bottle to take away with him, he would never come back again, for he liked to hit that second bottle as soon as he got into the cold morning air. They said he was such a clumsy sailor that his skipper would have fired him long ago, if it hadn't been for the half bottles he arrived with and which were taken away from him the moment he sank into his bunk.

When that night, while I was cleaning away the supper, Skipper Arie Kos and his crew stooped into the cabin and the Black Skipper said: "Let's get a Liar," I hurried, for I wanted to be snug, wrapped up in my rags behind the partition before he arrived. Kos said: "Let's get Bokke Prins—I'm sick of the children's babble of the others," and the Black Skipper ordered Bonk to go ashore and get three bottles of Geneva.

It was so long before he came back, that I was nearly asleep, cold and disappointed. I was sure that Bokke had been snatched up by some other botter in the harbor as we were lying so far out. But after what seemed at least an hour I heard the splashing and crunching of oars drawing near, a thud when the boat hit the ship, and Bonk's voice saying: "Steady, sir, let me give you a hand." I heard another voice mumble something shapeless, a high-pitched voice like a woman's, and I sagged back in disappointment because I was sure this couldn't be Bokke. Bonk must have caught some second-rate Liar, loitering on the quay, who hadn't been able to find a drink yet.

But whoever it might be that was ushered into the cabin, he had certainly been able to find a drink. The high-pitched voice was so drunk that it strung words together like a child of two stringing colored beads. There was a lot of stumbling, scraping and hiccuping and I understood that the drunk had entered the cabin with his clogs on. I was about to turn away and go to sleep when I heard the Black Skipper say: "Oi-oi, Bokke; how are you, my boy?" The high-pitched voice chirped and giggled and slurred a string of words of which I understood only one: "Thirsty." There was a plop of a bottle being uncorked and the glugglug of gin in glasses; I felt angry with Kris Muis, because he obviously had pulled my leg. Bokke Prins must be the worst of all the Liars. The only thing I couldn't understand was why the Black Skipper should have spent so much money to have a speechless drunk hauled all the way from the harbor. Three bottles of gin were worth a fortune.

They sat drinking in there for the better part of an hour. The noises the drunk made got less and less human. He played a lopsided little tune on a mouth organ which ended in a slobber of spittle. He giggled, cooed, gave feminine little shrieks; his voice got higher and higher until he sounded like a baby chortling to itself in its cradle. If I hadn't been so cold and so tired I would have dragged myself to my basket where Murk lay already snoring, but the idea of having to unwrap myself and crawl all the way through the icy cold was so unpleasant that I just sat there uncomfortably and dozed.

I must have been asleep at one time because when I woke up something had changed and I couldn't remember when this had happened. A soft man's voice was talking behind the partition, a voice so melodious and fascinating that I thought someone else had come in, but it was unmistakably Bokke's. It spoke with the soft, slurring Urker accent, and was so beautiful, that I listened to it for a while, without realizing what it was saying.

The cabin was so silent that I could hear the water lapping against the side of the ship, the sleepy shuffling of our leeboard against Arie Kos's botter, the faraway squeak of the rudder stirring in its hinges, the soft tapping of ropes against the mast. The voice seemed to be alone in a world of wind and water.

It was telling the story of a girl, who had lived on the Island of Schokland before the village of Emmeloord had been submerged. I knew of the village of Emmeloord; it was the one whose bells could be heard ringing when the ground seas of a gale stirred them in the depth. I had often wondered what Emmeloord had been like, and the voice told me.

A wind-swept village of small red houses huddled close together, peeping over the dike at the Zuider Zee with their attic windows, barred against the gales. The girl was called Mensje and she had a lover called Jan Viool who was a sailor for the East India Company. They were to marry after his next voyage, and Mensje had started fitting out her hope chest when one night she had a curious dream.

She saw Jan standing at the bottom of a broken red tower. She couldn't make out whether it was night or day for the light was very strange: a curious blue that sometimes changed to green. The tower was covered with a sort of creeper the like of which she had never seen before. Jan stood there, clad only in his trousers, a blood-soaked kerchief knotted around his head, and he was calling her. The curious thing was that although she saw him calling she didn't hear a sound. She saw his mouth move in a deep heavy silence, as if he was trying to make himself heard through a thick glass plate. She tried to understand what he was calling and he tried to make himself understood, but the heavy silence was impenetrable, and she woke up with a feeling of great urgency. She was sure he was in danger and that he wanted her to do something for him but she had no idea what it could be.

The next night she had the same dream again. Again she saw him standing at the bottom of that curious tower in that green light changing to blue; again he tried to make her understand what he was saying, but the heavy glass silence remained impenetrable. Before she woke up, however, it seemed as if his message had been brought back to two words: two words he kept on repeating time after time, forming them slowly, pleadingly with his lips. He was still repeating them when she woke up, without any idea of what he was trying to say.

During the month that followed she had the dream several times. It was always the same: the tower, the creeper, the green light, and silence, and Jan, weary and wounded, trying to make her understand two words, two words only. And every time she woke up in tears, because she had no idea what they were.

The fortnight after she had dreamed the dream for the last time the news came that Jan's ship was missing. People came to comfort her, but although she let them say what they wanted in order not to hurt their feelings, she didn't for a second believe that Jan was dead. He was standing somewhere at the bottom of a red tower in green sunlight calling her, and she would help him, if it would cost her everything she had.

But there was nothing she could do. She thought of boarding a ship to the East Indies but nobody knew exactly where the ship had got lost. She decided to remain where she was and to wait until, somehow, they would be able to reach each other through the thick glass plate that separated them. She dreamed the dream many times after that and she began slowly to realize that the first word was "your" and that the second word had an "o" in it; but she never found that second word.

Her waking life became less and less important to her. She would have wanted to sleep and dream forever, if there hadn't been the hope that someday someone would come who would bring her news about Jan or his ship.

Every night she sat listening in the lamplight, knitting socks for him, alone in her little house; and whenever she heard the distant splash and rattle of an anchor dropping in the bay, she would put on her shawl and go out in the night and climb the dike to wait for the first boat coming ashore. Whatever the ship, she would invariably ask the same question: "Have you met the *Rising Hope*, the flagship of the East India Company?" The men in the boat would always be nice to her, for she was a pretty girl with the innocence of the faithful in her eyes. They would say: "Not that we know of, but we have passed so many ships in the distance which we didn't recognize that it's quite possible." Then she would ask: "Have you heard any news about Jan Viool, a sailor? He may have changed ships abroad." Then the men would get uncomfortable with pity and self-consciousness and say: "No."

This happened many times during the months that followed. She must have asked those questions on dozens of nights; misty, moonlit, stormy or rainy nights. She asked it in snow and hail, shouting against the gale or whispering in the summer breeze; but every time she got the same answer. She would always say: "Thank you, gentlemen," politely, and walk back along the dike: very pretty, very brave, and resume her knitting in the lamplight, alone.

One night, almost a year after Jan had got lost, a night when there was no moon and no breeze and fog enclosed the Island of Schokland, she looked up in the lamplight, amazed, for she heard distinctly the splash and the rattle of an anchor dropping in the bay. That was very strange, for there was no wind and no visibility; the ships in the harbor were lying dead, the ropes silent against the masts, and everybody in the village was asleep in the comfortable certainty that no ship could reach the island that night.

She got up, put her shawl around her shoulders, went out and climbed the dike. She had been used to walking along it to the jetty, for that was where all boats moored; but the night was so thick with fog that she couldn't see one step in front of her, and so she stood still, listening.

She heard distinctly the creaking of oars approaching in the fog, the murmur of water against the bow of a boat, she even heard the oarsmen sighing and the soft clanking of the rudder chain, but she saw nothing. The sounds seemed to come straight at her, and for the first time since Jan had left she became conscious of being alone.

Then there was the scraping of an iron keel on the basalt of the dike, the rumbling of oars being pulled in, the splashing of people getting out and wading through the shallow water; then, suddenly, there came a faint light climbing toward her, with the scraping of hobnailed boots on the rocks.

The light came nearer and nearer, until she saw that it was a very old-fashioned lantern. Then it stood still, and the steps fell silent. She saw only that lantern, and nothing else; but she knew there must be men around it hidden in the fog, and she asked her question without seeing whom she was addressing.

"Have you met the *Rising Hope,* the flagship of the East India Company?" she asked, and for the first time she realized how often she had asked it before. The lantern shone motionlessly in the fog, and she was about to turn away when a voice said: "We have."

She took a long time asking her second question, for she had suddenly become afraid. This was the answer she had been waiting for, for almost a year; but now that she finally heard it a cold fear started creeping up her legs. "Have you heard any news about Jan Viool, a sailor?" she asked. "He may have changed ships abroad."

Again the lantern shone motionlessly in the fog for minutes on end, before the voice answered: "We have."

The fear had crept up so high now, that it nearly numbed her lips. "Do you know where he is?" she whispered.

Again the voice answered: "We do."

Then she asked her last question, and even before she had spoken she realized that it was going to decide her life. Asking that question was the bravest thing she had ever done; but as she had decided that she would help Jan even if it would cost her everything she had, she looked at the motionless lantern bravely and said: "Could you take me to him?"

The silence that met her question lasted so long that she repeated it. Then the voice said: "We can. But it will cost you a lot."

"It doesn't matter," she said. "You can have anything I possess; tell me your price."

The voice answered: "It will cost you your soul."

And that was the moment she knew what had been the second word of the two Jan had tried to make her understand in all those dreams. It was "soul."

The Liar's voice behind the partition fell silent. I heard the plop of a bottle, the small sound of Geneva poured into a glass, and they were the only sounds. Nobody stirred in the cabin; they were more silent than if they had been asleep, for there wasn't even a sound of breathing. Then I heard the Liar smack his lips, and the sharp click of the glass as it was put down on the platter.

Mensje, said the Liar, was the girl we have all been dreaming of all our lives. Her love was so unselfish that she said to the lantern: "All right, take me," giving up Heaven for that one vision: the weary, wounded Jan of her dreams, talking to her, as silent as a fish. If the voice had told her to go through fire to save him she would have done it; she was so generous and gentle that she understood that her love was worth more than her soul. She didn't want to live another sixty arid years, turn into a bedridden mummy in a nightshirt before she died, and then to lie rigid in her grave, her skeleton hands crossed on her barren chest, to get up in that nightshirt at the sound of the Last Trump and face God alone. She would rather sink to the bottom of the ocean, a swollen sack of shark's food, if that meant sinking into the arms of her lover.

Ah, said the Liar, she was the woman we all saw once, for one fleeting second: shaking a mop out of an attic window, or smiling at us as she passed carrying a basket of fish, and when we turned round to look again she had gone forever. He sighed, and there was another sound of Geneva, again the smacking of lips, and another sigh.

When he spoke again his voice was more beautiful than ever. It sounded like the mellow flutelike pipes of the church organ that always made me feel like weeping. It sounded as if the love of Mensje throbbed in his voice, and I wished there was a hole in the partition for I wanted to see him. But there was no hole; the picture I made of him in the darkness was of a wonderful man in robes with a beard, somebody like Jesus, whom I had never really liked before.

Well, said the Liar, she went. She didn't go back to her house to pack a bag or put on clogs; she went as she was: in her slippers, her shawl around her shoulders; the knitting needle, which she had stuck in her hair when she heard the splash and the rattle of the anchor dropping, went with her. The lantern guided her down the dike toward the sea, and she heard the splashing of boots in the water as the invisible men waded toward their invisible boat. Nobody offered to help her, so she put her slippers in her apron, gathered up her skirts, and waded after the lantern through the icy water. She saw the flank of a boat glistening in the fog, and had to climb into it unaided. The moment she sat down, dripping, on the middle bench, the oars rumbled out, the keel scraped free of the rocks, and the boat swung around in the darkness.

The lantern light had gone and she sat there quite alone, shivering in the fog with the sound of oars plowing the water all around her. She sat there for almost half an hour; then the lantern light flashed on again and she saw the dark, glistening wall of a big ship's side rising up beside her. A rope ladder was thrown down to her and she climbed it. The little swinging moon of the lantern followed her and made her climb into her own shadow.

She reached the rail, and climbed it, and stood on a vast deserted deck. The lantern appeared beside her and the voice said: "Follow."

She was taken to a small cabin, that at first looked quite ordinary. The lantern was left with her, the voice said: "Go to sleep," and then there was the sound of a door shutting and of a key turning in the lock.

When she began to undress and put her shawl on the little stool in the cabin, she realized that it was not an ordinary cabin at all. When she tried to lift the stool, to put it nearer to the bunk, she couldn't move it because it was too heavy. It was made of stone. She looked around her at the small objects that had seemed so normal at first glance; they were all made either of lead or stone. When she had undressed and climbed into the bunk and tried to lift the blanket, she had to use both hands for it was a rug of closely knitted iron rings. She wriggled her way underneath it, and when she put her head on the pillow it felt hard and unyielding. It was filled with sand.

She lay on her back, gazing at the ceiling, getting colder and colder under the iron blanket and on the pillow of sand. She folded her hands to pray; but before her fingers had met she stopped and lay still, for there was no use any longer to pray for her soul. She shut her eyes and thought: good-by life, good-by sound of the wind in the drying nets, good-by smell of freshly ironed aprons, good-by Schokland, my home, good-by.

She felt very sorry for herself when she thought that, but then an image dawned in the darkness of her closed eyes: a red tower, covered with unknown creeper, and a boy with a blood-soaked kerchief around his head calling her name. She smiled, because she realized that there was no point in saying good-by to anything; her life was him. With that smile on her lips she fell asleep.

When she woke up again the lantern shone no more. The cabin was light: the curious blue-green light she knew so well from her dream. The first thing she saw gave her a shiver of terror: her hair seemed to be standing on end, it rose right to the ceiling and moved softly, waving about. She was so cold that it felt as if her body wasn't there any longer; when she swung the blanket aside it was much lighter than it had been the night before.

But she didn't notice this, for when she swung the blanket aside she saw a sight that nearly made her heart stop: the lower part of her body had changed into a glistening fishtail.

While she lay staring, aghast, at her scales and the forked fin that had once been her feet, a swift shadow passed above her. When she looked up she saw it was a little fish, that had swum in through the open porthole and now floated in the middle of the cabin. The little fish stared at her curiously out of the side of its head with one gold eye, then it turned, swam around the lantern, dived, and nibbled at her clothes. When she slowly stretched out her hand toward it, it flashed away, a streak of silver, and shot out of the porthole into the green light. She rose on her elbows and was amazed how light she was; then she looked out of the porthole and saw where she was.

The ship was lying in the deserted market place of a village of ruins. On the other side of the market place was a roofless church of red bricks, its tower broken; and the tower was covered with the curious creeper that she had never been able to recognize until this moment. It was seaweed.

She got out of the bunk, but never touched the floor, for she floated. Her tail was very strong; when she made a movement of walking she shot ahead and bumped her head against the wall, but her cry of pain was soundless. She understood that she was now in a world of gentle movements and silence.

She tried to open the door but found it was still locked; then she swung around and a quiver of her tail sent her soaring toward the porthole. She stretched her arms through it and tried to make her body follow, but the porthole was too narrow. Then she gave one strong sweep with her tail, and with a tearing pain she shot out into the green light, rose high up in the sky, turned, circled over the roofs of the ruins, and descended gently at the bottom of the broken tower, the very spot where Jan had stood.

While she hovered there sadly, looking around for her lost lover, an old man crossed the market place with slow long steps, rising into the air at each step as if he danced. She stirred her tail and flashed toward him so fast that she had to rise over his head and circle around before she cautiously descended beside him. He was a very old man with one eye and old-fashioned clothes; on the top of his bald head was a brand-mark of a skull and cross-bones, and she understood that he was a pirate. She had a moment of fear, but the thought that she could flash out of his reach with one sweep of her tail gave her a feeling of security. The old man didn't look a bit amazed on seeing her; his one eye gazed at her sadly, as if the sight of her filled him with pity.

She wondered how to communicate with him in this soundless world, but he took her head between his hands, pressed his cold lips against her ear and she heard a whisper. "Jan Viool has just left." Then the old man pointed at the green dusk behind the town, and moved his lips as if to say good-by. She hesitated, for the dusk seemed to be filled with fear: slowly rising in blue circles, waving with the limp dead trees of seaweed, floating with the fleeting shadows of unseen fish. But she thought of Jan and his despair, swung her tail and shot away into the terror of that unknown world, her long hair streaming behind her, spurred by the one hope left to her: that one day, one night, she would find him.

When the Liar filled his glass again, he did it slowly. When I stirred in my rags I did it slowly. It seemed as if the world was entirely silent now; as if we had all sunk to the bottom of the ocean, unnoticed. He didn't sigh any more or smack his lips, and the click of his glass being put back on the platter was a soft thud. When he spoke again his voice was much slower, as if he was the only one who could speak under water and as if every word he said was precious to us, mute fish, gathered around him to hear the news he brought from the land we had lost.

She went, he said, from town to town. She had never known that the bottom of the sea was dotted with submerged villages and cities in which the drowned sailors waited for Judgment Day. She passed through scores of them and found that in every city there lived different people: Dutch, Norwegians, Greeks, Turks. There were cities entirely peopled by women, and villages in which only children lived. Everywhere along her way between the towns she found the silent wrecks of sunken ships, with weeds growing up their rigging and little fish playing around the mouths of their guns. It was the crews and the passengers of those sunken ships that peopled the ruins of the sunken towns.

But everywhere she arrived she got the same message whispered into her ear: "Jan Viool has just left," and every time the one who gave her that message, man, woman or child, pointed at the green dusk ahead of her.

She swam through the North Sea, the Gulf of Biscay, along the coast of Africa, until she arrived at a little village at the edge of a forest as dark as ink. The village was peopled with Portuguese fishermen, with rings in their ears, blue breeches, and long red caps on their heads with tassels which stretched out behind them when they walked with the long, dancing steps of the drowned. After one of these fishermen had taken her head between his hands again and whispered: "Jan Viool has just left," his hand rose slowly and pointed at the forest.

She wavered, for the darkness ahead of her looked so threatening that she couldn't find the courage to swing her tail and shoot into it. The fisherman saw her fear, took her head in his hands again and whispered: "Wait here." She nodded, saw him dance away into the dark inside of a roofless building, the windows of which were barred with rusty iron bars. After a while she saw the red cap emerge again from the darkness, the fisherman danced out into the green light, and behind him came a row of five people: black, naked people, their left legs linked by a chain. She understood that they must be Negro slaves, drowned while crossing from Africa to America, and wondered what the fisherman had brought them out for.

The fisherman took the head of the first Negro in his hands and pressed his lips against his ear. He whispered for a long time; the Negro nodded and his dark, dead eyes glanced at her. A silent crowd had gathered around them: Arabs in red cloaks, naked Negro girls, Turks with turbans on which still flashed the glitter of diamonds that had once been worth so much. Then the fisherman shook the Negro by the hand, and the five chained men bobbed slowly toward her until they had reached her. The first Negro put out his arms and took her head between the pale palms of his hands. She felt the brush of his thick dead lips against her ear, and heard him whisper: "Follow me."

Before she vanished into the inky darkness of the forest, following the slow procession of the five chained Negroes bobbing along, she looked around once more and saw the crowd staring after her. The fisherman stood alone in the circle; when he saw her glancing back at him he took off his red cap and waved slowly, a last good-by.

The voyage through the forest lasted for weeks. It was so full of creeping fear and sudden streaks of terror that she got exhausted by darting aside all the time, away from the shadows that swooped down on her from the tangle of the high dead trees. The trees were peopled by monsters: sharks, inkfish, horrible crabs. They all attacked her: the sharks like streaks of white lightning, turning around on their backs as they swooped down, their white bellies flashing past her as she darted away from their terrible fangs in the nick of time; the inkfish spurting darkness, slowly slithering down the trees, their slimy tentacles groping for her in swirling clouds of ink; the crabs swinging out arms as long as derricks, with wide-open claws, snapping shut just behind her glistening, flickering tail. Every time she managed to escape from the attacks of the monsters, and to rejoin the faint shimmer of the five chained men below her, whose path was lit by tiny luminous sea horses, dancing ahead like glowworms, playful sparks in the utter darkness of the sunken jungle between the continents.

When at last, exhausted, she reached the other side of the forest, she emerged into a desert overhung by solid green clouds. She had no idea where she was, but when she saw sticking out of the clouds the keels of ships, and hanging anchors slowly stirring in the circular tide, she understood that the Negroes were moving toward the center of a sea of weeds called the Sargasso Sea.

She had often heard about this sea. Sailors said that all the wrecks of the ocean that did not sink were slowly dragged toward it, to end up in the weeds and join the ghostly fleet of barnacled hulks with broken masts covered with seaweed, slowly spinning around the center of the Sargasso Sea which no human being had ever set eyes on. She remembered that when she was still a child at school an old fisherman had once told them the story of how the Sargasso Sea came into being. Jesus, the old man had said, on finding out that the land was peopled with sinners, got so disgusted that He and His apostles boarded a ship called the *Aldebaran*. In it they sailed the seven seas for centuries, and whenever a ship was being drowned by a gale and battered by waves, there would at the ultimate moment appear a blue light on the horizon, and a cross would shine in the stormy darkness: the *Aldebaran*, coming to save them. But, so the old man had said, Jesus discovered in due course that the sailors were just as disgusting a crowd of sinners as the landlubbers had been. Hopeless and tired, He had ordered His apostles to drop anchor in the loneliest spot of the Atlantic Ocean and wait there for Judgment Day. Like all ships lying still, the *Aldebaran* had started to grow weeds and barnacles. The weeds grew and grew, until they had completely overgrown the ship and covered the sea for miles around.

So when, on a dark green morning, she reached a rusty chain going straight up into the clouds, and the five Negroes sat down on the blade of an enormous anchor sticking out of the desert sand, she knew where she was. The old Negro who was the first of the gang crossed himself and then pointed upward with a pale hand to where the chain vanished in the clouds of the weeds. She hesitated for a while; but then she thought of Jan's desperate face, rose slowly along the chain and vanished in the clouds.

She seemed to rise through that swirling green mass of weeds for a very long time; then she saw a light overhead, a soft white glow like that of the sun hidden by the thin mist of a winter morning. She saw, as she got nearer, the bottom of an enormous ship, so overgrown with barnacles and mussels that it looked like the ceiling of a grotto that had been born when the world was very young. Somewhere among the rocks was a crack of light, and she swam toward it.

Amid the mussels and the barnacles she found after searching for a long time, a huge rusty iron ring, like a door knocker, and using all her strength she swung it to and fro until at last it knocked. There was a sound of heavy bolts, a creaking of huge hinges, and the crack got wider until a flat beam of golden light shone into the green darkness of the weeds like sunlight falling into a wood.

In that light she saw the face of a very old man with a white beard appear, and his blue innocent eyes gazed at her in amazement. He must be one of the apostles, and somehow she knew instantly that he was Peter. When she spoke she discovered that she had suddenly got her voice back; it sounded faint and distant, but it was unmistakably hers.

"Could you tell me," she asked, "where I can find Jan Viool, a sailor?"

53

"Who are you?" the old man asked gently.

"I am his girl," she said.

Old Peter looked at her intently, and then his face changed; as if only at that moment he realized that she was a mermaid. "You are just a few days too late," he said. "He went back to the Island of Schokland the day before yesterday, alive again."

She felt a terrible sadness and at the same time a great joy overcome her, and when she repeated: "Alive!" she felt something warm go down her cheeks, the first warmth she had felt since she had woken up in that cabin of stone, long ago.

"Yes," said Peter, while shutting the door. "He has been lucky: some fool ashore has given up his soul for him."

She didn't know what to say any more. She saw, through her tears, the sunlight shrink to a vanishing crack; then it was dark again around her, and she sank slowly down along the chain until she was back in the desert, where the huge rusty blade of the anchor lay waiting to be lifted from the sand at Judgment Day.

She sat down on the anchor, and wept. The Negroes had gone, and she was quite alone. The thought of wandering among the drowned forever without even the hope of ever reaching the man she loved made her very sad, and for a while it seemed to her as if now there was nothing left to live for. But then she thought of his despair when he would arrive in the Island of Schokland and find her gone, and it was that thought that made her sweep her tail and shoot back into the horror of the black forest, across the nightmarish miles of sunken jungle, across ocean and seas, until at last she reached the dike over which she saw the timid roofs of Emmeloord peeping at the horizon.

On the dike stood a lonely man, staring sadly at the sea. She rose from the waves and waved, but he didn't see her. She called his name, but he didn't hear her. She pleaded, shouted, jumped out of the water with a burst of silver spray, lashing the waves with her tail; but he saw and he heard nothing. He sighed, and he turned slowly around, and vanished behind the dike to go into the little house, in which she knew he would lie down to sleep and dream of a girl, standing at the foot of a broken red tower covered with seaweed, smiling at him through a green glass plate, and forming three small words with her lips which he would, one night, perhaps understand.

The Liar sighed, and uncorked the bottle. He took a long, long drink, after which he smacked his lips sadly, but then he said: "This is not the end of the story."

54

Jan Viool became the lighthouse keeper of Schokland and remained a brooder until the end of his life; but the mermaid, who was immortal, realized in the end that all men were brothers, and her love became like a fountain: it shot up toward one sailor, but it rained down on all of them. She remained in the sea around the Island of Schokland until this day, and every time a storm is brewing the fishermen hear a soft girl's voice, singing above the murmur of the waves. When they hear it they furl their sails, lock their cabins and go home to wait in bed with their wives until the gale is over, which they know will come before the dawn.

There she swims, said the Liar's voice with a hiccup, the only woman we have all looked for all our lives, and whom we will go on looking for until the Last Trump will make us one.

There was a long silence; then a voice said: "Where's my extra bottle?" and it was the high-pitched drunkard's voice again that I had first heard when the clogs entered the cabin.

I did not hear him leave; I woke up the next morning in my dog's nest on the ropes with the furry warmth of Murk close to my face. Overhead clogs were banging, and I heard the rattle of blocks as the mainsail was hoisted by Krelis and Bonk. The trap door in the partition was open, and I scrambled out before the wet anchor chain would pile up on my bed. I climbed out of the men's bunk, and when I emerged in the open I saw the Black Skipper standing at the helm and he saw me.

He beckoned to me and asked: "Like to look again, child?" and I nodded and said: "Please, sir."

He took me on his arm again, and I saw the fleet leave: hundreds of sails streaming out toward the rising sun. At one moment an Urker botter foamed past us very close and I saw, peeping over its side, a fat piggy face with a tiny Urker cap on and blue watery eyes, that blinked at the flashing silver of the sun on the sea. I thought it was a stupid fat man about to go sick, and then I heard the skipper say: "Look, there's the Liar. Boy, he must have a hangover after all the Geneva he got out of me!"

I didn't believe it until Krelis described him. The man who had sounded like Jesus was a drunk with the face of a pig, gazing sickly at the big wet sea. It took a long time before I got over the damage his face did to his story.

I SAILED ON BOARD THE HZ 69 FOR THREE MONTHS, BEFORE THE DAWN OF terror befell me.

I got to like my work; I became Krelis' friend and Bonk's mortal enemy, but I had an ally in Murk, who was also Bonk's mortal enemy because he would open the trap door in the partition and, on his way there, would walk over Bonk's face as he had once done over mine. I fell overboard in Enkhuizen harbor; was hung during punishment hour on Sunday in the bay of Monnickendam, after I had smashed up one of Krelis' clogs to make a boat out of the other; and every time we sighted the white tower of Schokland lighthouse in the distance I thought of the mermaid, and listened secretly for her song. The story that the Black Skipper raised his fist and shouted: "I'll have you yet one day!" whenever Schokland lighthouse came in sight was not true; the only thing I ever overheard him saying in reference to the lonely widow was: "There lives one hell of a female," that was all. We were struck by a gale near Urk which made me seasick again; we lay becalmed for two whole days south of Wieringen, and I had plenty of time to look at the wicked dam. It looked innocent and feeble, only a couple of yards of mud sticking out of the water at high tide. While we lay becalmed there, I overheard much talk of the blowing up, and somehow it seemed that the Black Skipper had much to do with this; I even thought for a breathless hour that we might be going to do it ourselves; but nothing happened at all.

I found a sea mouse's life was a happy one; I could think of no brighter future than to grow up into a sea boy, then into a deckhand and then into a skipper with a botter of my own, without ever going ashore again except on Sundays in the golden towns. Whenever I heard the giants talking about going home I felt miserable; but luckily the Black Skipper always said: "Why should we?" and Krelis always answered: "Why indeed."

56

But then came the half hour of dawn during which all this was changed. After that half hour I had but one timorous longing: to go home.

The night before we had put out our nets in the moonlight as usual. It was a soft misty night, with little wind and wisps of laughter and harmonica music floating in the rising haze. I went to bed snuggled up with Murk on my lap and fell asleep instantly.

I half woke during the night because of a growing noise of whistling wind and thumping water, and the loud banging of the main beam, but I went to sleep again when I heard clogs overhead and realized that Krelis and Bonk were shortening sail. The waves rocked me to sleep as they had done so often before.

I was woken up by an earthquake, a shock so tremendous that it seemed to split the ship. With one jerk the world which had become my home crumbled to ruins. While I heard the men screaming in the bunk behind the partition, everything that had hung gently rocking overhead during all those months hailed down on me in a nightmarish bombardment: blocks, glass floats, lamps, bunches of iron hooks came crashing down with a shower of glass. The ropes, piled up beside me, which had sat there solidly without shifting even during the Urker gale, were flung sideways and piled up on top of me. Murk shrieked, and tried to crawl away across me, scratching my face.

While all this happened within one second below, overhead the ship seemed to go berserk. The jib slammed its sheet-block up and down its iron rail like a horse in a stable stung by a hornet. The mainsail rattled and banged its beam from one side to the other with explosions of flapping sails: the leeboard battered the side of the ship like a ram; the whole world seemed to swing around and hurl itself into perdition, as if the moon had crashed onto the earth.

Then there was a loud tearing noise, so terrifying that I couldn't regain my breath under the pile of ropes. The leeboard, after a last reverberating bang which seemed to fill the ship with its sound until it split its sides, was torn right off with the noise of a tree falling, and I understood that we were being dragged backward at great speed.

How I managed to free myself from the pile of rubble on top of me I do not know. I heard Bonk's voice far away screaming, screaming. I heard Krelis' voice barking senseless curses, and, while biting smoke and the stench of smoldering blankets began to ooze through the cracks in the partition, I heard the Black Skipper's voice in the pandemonium, shouting: "Haul in the net!" I crawled on top of the rubble, scrambled frantically toward the manhole, and tried to lift the hatch covering it. But however much I pushed I couldn't open it more than a crack, for the fallen jib pressed it down. I stumbled toward the trap door in the partition and tried to open that, although I knew that I couldn't do so from the inside. As I banged and kicked it senselessly, the smoke pouring in through the cracks choked me and I scurried back to the hatch and attempted to lift it again, gasping for air. Then I saw, my eyes on the level of the deck, a sight which froze me.

Through the clouds of smoke, billowing from the cabin underneath the slamming beam of the mainsail, I saw the streak of a yellow dawn. And silhouetted against it, so terrifying that the sight became forever imprinted in my memory, I saw the red wings of a Volendammer's sails. Never before had I seen a Volendammer so near; it seemed huge, evil and of boundless strength. It was racing down before the wind with a mainsail on the port side of its mast and its jib stretched on a beam on starboard; in the mainsail was painted in large white letters: VD 10. But apart from these two sails it seemed to carry a dozen others: topsails, leesails, staysails and ahead of it all the huge bulging cloud of the largest balloon jib I had ever seen.

I heard a splintering crash, and beams and woodwork came tumbling down on the foredeck; it was Arie Kos's botter, slammed against us as the Volendammer with incredible strength pulled both of us backward toward the yellow dawn, dragging us by the top cable of our net folded double. I saw Skipper Kos and his deckhand, frantic black shadows against the light, hauling in their net as Krelis and the Black Skipper were doing; I saw in the cockpit of the Volendammer ahead a crowd of men in red jackets with wide baggy trousers flapping in the wind doing the same. There seemed to be dozens of them, although I had always been told that the crew of a Volendammer numbered six. They seemed to haul in their cable much faster than Arie Kos and the Black Skipper did our net; I saw the murky silver of fish pouring in over our sterns, and heard among the banging, crackling and creaking noises around me the splatter of thousands of herrings jumping on the floor of the cockpit, until they piled up so thick that I heard the men's clogs crunching them.

Perhaps it was that sound that brought me the final realization of the disaster that had befallen us: whenever I had trodden on a single fish, Krelis had called out: "It's gold!" The herrings were more precious than money, women, sleep; our lives were lived to get the herrings safe and sound on board the buyers who would race them to Amsterdam. Now the herrings, the very reason of our existence, were being crushed, in hundreds.

The Volendammers stooped and pulled while hauling in the cable of

58

their dragnet with quick rhythmic movements, as if they were pumping; and every pull brought them nearer to the tangle that had slowly risen from the sea between us and them: a tangle of floats and ropes and net and fish. The precision and the speed of their movements filled me with despair when I looked at the slow, clumsy dragging of our and Kos's crew, who were being buried by their own catch.

And yet, somehow, the tangle in the sea between us seemed to get no nearer to the Volendammers than it did to us. This was the moment I had been innocently dreaming of as a child: the battle approaching, the initiation to manhood by blood and fire; but my terror at seeing the three ships draw closer relentlessly, slowly, was indescribable. I wept and choked and scratched away at the trap door and the hatch of the manhole like a frantic caged rat; if the jib hadn't rested on it like a rock and I had been able to scramble on deck it would have meant the end of me, for I would have thrown myself overboard in panic.

When the sterns of our three ships finally touched and the slaughter began, deciding who would cut the other's net first, I could hardly see what happened, so thick was the smoke by then that poured from the cabin. I heard the animal roar of angry men, when the first pole lashed out at the enemy and its sharpened hook bit into living flesh. I didn't recognize the voices any more; it seemed as if even my world of people was now tumbling down in ruins. All human silhouettes I saw staggering in the smoke, red with the dark glow of fire, bellowed with the same bestial roar; I saw the flicker and the blow of hatchets; I saw the balls of fire of burning wads of cotton waste fall all around me. I heard a stampede of splintering clogs; the gnashing of wood crushing wood as the three ships smashed into each other, and above it all the high-pitched screech of the wind, screaming in the Volendammer's rigging.

At first the nightmare raged and swirled around me; then it sprang up from the trampled nest of my cable hole itself. I felt a double lash of pain streaking down my legs and turned around with a scream. A demon seemed to be attacking me, trying to jump up at my throat, burying its claws in my flesh; it was Murk, trying in a frenzy of animal fear to force his way out of the cracking cave we were buried in together. I didn't realize that all he did was try to jump on my shoulder to get out through the gap of the lifted hatch. I thought he was attacking me, struck by the wave of madness that had washed my world away. Time after time he sprung up at me, his claws tearing my shirt and scratching my chest as he slithered down my body. The fishy stench of his snarl as he jumped at my throat set me howling with terror. I lashed out at him with flailing arms, took off my clogs and flung them aimlessly into the darkness, then I groped around for something to defend myself with. I don't know what I grabbed, but when he jumped up at me again in a last, desperate effort to escape, I smashed the thing I had in my hands at him, heard a sickening thud, and the impact flung me backward onto the rubble.

The silence that followed was so thick with disgust that I pulled myself up at the edge of the manhole as though I was trying to drag myself out of a hole in the ice. I gazed at the hell outside with wide stinging eyes. There was a loud tearing noise, followed by a howl of wounded animals; then an explosion that racked the ship, and I saw two huge red wings soar birdless into the sea. The wail of pain clamoring from afar was drowned by a beastly shriek of victory of many voices; for a second I saw a huge shadow with a spear stagger victoriously against the smoke, the yellow sky and the red rags of the Volendammer's torn mainsail; then the spear was thrust down. The silhouette fell headlong out of my view, and there was a piercing scream of pain.

I realized, in a senseless way, that we had won and that what I had seen flying through the dawn was the Volendammer's heart, but it made no difference. I hung clinging to the edge of the ice, when I saw, distorted as in a weathered mirror, a foredeck and a lifted hatch. Out of the gap peered a child's face, weeping, so contorted with unspeakable terror that it seemed to express everything I felt. It was the beaten Volendammer's sea mouse; and never as long as I live will I forget that face. After seeing that face, for a few seconds only of one yellow dawn on the Zuider Zee, war has never contained any glory for me.

THAT DAY I CAME TO UNDERSTAND WHY THE HUIZER FLEET ALWAYS returned home without notice.

After a fight the two damaged botters had to return home for repairs; and the rest of the fleet returned with them to give them protection. For once the Volendammers had picked up their countrymen's wreck, they would line up on the course to Huizen and wait for us. If the two damaged botters went home alone, they would doubtlessly be rammed and sunk by the Volendammers swooping down on them, all their sails hoisted, traveling at great speed before the wind. Even if the whole Huizen fleet protected the victors the Volendammers might still attack, try to cross the line of the enemy and do as much damage as possible in a single thrust.

I had never heard of a full sea battle between the two fleets in the recent past, but there were various waifs in Huizen with whom I had played in the street about whom it was said that their fathers had drowned when the two fleets clashed. For while the object of a three-man scuffle was only to cut the enemy's net, once the fleets met in battle the object was to sink ships. It depended how the Volendammers took their defeat, whether it made them mad or just angry.

When, hours after we had set out for home, Krelis opened the hatch of the cable hole and found me hidden in a corner, he picked me up and carried me to the cockpit. Both he and the Black Skipper were wounded; he had his arm in a sling and the Black Skipper wore a handkerchief around his head as if he had a toothache; one of the rings in his ears had been torn out during the fight. The cockpit was covered with the bloody pulp of crushed herrings; the cabin looked terrible. The floor was scarred with burns, the bunk a blackened hole from which the wet rags of burned blankets were hanging. Everything on the shelves had come down and lay scattered on the floor. The stove itself lay dead and upturned in a corner, and sunlight shone in through the chimney hole in the deck.

I remained silent for most of the day, but normal life seemed to come back slowly with the warmth of the sun. Yet something had been destroyed in that half hour of terror that I couldn't find again. I did not know what it was: a state of mind, a feeling, a faith; but whatever it was it didn't come back, even when I saw Murk limp to his favorite spot at the foot of the mast again, groggy and dazed, attempting to lick the tar out of his fur, as if he had already forgotten what had happened.

What I lost in that half hour was my childhood, but of course I couldn't realize that. I only realized in a vague, hopeless way that I no longer wanted to be a fisherman with a botter of my own. I didn't know what to want instead because there was no other life I knew of.

I overheard the men talking about the possibility of a battle between our fleet and the Volendammers. Other botters of our village came very close to us, and I heard the skippers shout: "Will you give battle?" But every time the Black Skipper waved his hand and shook his head. Krelis argued with him; he said that we might as well stamp out the menace of the Catholic pirates now as any other time. There was half a gale blowing and if the Volendammers came down on us before the wind and we let them through they would soon be forced to turn back from the shore and start tacking into the wind. That was the time to tackle them; sailing by the wind they were much slower and clumsier than we because they had to take in all their fancy linen.

But the Black Skipper just shook his head, he didn't even bother to speak. He looked very grim with that handkerchief round his head and the blood trickling down his neck, and somehow much older. I suddenly suspected that he didn't want to give battle because he was so old, and this notion ought to have made him lose much of his glory in my eyes. But the glory of war had been frightened out of me.

We didn't give battle; the Volendammers attacked us all right but we let them through. It was a moment which caused an echo of the fear I had felt that morning: Bonk at the jib, Krelis at the sheet of the mainsail, the Black Skipper at the helm, all staring tense and rigid at starboard. The roaring gush of the bow waves of a fleet of botters approaching, a sharp command from the skipper at the helm; then the jib swished down, the ship swung into the wind, and on each side of us the towering red sails of a Volendammer soared past. There were a few shouts and a stone crashed into our cockpit, but that was all; Krelis screamed: "Let's get them now! Let's get them now!" but the Black Skipper said: "Shut up," and brought the ship back on its course.

I knew we were approaching our village when I saw Krelis and Bonk that night hoist six baggy trousers on the flag line. I heard the echo of our bow waves as we sailed into the piers. Then there came what had once been the most glorious sound of my dreams: the cheering of the women and the children on the quay, but it was nothing like what I had imagined it to be; for one thing it sounded much fainter to us on board than it did to the cheering crowd itself. But the main reason why it didn't elate me the way I had always thought it would, was that I now knew what they were cheering about: the face of a Volendammer sea mouse, contorted with fear.

It suddenly seemed that of all the hours I had spent on board the Black Skipper's ship only one remained untainted by that face: the hour I had sat behind the partition listening to the voice with the soft Urker accent telling the story of the mermaid.

I felt very tired and dispirited and wanted to go home, never mind what Mem would do to me; but when we were about to make fast Krelis locked me up in the cable hole. I said: "I want to go home," but he answered: "No, no, you are a big boy now; tomorrow we will sail again." Before he shut the hatch he said: "And don't whistle or call through the hawsehole or I'll hang you." Then the light went out and I heard the sounds of a chain being padlocked.

I sat there for a while, and slowly the realization dawned on me that whatever I might dream and whatever I wanted, my life was being decided for me. I would never get off this ship again, but be forced to grow up into a sea boy and then into a deckhand and then into a skipper with a ship of my own. I got up, scrambled to the hawsehole and shouted: "Help! Help!" and "Mem! Mother Bout!" and "Let me out! Let me out!" but nobody answered. At first I thought that surely Mother Bout and Jaap and Bulle would be looking for me on board all the ships of the fleet and end up by finding me; but then I realized that nobody had seen the Black Skipper pick me up that night after I fell into the harbor. They must have found my clothes on the pier, hanging over the dead remains of a fire, and thought I was drowned.

The knowledge that in all the cable holes of all the botters in the harbor a sea mouse sat in the darkness, locked up like me, didn't give me any comfort. I didn't want to be a sea mouse any longer like Kris Muis and the others; I wanted to go home—I was a coward. I shouted, whistled, banged on the hatch and the partition, rattled the anchor chain until it grew dark; but all I heard was the sound of the water lapping against the sides of the ship, the creaking of wood of the botters rubbing sides, and distant steps of clogs on the quay. The wind rose, the tapping of the ropes against the masts grew to a rattle; nobody would ever hear me in that world full of wind and noise. I fell asleep miserably, cold and lonely without the warmth of Murk on my lap; he was promenading the quay with the other cats—nobody would ever dream of caging him.

I was woken up in the middle of the night by a sound of heavy rain. It drowned all other noises in the harbor, a monotonous relentless sound of utter melancholy. I came back to the surface of reality feeling as if the rest of my life would be like this: lying on my back in the dark, alone, listening to an endless rain. Then suddenly there was a sharp scratching overhead and a dotted line of tiny ticking noises crossed the deck. I understood it was Murk who had jumped back on board, sheltering from the rain; and the moment I realized that I heard the sharp click of a lock and a bang in the darkness, and a gust of cold air came toward me. I heard a soft meow, and then I was sprayed with drops as Murk shook the rain out of his suit.

It had happened so suddenly and unexpectedly, that I didn't realize that Murk, by opening the trap door, had set me free until I heard in my memory the voices of the Black Skipper and Krelis, that first night long ago: "Have you found out yet how the others got away?" and: "No, someone must have sneaked on board and let them out."

When Murk's wet fur touched my face, as he curled up to go to sleep the way he had been used to for all these months, I jumped and flashed out of the open trap door, the way the other mice had escaped before me.

WHEN I HAD LOWERED MYSELF CAUTIOUSLY ALONG THE HAWSER ONTO THE quay I peered along it for minutes, hidden behind a bollard before I dared venture into the open. The rain was so heavy that it soaked me instantly, but I didn't notice it. The rain had emptied the quay of giants; it had made them hurry for shelter like Murk had done.

I left my clogs behind and scurried across the quay to the smokery. As I sidled my way along it toward the first houses of the village, it was like coming home to a sunken world. The sound of water was tremendous, the rain fell in straight silver wires through the gaslight. I crept along walls and through the narrow wet alleys of dripping nets, until I had reached home. I had no idea what the time was, but it must have been very late for I had passed no lighted windows on my way, and the windows of our house were also dark. I climbed over the gate, ran through puddles and past gurgling gutters to the back of the house. There I looked up at the attic window, put my cold hands around my mouth and gave the soft screech of a sea gull.

The rain clattered on the tiles of the courtyard, gushed down from the roof, rustled in the dead rushes of the screen around the washing place. I screeched again, louder, but no one answered. The rain drowned everything.

I stood there screeching for a long time; then suddenly a wavering light appeared behind the flyscreen of the kitchen window. A huge shadow shrunk on the steamed glass, a hand wiped an opening in the moisture and I saw two anxious eyes peep out in candlelight: it was Mem.

I heard her voice from very far away calling: "Who's there?" and I answered, still the sea gull: "Me!"

The next instant the kitchen door was torn open and she appeared like a ghost in the doorway. Her head was covered with bits of newspaper and she wore a long white nightshirt, her hand on her throat. I went slowly

65

toward her through the rain. She lifted the candle, and the scream she gave made me dart past her like a wet cat into the safety of the kitchen, for I was sure that it had made all the fishermen of Huizen sit bolt upright in their beds.

She turned around, aghast, her mouth wide open, and she suddenly looked very human and nice, perhaps because she was without her spectacles and her teeth. "Darling!" she cried, put the candle down on the kitchen table and soaked herself to the skin by picking me up and pressing me against her and kissing me all over my face with a thin hard mouth. Then she let go of me, staggered toward the door to the attic with the arid front of her body clearly imprinted in her wet gown, opened the door and shrieked: "Jaap! Bulle! Come downstairs, he's back!"

There was no sound from upstairs. She had to climb halfway up and beat the attic floor with her bare hands, screaming: "Get downstairs or I'll smack you!" before I heard the thumping of feet on the ceiling. When she came back she looked at me with tears in her eyes, shivering. "Darling," she said, "look at you, I must make you something hot!" And then she scuttled toward the stove and began banging and clattering with pans, while Jaap and Bulle came creeping down the stairs, yawning, with tousled hair and very light eyes.

At first they weren't at all excited to see me. They said: "Hello" and "Oi-oi," rubbed their eyes and yawned again; then they climbed onto the chairs around the table and sat down with their faces in their fists, blinking at the candle and yawning.

Mem screamed: "Undress!" and lit the lamp. I took off my wet clothes until I stood naked in the kitchen. Then the sight of me seemed to make some memory stir in Bulle's head. He looked at me vaguely and said: "Coo; we thought you were dead." I said: "No, I was stolen by the Black Skipper."

Then their eyes woke up. "The Black Skipper?" said Jaap; he blinked, sat up and asked eagerly: "Then were you in the fight?" I said: "Yes," and then Mother Bout came tumbling down the attic steps with a blanket and a pair of bed slippers. She wrapped me up in the blanket, put me on a chair, said: "Put his slippers on, can't you see he is freezing?" Jaap and Bulle got off their chairs and put on my slippers for me, while she was rubbing my hair with a towel. It was a pity that she did it so roughly, for I felt that this was a moment that should have been beautiful: Jaap and Bulle kneeling at my feet, and a pan of milk steaming on the stove at dawn.

When I had my slippers on and Mother Bout had finished rubbing my head she sat down, her eyes wide and innocent in the lamplight, and said:

"Now tell us everything! Where on earth have you been?" And I began to tell my story.

I had never told a story before in my life, but I didn't realize this at first. All I had done so far was to listen and to talk, but I had never talked alone, there had always been others talking with me. I only realized that I was telling a story to three silent listening people, when I came to the moment that the Black Skipper had picked me up. I suddenly became conscious of the fact that if I told the truth it would do him harm, and I halted for a moment, at a loss. Then I heard myself saying: "When I found that my clothes didn't dry I set out for home, but at the harbor when I saw men in the distance I remembered that I was naked and I thought how angry you would be, and perhaps beat me, and so I stowed away on board the Black Skipper's botter."

It was a lie, so stupendous, that after finishing it breathlessly, I sat for a second waiting for Jesus to swoop down on me in hot revenge. But nothing happened but that Mother Bout's eyes filled with tears. "Poor darling," she sniffed, "I knew it was all my fault."

The stupendousness of my lie was topped by the stupendousness of the truth it had evoked, and I felt during that long moment as if my whole world of laws and conscience was sagging. How could it be that instead of slapping me, Jesus had come so justly down on Mother Bout who had indeed been the cause of it all?

But my voice went on without betraying the chaos in my conscience. I told about Murk and Bonk and the silver of the fish in the sunrise, of the triangular black expanse of the jib when Krelis opened the hatch that morning, of the needles in the frying oil, the smell of the coffee, the Black Skipper's spectacles and the glittering promise of the golden towns floating on the evening haze. Then Mother Bout uttered a sharp cry, as there was a hissing sound; the milk had boiled over.

We were given steaming hot mugs of chocolate and crunchy biscuits with more butter on them than we used to get in a whole day; she even sprinkled sugar on top of them. And when we had finished with the biscuits she brought out the tin with the colored portrait of the Queen on top, in which the Sunday sweets were hidden that we had never even seen, because she handed them out only to the gossiping women who used to come to visit her between the church services, in the stuffy parlor smelling of wax and mothballs that we were not allowed to enter.

The sweets should have been the biggest treat we ever had, but neither Jaap nor Bulle nor I took more than five, munching them without really

67

noticing what we were doing; and the reason was that I had gone on telling my story.

It was a story that amazed me as much as the others, gazing at me motionlessly in the lamplight, wide awake without hearing the wheels of the first milk cart rattling past on the cobbles. For although I told the truth, yet it was one big bunch of lies; for I got mixed up with what I had been told and what I had experienced. I found myself telling about a singing crowd carrying a helpless policeman in torchlight and flinging him through the window into the burgomaster's parlor. I told about the big conspiracy to blow up the dike as if I had sat in on all the secret meetings instead of only having guessed what the whispers behind the partition were about. I told, the saddest lie of all, how brave I had been during the terrific battle with the Catholic pirates; how I had seen the baggy trousers torn off the behinds of the cringing Volendammers, wailing for mercy; how the enormous hands of the Black Skipper had beaten howls of pain and humiliation out of them while Krelis held their arms and Bonk and I each sat on a squirming leg. I couldn't understand why I told this, for the face of the Volendammer sea mouse seemed to look at me in despair as if I was betraying something, a secret pledge that was worth more than all the flags and the cheers and the glory. But yet somehow the story I told was the truth. This was the way I would have told it if I had floated overhead like a sea gull and seen it all happen below me, instead of having been trapped in the cable hole full of smoke with Murk going mad in the darkness.

It was not until I began telling the story of the mermaid that the great truth came to me, like a sunrise in the chaos. The lamp remained lit, although the dawn had long since bleached its light. The three listening people gazed at me in wonder and didn't notice the growing sounds of the morning. When the mermaid sank slowly down the anchor chain through the waving green clouds of the seaweed, and sobbed on the rusty blade sticking out of the desert sand at the thought that she now had nothing left to live for, Mother Bout shook her head in pity and sighed.

Then I knew for the first time what I have known ever since, and I still have not decided whether to be glad or sorry.

I was a born Liar.

TWENTY-FIVE YEARS AFTER I HAD BECOME A LIAR, I PASSED ONCE MORE THE place where I had seen the face that I betrayed. I passed it in a car.

The Zuider Zee was no more. The big dam across its mouth had been completed long ago without anybody ever trying to blow it up; most of the land submerged by the great flood of 1302 had been reclaimed.

I had passed through the villages of my youth and found them unrecognizably changed. The harbors were dead, the smokeries, net-knitteries and shipyards had vanished and been replaced by bicycle works, radio stations and factories of anti-indigestion pills. The old costumes were seen no longer in the streets, except on very old people who had sunken below the general social level. Louts in plus fours and zoot suits chewed gum and smoked drooling cigarettes under the old elm trees, where once the fishermen had cursed the price of the herring and whispered about blowing up the dam. The clogs had been replaced by high-heeled shoes, and the "oi-oi" of yore by "hiya."

After this sad voyage through the land of my childhood I arrived at the border of the new polder that had once been the sea. I was in a dark mood, haunted by the wolf calls of a loudspeaker in the market place, where once old Henk's croaking voice had sung the praise of his smoked eels with an Arabian melody. But after I had driven through the gap in the dike, which was the entrance to the northeast polder, the newest part of our planet, I forgot what had happened to my past.

Where once the silver sheet of the sea had stretched out to the blue haze of the horizon, underneath that green sky the like of which I have never seen again, lay now a plain so breath-taking in its geometric vastness, with the straight lines of its canals and its roads all converging on the distant horizon, that it seemed for a moment as if I heard again that sickening roar of the cheering crowd on the quay after a great victory.

I hazarded into this strange forbidding land with a curious shyness. It

69

was unbelievable that so small a country as Holland could suddenly take on the vastness of a continent. The new land wasn't ready yet to be plowed and sown; it was still only a colossal flat expanse of water, roads and mud, under a sky with lonely sailing clouds.

The strangest thing about this plain was its utter loneliness. It seemed as if suddenly—with my car, my memories and my tweed cap—I found myself on the moon. I crawled along a muddy road, stretching straight into infinity, and passed close to a narrow hill with a house and a cluster of old trees rising from the desert of mud. Only when I saw a sort of quarry surrounded by a jetty with football goals in its center, did I realize that this had been the Island of Schokland. I looked for the lighthouse, but it was no longer there; it must have been demolished for its bricks, and used to harden the roads.

As I sat staring at the hill, which seemed to be a relic from Roman times in the emptiness of this new geometric world, I experienced a wintry feeling that must be known to very old people only. A world had vanished which was the source of my life; I sat there lonely, tired, helpless with the memories I seemed no longer to share with anybody.

I penetrated deeper into the new land, and as I did so I saw at long intervals the scaffoldings of new farms being built, sticking pointlessly in the mud. Next to them were little wooden shacks looking like hencoops, in which families seemed to live waiting until their houses would be finished, for I saw lonely laundry fluttering on lines but I saw no human being, not even an animal about.

In the heart of this boundless emptiness I hit upon a village of prefabricated wooden houses, and it was there that I heard the first sound since I had entered the northeast polder, except for the humming of my car's engine. I heard a choir of high-pitched children's voices singing in triple descant about a little horseman who fell in love with a little maiden and betrayed her.

I stopped the car and looked around for where the sound came from. It came from one of the prefabricated houses, slightly larger than the others, with steamed windows and a brand-new bell on top. When the little horseman had blown up the nunnery and shot himself, and his three friends had become monks, there was a confused noise of chirping voices and the stumbling of clogs on wooden floors; then the bright new doors of the shack burst open and from it poured a swarm of children, whose shrill little voices seemed to fill only a handful of sky with their tiny sparrow's sound.

Three little girls with white plaits flying came running toward me, swinging their school bags. "Are you going to Emmeloord?" they called. "Are you going to Emmeloord?"

I looked at them stupidly, for to me Emmeloord was a sunken village whose bells still rung when the ground seas of a gale stirred them; the village from which the mermaid of Schokland had set out for her pilgrimage of love. I said: "Yes, but you will have to tell me where it is."

"Road 65-B!" the girls chanted, thinly as high sea gulls, and they clambered into the car.

We set out to cross the moon again, and when I took one of the dead-straight mud tracks, leading to nowhere, at random, they cried: "That's 80-C! That one goes to Rutten!"

I asked where Rutten was; and they said it didn't exist yet, but they could point it out on the map. I took another road, which they pointed out to me, and then I asked whether Emmeloord existed. They laughed at the joke and said: "Of course! Emmeloord is Mom and Dad and Kees and us. It's a very big town, the biggest in the polder. One day the governor will live there in a stone house and there will be a cinema."

I asked whether anybody else lived there yet but Mom and Dad and Kees and they. They said no, Dad was still making it.

At first, as I drove into nothing with the three tiny voices of a new race of man chippering behind me, I felt older than when I had looked at the football goals in Schokland harbor. But when I asked whether there was anything growing in the new polder yet, they said: "Oh yes, the forest of Urk."

They said it with a curious conspiratory softness in their voices, that I seemed to remember from long ago. I asked them whether they had ever been there; and then they told me a curious story.

Around a little village on a hill called Urk there was a wood which had not been sown, but that had just grown up when the water receded. It was a very thin wood, and always misty, and the strangest things grew there: giant ferns, silver willows, toadstools as big as tables, and one night not long ago one of them, walking home from school along the edge of this wood, had seen something move among the waving reeds. At first she had not known what it was, and she was frightened for it looked like a dead tree following her silently, peering at her over the reeds. Then there had been a sudden rustle, a brown shadow had flashed from one shrub to the other. Dad and Mom did not believe her, but she knew what she had seen. It was a deer. Did I know how it had got there? It must have got there somehow, although Dad and the master said it was impossible as there were no deer in Holland for hundreds of miles around.

When I said that what she saw must have been the mermaid, they looked at me blankly and I realized that her story had died with the sea. When one of them asked: "Mermaid, what is that?" I didn't know the answer, for "a woman with a fishtail" would have sounded preposterous in this merciless new land.

When I put them down at a muddy crossroads, about a mile from a little wooden shack with a smoking chimney hidden in the gathering dusk, one of them said to the other: "Careful, careful," and I saw her stoop to pick up a piece of bread that had fallen in the mud. She noticed that I had seen it, looked around at the shack a mile away as if afraid of being overheard, and then she whispered: "We always take that with us for when we shall see the deer again."

Then they rushed off, very small on that road under that sky, and I set out for home.

When I drove through the gap in the dike I no longer felt old and alone, nor did I feel that anything real had been lost. All that had happened was that a children's sea had turned into a children's land.

The Distant Shore *Part I* WAR

CHAPTER ONE

WHEN I ARRIVED IN ENGLAND EARLY IN THE WAR, AFTER ESCAPING FROM occupied Holland, I was appointed captain of an ocean-going tugboat on the Western Approaches.

I was amazed by this appointment, for I had been out of the service for seven years. I had started on ocean-going tugboats as a boy, worked my way up to mate in eight years' service, then I had quit and joined the Amsterdam Harbor Police, which was a nicer job. Dutch ocean-going tugboats are different from the busy little things one sees scurrying about in harbors, pulling or pushing the liners about. They are the same sort of vessel but three times as large, intended for salvaging ships in distress or towing drydocks and other large material across the oceans. After a voyage of seventeen months I had called it a day.

When I got my commission in London I told them that I didn't think myself good enough for it, but they laughed. As any man will believe it when people tell him that he is too modest, and as there didn't seem to be room for discussion left after someone had said, "This is an order," I went to the store, tried on several uniforms, got one that was too tight under the arms, and set out for my wartime destination with a suitcase.

The destination was Westport, a medium-sized harbor in the extreme southwest of England. I vaguely remembered it from a visit ten years before, when I had been a bosun's apprentice. I remembered a big, noisy port, a restaurant called Lyons, and a little tattooist's shop with a notice in the window: "Three-colored mermaids, painless and indelible, 2/6 per square inch." I remembered also an artificial hill in the middle of the town, with a tower on top and a gilt angel on top of the tower. Someone had told me that it was a symbol of the independence of Westport: the hill and the tower had been erected in honor of a man who had not discovered America, and the angel spreading its wings toward the New World faced the wrong way.

When I came back to Westport, one foggy autumn evening in 1941, the things I remembered were still there, but little else; the rest had been bombed out of existence. The center of the town was a waste of dunes of rubble, dotted with broken chimney stacks and twisted girders like tree trunks after a forest fire. There wasn't a single house left standing, but the tower on the artificial hill had survived.

The angel still faced east defiantly, its gilt blistered and one of its wings broken, but the prim little lawns with the heart-shaped flower beds and the evergreen shrubs trimmed to resemble cocks and poodles that I remembered from my visit ten years ago had changed into a nightmarish jungle. In the straggling grass, among the ruins of what once had been ornamental benches, scores of lovers rolled about, as uninhibited as animals. Only the women looked different from one another in the dusk; all the men were in uniform. In the middle of the jungle stood a huge, blistered notice board on thin poles, saying: "Carpet beating strictly forbidden."

My marching orders told me that I was billeted in the Grand Hotel on the Esplanade, and so I started toward the harbor. As I turned a corner I suddenly found myself facing the little tattooist's shop. The top floors of the building had gone, but the basement with the shop was still there. Its window had shrunk to a solitary pane in a shutter of asbestos, and showed a new notice: "Names and hearts removed without a trace." Under the circumstances it seemed a grim joke.

I found the Grand Hotel without much difficulty. It was one of two huge lumps of masonry left standing on the boulevard that skirted the harbor. The first was a block of flats called "Seaview," then there was half a mile of rubble, and after that the Grand Hotel. I worked my way toward it through a teeming crowd of sailors of many nationalities, British soldiers and R.A.F. men, through which dispatch riders on motor bikes weaved at great speed. When one of them stopped and took off his crash-helmet I saw that they were girls.

The Grand Hotel was a somber three-storied building with a mock-Grecian façade. I expected it to be requisitioned as a naval billet, but when I entered through the swing doors I saw that this could not be true. In the hall sat a crowd of old ladies in wicker chairs, with little doll's coffee sets on wicker tables in front of them, listening to the nine o'clock news. They were an island in a sea of uniformed males, who stood about sipping cocktails, and drowning the bland voice of the B.B.C. announcer with shouts and jokes in a language I hadn't heard for a long time. It was Dutch.

Apart from the last stand of the old ladies, the entire population of the Grand Hotel seemed to be Dutch. I saw only two kinds of uniforms: pilots' and sailors'. The pilots were of the K.L.M., the Royal Dutch Airlines, and the sailors wore the same uniform as I. I carried my suitcase to the desk and was greeted by a surly old porter with the words: "Jesus! Another one!"

By his side sat a lady with glasses, who gave me a motherly smile and said, "Welcome home, Captain; I hope you will be very happy here. Your room is No. 77, very nice and warm because it is just over the Turkish bath." She turned to the old porter and said, "Take the Captain to his room, Francis, and make sure that he gets a towel of his own."

The porter grabbed my suitcase, tried to lift it, said, "Jesus" again, and then, "Follow me," in a tone that made me climb the stairs with apprehension.

The apprehension was right. Room 77 resembled the Black Hole of Calcutta. It had three sets of bunks in three layers, a window consisting almost entirely of asbestos, a cracked wash basin, a mirror with the word "chronometer" written on it with soap, and it was infernally hot. Clothes, shoes, caps, bits of newspaper with the remains of meals, and empty beer bottles lay strewn about. The beds were unmade and the ceiling covered with crude drawings of the female anatomy, obviously made by the occupants of the top berths.

I wondered which one would be mine; the porter helped me out. He dumped my suitcase among the rubble and said, "You're up on top there; Captain Wolters' bunk. He killed himself last week." He turned to go; before he closed the door behind him, he said, "And don't piss in the wash basin, there is a perfectly good lavatory at the top of the stairs."

I said, "Thank you," and fumbled in my pocket for a coin.

He saw it and spat. "Keep the change," he said, "all I want is peace."

I managed a smile, and said, "So do I."

He looked at me with one eye closed, like a photographer, and said, "You'll have it, Captain, before you know what hit you. The average life of you boys is three months." Then he added, enigmatically, "Ask Miss Headland," and shut the door.

I was tired, but very much awake. I took off my jacket as it was hurting me under the arms; then I decided that I might as well undress altogether and go to bed. I had some difficulty in finding room for my clothes; I ended up by putting them on the only chair in the room, which stood in the middle of the floor.

After I had climbed into my bunk and lay down to sleep I saw, on the wall next to my pillow, a poem written by a schoolmastery hand:

> There is an old belief
> that on some distant shore
> far from despair and grief
> old friends shall meet once more.

I wondered whether Captain Wolters had written this, and decided he hadn't, for it looked more than three months old.

I remember vaguely the sounds of voices and the splashing of water that half woke me several hours later, but I didn't bother to look down and introduce myself. Not only had the heat doped me, it seemed hardly worth the trouble.

Toward dawn I was woken up by a loud banging on the door, and a voice shouting, "Captain! S.O.S.!" I recognized the voice of the old porter.

Nobody else in the room seemed to have heard it; the hot silence was full of wheezes and snores. The door was opened and the light switched on; the porter came in, muttering, and shook the shoulder of a shape in the middle bunk of the tier opposite me. As the shape did not react, he repeated his call, "Captain! S.O.S.!" then he muttered, "Jesus! drunk as an owl," shuffled out of sight, and there was a sound of water.

He came back with a dripping face towel in his hand, which he rubbed in the shape's neck, calling: "Coo-coo, Captain," and "Wakey-wakey," as if he was in a night nursery. The shape woke up, cursing, kicked off its blankets, and two bare legs were swung out of the bunk. They looked very young.

After the porter had left, their owner came out into the open. He was a fair-haired boy; his tousled hair gave him an almost childish appearance. He groped among the disorderly pile of clothes on the chair until he had found his own; I watched him with amazement. He seemed far too young to be a captain; I thought that he must be an airman until I saw him put on a jacket with four stripes on its sleeves. They looked incongruous on him; in my tugboat days captains had been at least forty-five, he looked as if he had just left naval college. He dressed with an amazing speed considering his condition; when he left the room he had the good grace to switch off the light, and left me wondering in the dark. On my way to Westport I had felt nervous and insecure at the idea of being the captain of a tugboat; after seeing him I felt like an old hand at the game.

As I tried to fall asleep again I had a curious feeling. It had to do with memories and loneliness, with old standards crumbling and a growing new fear. I felt as if I was about to cross a shadow line; as if for me the war had not yet really started, despite the things that had happened during my escape. I suddenly felt a great sympathy for the unknown boys, wheezing and snoring around me. I remembered the poem on the wall with a sensation of beauty and understanding; as if I had already set out toward that distant shore, as if we already were old friends, before I even knew their names.

I lay in the darkness and heard the town wake up. I heard the distant booming of hooters in the harbor, the growing and diminishing roar of the first motor bikes streaking past. I thought of the girls with the crash-helmets who rode them, the sheltered lives they had left to pin up their hair and put on breeches and roar through the dawn, knowing more about two-cylinder engines and death than they had ever known about algebra and love. I saw the solitary pane in the asbestos window grow pink, and thought of the boy with the four stripes on his jacket. For the first time in my life I felt old, and yet I wasn't even thirty.

Next morning I had breakfast in a huge dining room full of bleary-eyed characters with hangovers, seated untidily at long tables with communal teapots and huge sugar bowls that looked like sand pits after playtime. The only spots of defiant tidiness in that dining room were the little one-man tables at which sat the old ladies reading *The Daily Telegraph* and *The Times*.

During breakfast an airman came in, followed by a tired private carrying a huge bunch of bananas. The airman ripped off a strip of bananas at each of the little tables, offered them to the old lady behind it with a bow and a flowery little speech; then he slumped into a chair at one of the long tables and said, "Hell's bells! They nearly got me this time." Someone asked, "Where?" and the airman answered, "Three hundred miles west of Gib," before he yelled, "Lily! Breakfast!" Nobody commented upon this.

After breakfast I reported at Headquarters, as ordered. I was directed to a small red brick building at the end of a pier, carrying His Britannic Majesty's Coat of Arms and the legend hewn in granite: "H.M. Customs and Excise." On the heavy oak door a piece of three-ply had been nailed, saying: "R.N.A.N., OTWA, R.H.Q., Knock."

I knocked, a voice shouted, "Ja!" and on opening the door I heard a multiple twittering of radio signals, as if I had entered the birds' gallery in a zoo. Three wireless receiving sets were lined up on a bench along the right-hand wall with loud-speakers above them; the left-hand wall was empty but for an enormous desk. Behind it sat an angry old tugboat Captain, faced by a young Lieutenant Commander of the British Navy, who was busy cleaning his nails. I remembered the Captain's face from an earlier occasion: he had been a member of the jury when I passed through the ordeal of the Mate's examination for ocean-going tugboats. I had been frightened by him then; when I told the story of the examination later I had made fun of it, because it consisted mainly of shouting; whoever bellowed the usual tugboat service commands loudest was sure to pass with praise. Now I was frightened of him again.

He talked to me in a husky voice, and every word seemed to travel across to me on a widening ring of gin fumes. What he said was difficult to understand because of the frantic twittering of the loud-speakers on the opposite wall. I understood that my ship, the *Zeeland*, was at present in dry dock for repairs, and that this was fortunate because it enabled me to acquaint myself again with the service as a guest on one of the active tugboats during the next week. He talked in an angry voice about the noble character of OTWA, calling it at least six times: "The Red Cross of the ocean." Apart from this obviously hackneyed phrase, which he uttered with the impatient boredom of an overworked man, the only thing I understood from all he said was that OTWA was short for "Ocean-going Tugboats Western Approaches." But suddenly one word made me sit up: the name of the Captain on whose ship I would be a guest until the *Zeeland* was put back into service. The name was Dop.

I knew Jan Dop very well indeed. We had gone through the same year of Naval College and sailed together off and on on various trips until I quit. He was a nice chap but a bit wild: when I had thought of him at all since the beginning of the war I had pictured him sitting quietly in some apartment somewhere in Rotterdam or Amsterdam with a girl, planning boyish excursions into the black market. Hearing his name that morning was like seeing a raft swirl past; I asked the old Captain, excitedly, where I could find him. The Captain said, "Wait a minute," and shouted at the radio desk, "Hey! Whereabouts is the *Vlieland?*"

One of the three men sitting with their backs to us answered, without looking round, "Just passed B.R. on his way home, with a tanker in tow."

"Bishop Rock," said the Captain. "He'll be back in about four hours; you report here at 11 A.M. Good-by."

When I came back at eleven I found the old Captain in a rage. He was banging the table and shouting at the top of his voice, but no one paid any attention to him. The loud-speakers twittered; the three men sat underneath them with their backs to him, scribbling; the English officer had finished cleaning his nails and was now carefully filling his lighter. When I came in the old Captain started to shout at me.

"The bastards!" he screamed, "the sneaking sharks! This is the second they have got within two weeks! If from now on my ships don't get fighter cover, or are at least fitted out with guns that can shoot level, I'm quitting this job!" He shouted these last remarks at the British officer opposite him, who didn't look up, but went on filling his lighter. I understood that a tugboat had been sunk by a U-boat, and thought for a moment with a feeling of nausea that it was Jan Dop's. But when I asked the old Captain he answered, "No," in a tone as if he regretted it. It was the *Friesland,* he said, with Captain Daamen, the youngest skipper of the fleet but the best. It was always the best who went first in his bloody war. I realized that Captain Daamen had been the boy I had seen woken up by the porter the night before.

Dop's ship came in half an hour later. I watched her through the steamed windows of the office. She rounded the pier at reckless speed and backed roughly into the row of tugboats opposite; I heard a splintering noise, and saw her mast tremble as her stern hit the quay; in our old days Dop would have been called on the mat for this. His crew was still mooring when I saw him jump ashore off the poop, followed by a man in a gaudy uniform that looked like an admiral's.

When he came into the office he was very noisy and very nervous. When he saw me he fell silent. He looked at me for a moment, his mouth open, and it was a moment of uncanny truth; never since have I seen him show his secret so plainly. He was a man terrified out of his wits.

He recovered in a flash, shouted, "No!" and practically jumped on my neck. He was exactly like the old Dop I had known: happy-go-lucky, breezy, and loud. He completely hid the terror which I had seen. He slapped my shoulders, pulled my hair, thumped my chest, and shouted the curses that are the Dutchman's only expression of strong emotion. Then the old Captain called, "Hey, you two! Go and play outside, don't keep this bird waiting, he has to go on!"

The bird was the man I had taken for an admiral from afar; he turned out to be the captain of a Yugoslav tanker. I remember the strong smell of petrol he brought into the room, and his dazed dark eyes. Dop and he filled out a number of forms, stating what had happened to his ship, where Dop had picked him up, what opposition they had encountered from the enemy, what course they had taken to get here, and how long it had taken them. Dop was very matter-of-fact about it all; it was obvious that he had done this many times before; but the Yugoslav Captain was dazed and went on rubbing his eyebrows, trying to remember exactly, formulating painstaking answers in an English entirely his own. After they had signed the forms and Dop had said, "Well, that's it, Skipper. Be seeing you sometime," the Yugoslav rose solemnly to his feet, put out a grimy hand, and said, "Aye wande zenk yu ver zavink my sheep." Dop shook hands quickly, said, "Any time, Skipper, any time," and whispered to me, "Let's beat it."

The old Captain called after us, "Hey, your pills!" when Dop had already opened the door to go out. He hurried back and grabbed the envelope offered to him. The Captain said, "And no monkey business you two; be either at your flat or in the hotel. I don't want to rouse the whole bloody town again in the middle of the night, trying to hunt down Captain Dop on a binge." Dop said, "O.K., O.K.," good-naturedly, and shut the door.

Outside was a lovely autumn morning. When we stood in the wind Dop grabbed my shoulders, held me at arm's length, and said, "Fancy seeing you here! God, this is wonderful." Then he put his arm round my shoulders and we walked clumsily down the pier. His arm trembled.

It was difficult to choose from all the questions I wanted to ask him and all the things I wanted to say, so after a few moments of silence I asked him what the pills were the old Captain had given him. He said, "Oh, stuff to sleep. They used to give us a tin at a time, but after Wolters swallowed them all at one helping and killed himself, they started handing them out three at a time after each trip." Then he looked at me with a grin and said, "God, I'm glad he did it, the dope, for otherwise you wouldn't have turned up."

I didn't understand this, and he told me that Wolters had been one of the two captains of the *Zeeland*, I was to replace him. Dop was sure he hadn't wanted to commit suicide, but had taken the stuff when he was drunk. When I asked him what he meant by "One of the two captains," he gave me the first concrete information about OTWA I had received so far. Each tugboat had two crews, one took over from the other the moment the ship came in from a trip so that it could sail again instantly if necessary. During the trip no one on board shut an eye, it would be impossible to keep the ships in constant readiness without having two crews. That was why the officers lodged in the Grand Hotel and the crews on an old channel steamer lying in the harbor. No one slept on board.

I thought at first that we were on our way to the Grand Hotel when we walked along the boulevard; but when we got to the door and I stopped he said, "Are you crazy? I've got a flat."

"A flat," I repeated.

"Yes," he said, "didn't you know? I am the only Dutchman in this town who has got a flat of his own. A flat and a girl." When he said this he grinned, with the look of boyish bravado in his eyes that I remembered best about him. It was that look that had made me assume during the past year that he was sure to have found a job in the black market. Seeing him grin like that gave me a feeling of great friendship for him, and I grinned back and slapped his shoulder, and said, "Good old Dop. What is she like?" He winked and said, "You come and have a look, chum. The best peach on the tree."

The flat was on the top floor of the other clump of masonry left standing on the boulevard: the block called "Seaview" which I had passed the night before. There was a lift, but its gate carried a lopsided notice "Out of order," which looked as if it had hung there for years. We climbed ten flights of gritty stairs, two flights to a floor. On each floor were three identical doors with aluminum numbers on them. The top floor was the lightest, for in the ceiling was a broken skylight that had once been covered with asbestos and through which sunlight now poured in. The floor beneath it was stained by rain and soot in an irregular pattern, which looked like a map of Africa. Dop stopped in front of the left hand door, No. 12. The top of the "2" was loose, and the number hung upside down. He pulled a key from his pocket and opened the door. The flat was silent, it felt as if no one was there. The door opened directly into a small kitchen dining room, very tidy, with red checkered curtains on the window. Dop took off his cap, threw it on the table, and called, "Hey, where are you?" Then a door in the far corner of the room opened, and a girl came in.

She looked about twenty-three, and was tall and blonde. She wore her hair loose with a white ribbon in it, and was dressed in a blue dressing gown. She had big blue eyes, very pretty, and a shy, large mouth. I liked her.

"This is Stella," said Dop.

She gave me a smile, but her eyes stayed earnest; she looked at me as children look at people they see for the first time: a look of grave observation, that was entirely unself-conscious.

Dop went across to her, took her in his arms, and gave her a mighty hug. "Did you sleep well?" he asked; and she nodded and kissed him.

Then she asked, "Did you have a nice trip?" Her voice was husky and lower than I had expected it to be.

"Oh, all right," said Dop. "A Yugoslav on fire. He was very co-operative." He kissed her and ruffled her hair; her eyes were so frank that it was almost embarrassing to watch. She was obviously very much in love.

"Well," said Dop, "sit down, chum, and make yourself at home." The girl asked whether I'd like something to eat, and I answered, "No, thank you." Dop said, "Don't be polite, have something to eat while I have a wash. She makes the best beans on toast in the world."

I sat down at the table; Dop left the room by the same door through which the girl had come in, and he left it open. While she was taking out bread from a bin and lighting the gas stove I heard him humming in the next room, and the splashing of water.

She cut the bread into slices and put them under the grill; then she opened a tin of beans, shook the contents into a little pan and put it over the flame. I wondered what else she would do to make the best beans on toast in the world, but she did nothing else. She made the toast, buttered it, and heaped the hot beans on top, that was all. Dop must be very much in love, too.

While she was doing this she asked me a few friendly questions; whether I was new in the service and that sort of thing. Her soft, low voice had a quiet quality which was somehow soothing. I realized this when I felt myself relaxing on that kitchen chair for the first time since I had come to Westport. For the first time I realized how tense I had been, how afraid. I suddenly became conscious again of the tightness of my jacket, and I asked her if she would mind if I took it off, for it pinched under the arms.

As I said that she looked at me again with her grave blue eyes, and said, "Give it to me, perhaps I can alter it for you."

I mumbled something polite, but she didn't listen and I handed her my jacket. She held it up by the shoulders, then looked at me, sizing me up, and said, "You come with me. Perhaps I've got something for you."

I followed her through the door in the corner into a bedroom with a double bed and a wardrobe. Another door into the room stood ajar and I saw Dop, stark naked, bent over a wash basin, washing his face. She put my jacket on the bed and went to the wardrobe. On top of the wardrobe was a big photograph in a leather frame of a young man in uniform; on it was written: "I'll walk beside you."

She opened the wardrobe, looked among a row of suits hanging on a rod inside, took one out, lifted the jacket off the hanger, and said, "Try this." It was a mate's uniform.

I tried it on and it fitted. Dop's voice called, "What are you doing?" from the bathroom; then he came in, in slippers and a dressing gown, drying his hair with a towel.

"I'm trying to find him another jacket," said the girl. "Does that one fit you?"

I said, "Yes," a bit embarrassed for Dop looked as if he didn't like what we were doing, and I suddenly realized that the uniform couldn't be one of his. He was a captain, and much thinner than I.

She said, "If it fits you, I'll change the stripes for you. Are you sure it fits?"

I said, "Yes, perfectly."

"Don't say it does if it doesn't," she said, like a grownup to a child in a shop. "Try the armholes; put your hand inside and see how much room you have."

I did so, and said there was plenty of room. She said, "All right, give it to me." After I had taken it off, she took the two jackets to the kitchen.

When she had gone I whispered to Dop, "Sorry if I . . ." but he didn't let me finish. He whispered, "Ssht. I'll tell you later," and then added, aloud, "Come, let's have some grub!" He shut the doors of the wardrobe; the portrait on top of it wobbled. We went back to the kitchen.

We sat down at the table and ate our beans on toast, while she snipped the stripes off my old jacket with a pair of nail scissors. While we were eating I noticed her hands; they were large and red like a boy's, she fumbled with the tiny scissors clumsily. Somehow this was moving; the best beans on toast in the world out of a tin and the clumsy sewing made me realize that she was an amateur, like all of us. Dop had sailed into the harbor with great gusto as if he was the best sailor in the world, and crashed his stern into the quay; I would soon have to sail a tugboat and make everybody believe that I had done so all my life, while in reality I had no idea any more of the maneuvers and the commands I had bellowed so juicily at my examination, nine years before. We were all amateurs: the drunken boy who had died that morning, the girls on the motor bikes, the angry old Captain in Headquarters; she was one of us. She played at being a good cook and an expert housewife; she was very sweet.

I would have felt at ease with her but for the uniform from the wardrobe and the wobbly portrait on top of it. I think that somehow she frightened me a bit, not as a person but as an enigma. When I had come in she had made me relax, because she had seemed part of the world I knew: one of Dop's girls. Now I realized that she wasn't; she was part of that other world across the shadow line, into which I had not yet entered. She was part of the war.

When she saw that we had nearly finished our beans on toast she got up and made coffee with a percolator. While we sat sipping it Dop told me about OTWA. He was not nervous and loud any more, but matter-of-fact and quiet. He told me that OTWA had three stations along the western seafront; Westport was one of them. Every station had two or three ocean-going tugboats in service, whose task it was to pick up the lame ducks left behind by the big convoys that sailed from America to England on the Western Approaches. "Lame ducks" were ships that had either been hit by bombs from airplanes, or by torpedoes or gunfire from U-boats, and whose engines had been put out of order so that they couldn't keep up to the convoy's speed any longer. As the convoys by now numbered several a day and were steadily increasing in volume, there were a great number of lame ducks about, and it was not unusual for a tugboat to turn around and sail again with its second crew the moment after it had brought someone in. In the beginning it hadn't been so bad, this station; they had started with five tugs, now there were three left, and no replacements had arrived so far.

I asked him what the Royal Dutch Airlines were doing here, and he said that they were operating a service between England and the Near East via Gibraltar. He said it curtly and with a glance at the sewing girl, as if he didn't want to discuss it in her presence. She said suddenly, "You ought to take your pills now," but he answered, "No, I'm going out again."

She looked up from her sewing with alarm in her eyes. "You haven't got to sail again, have you?"

"No," he said, "I'm going out with him. I must introduce him to Van Dam."

She looked at me with a smile, but her eyes were reproachful. "Don't keep him too long," she said, "he must sleep, otherwise he'll go to pieces when he has to sail again, tomorrow."

She said it casually, as if it was a perfectly normal thing to say; if Dop hadn't got angry I wouldn't have thought about it twice. But he got very angry; he shouted at her, "Who the hell is going to pieces? I've never gone to pieces in my life! Don't start mixing me up with someone else! I . . ." He would have said a lot more, if she hadn't got up and kissed him.

It was a curious moment; I don't think I'll ever forget it. I saw his insensate terror dwindle and vanish under her kiss. I was envious of him, although my vague fear was nothing compared to what I had seen in his eyes the first moment I saw him in that office. I had seen it in his eyes again when he started to shout at her, and now I saw it taken away from him by nothing but a kiss.

It worried me, his fear; I had seen many people in action so far, who did things that on the face of it were more dangerous than the work of OTWA, and they hadn't been nearly so jumpy. The R.A.F. boys, swarming out over Germany every night, certainly had more reason to be afraid than we had, and yet from what I knew of them they were in much better shape. There must be something to this OTWA business that was different, something I didn't know yet. But as I thought this I remembered the Dutch airman, who had come into the breakfast room that morning with the bananas, and I realized that he had had the same look in his eyes when he sat down at our table. It was a mystery, and I didn't like it.

Dop got up and went into the bedroom to dress while she finished her sewing. We talked a bit; that is to say, she did the talking. She had the Englishwoman's admirable capacity for making conversation on trivial subjects in awkward circumstances. She talked about how nice the civilians in Westport were; there was a Mrs. Bell who constantly gave little parties for the forces with raffles and soft drinks, and I must ask Jan to take me to the Savage Club one night where sweet old gentlemen sang songs and played snooker, and where anybody from the forces could get up whenever he liked and give a little lecture on his adventures or recite a poem in his native language; that was why the club was called "Savage." It was the kind of chatter that looks silly written down, but is a relief to listen to when you are at a loss what to say new. By the time Dop came back she had finished my jacket.

I put it on, and, after having assured her once more that it fitted, I started taking my things from the old jacket and putting them into the pockets of the new one. As I put my wallet into the inside pocket I noticed a little tab sewn onto the lining with a name on it: H. F. Barger. It struck me like a blow. "Not Henk Barger?" I asked, for we had been friends for three years. We had sailed together first as sailors and finally as mates' assistants on the tugboat *Terschelling*, before we both passed our examination and were commissioned on different ships. Dop said, "Yes, yes," hastily, and nudged me hard. I must have looked rather stupid, for when she turned away to get his coat for him, he whispered, "Don't look like a fool! I'll tell you later."

When I said good-by to her and thanked her for the jacket, she gave me a big smile and said, "Do come and have dinner with us sometime." But by then I knew the English well enough to realize that this meant nothing, unless you agreed upon a date. I concluded that I hadn't been much of a success with her, and that she didn't approve of me barging into Dop's life and keeping him up when he should have been in bed.

It was a pity, for I liked her.

When we got out of the building, Dop took me along the crowded quay and through streets lined with rubble to the cellar of a ruin, that had once been the town hall. In the cellar was a canteen for allied forces called the "Social Center." In it I found hundreds of sailors of all nationalities, dancing in a dense smoke with tired girls to music from three loud-speakers, or sitting at small tables against the wall sipping tea or Coca-Cola. The noise was so deafening that we had to shout; Dop shouted that it was the only spot in Westport where we could talk privately.

I found out that this was indeed true. Once we had found a table and two free chairs in a far corner, and Dop started bellowing at me, it seemed as if after a few moments the infernal noise isolated us completely from our neighbors, who sat so close to us that we rubbed shoulders. We shook our heads to two girls, who came to ask us in deaf-mute language whether we would like a dance, and ordered two Coca-Colas from an overworked waitress who dragged a huge untidy tea-trolley through the crowd; then Dop started to talk.

At first I was so distracted that I didn't really listen; but after a while I forgot that he was shouting and that the whole situation was preposterous. The din and the smoke seemed to isolate his pale, tense face. He looked younger than I had ever seen him, with his cap on the back of his head and his thin hands nervously breaking up a matchbox. His captain's stripes began to look as incongruous on him as they had looked on the boy whom I had watched dressing for death last night. He began by apologizing for shushing me in the flat, when I had begun to talk about Barger. There was nothing mysterious behind it, he said, only he didn't want Stella to get upset by talking about people who had been killed in action. She was a sensitive girl, who before the war had lived quite out of this world; she came from one of the Hebrides. She had volunteered at the beginning of the war and been landed in the air raids and the hell-hole of Westport without any transition. I asked what her job was, and he said that she had been secretary to the Dutch Airlines' Headquarters until she had started to live with him in the flat; now she devoted all her time to looking after him.

I didn't ask about the portrait on top of the wardrobe, but he must have sensed the question in my mind. Perhaps I looked a bit noncommittal when he talked about her as if she was still a Victorian girl keeping a diary on a misty island at the edge of the world. He said the photograph was her brother's; he had been drafted into the army early in the war and was now fighting in the desert. They were devoted to each other and she wrote him a long letter each week.

I began to get a bit fed up with all this talk about Stella; like all people in love he would have talked about nothing else if I had let him. I wanted to know about Barger, and he told me that Barger had been the previous tenant of the flat. Before he died he had given Dop a duplicate of his key, because he had rented the flat for the duration and didn't want it to get out of the hands of the Dutch. He had given the key on condition that Dop in his turn would have a duplicate made, once he moved in, and give that to another Dutchman on whom he was to impose the same condition.

He asked if I had known Barger well; when I said I had he glanced at me, then he looked back at his hands that were brushing the remains of the matchbox into a neat little heap on the table. He hadn't known him very well himself, he said, but he had seemed a nice chap. I asked how he had died; he shrugged his shoulders without looking up and said, "Oh, the usual thing: intercepted and gunned by a U-boat before he got to the duck he was to pick up." I asked why this was usual, and he answered, "The tricky bit is between here and the ship you are going to pick up. Once you get there you're all right; for the duck is armed, and we are not."

I said, "I see," but I didn't, not until a good three minutes later. We sat silently in the infernal noise for a while, Dop brushing the remains of the matchbox into an ever neater heap, while the truth slowly dawned on me. "But surely you've got some sort of cannon on board?" I asked.

"Oh yes," said Dop, "we've got a pom-pom. But it is vintage 1926, and it's not aircraft that are bothering us, it's U-boats. If you want to attack a U-boat with the thing you might as well try a peashooter." He looked up and grinned. "What's more: the thing won't shoot level," he said.

The disheveled waitress passed with her trolley and snatched our empty Coca-Cola bottles away, upsetting the neat little heap Dop had made of his matchbox. "Anything else?" she asked, and we shook our heads. "Let's go and have a drink somewhere," said Dop.

We worked our way through the dancing crowd, our eyes stinging with smoke. When we got outside in the cool dusk and the faint powdery smell of the ruins, I thought of the pilot I had seen come home that morning. I asked, "The planes of the Royal Airlines—aren't they armed either?"

"No," said Dop.

We had a drink in the bar of the Grand Hotel. It was full of Dutchmen; few were sober. After our third drink Dop fumbled in his pocket and took out a key. "Here," he said, "tuck this away somewhere and forget about it until you need it."

I knew instantly what key it was, but to give myself time to think of something to say I asked, "What the hell is this?"

Dop eyed me unsteadily; he was getting drunk. "I promised Barger," he said; "but so far I didn't know anybody here whom I considered good enough for the flat. I'm jolly glad you came; this takes a load off my mind. A promise is a promise. A man ought to stick to his promises. God knows there is little else left to stick to. Here." He closed my fingers over the key; his hand was hot and moist. "Put it away, forget about it, and if anything should happen to me: use it. Promise." His hot hand still held my fist, and he tried to focus his eyes on mine. "Promise that the moment you use it you will have a duplicate made, which you will give to your best friend."

I said, "Don't be silly. If anyone will survive this war it's you."

He shook his head slowly, his eyes closed, with drunken stubbornness. "You put it away and forget about it," he said. "And when you give the duplicate to your best friend, make him promise the same. Let's keep Barger's memory hallowed."

I said, "I don't want your bloody key, you're drunk."

Then he brought his face very close to mine, opened his eyes and asked, "You want me to bash your face in for you?"

I sighed, said, "O.K.," put the key in my pocket, and started trying to take him home.

By the time I succeeded I wasn't sober any more either. We weaved our way through the crowd on the boulevard arm in arm, shaking hands with people. After we had finally reached the house and started climbing the ten flights of stairs, we got out of breath once or twice and sat down, giggling. Dop tried to pick himself up when we stood in front of the door with the inverted "2," but he didn't succeed. I wanted to open the door for him with my key, after I had asked him several times for his. The moment he saw the key he sobered up instantly and slapped my hand. I was angry for a second, until I saw his face. He looked at me with such loathing that I suddenly felt sorry for him.

"What the hell do you think you are doing?" he said. "I'm not dead yet!"

He took out his own key, managed to put it in the lock at the third try, giggled, and said, "You'll sail with me for the whole of next week, so we are b-both bloody asses." Then he opened the door and staggered in.

I didn't wait for him to shut it. I went home.

CHAPTER TWO

THAT NIGHT I WAS WOKEN UP BY THE OLD PORTER MYSELF. HE SHOOK ME BY the shoulder and called, "Captain! S.O.S.!" He must have banged on the door and shouted before, but I hadn't heard him.

I swung my legs out of the bunk as I heard a splashing of water in the corner, for I didn't want the wet face-flannel treatment. My head felt as if my brains had got loose; I must have got pretty tight the night before. I dressed as quickly as I could, and managed to pick out my jacket from the heap of clothes on the chair without trying them all on because it had Barger's name on it. When I came down to the hall I saw the old porter sitting behind the desk in his shirt sleeves. On the desk was a glass of water with a set of dentures in it. He gave me a toothless grin and said, "Good luck, Captain"; then he vanished behind the desk. He obviously had a bed there.

When I got out into the open it was pitch dark and cold. The wind had freshened but there must have been a lot of cloud, for I didn't see a single star. I saw nothing at all. I stood there cursing under my breath, when the thin beam of a blacked-out torch darted at me and a voice said, "Looking for something, chum?"

I said, "Yes, the tugboat *Vlieland*."

The spidery beam slid down my sleeve and caught my stripes. "Sorry, sir," said the voice. "Let me take you there, sir."

I said, "Thank you, that's very civil of you," and followed the faint pin-point of light that the torch made on the pavement in front of my feet. I heard heavy steps of hobnailed boots beside me, but I saw nothing; I had no idea who it was. The voice chatted on the way with a broad cockney accent, warning me when we stepped off the pavement; the torch carefully picked out the obstacles on the pier when we got there. To each sentence the voice added "sir"; by the time we got to the ship and I saw him in the faint mooring light shining down from the poop, I had already realized that he was an M.P. I thanked him, wondering for a moment whether I should shake hands with him; he saluted smartly and I saluted back.

When I got on board ship I was quite prepared to salute some more; I had found that it gave me a nice feeling of authority for which I didn't find any justification inside me. But nobody did; for one thing the shadowy shapes I discerned on the aftdeck hadn't got anything on to salute at. I didn't see a single peaked cap; some of them wore knitted things with a tassel on top, the others nothing but hair which needed cutting. I addressed one of the shapes as it passed close to me, and said, "Would you take me to Captain Dop, please." The shape answered, "Who the hell are you?" and I told him my rank and my name, rather primly. He said, "O.K., keep your shirt on. This way." At that he vanished completely.

I groped my way along the rail, muttering, was whistled at from the darkness, stumbled several times, hurried up by a hissing voice ahead of me; when I finally got to the chartroom, where a dim oil light was burning, I was ready to give him a piece of my mind. He was a small swarthy man in a jersey covered with grease, a dirty towel round his neck. "He'll be around in a minute," he said, "wait here." I asked him whether he was the Admiral, and he answered, "No, the cook" indifferently.

I sat waiting in the chartroom for a good ten minutes before Dop turned up. It was the first tugboat I had been on for seven years, and things seemed to have changed in the meantime. I remembered the chartroom of the tugs I had known as fairly tidy places; this one was in an incredible mess. The chart on the table was scribbled all over with pencil marks and lines, and covered with rings like a pub table. I counted eight empty mugs, cracked and grimy, among the litter on that table; the rest was bottles, candlesticks, socks, crumpled-up signal flags, empty cigarette packs and a moldy rope-soled shoe. The cabin itself looked as if it hadn't been swept for months; the floor was covered with dirt and crushed cigarette stubs; in one corner lay a pile of empty bottles.

When Dop arrived he looked awful. He had dark rings under his eyes, and was unshaven. "God," he said, "we certainly hit it good and proper last night; Stella gave me hell." A boy wearing a sleeveless goatskin jacket over a sweater came in. "What have we got tonight?" he asked.

"A Norwegian in square 686," said Dop, "with a cigar hole in number one hold."

"Tanker?" asked the boy.

"No," said Dop, "wheat."

The boy said, "Good. Ready to go?"

"If everybody is there."

"Everybody but Martens."

"O.K.," said Dop, "the hell with him. Let's go."

When the boy had gone I asked who he was, and Dop said, "My Mate." He threw his cap among the rubble on the table, opened three drawers crammed with junk before he found a pencil; when he found it the point was broken, and he threw it away without looking where it fell. I gave him mine.

He said, "Thanks," and made a cross on the map about sixty miles due west of Bishop Rock. "The duck is here," he said. "It's wheat which will get soaked, that means no fire. The wind is south-southeast, force six, so we can sail the last ten miles if it doesn't get too light."

"Sail?" I asked.

"Yes," he said. "Jerry will be hanging around the wreck, and at night the only means by which he can spot us coming is the sound of our propeller. So if we sail the last bit we'll be able to sneak up on the duck without Jerry knowing we are there, before we have floated our line across."

"You don't shoot your line?" I asked, for that was what we had been used to doing in my days. Each tugboat carried a little cannon like the whalers use for their harpoons, and with it we shot a flare with a thin line attached to it across the deck of the vessel in distress. They hauled in the line and we attached our hawser to the end of it.

Dop said impatiently, "Hell no! The whole point is that Jerry mustn't spot us until we are well within the range of the duck's guns; if we started shooting lines we might as well light ourself up with Bengal fires to help him take aim. We approach the duck to the windward, float a cask with the line attached to it, and when the cask hits the duck's side, she picks it up."

I asked whether the duck knew this, and Dop said, "Of course. Every captain sailing in a convoy gets a set of sealed envelopes before he starts, to be opened in various cases of emergency. Ours is envelope D: "If disabled by enemy action and left behind by the convoy." In it he finds a set of instructions which we composed for him: Don't use your wireless, your position will be reported to base by the convoy's escort. Try to keep your vessel afloat as well as you can, and put out any fires as quickly as possible. Above all: Don't waste your ammunition by having pot shots at any U-boats that may surface around you while you are waiting for the tugboat; don't answer their fire, not even under the severest provocation; the U-boat won't sink you until it can take in the tugboat as well, so save your ammunition until we have made fast, then give them hell."

"What else?" I asked.

"Oh, some blurb about not betraying our presence when they sight us, and not giving wheel unless instructed to do so, and a set of day and night signals," said Dop. "But the wireless and the shooting business are the most important. We don't want the ducks to give the show away and attract all the U-boats in the region, while we are creeping toward them without as much as a slingshot to hit back with." The boy with the goatskin jacket stuck his head in and said, "Ready when you are." Dop said, "O.K.," and we went to the bridge.

In the cold, windy darkness I thought over what Dop had told me downstairs. It wasn't difficult to understand, but I found it hard to stomach. I had never thought of myself as a hero, and never felt any desire of being one; a job that seemed to consist mainly of being shot at without being able to shoot back didn't appeal to me at all. Before we sailed into the open I had the thoughts that must be common to anyone about to go into action for the first time. I thought how the devil I could wangle it so that this would be the last time. I thought of any special qualities which could make me eligible for a safer job; looking at it from Headquarters' point of view I decided that I had none. I thought of having an unfortunate accident, which would crush my foot or my left hand; but even while I thought so I knew that I hadn't got the guts to do it. I tried to bring out my better self by thinking of the others on board and all the boys of OTWA, who were running the same risks as I and didn't squeak about it. When that didn't work either, I stimulated the secret feeling common to all soldiers: that nothing could happen to me; that, if not immortal, I was sure of a long life and would die in bed. I remembered a fortune teller whom I had gone to see before I left Holland; she had predicted many narrow escapes but a long, long life for two guilders. During my escape, whenever I had found myself in a tight corner, the thought of that fortune teller had comforted me; now her prediction seemed as cold as a dead fish.

Perhaps I had too much imagination; I foresaw everything that would happen, down to the minutest detail. Although I had never seen a U-boat in my life, I saw a vivid picture of one, surfacing right beside us. I saw its commando tower, or whatever the thing was called, opened from the inside, and a dozen Fritzes climbing down on to her deck. They uncovered the gun, pointed it at us, and while we were dashing from side to side on a zigzag course, I heard the sharp reports of the shots, the screaming of the shells, and the sickening explosions when they burst all around us, sending up milk-white fountains of water. I didn't get to the actual direct hit which would tear open the ship and fling me into the sea to drown, a dismembered bleeding lump; before I got that far I was already so sick with terror that I had to force my mind on to other things by talking to Dop, or by looking at the dull glint of the piece of rail I could see in the darkness and trying to make out whether it was mahogany or teak.

When the swell got us and the ship started pitching and rolling I got better, for something unexpected happened: I was seasick. Somehow I had never foreseen this, although it stood to reason. A tugboat is a lively ship; I had known captains who felt queasy every time they hit the first swell, after as little as two months' shore leave. So far I had been so busy worrying what to do now I was a captain that I had overlooked seasickness.

I stood on the bridge, swallowing and belching, for as long as I could stick it; when I felt that I couldn't any longer, I said to Dop, "I think I'm going to lie down for a minute, call me if anything turns up."

"O.K.," he said, "take the couch in the chartroom."

I vomited over the rail as soon as I got down the stairs from the bridge, realizing too late that I was on the windward side. Somehow the thought that the traces of my seasickness would be visible to anyone looking overboard after daybreak was very humiliating. I even had a mad flicker of a thought: a U-boat captain seeing it through his binoculars. I decided that

94

my imagination had got beyond a joke, and staggered into the chartroom, for a moment disgusted with myself.

I lay on the couch, listening to the shuffling of the oilskins against the wall overhead, feeling so sick that I didn't care any longer whether we were sunk that night or not. The boy with the goatskin jacket came in several times, to look at the chart or to get something; I didn't know which and I was too ill to care. I didn't even care about him seeing me in this condition: a full-grown Captain in parade dress, lolling about on the couch, green in the face. But whatever I may have looked like, he didn't give it a second thought; he didn't even glance at me. When he came in the third or the fourth time, he reached over me to take off a couple of oilskins, dragged the cold cloth across my face, and said, "Sorry." I realized that I hated him, and that it had started to rain.

After that I must have fallen asleep, for several times I half woke up because I thought I heard gunshots in the distance. Once or twice the ship suddenly shuddered and seemed to rise on her hind legs; the seconds after that happened I lay breathless, trying to listen. But nothing happened; we must have hit a white horse.

I was woken up by a sound, or rather a lack of sound. The one pair of oilskins left suddenly shuffled much more loudly against the wall with the rolling of the ship; it took me some time to realize that the engine had been stopped. I got up, put on the oilskins and went to the bridge.

The moment I got into the open a cold hard rain hit me in the face and sobered me up. I didn't feel sick any longer, nor afraid. I felt a brittle excitement which made the whole thing seem almost fun. I had to hold on to the rail of the stairs and the bridge, for despite the fact that I now felt as clean as a whistle I was oddly weak in the knees. A murky dawn was breaking, and in it I saw a sight that almost made me laugh, it was so incongruous: a trawler's sail attached to the mast of a tugboat. It was a clumsy, flapping affair, and didn't seem to do much good; only occasionally it strained in the wind and then it made us heel over with an exhilarating feeling of recklessness. I remembered the feeling from my boyhood, when I had rigged up a bathtub with a sail and messed about in it with a couple of friends in the harbor of our village. I suddenly felt good, better than I had felt ever since I set out for Westport. Despite the rain I wanted to light a cigarette, if only to prove to myself that I had recovered from my seasickness, also because I had a foul taste in my mouth and my tongue and palate felt very dry. The moment I took out my lighter someone put his hand over mine, and said, "Are you crazy?"

It was the boy with the goatskin jacket, now clad in glistening oilskins, his wet hair matted over his dripping forehead. I said, "Sorry," and decided that if he spoke to me again I'd grab him by the scruff of his neck and fling him off the bridge. I was a captain, damn it all; I had been mad to worry whether I could tackle the command of a tugboat after all these years. I could sail any bloody tugboat in the business a hundred times better than any of these louts in their fancy dress.

I felt on top of the world just then; shaky, but on top. Then a whistle chirped twice from the fo'c'sle. I heard Goatskin's voice say, "There she is, abaft the beam on . . ." He may have finished his sentence, I didn't hear it. A frantic whine came whistling at us from the sea, rapidly growing in volume until it sounded like the screaming wheels of a streetcar rounding a corner. I never heard the shot, for the mast and the sail came toppling down with a terrific noise. Dop's voice shouted, "Hard starboard!" I heard the ringing of the engine room telegraph, the rattle of the steering engine. Then another whine came whistling at us, and passed right overhead with a sound that I felt in my teeth. This time I heard the shot: a high metallic twang in the distance, as if someone had hit an iron railing with a stick. Perhaps it wasn't the shot, perhaps it was something else; I had no time to wonder, for at that moment a colossal sound right overhead frightened the life out of me. It was my first moment of fear in face of the real thing; when I realized that it was the ship's siren I burst into a loud laughter, which I managed to check as soon as it occurred to me that it was hysteria.

The siren screamed for minutes on end; then the ship seemed to jump bodily out of the sea and throw herself on her starboard side. My feet slid from under me; I was flung down the full length of the bridge and hit the starboard rail with a sickening thud, that knocked the breath out of me. I lay there gasping for a while, expecting to feel the water, for it seemed impossible that any ship could stand up to this; but I regained my breath and felt the ship right herself. I heard shouting and a loud clatter of iron; then there was a sudden burst of gunfire, very close to. A quiet voice said, "Well, she's handing it out good and proper, the old bird."

It was Goatskin. He stood looking at something over the rail as if he had remained on his feet all the time. Perhaps he had. Perhaps he was God. I dragged myself up to my knees in a praying position and managed to get back on my feet, despite the fact that vital bones in my body seemed to be broken. He glanced at me and asked, "All right?" I nodded, unable to speak, with a lump in my throat and a hot prickly feeling in my eyes. I hated him to tears.

I looked over the rail. The cannonade thundered overhead remorselessly, like five pneumatic drills gone mad. I saw the Norwegian: a dark hull, her bow sunken right up to her fo'c'sle. From her poop and her foredeck spurted the vivid flashes of gunfire. Our siren had stopped screaming when we were flung aside; now it yelped again, two short blasts. The guns on the ship alongside fell silent.

I expected them to start up again any minute while we maneuvered toward her stern and shot a line across; but they didn't. They didn't start up again until a good deal later, when we had already made fast and started towing. I stood looking back at the high stern of the ship when I heard that sickening whine again. The very moment I heard it the siren started screaming again, and was drowned by the thunder of guns abaft. I never knew whether the shell passed overhead or came anywhere near us at all; anyhow, it missed us.

After that nothing else happened in the way of shooting; we just towed the ship home in the growing daylight, that was all. I never saw the U-boat, and I still didn't know whether my picture of the Fritzes climbing out of the commando tower was right. I stayed on the bridge with Dop and Goatskin for the rest of the trip. The cook brought up tea at one time that looked all right, but made me seasick again. I took only a sip or two, and managed to keep them down until we got home, but it was hard work. Only when we sighted the harbor did I realize that I had hardly been afraid.

The moment I thought this, I got it. It started in my calves and crept up to the back of my knees: a trembling, so uncontrollable that I had to cling to the rail to keep myself from sitting down. I thought I was the only one, until I saw Goatskin's face. He was not God any longer, he was green.

Dop took me by the arm, once we had moored, and said, "Well, that's that. Let's nip across to Headquarters and get the form business over with." His hand trembled as his arm had done when he put it around my shoulders the morning before. I remembered someone had told me once that fear came only before and after the danger; I had forgotten who it was, but he was right.

We got the form business over quickly. The Captain of the Norwegian had been brought on board our ship by a British Navy launch, when we handed over his vessel to two small tugs in the outer harbor who would tow her the rest of the way up the coast. He was a quiet man with very blue eyes and very tidy; he looked as if he had come straight out of the barber's after a nice thorough shave. He thanked Dop politely for bringing in his ship and Dop thanked him for putting up such a good show with his guns. The Norwegian raised his eyebrows slightly and asked, "Well, wasn't that what you wanted?" Dop said it was, and we went home feeling a bit silly, as if the Norwegian had told us in so many words not to make such a fuss about a normal operation which had proceeded according to plan.

I took Dop home because he insisted. The flat was there, he said; Stella would be waiting with food anyhow, we had been in this together so we might as well finish it off with some grub and a chat. I knew it was wrong, that she wouldn't want to see me at all. But the prospect of going to bed all alone in that untidy room, after swallowing the pills the old Captain had handed me, made me give in.

When Dop opened the door and we entered the kitchen I was struck by the same uncanny feeling as the day before: a feeling of emptiness, as if no one was there. Dop called again, "Hey, where are you?" The door in the corner opened and she came out exactly as she had done the day before: in her blue dressing gown, a white ribbon in her hair.

But when she looked at me it was different. Her grave blue eyes did not observe me any longer like a child's; she gave me a look of such instant understanding that I suddenly felt my knees again. I grinned at her and said, "Hello, how are you?" in a voice that must have sounded like a parrot's; then I sat down at the kitchen table, fighting a childish desire to drop my head on my arms and cry.

I got over it. I told myself that I was a sentimental fool, a coward who had come home to roost, and I believed it. I sneered at myself as I sat there, making polite conversation and watching her grill the toast and heat up the beans; my knees trembled all the time, although I grasped my knee caps until my knuckles went white.

When the beans on toast were put in front of me by a red hand that looked like a boy's, I knew I wouldn't be able to eat them however much I tried. My eyes filmed over, and I believed it was the steam until I felt a hand on my shoulder and heard her low, soft voice say, "Don't worry, you'll be all right. The first time is the worst."

I felt like screaming "Goddam you!" and bursting into tears. I got up, said in a general way, "Thank you; I think I had better go home now," and managed to get out of the door without making a fool of myself.

I got to the hotel somehow, went upstairs to room 77, took off my clothes, threw them on the chair, and swallowed my pills with a gulp of water from the dirty glass on the washstand; when I finally fell on my back in my bunk I couldn't be bothered to pull up the blankets. My head fell aside, spinning; I saw the poem and closed my eyes with a sour taste contracting my mouth.

I decided then and there that I would not go back to the flat until I had found a woman of my own, to kiss me and take my fear away as Stella had done to Dop. I knew now that that kiss was the only cure. I was jealous.

I sailed with Dop twice more that week. The fear didn't get better, but the seasickness did. The fear had nothing to do with what actually happened, for we weren't gunned at all, but with the thoughts of what was going to happen. Nobody can tell me that he ever got to a point where he was not afraid in action; he may have come to know his fear so well in the end that he could take it for something else. But our fear was worse, because we were powerless. We couldn't hit back.

When I was in London someone told me that at the beginning of the blitz people got very worked up and defeatist because they felt defenseless against the bombs; they almost gave up until a couple of gunboats started pounding shells at the sky which were perfectly pointless, but made a heartening noise. The person who told me this didn't think that any enemy aircraft had ever been hit by those shells, but their effect on the population was tremendous. I wondered whether we would feel better if we started to work our pom-pom in the face of the gunning U-boats, and I asked Dop this. He said it would be pointless, our only hope was our small size and our maneuverability. Even if the pom-pom was modified so that it could shoot level, it was so weak, and so difficult to train as we were tossed about so much, that we might just as well save the manpower and concentrate on zigzagging. I wondered whether he was right. I was sure that I would have felt a lot better if we had been able to make some noise ourselves even while knowing that it was just noise and nothing else.

Then I began to suspect something: perhaps the men of OTWA didn't want any guns. I was surely not the only one who went weak at the knees when he was being shot at like a helpless rabbit. There must be some thought or some emotion unknown to me, that made these boys so nauseatingly brave and so disdainful of the enemy's sharpshooting.

The one who gave me a possible explanation was Captain Van Dam, my opposite number, with whom I was to share the command of the *Zeeland* after she came out of dock. I went to see him the day before my first command was to start at midnight. He lived in the Grand Hotel in room 50, which he shared with three other Captains. Room 50 was called "The Club," because the four Captains were old compared to the rest of the population of the hotel; none of them was under forty.

When I knocked on the door of room 50 no one answered at first, and I listened with my ear to the crack to hear if there was anyone in. I heard a curious noise, as if someone was sharpening a pencil with a badly oiled machine. I knocked again; a voice called, "Come in"; when I opened the door the first thing I saw was a cage with a canary in it, making the noise. A man sat with his back to me in a low chair, reading a newspaper. He was in shirt sleeves with his waistcoat on, and on the back of his head was a bald spot the size of a guilder. He turned around when he heard me, and I was reminded of the forced visits I had paid to the local police station of our village when I used to scale the wall of the vicarage garden to steal the parson's pears. The man in the chair looked at me exactly as Sergeant Bulters, the head of the local constabulary, had done.

I knew the man was Captain Van Dam, for I recognized him from the photographs. He was an old professional, and before the war he had towed a dry dock from the Clyde to Australia round the Cape of Good Hope which had given him a fortnight's fame. He was one of the best deep-sea-towing experts alive; thinking of him during the preceding week I had felt an awe which I would not have experienced if I hadn't been drafted back into the service. It was the kind of awe I would have felt for him when I was still a mate with aspirations; ten years had fallen out of my life.

I had not been prepared, however, to feel twenty years fall away, and yet that was exactly what happened when the stern regard of his pale blue eyes hit me for the first time. I almost expected him to say, "What? You again?" and to hear myself answer, "No, sir, it wasn't me. I just climbed the wall to see what the others were doing." Instead he said, "Yes?" and I introduced myself. "Good day," he said, without getting up. He folded his newspaper, pointed at a chair underneath the cage with the canary, and said, "Sit down."

I sat down, my cap on my knees, and looked around. The room was spotlessly clean and so tidy that it hurt. On the wall was a calendar with a picture of the Dutch Royal family, and a lithograph of the Monarch of the Glen; the rest were family photographs, concentrated in little clusters over the four beds: matronly woman, fat children, babies on sheepskin rugs and provincial wedding groups. By the side of each bed hung the ghostly shape of a bunch of suits on hangers, covered with a dust sheet; one of the shapes was partly uncovered, and I saw a sleeve with very worn captain's stripes, shiny at the elbow. The sight of that sleeve made me feel as if I was masquerading, a kid playing at being a sailor.

"What can I do for you?"

He looked at me with those pale blue eyes as if he had been watching me for some time and decided that I had gaped enough.

I asked him a few questions about our ship and the routine; he answered them precisely, without any attempt at making conversation. I had the feeling that he disapproved of me, not as a person but as an amateur. I mentioned something about the *Vlieland* being rather untidy, and for a moment he looked as if that would set him talking. He knitted his eyebrows and pursed his thin lips as if he was tasting something bitter, and I waited for him to give a regimental sergeant-major's speech. But he said nothing. His face relaxed; he took a cigar out of the breast pocket of his waistcoat, snipped its tip off with a little surgical instrument hanging from his watch chain, produced a brass lighter which sprang to flame like a torch, and lit the cigar with care. After he had pocketed the lighter again he looked at me through the smoke with one eye closed, the cigar clenched between his teeth, and asked, "Made any sorties yet?"

The word was so old-fashioned that it took me a moment to realize what he meant. Then I answered him that I had made three sorties so far.

"Liked them?" he asked.

I thought I had him taped by then; he was one of our frank boys. Two could play at that game, so I answered, "No."

"Why not?" he asked.

It was such a preposterous question that it took me a moment to decide whether to get up and leave after patting the bald spot on his head, or to carry on this stage dialogue. "I don't like being shot at without being able to shoot back," I said. "It makes me nervous."

He eyed me coldly for a while; then he said, "That is because you have got the wrong approach to your work. Stretcher-bearers on the battlefield can't shoot back either."

I said that was quite a thought, and began planning how to get out of the place quickly. But I had put him on the rails, and pushed him off; now he was running downhill all by himself, nothing would stop him until he reached the terminus. He took the cigar out of his mouth, and addressed it as if it was me he was holding upright in his stubby fingers at a hand's width from his face. War had nothing noble or sensible about it, he said; it was just an epidemic of madness sweeping the people ashore, and anyone who got caught by it deserved to have his eyes gouged out by a fellow patient. He would rather be shot to hell ten times over, trying to bring in a helpless wreck, than join the lunatics by shooting back. "Shooting back!" he snorted, as if I had suggested something stupid in a complicated maneuver; "Be glad; the fact that you cannot shoot back gives you a chance to remain sane among all this murder."

I thought that the word "murder" was the terminus, for he stuck his cigar back between his teeth. But it wasn't; he took the cigar out again and added, "What's more, if you are a good sailor you won't get hit. The German will be hanging around the wreck; you aim two squares above the one your wreck is in. Pass it for one square, then turn around and close in. Ten to one you are well within the range of the wreck's guns by the time the German spots you. If you aren't and he starts gunning you, don't zigzag, for that is asking to be sunk. When the first shell comes, turn your arse toward the gun and travel backward. They'll plonk about a dozen rounds over your head in front of you, then you'll find there will be a pause. While they are dithering you travel forward again, and so on. Just use your brains. But above all: no drink, and no women."

That was the terminus all right. After he had put his cigar back again, he shut up like a clam. I tried to make him talk a bit more about this idea of remaining sane in an epidemic of madness, for it sounded as if he had got something there. But he just grunted and picked up his newspaper again.

When he started to read it I left.

I met Van Dam again a couple of hours later, when I went to look over the ship. I thought I might as well get an idea what she looked like before I crawled on board in pitch darkness at the first S.O.S. I had expected her to be deserted except for the stoker who was to keep the steam up, but I found her fully manned.

Van Dam was there and he spotted me the moment I stepped on to the poop. He came marching toward me with brisk little steps; he was much shorter than I had thought when I saw him sitting down, and he had a large behind. "Glad you came," he snapped when he got to me. "I'd like to show you the condition I expect to find my ship in when I take over from you at the beginning of each sortie. You may like living in a cabin that looks like a gipsy's caravan after a collision; I don't. So please be good enough to tidy up your mess before you knock off."

I thought of a number of humorous and withering answers I could have given him after that little speech. I thought of them while he was showing me around the ship; they were good but too late.

The ship was in apple pie order. War didn't exist for Captain Van Dam, it stopped at his gunwales. I wouldn't have called her a model of sanity; she seemed to me a model of pernickety and futile tidiness. Every spot of brass was polished to gold, there wasn't a scratch in the varnish on any of the rails; while I followed him around, I spotted an old man with an upturned pipe touching up the varnish on the thresholds. The table in the chartroom was so clean that you could eat off it; the charts were meticulously rolled up, and so neatly stacked in the rack that I was sure someone must have brought the edges into line with a ruler. In the pen tray were three pencils: one red, one blue, one black, sharpened to a point where they began to look dangerous. The leatherette couch looked like a gynecologist's; if it had been covered with a sheet he could have taken anyone into that chartroom and charged five guineas per visit.

When we had finished the tour, he said, "I was told in Headquarters that you were to have the first watch, but I changed this. I know this ship, I want to find out if she is all right after her repairs." I asked him what had been the damage, and he answered, "Superstructure shot away."

I thought this took a bit off the bloom of his advice that morning, which had sounded rather convincing at the time. Perhaps he hadn't thrown his arse round quick enough. He must have suspected my reflections, for he said, "It was Mr. Wolters' contribution." I saw his point, but I thought that all the same he might be a little more lenient toward the amateurs, at least once they were dead.

Before I left he asked me, "Have you briefed your crew yet?" and when I answered, "No, I haven't even met them," he gave me one of those glances that are supposed to kill, and said, "I see." After that he turned briskly round and marched away on his short legs. Seen from the back he looked like a duck.

I met my crew that afternoon. I didn't exactly brief them, I just shook hands with them, chatted a bit with each one, and got their names mixed up. They looked a sensible, competent lot; I particularly liked the chief engineer, who had the nice homely quality about him that results from a single-track mind. To him, war or no war, nothing was more important in the world than engines. I was not so happy with my Mate, a thin nervous youth called Waterman. He seemed to have a lot of good will, but little experience. From what I knew of Wolters, the two of them between them must have had quite some luck, to get through four months of OTWA without anything worse than a superstructure shot away.

It was because of the reactions and the attitude of my crew that I first realized that I no longer considered myself an amateur. I was a professional all right, a bit stiff in the creases after seven years among the mothballs, but one of the old guard. I was surprised at this, for the change had come without my noticing it. But for my two brief encounters with Captain Van Dam I would have approached these boys differently, trying either to please or to impress them. I had done neither; I had just looked them up and down, shaken hands with them and forgotten their names when I got to the next man. When I left they eyed me with a curious relief, as if I had somehow convinced them that my presence on the ship would give them a new chance.

I had dinner in the dining room of the hotel. In the far corner was a table for eight, where the Club used to dine; four captains and four engineers of prewar standing. So far I had eaten with the untidy crowd at the long tables, where pilots and sailors sat down indifferently wherever there happened to be a free chair. As I passed the Club table that night, Van Dam called me. He said, "De Groot here has found something wrong with the auxiliary bilge pump, and he would like to talk to your chief engineer about it. Is he around?"

I answered that I would have a look, and turned to the noisy crowd rather unhappily, for I was sure that even if my chief engineer was there, I wouldn't be able to pick him out. But I had hardly made a move, before someone got up in the distance and called, "Looking for me, Skipper?" He was the homely character, it must have been telepathy. I beckoned to him and he came running, his napkin in his hand. I introduced him to the Club as "Mr. Er . . ." Van Dam asked us to sit down. While we were talking, Lily the waitress put plates in front of us, and before I noticed what had happened we were eating with the Club, as if we had been tacitly accepted as members.

I could understand that they accepted my chief engineer, for he was indeed a professional; what surprised me was that they included me, after the parting look Van Dam had given me that afternoon.

After we had finished our meal and I had accepted a cigar from one of the bald heads, I left the dining room with the thing between my teeth, feeling somehow fatter. As I went out through the door I saw someone staring at me with unfriendly eyes. It was Goatskin; he obviously had his thoughts at seeing me, the new member of the Club. But whatever his thoughts may have been, I had my little moment.

As Van Dam had taken over the first watch and I had at least twenty-four hours ahead of me with nothing to do, I decided to start by devoting two of them to meditation. There were a couple of things I wanted to work out in my mind before sailing on my first operation, so I went to the only place in Westport where one could think privately.

As I entered the cellar the infernal music from the loud-speakers hit me like a barrage of naval artillery. I worked my way through the dancing crowd, and managed to find a free table underneath one of the loud-speakers. I sat down, shook my head at several girls, ordered a cup of tea, and started thinking.

I put my lighter on the far edge of the table: that was the lame duck. On the edge nearest to me I put my pencil: that was the U-boat. In the center of the table I put a match: that was me.

I put myself there because Dop had told me that U-boats rarely got between the tug and the duck, for fear of drawing the duck's fire. They usually began to close in on you from the rear when you got near the duck. I hadn't quite understood why they should do this; if I was a U-boat captain lusting for a tugboat I'd go to meet her on her probable course, and finish her off in peace. Dop had answered that they were greedy; they didn't want to lose sight of the duck and lay there licking their lips for hours, waiting to kill two birds with one stone.

It all sounded rather vague and emotional to me. I was still a bit confused, for I had been living in a sort of daze ever since I sailed with Dop for the first time; but even so I was conscious of something illogical in the whole U-boat–tugboat relationship. Why didn't the U-boat finish off the helpless duck, before the tugboat arrived? Dop had said, because the guns of the U-boat were inferior to those fitted on the Allied merchant ships, and so they stayed out of range. I thought that was odd, but I didn't see any other explanation for the U-boat's behavior. Then, why did the U-boat, instead of closing in on the tugboat once it had spotted her, insist on gunning her from a distance? Surely the Germans must know by now that we weren't armed? Dop had said, because they wanted to stay out of the range of our pom-pom. It seemed silly, for the pom-pom was harmless. Then, why those mysterious bursts of a dozen rounds Van Dam had told me about? Why didn't the U-boat keep up its fire? There was something fishy there; but as I had no means of solving the mystery, I sighed and started working out positions with my toys on the table.

Van Dam's advice had impressed me. His bit of common sense about approaching the duck was obviously sound; and his recipe for dodging gunfire was a cunning idea: the moment you are shot at, turn your stern toward the U-boat, thereby diminishing yourself as a target to your smallest possible size; then travel backward. Dop had told me that U-boat guns had a lot of kick in them, but they were only auxiliary armament; they had none of the elaborate range finders that made surface ships so deadly. It could safely be assumed that no one, staring at a pinpoint in the distance through his binoculars, could make out whether it was traveling ahead or astern; they would naturally suppose that the rabbit was running away from them, and direct their fire accordingly. The idea of a rabbit running backward was a novelty.

But when I started working out Van Dam's idea on the table it looked less convincing. My aim was the lame duck; I had to get into the shelter of its guns as quickly as possible, and I couldn't quite see how to get there by traveling backward away from it. After some thought, under the screams of "You made me love you," I hit upon the idea of traveling backward toward the lame duck instead of away from it, thus facing the U-boat, and making it believe that I was heading for it. It seemed I had got something there, until a teacup was put slap on the match by the waitress's hand. It gave me quite a shock, because it looked like a direct hit; sipping the black tea I concluded that this was probably exactly what would happen. Jerry might be slow witted; he was certainly not stupid. I put my lighter back in my pocket, took out my notebook, and began to work out positions on paper.

I sat in the Social Center till closing time, and drank five cups of tea. When I finally went out into the night air I felt depressed. Upon close scrutiny Van Dam's panacea didn't work; he must have said it just to impress me. The only thing that kept me doubtful was the undeniable fact that he was still alive after six months of OTWA, and so sure of himself that he made people varnish his thresholds.

I slept badly that night, and spent most of the following day hanging around Headquarters waiting for the *Zeeland* to return. She came in toward dusk, a fat Greek in tow with a list of forty-five degrees. As soon as she was moored I asked Headquarters to summon my crew; I wanted to do some drill in the outer harbor while it was still daylight.

My crew reported with a speed that impressed me; the old Captain in the office might be a foghorn, he certainly worked his ropes fast. Van Dam came in with the Greek Captain to deal with the forms as though he had arrested him, and was now going to enter his offense on the charge sheet. When he saw me he said, "She's all right but for that bilge pump; see to it that your C.E. puts it right." I said I would, and asked whether she was lively on her rudder. "Yes," he said, "you'll find that you'll have to give counterwheel the moment you start pulling her around. Anything else?"

I said, "No, thank you, that's all for the moment," and went on board.

I was nervous when I gave my first order; when I pulled the engine-room telegraph on "Slow astern" for the first time I felt as if I was going in for an examination. Not only did my crew watch me critically; I saw faces behind the steamed windows of the office. The first three minutes I cursed the moment I had thought of trying her out; it would have been better to start at night and get the feel of the ship on my way to my first operation;

now I was just sticking my neck out. But once we headed toward the open I felt better, for I concentrated on the ship.

She was a lovely ship, lively and very fast. When I pulled the stops for the first time and let her have it, she seemed to lift her bow like a speedboat and trailed a wake that was impressive to see. The boy Waterman, who was with me on the bridge, said she made sixteen knots under top pressure, and I could well believe it. When I stood in the speedwind, and the bloom of the spray settled on my face, I felt an unexpected exhilaration. This was my first command; with a ship like this it was worth making a good job of it.

We maneuvered in the outer harbor until it was dark. When we put in, the Chief came to the bridge, wiping his hands with a wad of cotton waste and his forehead with his sleeve. "Blimey, Skipper," he said, "you certainly kept us busy." I had. I must have swung her round, switching from full ahead to full astern, at least a dozen times. I had made her spin in narrowing circles, until she listed so much that I had heard things in the chartroom slide and the bell had started ringing itself. I had found out that she was indeed a lovely ship; you couldn't expect her to do more and still be called a tugboat. I had found out also that my crew was all right, with the possible exception of the boy Waterman, who was very jumpy. But when we went ashore, after mooring her as if she was a crate of eggs, and set out for the Grand Hotel, he trotted beside me, chippering excitedly as if I was his uncle. Whatever the practical results of that bit of drill might be, it had established me in the eyes of my crew as a methodical man who knew what he was doing.

I had dinner with the Club again, and felt fine and confident. When at last I lay on my bed, the confidence ebbed a bit, as a suspicion grew in me. All I had been doing was trying to convince other people that I was a man who knew his job; I had better watch out not to believe it myself too soon, or I would be sorry.

I had no experience as a captain, and didn't know yet that you are as good as your crew think you are; if they think you stink, you had better change ships or you'll begin to bungle things. I don't know why this should be, but there you are.

When the call came I felt as if I hadn't slept at all; my watch said it was half-past three. I dressed quickly and hurried to Headquarters, finding my way with the torch I had bought the day before.

When I entered the office to get my instructions, I found them waiting for me, written on a memo form. It was an Englishman, 16,000 tons, cargo agricultural machinery, hit by a torpedo in No. 4 hold, rudder and propeller shot away, position square 365. That meant a good hundred miles west of Bishop Rock; a good ten hours' sailing. That meant daylight.

When I got on board, I felt worse than I had ever felt before; I felt like shooting myself. I went to the chartroom and started plotting our course on a chart which Van Dam's slaves had tucked away so neatly that it took me minutes to find it. The pencil had been sharpened so meticulously by the slaves that I broke its point the moment it touched the paper. I closed my eyes tightly to fight back the tears and thought, "God, help me." I thought of my father, and prayed to him to be with me and help me; he had been dead twenty years and wherever he was, it was a long way away. I prayed to my mother, but although she was nearer, smiling anxiously, she seemed helpless with her flowered apron and her frying pan. I must have been a nice heartening spectacle for the boy Waterman to see when he came in. He coughed respectfully, and said, "Skipper?" I opened my eyes but didn't look around. I looked at the chart; Bishop Rock swam in a haze. I said, "Yes?" He said, "Rea-ready when you are." His voice broke on the "ready," and that cured me.

This was the spot where Van Dam had stood forty-eight hours before; and he had made room for Christopher Robin saying his prayers. I don't know where it came from, but I started to hum, "Hush, hush, whisper who dares—Christopher Robin is saying his prayers." It somehow made all the difference; I went to the bridge with a confidence and a calmness that seemed miraculous. I gave my orders in a voice so quiet with authority that I could hardly be heard, and I felt Waterman's presence edging nearer in the darkness, nervously. I was such a center of self-assurance and experience that I even impressed myself. I just was one hell of a good Captain. My crew was lucky that fate had sent me, they had got nothing to worry about. It was a touching sham; I had just slipped into the character the boy Waterman had offered me when his voice broke.

I stayed on the bridge from the moment we sailed: old Captain Ironsides lighting his pipe, and pacing up and down at hiking speed on his sturdy sea dog's legs. A yellow dawn broke through thin cloud and grew into a murky day. The sea was tired, a bored gray swell kept us rocking mechanically. I didn't realize how lucky I was that there was so little wind, as I still hadn't quite got over my seasickness; I even ate the bacon and the mashed potatoes cook brought me without giving it a second thought, and I drank two cups of his coffee. I thought, while pacing, how silly I had been ever to leave the tugboat service; this obviously was the job I was born to do.

The Chief came to the bridge halfway and talked about the bilge pump. He had fixed it. I nodded approvingly without taking my pipe out of my mouth, and he retired, mysteriously satisfied. I saw, every time I turned on my heels on the starboard side, a scratch in the varnish on the rail. After I had seen it about six hundred times without registering, I suddenly noticed it, stopped, rubbed my finger over it like a housewife testing a mantelpiece for dust, whistled the bosun, and told him to put it on his list. He asked, "List?" I frowned. Surely he had a list of minor jobs to be done? He said he hadn't; I ordered him to buy a notebook tomorrow. My bosuns used to have a little notebook to write their jobs in, to be checked as soon as they were done. He could get one at Woolworth's for sixpence; he could add the sixpence to the petty cash account. He left, mysteriously satisfied.

It was the boy Waterman who spotted the U-boat; I was thinking of Stella when he called me. I saw her standing with her back to me at the stove, making beans on toast; her hair looked soft and shiny. Waterman said, "I think there is one, Skipper."

I took over his binoculars and saw my first U-boat. A low, gray shape in the haze.

I had a moment of coldness. My cheeks contracted and I felt the quiver in the back of my knees again. At the same time it seemed as if I was watching myself with curiosity: a man who couldn't play chess, but only knew one opening.

I played my opening with a gusto that had an almost humorous edge of complete despair. I called the engine room through the blower and told the Chief that we were in for some quick maneuvering. Then I spun the ship around until she ran away in a straight line from the U-boat, and switched to full speed astern. The moment my hand left the handle of the telegraph, the first shell came whistling at us. It passed so close overhead that I ducked; when the rumble of the explosion sounded thickly ahead I looked up and saw the cauliflower collapse in the wake we had made, about seventy yards in front of our bow. But for Van Dam's little hint, Jerry would have scored a direct hit with his first round.

The boy Waterman didn't know it was Van Dam he had to thank for still being of one piece; nobody knew but me. I realized that when I saw their faces. They looked at old Captain Ironsides with such reverence that I almost turned around to see who was standing behind me; then I slipped back into character.

Captain Ironsides was as cool as a cucumber. He moved his ship about with geometrical precision. The shells and the ship seemed to perform a slow, formal dance, to the accompaniment of whistles and a kettle drum;

every move followed a rigid pattern. At first I felt tense, then relaxed, then tense again with the quiver in the back of my knees returning, as the notion dawned on me that this couldn't go on forever. This was just crazy. Then, suddenly, the music stopped. Jerry had spent his dozen rounds.

This was the opening as far as I knew it. I fell back on to my course, full speed ahead, and waited, suspended in a vacuum. The duck we were heading for must be just behind the horizon, but she was not yet in sight. I raced toward her as fast as I could; then I spotted a flash in the haze abaft and switched to full speed astern with a quickness that was purely automatic. The ship quivered, pitched; the bridge was set trembling until everything rattled; then we ploughed back on our wake. The whistle again passed close overhead, again the shell struck ahead of us. The dance started again until the dozen rounds were spent. By then I was sure that Van Dam had it taped. We could go on doing this for as long as our coal lasted, and that was a lot longer than Jerry's ammunition would last. The only thing that amazed me was that Jerry didn't get wise; but he just didn't.

We went through the intricate pattern of our dance four times, and in the end the shells began to strike very close. Then hell broke loose on the horizon. We heard two salvos soar overhead like low flying planes; then four fountains of milk spouted far behind us. Whatever was the matter with that duck, she certainly had good eyes.

That first salvo from the Englishman had an odd effect on me: it dried me up completely. I pulled the telegraph on full speed ahead, but it was no more than a reflex. After that I just stood there on the bridge, grinning like a cretin, feeling my knees turn to jelly.

I leaned back against the rail, trying frantically to think of something to do or to say next, for I hadn't got the faintest idea, I couldn't even think of the names of the most familiar objects, like "line" and "hawser"; I just stood there, speechless, while Captain Ironsides floated away and left me behind: an actor who had forgotten his lines.

When we got alongside the duck I stared at it in a dull panic. This was a job I had tackled at least a hundred times before; I had even passed an examination going through all the moves; I could dream them. But at that moment I just hadn't got a clue. I didn't know whether to attach a rope to her mast and pull, or to put my nose under her smashed tail and push her. Then a cunning thought slid out of the jungle of my confusion, like a snake. I gave the boy Waterman the falsest smile I must ever have produced, and said, "Well, Mate, now let's see what you can do. You take over." He woke up from a sort of daydream, blinked, swallowed, and said,

"Aye aye, Skipper." As he started blowing his little whistle and shouting commands with his high piping voice, I tried to light my pipe. I tried three times; then I gave up, for I was sure that by then the shaking of my hands was getting too obvious.

I watched the proceedings in a haze. Once or twice I became conscious of Waterman asking something, I had no idea what. I just said, "No, no, you go ahead; this is your show," and went on sucking my dead pipe, looking quizzical.

Whatever the boy Waterman did, he made a job of it. Within twenty minutes we were on our way home with the duck in tow, deafened by the thunder of her guns that went on pounding overhead with exhausting regularity. I remembered at one moment that Dop had done something under similar circumstances, something rather important; but I couldn't for the life of me remember what.

I remembered it a good twelve hours later, when we were nearing home. I was lying on the consultation couch in Van Dam's clinic, when the boy Waterman came in. He seemed anxious to say something, but unable to decide how to begin. I raised my eyebrows in a gross imitation of the absent doctor, and asked, "Well?"

He said, "I'm sorry I forgot the hooter, Skipper. I know I should have signaled them to hold their fire, but I don't know what came over me. I just forgot. I'm sorry."

I gazed at him for a moment from an utter, dizzy emptiness; then I remembered what I had forgotten: the signals with our siren, to direct the duck's fire. One long blast for "Fire" and two short ones for "Hold it." That was why the Englishman had gone on pounding away with all his guns, long after the U-boat had stopped being dangerous; he had stuck to the letter of the instructions in envelope D with religious fervour, waiting until his guns turned red for us to signal him to hold his fire.

It was shocking, and I couldn't think of anything to say. The poor boy had had more reason to forget those signals than I had; he had been pushed into the command of a tugboat while he was staring dreamily across the rail, thinking of flowers. I was about to say something disastrous to my prestige, when suddenly the snake slid out of the jungle again and hissed: *that's quite all right, you didn't do badly.*

I said, "That's quite all right, old man, you didn't do badly."

He said, "Thank you for not ticking me off on the bridge. That—that's what I really came in to say."

The snake hissed *Get along with you*, and I said it, with a fine, fatherly smile.

He went away and left me lying on that couch, stunned. I had fooled myself all my life, until I honestly believed that I had an accurate idea of what I really was like. Fooled was the word, indeed.

The devil knows what was the matter with the last cup of coffee Cook brought up for me as a treat, just before we entered the harbor. It must have sat on his stove boiling for hours. It made me seasick, the moment I had finished it. For the next hour or so I was so busy keeping it down that I hardly registered what happened.

We handed the Englishman over to the Navy tugs; we took her Captain on board, sailed into the harbor, and moored. The Englishman was of the tubby, chatty type; but I was not responsive. I just looked stolid and stern, with my jaws clenching my pipe and my hands clasped behind my back as if they were grafted together. I needed all my concentration to keep myself from throwing up.

When we moored, the tugboat next to us was very lively. It was Dop's, and she was obviously about to leave. I found Dop in the office reading his orders. He asked if I had done all right, and I said I had. He looked curiously happy and excited, and behaved as if he was dying to tell me something. The Englishman said, sportingly, "The nicest piece of dodging I've seen for a long time. I must say you chaps know your job all right." I would have enjoyed this more if I hadn't felt so sick; at the moment all I thought of was how to get the form business over as quickly as possible.

We got through the forms at record speed; the Englishman barely got the chance to mumble the traditional "Thank you for bringing me in." I said he was welcome anytime, and started to hurry out before finishing the phrase; then a voice I hadn't heard before stopped me. It was a very British voice, so bland that I had the momentary delusion that one of the wireless operators sitting with their backs to us had switched on the B.B.C. news. It was the British Lieutenant Commander, whom so far I had only seen cleaning his nails, filling his lighter, and smoking a long pipe. "By the way, Captain!" he called after me. "You didn't get a clear picture of the U-boat, I suppose?" I said no, not very clear; just a long gray shape in the haze. "You said she gave you four bursts of a dozen rounds each; did you notice by any chance whether she dived between those bursts, or did she remain surfaced?" I said I hadn't noticed; I was too sick to ask why the hell he thought she should have dived. He gave me a smile, said, "That will be all, thank you," and I made for the door. I had my hand already on the knob when Dop caught up with me.

He whispered, "We're going to be married!" I said, "Good! When?" He said, "As soon as I come back from this trip. You must be best man." I said, "O.K."; then I just had to get out, and fast. The moment I had shut the door behind me I vomited in the darkness.

The English Captain opened the door again when I had just about finished. I was already feeling relieved that no one had seen me, when I caught sight of a dim shape close to me before the door shut off the light. It had only been a second, but long enough to recognize the shape. It was Stella.

I stumbled home to the Grand Hotel, convincing myself all the way that she had not recognized me. When I entered the hall the old porter rose from his grave behind the counter on hearing the swing doors swish. He narrowed his eyes, recognized my uniform, produced a bottle wrapped in paper and said, "Want a drink, Captain? Canteen price." When I answered, "No, thank you," and hurried on, he called after me, "All right, you stingy bastard; lie down and rot!" He was a curious old boy, he hated our guts. Perhaps it was only the war he hated, because it had upset his nicely organized life just when his sun was setting, and we were the only part of the war he could get hold of to show how he felt about it.

When I lay on my bunk in the darkness, listening to the wheezing and snoring round me, I felt so sick that I hardly dared move. I trembled all over, and had a splitting headache. I thought that I would have to get up and go to the lavatory at the top of the stairs, until I realized that it was not that kind of sickness.

I wanted a kiss, to take my fear away. I wanted a woman, any woman, so badly that it made me groan. It wasn't the coffee; it wasn't even the fear, although I now lay there shaking like a leaf. I was just sick with desire.

When I realized this I was already so drunk with the pills that it struck me as funny. I sniggered, and as that caused another wave of nausea I began to hum. I remember humming: "Onward, Christian Soldiers," and thinking it a wonderful joke. I must have fallen asleep soon afterward.

CHAPTER THREE

I WENT TO HEADQUARTERS THE NEXT EVENING TO TELL THEM THAT IF ANY-thing came up before midnight I would be in the Social Center.

Van Dam wasn't back yet, but Dop had just come in. When I entered the office the Captain of the duck which the *Vlieland* had brought in was being taken through the paper routine. I didn't register what he was like or his nationality; I never looked at him, for it was Goatskin who sat filling out the forms.

I knew instantly that Dop had been killed, even before Goatskin looked up and I saw his face. I didn't feel any particular shock; so much had happened during the ten days since I had met Dop again that my sensitiveness had got a bit blunted. My first thought was not "How terrible," or whatever else one thinks in normal circumstances on realizing that one's friend is dead; my first thought was "What happened?" for it seemed odd that only one man out of an entire crew should have been killed by U-boat gunfire. Perhaps he had fallen overboard.

Goatskin told me that he had. They had been strafed by machine-gun fire from a plane, on their way to the duck. The plane had strafed them twice; Dop had caught it the second time. He had refused to take shelter until the very last moment; when he had tried to duck behind the rail it was too late. The plane came in from starboard, he was standing on the port side of the bridge; he had no time left to run across the bridge for shelter, so he had tried to climb over the rail and sit on the navigation light. At least Goatskin assumed that this had been his train of thought, otherwise it couldn't be explained why he had suddenly tried to climb over the rail. He had been hit when he straddled the rail; he had arched his back, clutched his side and fallen overboard. They had stopped the ship and circled, but there had been no sign of him.

After Goatskin had told this, the old Captain started to bellow again and to thump the table, trying to frighten the British officer opposite him with the threat that he would quit this job unless his ships got fighter cover. The officer listened to him impassively, smoking his long pipe. The old Captain made a mistake when he included, "Guns that could shoot level" with the conditions of his ultimatum, for in this case it did not apply. The officer let it pass; he didn't betray the fact that he had noticed the mistake. Perhaps he was thinking of something else.

I didn't remember the key until I had followed Goatskin outside and heard him say, "I had better go and tell his girl." He didn't sound happy at the thought, so I said, "I'll do that, if you like."

We were walking down the pier; when I said that he stopped and looked at me with the same expression in his eyes I had noticed when I left the dining room after my first meal with the Club. I didn't understand why. "What's the matter?" I asked. "Nothing," he said, and walked on.

I should have let him go; but I caught up with him, feeling rather foolish. Somehow I still had the notion that people had to be comforted after a loss. Although he had told the story of Dop's death so crisply that it had sounded as if he was dictating a cable to his local newspaper, his face looked haggard. He didn't say another word until we got to the bottom of the pier. There he said, "Well, enjoy yourself," and turned briskly away. This time I should have caught up with him, grabbed him by the collar of his goatskin, and asked him what the hell he meant by that. But I let him go.

On my way to the flat I thought of an explanation for his attitude. Perhaps he knew about the key business, and had only realized that Dop had given it to me when I offered to go and see Stella. Perhaps he had expected to be given that key himself; Dop and he had seemed to get on well together. So either he was hurt that Dop had not considered him his best friend, or jealous because he had expected to take over the flat himself.

I didn't think about the flat at all. I thought about Stella and how I was going to break the news to her. I had never told a woman that her husband was dead, and I felt sorry that I hadn't let Goatskin tackle the job when he said he would. When I had climbed the stairs and stood on the map of Africa in front of the door with the inverted "2," I leaned against the wall staring at the lock. I tried to figure out what would be better: to knock or to use my key. I had been climbing the stairs with the key in my hand and it had grown warm by now. I listened at the crack but didn't hear a sound; I knocked once.

It was a feeble knock, and nobody answered it. Even if she was in the flat she could hardly have heard it. I was about to knock for a second time, when I heard steps mounting the stairs, and I decided to wait until they had gone. I heard them shuffle about on each landing, between climbing the flight of stairs; when they got to the floor below me I heard knocks. I decided it must be the milkman; when the steps mounted the last flight and he came into view it was a postman.

He saw me, said, "Good morning. Lovely day, isn't it?" then he shoved a letter under Stella's door, knocked, and turned to go. When he was already descending the stairs, he asked, "Waiting for No. 12?"

I felt embarrassed, and said, "Yes, I don't think she's in."

The postman said, "She's not in? Then it's the first time since I've been on this round. She never goes out, that one." As he turned the corner between the two floors he called, "You try again!" and vanished. I listened to his steps until they were gone; then I put the key in the lock, turned it and opened the door.

The kitchen was empty, the door to the bedroom stood ajar. On the mat lay the white square of the envelope which the postman had pushed in.

I was sure she wasn't there, for the flat had a feeling of emptiness. Then

I remembered that it had had that feeling both times I had come in with Dop, and I was not so sure any more.

I coughed, but didn't hear a sound. I thought that she might be out after all; perhaps I had better leave a note on the table asking her to call me when she came in. Of course I was sure all the time that she was in, for if Dop had been still alive he would have come home at this time. But somehow I wanted her to be out so much that I just believed it.

I picked up the letter from the mat to write the note on the back of it. Before I turned it around I read the address. It was a bill from the Southwestern Electricity Board to Captain David de Jong, K.L.M., 12 Seaview, Esplanade, Westport. "K.L.M." were the initials for the Royal Dutch Airlines.

As I stood looking at the letter I heard a sound from the bedroom. A sound as if someone was choking. It gave me a shock; I forgot about my embarrassment and went to the bedroom door.

The bedroom was empty and tidy. The bed was made and covered with a chintz spread. The face in the leather frame on top of the wardrobe smiled at me fixedly. I called, "Stella?" softly, but with an alarm in my voice that I had not intended. Then I heard a sound from the bathroom; the same sound I had heard before. This time I recognized it; it was the sound of vomiting.

I stood there for a moment, motionless, listening. I thought I ought to go in there and help her, but I didn't quite know how. I remembered that when I was sick as a child my mother had held my forehead for me with a quiet cool hand. My hands were hot and sticky, and I didn't know her well enough to be of any comfort to her in such a humiliating position. I really didn't know her at all.

I went back into the kitchen, looked around, and sat down. I took off my cap and put it on the table. I noticed the letter again, and for some reason I got up and put it back on the mat, face downward. Then I went back and sat down again; put my hand on the table and drummed with my fingers. When I took my hand away there was a damp patch on the polished surface; I wiped it off with my sleeve. I remembered that it was she who had sewn on my stripes, how her red boy's hands had fumbled with the nail scissors, how kind and sweet she had been. I felt very sorry for her, and didn't want to go away any longer. I was the only one who could be of any use to her in this, if only by letting myself be talked to. I was the only one who had known Dop as a normal carefree chap, the way she must have known him; Goatskin knew only his tense, noisy side. If I had a girl and someone had to tell her that I had been killed in action, I

116

would hate the idea of the boy Waterman going to see her to break the news, for he had no idea what I really was like. He would come to announce the death of old Captain Ironsides; the poor girl wouldn't know who he was talking about.

As I sat there, waiting, I hardly had any thoughts at all; I just listened. I heard no more sounds from the bathroom, and I wondered what was happening. I wondered why she was sick; perhaps she knew. Perhaps my cough had given me away; perhaps opening the door with my key and not calling, "Hey, where are you?" with Dop's voice had been all that was needed. Then I heard the sound of a toilet being flushed.

At first I thought it might be at the neighbors'. The flats were very noisy; while I sat there waiting I had heard steps and voices on the other side of the kitchen wall, and a blast of music from a radio being tuned in. Then the hissing of the tap filling the cistern suddenly got louder, before it dimmed again. I knew she had come out of the bathroom into the bedroom. I stood up and waited for her to come in.

She took a long time coming in. At first I thought she must be standing there in that room, listening, as I was in the kitchen. Then I heard a soft stroking noise, and a clatter of something being put down on a glass surface. I realized that she had been brushing her hair at her dressing table.

That gave me a moment's doubt whether she knew after all, whether she even knew I was there. When she came in I didn't doubt any longer. She came in exactly as I had seen her come in twice before. She wore her long blue dressing gown and the white ribbon in her hair. She smiled, but it was not pretty to see. Her face was as white as a sheet, and she had painted herself a bright red mouth which looked horrible. I had never noticed that she used lipstick before, although I think she must have; perhaps she had put on no more than usual this time, but her face was so white that the mouth made her look like a clown.

It was the color of her face that gave her away; her eyes expressed nothing. She looked at me steadily and with a desperate gentleness, and said, "Hello." Her voice was steady, but very soft.

I said, "I'm sorry," and thought of what to say next, but she didn't let me.

She said, "Would you like something to eat?" and I answered, "If you like," for anything else would have sounded sillier. She went to the stove and started going through the routine of making beans on toast.

I remembered Dop telling me she made the best beans on toast in the world, I remembered the time I hadn't been able to eat them. I wanted to tell her how Dop had died, and that he couldn't have had much pain; but I decided to wait until she asked me.

She stood with her back to me for a long time; cutting the bread, putting it under the grill, opening a tin, emptying it into the little pan, putting it over the flame. She said nothing and the silence became so oppressive that I couldn't stand it any longer. I said, "He was killed by m.g. fire from a plane and fell overboard. He can't have felt anything; he must . . ."

Before I had finished she turned around, crying, "Don't talk about it! Don't!" Her face was so haggard that I suddenly felt cold. Then her eyes seemed to fill with that gentleness again, and she added, "Please." She said "please" in exactly the same tone in which she had said, "Don't worry, you'll be all right," and I couldn't bear to look at her any longer. I turned away, and said, "I'm sorry, I know how you feel. Let's have something to eat."

I sat staring at the emblem of my cap on the table until she took it away and put a plate in its stead. I said, "Thank you," and wanted to start eating, but I had nothing to eat with. She put down another plate and sat down herself; then she saw me staring, said, "Oh, I'm sorry," got up and fetched knives and forks.

We sat eating in silence for a while. I concentrated on my plate, but occasionally I glanced at her hands. She was eating too, and I wondered how she managed it. I thought how very English she was, how she must have been brought up in that curious tradition of never showing any feelings in order not to embarrass other people, until it had become engrained in her character. As we ate on I began to feel very alien to her; I wished she had broken down and wept, or just been unable to eat like that. It would somehow have made me feel a lot better.

Halfway through the meal she asked, "When do you want the flat?"

I said, "I don't want it at all. I want you to stay here and carry on until you have made up your mind what to do."

She said, "I wouldn't want that. You promised him that you would take over, otherwise he would never have given you the key. I want you to keep that promise, it's important."

Then I just couldn't stand it any longer. I put down my knife and fork, and said, "Look here. He was my best friend. He was killed this morning. I'm not an Englishman; I cannot just sit here and eat beans on toast and behave as if he never existed. I . . ." She put her hand over mine and clasped it, hard. Her hand was very cold.

"Don't," she said; when I looked up I saw that she had bent her head, her long hair hung down by the sides of her face. I felt ashamed to think it, but she looked beautiful at that moment. I wanted to look away, but she lifted her head and looked at me with such concentrated strength in her eyes that I couldn't. Her eyes seemed to have the experience of all the generations of sailors' wives of her island behind them. While she sat looking at me I had an odd feeling, as if we had sat like this many times before. As if I had as much experience of bringing messages of doom as she had of receiving them. Perhaps I had gone through this before, in a dream.

It was that feeling that made me accept her attitude as inevitable. I said, "I'm sorry; it was stupid of me. Is there anything I can do?"

She thought for a while, then she answered, "I'd like you to come in after you get home next time, and have a meal with me. Then we can talk about the flat and decide what to do."

I said, "O.K., I'll be seeing you," and left.

I didn't go back to her until a week later. I sailed three times that week; twice I got home between midnight and three in the morning, so tired that I couldn't be bothered. There was of course another reason why I didn't go, but I kept it nicely tucked away, well out of reach of my consciousness.

The first two times we sailed for nothing. We didn't encounter any U-boats, but when we got to the square in which the wreck had been reported, it was gone. Both times my wireless operator came to the bridge, after some pointless circling, to say that Headquarters had reported the wreck lost, and could we please pick up survivors. We cruised about, looking for them, but there weren't any. The first time we found nothing at all, the second time only some wreckage floating about.

The third time, when we neared the appointed spot at daybreak, we heard a dull thud behind the horizon, and after a while saw a new cloud slowly rising out of it. When we got nearer we heard the sharp, metallic reports we knew so well; they were shots from a U-boat gun. It somehow seemed a decent thing to do to keep on our course and race to the duck's assistance, although our assistance couldn't amount to much. I ordered the bosun to uncover the pom-pom and bring it to the ready; he looked doubtful when he went to obey this command, as if I had asked him to put the old tricycle from the attic in running order.

We never got near enough to see what had actually happened; before we got there a U-boat surfaced close to us.

This time I saw it very clearly: an ugly gray thing, much smaller than I had expected; water oozed from its nostrils when it came up, and until it was up all the way the gun sticking out of the foredeck seemed to be traveling by itself. Then the lid of its conning tower was opened and a lot of busy little men came tumbling out; when they ran toward the gun I shouted at the bosun, "Fire!" The bosun and a couple of sailors turned what seemed to be an incredible number of wheels, handles and gauges; the thing swung around on its pedestal with screams of rusty iron, then it went off.

It made one hell of a racket. I never saw any bullets get anywhere at all. The thing just spat fire and sounded as if it had six barrels instead of two; as far as I could make out from the bridge it was aiming in a general way at the sky. The effect, however, was surprising: the busy little men ran back to the tower as if they were being swept away. One of them went on fumbling heroically with the cover over the gun for a second, then somebody shouted at him from the tower like an angry mother on the beach, and he scurried back. The moment the lid was closed there was a loud curse from my bosun in a sudden silence. He looked at the bridge, made a gesture of helpless rage, and shouted, "The bloody thing's got stuck!" then he turned around and kicked it, after which he grabbed his foot. The U-boat went under with a lot of bubbling noises, and at an astonishing speed; then it vanished completely. I wished I had been sailing an ice-breaker instead of a tugboat, for during the minute she was going under I could have rammed her easily.

As it was, we went on at full speed toward the spot where the wreck had been reported. It wasn't difficult to find, for the cloud, although much fainter, still floated over it. I knew the duck had a cargo of agricultural machinery. Judging from the way she had blown up I could imagine what kind of machinery it had been; they couldn't have had any time for lowering lifeboats. We met some wreckage and spotted a raft; when we got nearer we saw it was empty. Sparks came to the bridge and said he had just picked up a signal from Headquarters that the duck had fallen silent after squeaking for a bit, which meant that she had been sunk in action, for according to envelope D a duck was to squeak only when subject to a direct attack. I swung around at full speed and began running for home.

As I had expected, the U-boat surfaced on our course. This time we had no duck to run to for shelter, and although our pom-pom was permanently out of order I decided to put up a show as if it was working. The moment we saw the U-boat surfacing over starboard I headed right at it, even though it was still a long way away. I saw through my binoculars the mannikins tumbling out of the tower, uncovering the gun and pointing it at us. When the first shell came whistling at us and fell short, I took over the wheel myself and started zigzagging. Although the ship was very quick on her wheel I couldn't zigzag fast enough for a good gunner, and while the shells came whistling and splashing ever closer, I became convinced that this time we would buy it. But an amazing thing happened: when they were just about to pot us, they stopped; the mannikins covered the gun and ran back to the tower, the lid was closed, and the U-boat dived. When they did this they were still well beyond the range of our pom-pom even if it had worked and been able to shoot level. I seemed to be lucky that day.

I called the engine room and told them to give her all they could, that if we wanted to get home we had to run faster than a U-boat. I wouldn't have been surprised if my Chief had refused to put up the pressure, for he was that kind of man; he had no notion of what was going on in the world outside his engine room and would rather be blown to bits by a direct hit than by an exploding boiler. But he obeyed; never had I known the *Zeeland* to run faster.

Our speed for some reason put my crew in an exhilarated mood. They stood laughing and slapping each other on the shoulder, looking at the bow wave and the wake; the boy Waterman asked me whether it would be all right if he timed her. When I said, "No," he looked disappointed; he seemed to have forgotten the U-boat in the excitement of going so much faster than God had meant us to.

The U-boat surfaced again, this time behind us. Again she lashed out with a dozen rounds without scoring a hit, although several times I ducked with my heart in my mouth. After the dozen rounds were spent, the mannikins went through the same rigmarole of covering up the gun, running back to the tower, closing the lid and diving, letting us, by this incomprehensible waste of time and opportunity, run away from what was almost certain death.

The U-boat surfaced twice more, before we got out of her reach. Every time she was further away; every time she did the same: surfaced, uncovered the gun, shot a dozen rounds, covered the gun up, and dived. I followed her antics through my binoculars; they left me in a pensive mood. I didn't hit upon any logical explanation for this diving business, but although it had certainly saved our lives I somehow didn't like it. I didn't like it a bit.

We got home about midnight. When I went to the office to report, the old Captain wasn't there; he had obviously gone home when he heard that there was nothing doing. The only ones there were the wireless operator on night shift and the British officer. The W.O. was reading a book with his feet on the radio bench; only one of his loud-speakers twittered faintly, but he didn't seem to be listening to it. The officer was cleaning his pipe, a messy business; while we talked he went on mucking about with soggy cleaners and bits of paper he wormed inside the hole in the pipe's head, and filled the room with the stench of tobacco juice.

I told him that this time I had seen the U-boat close enough to give him a full word picture. While I gave it to him he didn't look up once. He asked, after I had finished, whether she had dived between shooting her rounds; when I answered, "Yes," he looked up with a happy smile as if this was good news. He was then sitting with a soaked cleaner in one hand and a dirty piece of twisted paper in the other, undecided where to put them; I am sure he would have shaken hands with me otherwise. He said, "Splendid! This helps us a lot. I'm sure we have spotted him now."

I asked whether he would mind telling me what he was talking about, as I was rather interested. He said, "Of course, old man, of course. Do sit down."

I sat down, while he wrapped his nasty business in a sheet of typewriting paper, folded it into a neat little parcel, and dropped it in the wastepaper basket. Then he said, "The U-boat that has been pestering us is a very old one, used by the French for gunnery practice, and taken over by the Germans for the same end. Its captain is called Hasenfratz, he's an old instructor and trains crews. Until a week ago he seemed to do only gun training, but it looks now as if he was given a cigar to spend on each trip, for he could never have sunk those ducks by gunfire alone. His gun is too small, he wouldn't have a hope against the stuff most of our merchant ships are fitted out with now. So all he is doing, really, is target shooting."

I asked, "On us, you mean?"

He said, "That's right. You chaps are the perfect target for training. You are small but not too small, slow but not too slow, armed, but insufficiently, and you put up one hell of a fight in the way of dodging fire. Old Hasenfratz could ask for nothing better; but as he is a Jerry, he sticks to the drill, and allows his pupils only a dozen rounds a go. After that they dive and surface again. You didn't notice how long they took between surfacing and firing the first round, did you?" I said that I didn't, but that they were pretty nippy about it. "I had to make a lot of inquiries before I reached my deduction," he said. "I found out from our people that our record time between surfacing and shooting the first round is fifty-five seconds."

I said, "Fancy," and he looked at me for the first time in a way as if he really saw me. "Pretty hard on you chaps," he said, "to realize that you are being used for target practice. I don't think we should make it generally known."

I said, "You might consider filing an application on our behalf for better guns, if you can fit it in."

He said, "No need to get cynical, old man, I'm doing my best. I've been pleading for you ever since I got commissioned here. I am sure that by now they are putting my reports in the wastepaper basket without even reading them, for they are always the same. I think it's a shocking shame to let you chaps face the music with the antique stuff you have got; but now look at it from their point of view. I can't tell you how many convoys come in on the Western Approaches, but you must have a pretty accurate idea yourself from the way you are being kept busy. Out of all the ships making up those convoys a very low percentage gets lost or disabled; in their eyes you just aren't worth bothering about, neither the ducks nor you. The moment a ship gets left behind by a convoy it is written off; if you manage to salvage one or two it is sheer profit. I'll go on pestering them on your behalf until they go black in the face, and transfer me to get rid of the buzzing in their ears; but if you ask me my honest opinion: you won't get your guns until every single merchantman in the Allied fleet has been properly fitted out. I'm sorry, but that's how it is."

I looked at him for a while without saying anything. He was not a bad chap after all, and I was sure he had done all he said he did. But somehow I felt like bashing somebody's face in. I said, "So, if I get you right: all we are is just a set of clay pigeons for Captain Hasensomething."

He looked at me the way Stella had looked, when I wanted her to show some reaction to the news of Dop's death. "I'm afraid you are," he said. "But you might care to consider that you are not the only one."

That reply brought me so near to screaming point that I had some difficulty in getting up and going out like a sensible, well-mannered hero. But it made me understand something about the English that I had not realized before, and that explained in a way how they had managed to stick it for so long, alone against overwhelming odds, without flinching. They were merciless toward everybody, including themselves.

When I got out of the office I was in a black rage. I suppose I should have felt a more complicated emotion; but the idea that all we were— with our fears, our hopes, our philosophy, our love—was just a set of clay pigeons for a German artillery instructor, was such a monstrous idea that all I could do to defend myself was to fly into a helpless rage. I stamped along the pier and the Esplanade, my fists in my pockets, muttering, "Hasenfratz!"

By the time I got to the Grand Hotel, I had so much explosiveness bottled up inside me by the sheer repetition of the name "Hasenfratz," that I only realized I hadn't been given any pills that night when the old porter rose from his grave, brandishing a bottle wrapped in paper, and whispering, "Want a drink, Captain? Canteen price." It was the glass with the dentures that reminded me, for it was the same type of glass that was on all the washstands in the hotel, and to me they were associated with gulps of tepid water washing bitter pills down.

I asked him what he had got there. He unwrapped part of the bottle and showed me it was Scotch. I said, "O.K., I'll have it. Canteen price," shoved a pound note across the counter, and went away.

He squeaked, "Hey, hey! It's one pound five!" He shouldn't have said that; I turned slowly round, came back and said, "Listen, Hasenfratz, one more squeak out of you and you'll be sorry for a long, long time."

He eyed me as unflinchingly as a stuffed parrot, and repeated, "That will be one pound five." His eyes had the same strength behind them that Stella's and the officer's had had; God, they were tough, these English.

I said, "How would you like it if I wrung your neck for you?" and he answered, "Fine."

I gave him two sweaty half crowns from my pocket; only then did he blink. It looked as if the lids covered his eyes from the bottom up; he looked more like a parrot than ever. He said, "Good night, Captain, happy dreams," and sank back into his grave.

I stood for a moment in doubt whether I would empty the glass with the dentures on his head; that was the state of mind Captain Hasenfratz had put me in. Then I turned round, groped my way to a corner of the darkened hall, sat down in a twanging club chair, opened the bottle and took a swig. The Scotch tasted foul; I knew instantly that it was some beastly hooch he had concocted himself in the basement and poured into an empty bottle. I thought of a means to prove this, and considered going back to the counter and offering him a drink of his own stuff, then I would know all right. But I couldn't be bothered; I just sat there in that corner, staring across the dark mausoleum of the hall at the dentures on the tombstone, swilling hooch and thinking.

I thought of how the others would take it when they came to know what the U-boat was doing, that had sunk two of our ships and kept us in a state of continuous fear that amounted to neurasthenia. I wondered how Van Dam would feel with his lovely little theory about us being stretcher-bearers on a battlefield; whether he would still be so damned snooty about shooting back if he realized that he was bearing stretchers at the wrong end of a shooting gallery. I wondered whether Captain Hasenfratz's pupils who had bagged Frankendaal and Daamen had got a prize for scoring a hit: a teddy bear, or a bottle of perfume.

I tried to see the whole thing from Hasenfratz's point of view, and as soon as I did this found out that I couldn't hate him any longer. When I was still in Holland during the occupation, British planes had nipped across frequently on little training excursions, bagging trains and bridges; although occasionally a passenger train or a tollkeeper's house had been blown up, we had never taken this in bad grace, we had understood that everybody had got to learn. I could not make light of a tollkeeper's wife and children being blown sky high, and at the same time sulk because someone else was doing some practicing on me. I wasn't even a civilian, I got hooch at canteen price; so what was I whining about.

Now I had solved all the mysteries that had seemed to surround me so thickly when I first got to Westport. I had crossed the shadow line good and proper, and was now one of the initiated in the brotherhood of Christian Soldiers. I didn't blame Captain Hasenfratz for anything, I didn't even blame Headquarters for not giving us guns. After my fifth swig I didn't even blame Van Dam any more, for having found his own little design for dying and being high and mighty about it; if anything I was envious of him, for I could do with one myself. I tried to think of all the arguments for this war being a holy one, that had sounded so convincing when I was still living under the German occupation, and not being shot at by Captain Hasenfratz and his kindergarten. I thought of Hitler's hysterical speeches over the radio, exterminated Jews, defenseless people beaten to death in the concentration camps; but it was not enough to make me get up and brace my shoulders and stride out through those swinging doors, longing to be shot at again by an artillery instructor for the sake of freedom of conscience and democracy.

I might have kidded myself into accepting some sort of higher purpose for being the bull's-eye in a shooting gallery, if I hadn't had so much hooch inside me by then. The hooch didn't make me drunk, it made me objective. I was just a man terrified out of his wits, a coward, trying to sip courage from a bottle. That was the nasty part about it; I knew how I would feel when I had to sail again. I wished the British officer had never told me.

Once I had got to the ugly truth at the bottom of the bottle, I felt so sick with fear that I sat there whimpering; I just had to talk to somebody about it, dilute the concentration of fear in my system by sharing it with someone else. I thought of the people to whom I could talk about it and who would make me feel better by getting frightened themselves; I could think of no one. It wouldn't make the slightest difference to Van Dam, whether he was being shot at by a skilled lunatic or an unskilled one; Goatskin would recognize my fear at a glance and disdainfully brace himself against anything I could tell him. The only one who would be impressed by my story was the boy Waterman; but he was too easy. And as I had to sail with him again tomorrow the idea of having two sets of chattering teeth on my bridge didn't appeal to me. The only one I could think of was Stella.

It was surprising that it should have taken me so long to come to the decision to go to the flat. I had needed a bottle of hooch and Captain Hasenfratz's assistance to get up and face those blue eyes again. I got up, went out, walked through the chilly night air along the crowded boulevard gingerly, convincing myself that I was not drunk by making bee lines at lampposts. I sailed from post to post, keeping my eyes fixed on the guiding lights, until I reached the entrance to Seaview. When I got there I knew that I was lucky not to have broken my neck on the way. I was very drunk.

I climbed the stairs slowly, pausing for breath on each landing. When I got to the top floor I felt as if I had climbed the mast of a windjammer at sea, and I clung to the doorpost. On my way I had made a little plan: I would tell Stella everything about Captain Hasenfratz, fly into an incoherent rage, and she would help me out of it with a kiss. But when I stood there, clinging to that doorpost, I knew I couldn't even get all the syllables of that name out in one breath; it would take me so long to say "Hasenfratz" that I would break down halfway.

I felt very sorry for myself, particularly sorry because I had allowed my little plan to float to the surface of my consciousness, a troubled sea of hooch. If only I had been able to enter that kitchen as a nice, clean, innocent soul, beset by the terrors of a nasty, cruel world, I would have slid into the double bed as if I had never expected such a thing. But as I stood there, clutching the doorpost, the little plan was forced to the surface by hiccups smelling of gas. And that was not all; while I stood wondering with one section of my mind why people ever bothered to put their heads in a gas oven when they could achieve the same end so much more pleasantly by buying a bottle of Scotch at canteen price, another section dealt with the last mysteries of Westport still hidden in the dark. I realized that they hadn't been true mysteries, that I had known the truth all along, but just managed to keep my gaze on heaven.

I had suspected that Stella was a tart when I had seen the photograph on the wardrobe and Barger's name inside the jacket she took from it; I had known it for certain when I found that letter on the mat addressed to Captain David de Jong, K.L.M. De Jong had obviously lived in the flat, so had Barger, so had Dop. Perhaps there had even been others between;

Stella had not moved into the flat when Dop took it over: she went with it. I tried to remember the exact moment when I had known this; it had been even before I found that letter on the mat. Although I was thinking of people putting their heads in the gas oven at the same time, and sniggering at the idea of having poured the water with the dentures into the porter's grave, I remembered it all right. Goatskin had told me when he had turned at the end of the pier to leave me on my way to Stella, and said, "Enjoy yourself."

Enjoy yourself, for no one knows what the morrow will bring. I tried to put the key in the lock and succeeded at the third try; just like Dop had done when I had taken him home drunk that night. Perhaps I was Dop; perhaps our fear was so important in all of us, that to her it didn't matter what face or what name it carried. All I was about to do, was to step into a dead man's place in the ranks marching toward Captain Hasenfratz. *Serrez les rangs.*

I opened the door with a fine gesture, ready to find the kitchen empty. But it wasn't; she was sitting at the table under the lamplight, doing nothing. She looked at me the way she had done when I came in with Dop, after my first trip on his ship: with such instant understanding that it almost sobered me. I refused to be sobered, I said, "Here comes the next one!" intending it as a joke, but somehow it didn't come out funny.

She asked, "What has happened?" and the way she asked it almost sobered me again. She looked so sincere, so decent; what a pity she was just a tart. I wanted to answer her question but forgot what it was about. I wanted to say, "Hasenfratz," but knew I couldn't manage, and didn't even try. I decided to tell her the truth; I said, "I'm drunk." After that I felt very weak, as if it had taken all my strength to make that confession. I wanted to go through that doorway into the kitchen and sit down, but I dared not let go of the doorpost.

She got up and came to me. When she got near I smelt her through the hooch: a clean smell of soap. She put her arm around my shoulders and tried to make me let go of the doorpost. I resisted for a while, then I gave in. I felt very weak, walking into the flat, as if my knees bent lower and lower while I walked, like Groucho Marx. I thought we were heading for the table, but she steered me past it. I wanted to turn round and sit down; I wanted to give her a chance to tell me she was not a tart, but a clean English girl, smelling of soap. But she let her chance go by; she steered me into the dark doorway to the bedroom and switched on the light.

I saw the double bed rocking on a lazy sea, a U-boat covered with a chintz spread. I thought of a good joke: I would go down on my knees and look under the bed for Captain Hasenfratz. But when I did, it didn't work out funny; I fell, half on the bed, into a sea of sadness. I thought, "Jesus, I'll never be able to sail again," and wanted to get up; but something kept me down and turned me over; I was as helpless as if I was already a floating corpse, turning into corruption. I saw her face overhead, a vision of tenderness and understanding, and closed my eyes, waiting for the kiss that would turn it into corruption.

It didn't come. Instead I felt someone fumbling at my shoes and realized that she had begun to undress me. I tried to rise on my elbows in protest and despair; even though I was drunk, I didn't want it to happen in that way. I didn't want her to undress me and tuck me in and then undress herself and get into bed beside me; even though I knew that I was just closing the ranks, I did not want that horrible fact to be so callously revealed. I wanted to tell her that I wasn't the cynical character I pretended to be, that in reality I was as sentimental as a spaniel. I thought of myself as a helpless, gentle little boy who had never grown up; when I was on the verge of tears of self-pity and homesickness for the child's cot on which my mother had undressed me, Christopher Robin got in the way again. I wanted to get up and stride out of the flat, as impressively as I had strode out of the chartroom after the boy Waterman had called me with a catch in his voice; but she held me down. While she was undoing my tie I wanted to say, "Don't be so bloody noble about helping the poor sailors to forget their fears; be a tart and have done with it," but as this was too complicated to say, I said, "I'm drunk." My voice sounded so sad and sincere, that I looked up with tears in my eyes.

I saw her moving over me, shapelessly, as if I was looking at her through a glass of water. She didn't say anything; she undressed me quietly and expertly, like a trained nurse. I thought of the cure for all ailments: to bed with the nurse; I thought of God, and hoped He would have mercy upon us. When I felt I was naked I expected that now she would tuck me under, but I felt her putting things on me again. I looked up, couldn't focus my eyes, but vaguely discerned an expanse of green and white stripes, like an awning, and assumed they were pyjamas. I wanted to say, "Whose are these? De Jong's? Barger's? Dop's?" but it was too complicated. I said "Drunk," felt I had left out something, couldn't remember what, and said, "Sorry." Then something was pulled away from underneath me, and covered me with a gush of wind. I said, "Blankets."

After that there was a silence, in which I heard a slow rattling noise. I couldn't make out what it was until she began to speak, then I realized that it had been the dialing of a telephone. I heard her say that if a call came I was at the flat and not at the hotel. I thought she had a lot of pluck.

After that I just lay there without thinking, waiting for her to get into the bed. She took a long time; I heard rumbling noises and the sound of cupboards being opened and shut, and they went on for so long that I suddenly thought: she is moving out. I tried to call her, but didn't get further than a shapeless moan. She was by my side instantly, she couldn't have been far away for the moan had been a faint one. I tried to say, "Don't go away," but couldn't. I made some noises which must have been more intelligible than they sounded to me, for I heard her say, "Don't worry, I won't go away." Then I heard the click of the switch and the red glow of my eyelids went dark.

In the darkness thin lines of light crossed from horizon to horizon, like tracer bullets; some exploded into specks that floated down to the sea, like flares. I wanted to call her, for I was afraid; but I was too tired, I fell asleep.

When I woke up the next morning I heard a girl's voice humming, and the soft tinkle of small things on a hard surface. The girl's voice hummed a tune I had never heard; I realized that I was lying in Dop's bed and that Stella was washing up in the kitchen.

I listened to the tune and wanted to ask her what it was called, for I liked it. I never did ask her, for I fell asleep again while I was listening. I heard it many times later over the radio, bellowed by throaty contraltos or arranged for brass band. It was called "Ye Banks and Braes."

When I woke up for the second time she was standing beside me in her blue dressing gown, her hair long and shiny. She had a cup in her hand.

"Would you like a cup of coffee?" she asked.

I said, "Yes," and sat up. The moment I did so it felt as if I had left my head behind on the pillow, and I clutched it.

She said, "Here, take this. It will make you feel better."

I said, "Thanks," took the cup from her and drank a few sips. It tasted good.

"Is it sweet enough?"

I nodded and drank some more with my eyes closed, enjoying it. Then I looked up at her.

So far I had only seen her by artificial light, except the morning I came in to tell her that Dop was dead; but that didn't count, she had not been herself then. By daylight she looked more beautiful than ever. I searched her eyes for uncleanliness or corruption, but they were of virginal clarity. Perhaps our ideas of sin were as old-fashioned as our ideas of courage.

"You haven't been sitting up in the kitchen all night?" I asked.

"No," she said, "I put up the camp bed."

I nodded, as if I knew the camp bed, and went on sipping the coffee. I thought that I ought to feel embarrassed now, but I realized that it takes two for that. She wasn't embarrassed at all, she had been humming in the kitchen as if the man asleep in the bedroom had been living with her for years. Perhaps he had.

I remembered thinking this the night before, when I had been about to open the door with my key. It was curious that an obviously drunken thought should come back in the clearness of the morning and still make sense. Perhaps it was she who was sending out that thought, perhaps it had been she all the time. Perhaps she had heard me climb the stairs and lean against the doorpost, hiccuping; perhaps she had sat at the table, listening, waiting for what she knew was coming, and thinking the thought so strongly that it had penetrated the door and my alcoholic fog until it reached some center of awareness inside me.

As I sat sipping the coffee I realized that I was more quiet and clearheaded than I had been for a long time; when the name came back to me it seemed harmless. "Hasenfratz." I smiled as I pictured him: a red-faced German bully, scolding recruits. I remembered the angry mother's gestures with which someone had called back the boy who had gone on fumbling with the cover of the gun when our pom-pom started firing; I was sure now that it was Hasenfratz.

The quiet amusement with which I could recall that picture made me think of Van Dam, when he sat expounding his philosophy on war in his shirt sleeves. I felt for the first time as if I almost agreed with him, as if to remain sane under all this was more important than to be able to shoot back. I felt as if I was approaching some essential truth, which would enable me to see this war and all that happened in it in relation to the evolution of mankind. I thought of the First World War, and how the conquerors had been smitten with the diseases of the vanquished. I wondered whether this would happen again, whether the ideals and the mottoes that had sounded so sincere under the occupation had been just the symptoms of an epidemic of lunacy, a moral blindness that obscured our view of the truth. If that was so, then the conquerors after this war would be smitten by the same diseases they were now fighting. If we were the conquerors, we would turn fascist, chauvinist, anti-Semitic and aggressive, and be unable to do anything about it. In that case Van Dam was right; then the future of mankind would indeed be in the hands of the few who had somehow managed to remain sane, like him.

She took the empty cup out of my hands and said, "I'll run a bath for you; you take it while I make some breakfast."

She went into the bathroom and turned on the taps; then she crossed the room again on her way to the kitchen, humming. I felt so good that it made me wary; I started looking for the snake in the grass.

It didn't take me long to find it. I was sitting in that bed a happy man, because I was no longer alone. All that my superior thoughts of a moment ago amounted to was that she had given me a false feeling of security.

I was having my bath when the telephone rang. Stella answered it; I heard her say, "Hold the line, please," she sounded very secretarial. Then she opened the door of the bathroom and said, "You had better come out, it is Commander Wadlow." I said I had never heard of him. "The British liaison officer," she said.

I gave myself a hasty rub with the towel and put on a dressing gown and a pair of slippers I found in the corner. I remembered, as I went out of the bathroom, how I had seen Dop come out of it with the same things on. When I picked up the receiver lying on the night table and said, "Yes?" the bland voice of the British officer answered, "Oh hello, old man, I wonder whether you would be good enough to pop in sometime this morning. I should like to talk to you on the subject we were discussing yesterday. Do you think you can manage that?"

I said, "You mean about Hasenfratz?"

"That's right," he said, "I think we may have found a sort of intermediary solution, if you see what I mean." I didn't, but I said I would be round in about half an hour's time. He said, "Splendid," with the enthusiasm the British display only about completely trivial things, and hung up. When I turned round I saw Stella standing in the doorway. She had been listening and looked at me with eyes that made me feel proud and important. She was worried.

"Anything serious?" she asked.

I said, "No, no; just a routine thing," and thought how very British I sounded. I wondered whether this was going to be a new character: Captain Forthright, the African explorer. I decided to avoid it if I could; but I felt the need of some sort of character to hide behind, for by now I had become embarrassed all right.

I went into the kitchen and had breakfast. During breakfast I told her about Hasenfratz and his artillery school; after I had finished and saw her looking at me I realized that the way I had told it was so offhanded as to become silly. She knew instantly that this was the thing I had made all the fuss about last night.

"Does anybody else know about this?" she asked, and when I said, "No," she said, "I wouldn't tell them if I were you."

If I had known her well enough to be myself with her when sober, I would have asked her why not; but Captain Forthright answered blandly, "Of course. Could I have some more coffee, please?" I just checked myself from adding "old girl."

For some reason the atmosphere during breakfast got rather strained toward the end. I heard myself talking more and more blandly, until my upper lip seemed to have stretched to twice its length; and there was nothing I could do about it. Either I sat there as Captain Forthright having breakfast with Lady Cynthia in the Manor, or I had to get out. It was a relief when I had finished, could sneak out to dress, and beat it.

When I arrived in the office I found the British officer in the company of a gigantic pilot of the Fleet Air Arm, and we started to talk about Hasenfratz. The pilot was so large that I found it difficult to look at more than one thing at a time; my eyes wandered from the fruit salad on the expanse of his chest to his Buddha-like ear lobes, and from there to his straw-colored eyebrows and his enormous red nose. He was very hearty and talked as if he was addressing a barracks; his vast fat hands lay on the desk on top of each other like two sleeping piglets. It was amazing that a man could produce such a volume of sound and yet sit quite still.

The British officer said that he had told Harcourt about this Hasenfratz business and that Harcourt, who was the C.O. of our section of Coastal Command, thought he might wangle it so that one of his planes would nip out one day and plonk that floating kindergarten on the head; the more so as Hasenfratz now seemed to have started giving torpedo instructions as well. Because we all agreed that we had better keep this thing more or less to ourselves, he thought the best way to go about it was for me to give the signal when I came across Hasenfratz next time; so we had better agree on a code to be signaled to Headquarters by my Sparks the moment I spotted the U-boat on my next operation.

We agreed on a code; the big pilot said that he would be on the spot within the hour, if it wasn't too far out. I asked him what kind of treatment he thought he would give Hasenfratz, and he boomed, "Oh, I'll plaster him with D.C.s until I see his oil float up; so you had better make yourself scarce once we get going." I said I'd do my best to run away as fast as I could, but would he please remember that my top speed was sixteen, and that a tugboat was a fragile kind of vessel. He laughed, showing a pink cave full of healthy white teeth, and one of the piglets woke up and jumped on my shoulder as he said, "Don't worry, old man, we won't let off the crackers underneath your tail." I thanked him and left.

Once outside, I wondered what to do. Van Dam wasn't home yet, and as it was a nice morning I decided to go for a walk. I had a look at Memorial Hill and was amazed to find lovers in the straggling grass at this hour, rolling about underneath the notice "Carpet beating strictly forbidden." I walked the streets for a while, not really noticing where I was going, for I was thinking of Stella all the time. The feeling of security she had given me that morning might have been false, but it persisted. She had somehow stimulated the instinctive feeling that nothing would happen to me; I began to wonder why the discovery about Hasenfratz should have driven me to such extremes of abject fear last night. I knew the feeling was instinctive, and common to every sailor, soldier and airman fighting this war; and as things happened to thousands of them every day the feeling was obviously nonsense. Even so I felt as safe as if it was peace; the skirmish between OTWA and Hasenfratz was a battle of wits, and that morning I felt sure I could outwit him. I was even slightly disappointed at the idea that he would be plastered with D.C.s so soon; with Stella to come home to I felt sure I would have got him singlehanded in the end.

I passed a sudden bit of color on my way through the gray ruins; it was a flower shop with a tiny window in a large square of asbestos. The window was crammed with tight bunches of flowers and looked like a picture on a wall. I went inside and bought a pot with a little tree in it, from which bell-like red flowers dangled. The old woman asked whether I'd like it wrapped up; I thought I had better, because I would look silly walking about with that thing in my arm.

As she was wrapping it up in a newspaper, I asked myself why I thought it would be silly; and I saw myself coming down the street, a tugboat Captain carrying a pot with a little flowering tree. Only when I imagined what others would think seeing this, did I realize that I was in love.

When I gave her the little tree she was very sweet. She said, "Oh, thank you, it's lovely!" but she didn't kiss me. She took the pot to the sink and watered the little tree, then she put it on the window sill with a plate underneath it and turned it round until the side that carried the most flowers faced the room.

While she was doing this she asked how my discussion at Headquarters had got on. I told her what Wadlow had arranged; she listened with her back to me. When she turned round she didn't seem to be pleased about it.

"What are you going to do during the hour before the plane gets there?" she asked, and I said, "Same as I did before: keep him busy and dodge him."

"It seems an awfully long time," she said, and I answered that an hour went quickly if you were being shot at, and that on previous occasions I must have dodged them for longer than that. But while I was saying this I wondered if it was true. I had never checked the time; now I came to think of it, it might not have been as much as that. She saw me thinking about it and my face must have expressed a certain doubt, even though I was busy being Captain Forthright again. "Don't worry," she said, "you'll be all right."

I said, "You've said that to me once before."

"Well?" she asked. "I was right that time, wasn't I?"

I said, "Yes, I suppose so," which was a silly answer, but at the same time I was wondering whether she really knew, or whether it was just part of her routine. "Suppose I was not going to be all right one day?" I asked. "Would you know that as well?"

She said, "Yes," quite casually, as if I had asked her whether the milkman had been. I watched her, while she was opening a fresh tin of coffee and got down the percolator from the shelf over the sink, and my feeling of security waned for the first time since that morning. "How do you know?" I asked. "Are you psychic?"

"No," she said, still with her back to me, "I don't think so, I just know these things occasionally. Lots of people have it in my part of the world."

Captain Forthright said, "Must be jolly uncomfortable sometimes," and the feeling in the back of my knees returned, that had become such a familiar sensation during the past weeks that I had forgotten it meant something. She didn't reply to that one, but filled the percolator with water and lit the little spirit-stove underneath it.

"Did you know about the others?" I asked.

She turned round and faced me, her eyes were so full of that curious gentleness that I knew what would happen before it did. She kissed me. Her mouth was very soft.

I didn't put my arms around her, for it was not that kind of kiss, and I couldn't forget Dop. I had watched her kiss him in what must have been exactly the same way, for the feeling in the back of my knees vanished. I didn't realize that until later, after she had turned away again and gone on making the coffee. I had been right, that time I saw her kiss Dop when he was incoherent with fear and I had thought that her kiss cured him. I didn't care any longer whether she had foreseen the death of the others, for suddenly I was sure again that it wouldn't happen to me. It just wouldn't, I knew it. The certainty was so absolute, that it couldn't be the old instinctive feeling of all men in war; this time it was different, as if I had felt during one second the fullness of the future, the happiness of peace. Perhaps I was psychic too.

I didn't think of kissing her myself, until she turned round again to get something out of a cupboard on the other side of the kitchen. When she turned our eyes met, and she wavered a second, as if she expected me to.

But I didn't; I let her pass close to me and go to the cupboard without moving, without looking round after she had gone. For when I had seen her eyes again I had suddenly felt shy.

I knew at that moment that I was going to make a fool of myself over her. I still knew that she was just a tart, who took anyone that was coming in this key game of death; but at the same time I knew that very soon I would be explaining the others away until I would be convinced that she had waited for me all her life, and I for her. I remembered someone had said to me once that in every love affair there came a moment when you could still say "stop" for the last time; if you let that moment pass you were done for and had to see the thing through to its bitter end. I knew this was that moment, and I let it pass. I knew what I was letting myself in for and how it would end; yet I let it pass.

If I had kissed her it would all have been different. I would have found the woman I had longed for after every trip: any woman. I would have crushed the shyness of love that withheld me.

But I didn't, for her secret was that she made me feel I knew how it would end: in tears and misery and jealousy and bitter hatred and all the other tortures in hell, but not with my death. If I had still lived in the terrible urgency of fear, which had made me long to grab any woman before it was too late, I would have grabbed her; she had taken that away from me, she had made me certain that we had all the time in the world.

I was safe.

CHAPTER FOUR

THAT NIGHT SHE PUT UP THE CAMP BED AGAIN IN THE KITCHEN, AND I watched her doing it. I sat smoking a pipe in Dop's dressing gown, my stockinged feet on the kitchen table. I enjoyed watching her, she looked lovelier every hour.

During dinner I had discovered things about her face that I had not noticed before. While we were talking about whether it would be nice to have a radio and about a kind of chair they had in the Hebrides that closed you in entirely and was lined with sheepskin, I looked at her forehead, her eyebrows, her nose, her mouth, and wondered which it was that made her so beautiful. When I had first seen her I had thought her nose was too upturned and her mouth a bit too sensual; now I saw that I had been wrong. She had the kind of nose that I had only seen on English girls: the partition between the nostrils was lower than the nostrils themselves, and so delicately sculptured that it looked very vulnerable and sensitive; it gave her face a hidden nervousness that in contrast with the serenity of her eyes amounted to beauty. Her mouth was not really sensual at all when I looked at it that night, watching it while she talked. I realized that what I had taken for animal passion was human compassion, that she was not at all inverted in herself, but desperately concerned about other people. It seemed incongruous that she should live such a shut-off life; I remembered what the postman had said, and Dop telling me that she didn't like to go out and hardly ever left the flat. I had just taken it for granted at the time; now I wondered why she should be a recluse, it wasn't her nature at all. I was about to ask her, when I remembered what Goatskin had said. She must be aware of what people thought about her, and didn't like to face them for that reason.

After she had finished making the camp bed we had a cup of chocolate and talked some more. We were very snug in that kitchen, a tiny cube of light and warmth and cosiness floating in the great empty silence of a world at rest. She talked about her island; how the sheep grazing on the little aerodrome near her village scattered when a plane landed; there were people living in hamlets on the storm side who still thought that stars were specks of light shining through holes pierced in the sky. She told me that when she was a little girl she had heard a story about two lovers separated by the sea, who wrote secret letters to each other and put them in a little watertight box, with some charms and little presents, and then floated them across to one another with the tide. She had been so impressed by that story that she had written, "I love you," on a piece of ruled paper, put it in a tin, sealed the lid with candle wax and let it float away to the mainland, secretly, one early morning when the tide went out, hoping that someone on the distant shore would find it and reply.

When she said that I remembered the poem on the wall, and looked for some hidden significance in her story. But I couldn't find any, just a story about a little girl on an island; that seemed to be all there was to it.

While I finished my chocolate she went to the bathroom; when she came back she was wearing a nightgown. I suppose I should have felt a manly desire when she passed me; but although it was quite an ordinary nightgown it made her look very young and innocent, like a girl in boarding school going to bed. Perhaps it was her hair that made her look so young; she had plaited it into two braids and pinned them on top of her head. I saw for the first time how small and delicate her ears were, and how graceful her neck. She saw me looking at her and smiled; somehow that smile turned her into a child.

I didn't fall into the trap of giving her a fatherly kiss, and I thought that was a proof that I had all my wits about me. I felt warm and gay and contented when I switched off the light for her, opened the kitchen window and went into the bedroom. When I finally had got into bed I felt even better: warmer, gayer, more contented. I suppose I was just happy.

When the telephone rang, the luminous hands of the little alarm on the night table pointed at five to two. I let the telephone ring three times, and had already stretched out my hand to pick up the receiver when I heard the door squeak and felt the draught of someone passing close to me.

Our hands met on the telephone as it rang for the fourth time; she took my hand away and I felt something soft and warm touch the back of it. She had kissed it.

The telephone rang for the fifth time, then she answered it. She said, "Hello, yes?" and I heard a small mechanical voice quacking in the instrument. I couldn't understand what it said, but I knew. She listened to its quacking for a few seconds, then I heard her say, "All right, he'll be there in a minute." The bell of the telephone tinkled as the receiver was put back on the hook.

I asked the darkness, "Anything up?"

Her voice answered, "Yes, darling."

It was the first time she called me that; it was nice to hear, but at the same time it gave me a ghostly feeling, as if she didn't quite know whom she was addressing. As if in the darkness Dop and I and the others were one.

I wanted to get up, when I felt her cold hands on my face and then her kiss. I put my arms around her; as my hands touched her back I thought how thin the nightdress was, until I realized that she was not wearing it. I sank back on the pillow with her in my arms; her hands still clasping my face, her mouth on mine.

137

When the telephone rang again, twenty minutes later, I groped for it and knocked over the little clock. It fell on the carpet with a thud; the shock released the alarm and it started ringing shrilly with the telephone. It rang through the angry quacking of the old Captain's voice, asking what the hell was going on. When I said that I was just on my way out, he quacked, "Tell that to your grandmother! You're all the same, once you get into that bloody flat! Cut the cuddling, and beat it over here! There are people drowning, screaming for help!" Then he slammed down the receiver. The ringing of the alarm had slowed down; when I picked it up it fell silent.

I groped my way along the wall to the kitchen door and switched the lights on. She was lying on her back, her head on one side, her eyes closed. She might have been asleep, if her breathing hadn't come so quickly. I stood for a moment looking at her from a great peace. She was beautiful the way she lay there; but her face was almost tragic with the agony of love.

As I stood looking at her a new thought rose in me: I had to come back for her sake. To lie there like that, and again have the man she loved torn away from her by screaming bells and squeaking voices was more than she could bear. It was not I any longer, who had to be assured that I would be back, it was she. I went back to the bed and bent over her and kissed her cheek, and said, "Don't worry, I'll be all right." She did not react, but I knew that she had heard me. I covered her up, then I dressed. When I looked round at her from the doorway for the last time, she was still lying as I had left her: her head on one side, her eyes closed, her plaits like frayed silk ropes on the pillow. I switched off the light and went.

The great peace from which I had stood looking at her went with me; I moved within it all the way along the dark boulevard to the pier. I thought of what the old Captain had said, how we were all the same once we got into that flat, and it did not make any difference in my feelings toward her. I knew now that she was not a tart, but I knew also that I would never be able to explain to anybody why not. We shared a secret with the dead that no one could ever hope to fathom.

As I turned the corner to the pier a motorcycle came roaring through the night, and swerved on squealing tires, missing me by a hand's width. It stopped at the end of the pier; I saw the door of the office open and in its faint light a man in a duffel coat get out of a side car. He was so large, once he got to his feet, that the only one I could think of that size was Harcourt.

When I entered the office I saw I was right. I was glad he had arrived just ahead of me, for the old red-faced Captain looked as if he had been sitting there, piling up steam for half an hour, waiting to blow my top off. Harcourt's enormous presence shut him up.

Wadlow was there also, and with the two of them I had a look at the chart. The duck was an Englishman, with a torpedo hole on starboard in number two hold, sinking rapidly in square 539, which was nice and close. Harcourt said that he would zip back to base the moment I left, and fly the kite himself; everything had been lined up over there and he was ready to take off at a moment's notice. The weather was perfect, visibility clear, wind three, no cloud, temperature minus five. I could see it was, for our breaths steamed in the lamplight as we stood bent over the chart, talking.

Harcourt was worried that the duck might sink before I got to it; he couldn't wait to see Hasenfratz break up in boiling milk. He seemed to have a personal feeling toward the man; perhaps it was just his name that irritated him, for he went on saying it until it sounded as if he was putting a charm over him. After a while I expected him to take a little leather doll from his pocket and start sticking pins in it.

Wadlow seemed emotionally affected in the opposite way. He had been hunting the mysterious U-boat for so long in the maze of the reports of our operations that he had come to like the man, now he was no longer Commandant X, but a nice little human character called Hasenfratz. When we had agreed on our operation and were about to go, Wadlow said in a dreamy voice, "Pity we can't work it so that we could lay hands on the chap alive. There are a few points I'd like to see cleared up."

Harcourt scowled. "Ask the Skipper here to fish for him," he said; "then you can have his head stuffed with glass eyes and hang it on your wall with a brass plate saying Hasenfratz." He put the hood of his duffel coat over his cap, which suddenly made him look like a highwayman disguised as a monk. "Hasenfratz!" he said, for the last time; before he had brought out a rabbit's paw and crossed himself with it, he turned away and was gone. I heard his motorcycle spring to life the moment he shut the door; it took off when I followed him into the night, and streaked down the pier, blue flames spurting from its exhaust. Harcourt struck me as being a bit too enthusiastic to last. I wondered what would happen if I should not come across Hasenfratz this time, nor the next, nor the one after. Nobody could hate a name for that long.

The first thing I asked the bosun when I got on board was whether the pom-pom had been fixed. He said it hadn't; he had passed the order on to his opposite number when the second crew took over; when they had come home again and handed over his colleague had told him that Captain Van Dam had canceled the order. Captain Van Dam didn't believe in the pom-pom.

As I went to the chartroom I reflected that this was carrying the blessings of humanism a bit too far, and I decided not to accept it. It was a decision I could never have made the night before; I knew now that it was not fear that made me take it, it was just common sense. If I met Hasenfratz I was expected to keep him busy for an hour, a prospect that wasn't pleasing under any circumstances; without a pom-pom to keep him at bay if he edged in too close it was suicide.

I went back to the office and said, "Sorry, but I can't leave." The old Captain's mouth fell open; Wadlow, who was studying the chart all by himself, asked, "Why not?" in a quiet tone, that from an Englishman spelled death. I said, "On my last operation my pom-pom got stuck; I left the order for it to be put right, but Van Dam canceled it. I don't want to be a spoilsport, but I've got to let our friend play with me for an hour, and I'm not risking a good ship and a good crew by throwing myself at him without any gun at all."

The old Captain said, "Well, I must say!" Wadlow eyed me for a second as if I was a fish gone bad. Then he asked, "Can your C.E. fix it himself, or do you want me to ring the Section?" I said, "I'll tell him to have a go at it again, but he said before that he couldn't. So you had better ring the Section." Wadlow said, "All right," as if it was a famous last word, and started telephoning.

It took the Section an hour and a half to fix the gun. One of the recoils had got stuck and most of the time went in trying to find an antiquarian familiar with the model. When he finally arrived he looked as if he had been dug up from an old pensioners' home: a gnomelike old Corporal with gnarled hands and two fingers missing. He said, "Arr" five times, while looking at the gun by the thin light of a blacked-out torch, his eyes close to the metal, as if he was trying to read a pocket edition of the Bible without spectacles. After that it took him seven minutes to do the job. When I finally sailed, I sailed under a cloud.

Alone on the bridge, in the wind and the darkness, I wondered whether I would feel guilty if I should find the duck sunk and its lifeboats gunned, within the one hour and a half before my arrival. I decided I would have, if my insistence on having that gun fixed had been caused by fear. Now I was sure it wasn't I didn't see where I was to blame; and I knew that Wadlow, despite the way he had looked at me, thought I was right. It took an Englishman to see my point; I knew that Van Dam and the others, if they came to hear of it, would consider me a coward. It was Stella's final victory; she had given me the courage to let myself be called a coward.

I may have been sure on the bridge; I don't think if it had worked out that way I would have remained sure. But when we got to square 539, six hours later, the duck was still afloat and no U-boat in sight. We made fast and towed her home through a sunny cold day; the horizon was so clear that they could have seen us crawling along for miles around. But no one bothered us; it was hard to believe that there was a war on at all.

When I took the Captain of the duck on board outside the harbor, he told me that a U-boat had circled around him until we had come into sight, then it had dived and vanished.

Perhaps not only girls from the Hebrides were psychic; perhaps old German artillery instructors had a sixth sense too. It was a thought that didn't make me happy.

When I came home and opened the door with my key I found the kitchen empty. The door to the bedroom stood ajar. I called, "Hey, where are you?" and Stella came in, in her blue dressing gown and with the white ribbon in her hair. She put her arms around my neck and kissed me; I asked her, "Did you sleep well?" and she nodded and kissed me again with a hunger that choked me. She asked what the trip had been like, and I answered, "Oh, all right. An Englishman with a list over starboard; no sign of Hasenfratz." She said, "I'm so happy you're back," and I kissed her again and ruffled her hair. We were very much in love.

While she cooked the meal I had a wash. I tried to sing the tune I had overheard her humming when I woke up that first morning, long ago. I called to her, "Darling! How does it go?" She called back, "What, darling?" and I hummed the first bar.

When she started to sing it, loudly, so that I would hear, I went silently into the kitchen; as she finished I stood behind her without her knowing it. She called, "Now you sing it yourself!" and I started to hum it, softly.

She swung around as if she had been stung. When I saw her face, my cheeks contracted; never had I seen such horror in human eyes. We stood for a second facing each other, very close, motionless. Then she gave a sound, a moan so terrible and desperate, that I already was holding out my arms to put around her when she fell with her head on my shoulder, sobbing.

I tried to comfort her, by stroking her hair and saying soft soothing things, while I took her gently to a chair. She slumped down on it, flung out her arms on the table, and her head bumped down so hard that I heard it hit. She howled; never in my life had I heard anyone cry like that. I was frightened, I didn't know what to do with her, I got a glass of water and tried to make her drink it, but she wouldn't. She lay there, her head on the table, her arms with the red boy's hands flung out, howling.

All I could do was to sit down beside her, put my arm around her shoulder and stroke her hair, a helpless gesture of protection. I didn't understand why my starting to hum behind her should have upset her so much. She must have been all worked up; she must have nursed the others through ever-returning crises of fear and hysteria without a chance of letting herself go. Then her sobs turned into a name. "David!" she cried. "Oh God, David, David."

I felt such compassion and understanding and love for her that it didn't make any difference. I stopped stroking her hair; I just sat with my arm round her and waited for her pain to pass. During those moments I had a strange feeling, as if we were not alone.

After she had calmed down I put her to bed. She let me take her to the bedroom without caring where she was going. Her eyes were closed and her face was wet. I almost had to carry her; she collapsed on the bed. I took off her slippers and covered her with the eiderdown. I pulled up a chair and sat by her side until she fell asleep, exhausted.

Once she slept I dressed again; when I came back in the kitchen I smelt something burning and turned off the gas under the little pan with soup that had boiled dry. I wanted to go, but caught sight of the table on my way out. I went back to the sink, took the rag and wiped the table, then I went out.

I went out without a purpose; I thought I'd just take a stroll on Memorial Hill to give her time to recover. As I turned the corner I noticed a little locksmith's shop, between the tattooist's and the florist's where I had bought the little tree. I had seen the shop before, but now I noticed for the first time what was hanging in its square little window. Bunches of keys.

I don't know why I decided at that moment to have the duplicate of my key made. Perhaps it was just because I had promised Dop I would, and this was the first time I passed the shop with time on my hands.

The interior of the shop was very dark; as I entered it I saw only an old man's face and hands in the square beam of sunlight slanting through the little window in the shutter of asbestos. He had steel-rimmed spectacles on the tip of his nose, and was fumbling with something small and shiny gripped in a vice. He reminded me of the old corporal who had mended our gun.

I asked him how long it would take to have a duplicate of a key made. He answered that it depended on what sort of key it was. I said, "Oh, just an ordinary latchkey," and handed it to him. He grunted as he turned it round in the beam of sunlight, looking at it; then he frowned, shoved his spectacles on the bridge of his nose, muttered something, put his spectacles back on the tip of his nose, and peered at me, his eyes narrowed in the sunlight. "What the dickens do you boys do with those keys?" he asked. "This is the fourth one!"

I said, "Oh, we just lose them."

He asked, "Then why don't you have half a dozen made at a time? It would come much cheaper."

I said, "We've never thought of that, and I only want one, thank you."

He shrugged his shoulders, said, "Suit yourself. Money seems to be no object in this war"; then he pulled out a drawer in the darkness, rummaged in it, took the little glittering thing out of the vice, and put a key in its stead. After he had started filing, he asked, "What kind of place is it you boys live in? A boarding house?" I said no, it was a private house. He filed some more, filling the little room with shrieks; then he asked, "What happened to that young airman, the first one? I haven't seen him for a long time."

I said, "Oh, he's been transferred."

He asked, "Where?"

I didn't answer, but just smiled. He looked up, pushed his spectacles down, peered at me again with narrowed eyes, then he said, "Ah, I forgot. You're not supposed to divulge any troop movements."

I said, "That's right."

His file shrieked again for a minute or so, then he said, "You're not supposed to do a lot of things nowadays. It's quite a job to keep them all sorted."

I said, "That's right."

After that he didn't say any more. He finished his filing; my ears rang when he stopped. "Here you are," he said, sounding faraway; "that will be a florin." When I didn't seem to understand, he said, "Two shillings."

I paid him, and put the two keys in my pocket. When I left he called after me, "Good luck, sailor; and don't lose it this time!" I said I'd do my best.

I had known I was the fourth, before he told me. It didn't come as a shock to me; it wouldn't have come as a shock if I had found out that I was the twelfth or the fifteenth. I knew now that whatever our names might be, to her we were all one man, called Captain David de Jong, K.L.M.

I wasn't jealous of him, nor of any of the others, for I knew that I was going to be the last. One day she and I would wake up together, and it would be peace, and we would realize that it had all been a nightmare. I was so sure that I would survive the war that I didn't think of giving the duplicate of my key to anyone. I would just keep it, a token of friendship toward the dead.

When I came home she was still asleep on the bed, exactly as I had left her. I was hungry and so I spread some buns with Marmite and made myself a cup of tea.

The sun was setting, the shadow of the little tree lay across the floor and the table like dark foliage. I put on my slippers and my dressing gown after I had eaten; I was quiet in order not to disturb her. The neighbors' radio banged a symphony against the wall; in the flat below people were laughing and talking. I sat with my feet on the table, my chair tilted back, smoking my pipe, and drank three cups of tea. I felt tired for the first time since I had been woken up by the telephone, and realized that was forty hours ago. I didn't think I needed any pills to sleep, I felt relaxed and quiet.

I sat there thinking how good it would be if I could take her away with me to some faraway island, and sit by a log fire in a chair lined with sheepskin, with snow falling silently outside. I thought of the other girls I had known and with whom I had imagined I was in love; I knew now that it had not been love. As I sat there, thinking, while the shadow of the little tree slowly grew up the door opposite the window, I again had that strange feeling of not being alone. It was not a ghostly feeling; it was like what I had felt when I lay listening in the darkness to the wheezing and snoring of the sleeping boys round me during my first night in Westport, but much stronger. As if the distant shore had drawn very close while I sat there, with my feet on the table.

Perhaps the shore was not distant at all, in the sense of time and place. Perhaps it was right here: the table, at which all four of us had sat in turn, happy and at peace in the security of our love. I hadn't any wish or desire left, but for the one dream of taking her to that island, far away. And that was not a wish, but just an expression of my happiness and peace. If the distant shore was here, then I had reached a point of no return. I knew that I would never be afraid again and that death would hold no horror for me any more, for I no longer believed in it.

When I got up it was almost dark, I undressed in the dusk. When I touched her, Stella sighed and stirred; I did not want to wake her up but I couldn't take off her dressing gown while she was lying down. I tried to lift her off the bed, and she half woke up. She stood on her feet drowsily and asked, "What's the time?" with a sleepy voice. I said, "It's late, time to sleep," and opened the bed. Then I helped her take off her dressing gown and put it on the chair, supporting her with one hand. As we got into bed she said, "I must do my hair," but I said, "Ssh, never mind, sleep."

When she lay in my arms, her head on my shoulder, she mumbled, "So happy you're back," as if she was dreaming. Then she fell asleep, her hand cold on my chest.

I took it in mine to warm it, and floated away into that peace. It felt as if we were floating away together toward our island, enclosed in a little box, carried out by the tide of time.

When the telephone rang it was morning. Wintry sunlight fell into the room through the gap between the curtains. The moment it rang she gripped me so tightly in her sleep that I had difficulty in reaching it. As I picked up the receiver I saw that the time was 8:30 A.M., and wondered what could be the matter. Even if Van Dam had sailed instantly after we came in, he could not possibly be back yet; perhaps he was ill and they wanted me to take over.

When she heard me say, "Hello, yes?" she gripped me even tighter and began to tremble. I said, "Take it easy, darling, take it easy," and I heard Wadlow's voice in the instrument asking, "I beg your pardon?"

I said, "Sorry, I was talking to someone else. What's up?"

He said, "I rang you because I thought you might be interested to know that the United States of America have entered the war."

I said, "No kidding, on which side?"

"That is in very poor taste," he said, primly. "The Americans have done more . . ."

"All right," I said. "Sorry, I have only just woken up. How did it happen?"

He told me that Japanese aircraft had bombed the naval base of Pearl Harbor out of the blue, and done a lot of damage. I said, "Good Lord!" stroking Stella's hair, and whispered, "It's all right, darling, it's good news."

Wadlow said, "Isn't it. I suppose you realize this means that you will get your guns now."

I said that would be wonderful, and how long did he think it would take until we got them. He said he didn't know; but without divulging any military secrets he thought he could tell me that the first all-American convoy would be sailing the Western Approaches pretty soon. I was just beginning to wake up then, and, as always first thing in the morning, a brilliant thought occurred to me. I said, "Never mind about the convoy; how long do you think it will take them before they start shipping troops over here?"

He answered, "I haven't the foggiest idea, old boy. Why?"

I said, "Because I can tell you here and now that we won't get our guns until then."

He asked, "What on earth makes you think that?"

I said, "Oh, just intuition. I'm psychic."

He asked, "I beg your pardon?"

I said, "Never mind. Congratulations, anyhow, and thanks for ringing me," and I hung up.

When I turned round, Stella lay looking at me as if she was three years old. The fact that the telephone had rung with a message that was cheerful seemed to have taken twenty years off her age. I said, "Congratulate me. America has entered the war."

She said, "Oh," looking in my eyes for the snag.

I said, "Wadlow thinks that means that we'll be fitted out with guns now, instead of vacuum cleaners."

She still looked at me intently, as if she was undecided what I was thinking. "Don't you think so, yourself?" she asked.

I said, "Of course, it is wonderful news. Before the day is over we'll all be bristling with four inchers. If you look out of your window tonight, and you see a steaming wake flash past, that will be Hasenfratz going for a holiday. Now let's have some more sleep."

I closed my eyes and began to sink slowly back into a warm drowsiness. Her voice said, "You don't really believe it. You're just trying to be funny." I said, "Go to sleep, don't nag." She sighed on my shoulder. "And don't breathe down my neck," I said.

She was silent for a while, and I was nearly asleep when I heard her say, "You're the sweetest man I've ever known." That threatened to wake me up, but I decided to take it as it came. "You're an angel," I said. "Now shut up." She began kissing my ear, and I shouted, "Shut up!" with the ringing voice of Captain Ironsides. She lay very still after that, so still that it threatened to wake me up again. I said, "For God's sake, breathe." Then she began to giggle.

I realized that I might as well give up the idea of sleep. I turned round and faced her, but I didn't open my eyes. I felt her face very close to mine; her hair tickled my nose. I opened my eyes wide and saw hers very near, staring at me like an owl. I said, "If you don't go to sleep I'll put up the camp bed. I've got work to do. I'm tired."

She kissed me.

It must have been about ten when I fell asleep again; when she woke me up with morning coffee it was three o'clock in the afternoon. The sunlight had gone; as she drew the curtains I saw a gray wintry sky. I had a feeling of holiday and knew something nice had happened, but I couldn't remember what. As she sat down on the bed with her knees drawn up, after she had given me my cup, I asked her, "Something nice has happened while I was asleep. What was it?"

She raised her eyebrows, looking innocent.

I said, "I know, America has entered the war."

Her face changed. "That means bigger convoys, doesn't it?"

"Yes."

"Do you think they have got the stuff to protect them?"

"No. Not at this stage."

She looked at me for a while. "I thought that was it. Why didn't you say so this morning, if that was the truth?"

I said, "Give me some more coffee," and held out my cup; but she didn't take it.

"You were very sweet to me yesterday," she said, "when I got silly."

I said, "Sweet? I didn't do a thing."

"Yes you did. You put me to bed. And you didn't ask questions."

I hesitated for a moment whether I should let her go on. I knew that she was about to tell me things I didn't particularly want to know, and she might regret it later. I said, "I think it's silly to ask questions if you know the answers."

"Do you?" she asked.

I said, "Yes," and held out my cup again.

She bent forward and kissed me, then she took it, and went into the kitchen.

I leaned back and stretched and yawned. When I finally managed to close my mouth and open my eyes again, I found myself looking at the portrait on the wardrobe. He seemed a nice boy, if not very intelligent, but perhaps it was unfair to hold him responsible for his smile. I myself had had some pretty grim pictures taken in my time. As I lay looking at the picture I heard her voice say, "That's not my brother."

I had not heard her come in, and I felt a faint echo of what she must

147

have felt when I started humming behind her back. I didn't turn round; I said, "I never thought he was."

"Why not? Did someone tell you?"

"No, I was told he was your brother. But I didn't believe it."

"He is from our island. He's called Alan, and he is fighting in the desert. I write him a letter every week."

I wondered what she wrote, but I let it pass. "Does he reply?" I asked; but she wasn't listening.

"I write to him about the family and the people we know," she said, "and I make him remember little things we used to do together when we were children. We were neighbors."

I looked at him and his smile and what he had written on his collar: "I'll walk beside you." I thought of him, a boy from the Hebrides, slinking through the desert with a Tommy gun, taking a whispered communion from a cracked cup before stalking all the demons out of the Egyptian Book of the Dead. I knew I would never be able to do that; deserts had frightened me ever since I was a child. One week of his warfare would turn me into a raving lunatic. Next time I got into a state, I had better take a look at that picture and realize how lucky I was to have nothing to worry about but Hasenfratz. "All right," I said, "that's all I want to know." I turned round and reached out for the cup of coffee she carried.

"I'd like to tell you some more," she said, but I looked at her with authority and said, "You heard me."

She smiled, uncertainly. I realized that she was dying to tell me everything. Perhaps that was what she needed: to tell it all and get rid of it. But I didn't think I could stand that yet; I was not jealous and I didn't think I ever would be, but I wasn't sure.

"You tell me some other day," I said. "We've got all the time in the world."

Her smile grew until her whole face was radiant. "We have," she said.

CHAPTER FIVE

HASENFRATZ STAYED AWAY. SINCE THAT MORNING WHEN THE ENGLISH CAPtain had seen him dive as soon as we appeared on the horizon, he had not been spotted again. The ducks that were torpedoed might have been hit by him, but for over a fortnight he never surfaced near one of us. I was strafed once by a plane, but it caused no casualties because we all saw it coming and had plenty of time to run for shelter. It riddled a pail full of soup Cook had put outside to cool off; the ship reeked of peas and pig's trotters for hours afterward and Cook didn't calm down until we got home. Apart from that incident we might as well have been sailing in peacetime. We didn't even have sinkers any more; it looked as if the Germans just fired four or five torpedoes at each convoy, regardless, and scurried away before the wreckage came down from the sky. Goatskin, who had succeeded Dop in command of the *Vlieland*, thought it was because the Americans had entered the war and Jerry must be busy elsewhere. Van Dam shrugged his shoulders and said that it didn't mean a thing, for madness came in waves.

The first time I sailed, after Harcourt and Wadlow and I had made our little plan, Harcourt had come streaking down on a motorcycle. The second time he just rang up to find out what square the duck was in. The third time Wadlow had to ring him, and hold the line for almost a quarter of an hour until he was hunted down. The fourth time I asked, "I suppose our plan still holds good, in case I should come across Hasenfratz?" Wadlow answered, "Of course, old boy, of course." I said, "In that case, hadn't we better get hold of Harcourt and tell him to stand by?" Wadlow answered, "Don't worry, old boy, I'll do that the moment you have left." The fact that America had entered the war had an exhilarating effect on the British, they behaved as if victory was as good as won.

Perhaps it was, but I doubted whether Hasenfratz had been as easily convinced. Perhaps I knew the German mentality better because of my months under the occupation; I couldn't help feeling that our friend's absence from our course was to be taken as a warning rather than as a reassurance. But all I could do on my part was to keep my eyes open and our pom-pom well oiled; on every trip I made the bosun practice and shoot off a few rounds. We tried to find out where the bullets struck the water, but we never did. It was so eerie, that I had to convince myself by weighing them in my hand that what we put into the thing were indeed bullets and not duds; the bosun ventured that they might be striking behind the horizon. Wherever they were striking, it was a long way away.

My Chief, whose professional pride had been injured by the fact that a dotard with eight fingers had done in seven minutes what he hadn't been able to do in twenty hours, was fascinated and maddened by the gun. He filed away at it for hours, trying to make it dip deep enough to shoot level, but he didn't succeed. He broke a file and two hack saws on the thing, threw them on the deck, and started kicking it as the bosun had done. I began to suspect that we had been singled out unwittingly as the bearers of one of those ghost guns with a life of its own that I had heard talked about in the harbor pubs by sailors who had served in the last war. I got so above myself with self-assurance that I even thought I would regret it if the thing was finally replaced by a gun that let itself be pointed instead of taking its own aim. I knew that I was getting dangerously lighthearted, but I couldn't help it. I was just dreaming all the time, humming, smiling; when Hasenfratz came back I had forgotten how dangerous he was.

It happened on a cold, sunny morning, when we were on our way to a rudderless Dane in square 353. I stood on the bridge, looking at a faint feathery cloud high up in the empty blue sky. When I looked down again I was dizzy with gazing into nothing and dreaming about Stella and breathing the crisp, cold air. I saw something move in the sea on our port side about a hundred yards away from us; it looked like a stick being dragged very fast through the water. I was so far away from the war that, instead of recognizing it instantly, I gazed at it for over a second before I woke up; when I did I was so frightened that it took me another second before I could shout, "Periscope on port!" whistle, "all hands," and ring the alarm on the engine-room telegraph. What had frightened me was not the periscope itself, but the fact that it had taken me so long to react to it.

The U-boat surfaced almost immediately afterward, so close that I heard the water gushing from its nostrils as it rose. First I was sure it was Hasenfratz, then I looked at the emerging gun traveling by itself and thought it was someone else, for it looked much bigger than the one Hasenfratz carried. A minute later I recognized the conning tower and the rest of the ship; it was Hasenfratz all right.

While the bosun and his gunners rushed at our pom-pom, I saw the lid of the tower flap open, the mannikins tumble out; when they uncovered the gun I understood why Hasenfratz had been away for so long. The thing they started to wheel round at us was a monster; he had been fitted out with a gun twice the size.

I cannot say I was afraid, I was too busy thinking of a way out. But the feeling in the back of my knees came back. I felt it when I ran to the starboard side, as Hasenfratz swung round behind us. I yelled, "Hard starboard hard!" at the man at the wheel, and "Fire!" at the bosun; we turned at full speed, spraying bullets at the sky with a sound as if we were drilling macadam.

Hasenfratz got us on the side. There was a report, so loud that it shook the air around us; then a sound as if a colossal bomb came soaring down; I fell headlong on the bridge and thought: this is it. There followed a breathless silence, in which Stella quivered in a white emptiness, slowly stretching out her arms toward me, then another explosion, far away, so thick that I felt the sound rather than heard it. Before I had got back on my feet I heard people cheering.

As I looked over the railing I saw the bosun and the two gunners dancing on the fo'c'sle, slapping each other's shoulders, pointing overboard. I thought they had gone mad, then I looked overboard myself.

The U-boat was lying so close to us that I could discern the features of the Germans clearly. They were all sitting on their behinds round the gun, looking very stupid. A fat officer stood screaming at them, halfway out of the conning tower like the old woman who lived in a shoe. The gun itself looked strangely elongated, and pointed at the sky.

I shouted at the wheel, "Port!" as we were heading straight at them; we nearly skinned their nose as we swerved past. Even to me, who knew nothing whatever about guns, it was obvious what had happened to Hasenfratz's new monster: its recoil had stuck. What the madmen on my fo'c'sle were dancing and screaming about was that our recoil had got stuck too.

For a few seconds I was still aware of the danger we had escaped by the skin of our teeth; then the mood of the ship got me, too. I laughed until the tears ran down my face; I had to support myself at the rail in order not to sink on my knees laughing; when the befuddled Germans had scrambled to their feet and started filing back into the conning tower at the shrieked commands of the fat officer, one of them kicked the gun and limped the rest of the way. That just finished me; and not only me, it finished everybody. I even saw the last of the Germans double up with laughter, and then I did a crazy thing: I waved. I felt it was crazy even while I did it; but the German waved back.

It was a curious moment. In one flash of superhuman sanity I saw us finish our war then and there. I saw myself pull alongside Hasenfratz, lean over the rail, and say, "Now look here, chum, why don't we call it a day? This is just silly." Then the German who had waved was snatched down into the conning tower, the lid slammed shut, and the U-boat dived, blowing big bubbles.

We didn't see Hasenfratz again for the rest of the way. We picked up the duck and towed her home and put back into port underneath a black cloudless sky ablaze with stars, sparkling bluishly like diamonds. I tried, all the way home, to recapture the alertness I had felt during the few minutes between the moment I recognized the periscope and the moment the cheering started; but I couldn't. I just went on thinking of the German who had waved back, and the silliness of men shooting at each other; and then I realized what Stella had done to me.

When I was a boy on my first voyage I bought in Port Said one of those things one buys only on one's first voyage: a boudoir edition of Omar Khayyám's poems in English, bound in red leather, with a little lock and a key on it to keep it private. I remembered one of the poems that night; not its actual words, but what they said: That love is like a fountain, it shoots up toward one person and rains down on all mankind. It seemed rather romantic in connection with Stella and me, yet it gave the best description of what had happened that I could think of. I loved her so much that I felt a great sympathy for everybody round me; even for old Hasenfratz, who had been made to look so silly by his splendid new gun.

It was a wonderful feeling, and yet I knew it was somehow dangerous, but I could not think why.

When I told Wadlow about Hasenfratz's new gun he wasn't so interested as I had thought he would be. Hasenfratz was his baby, and several times during the past fortnight he had been worrying in an almost motherly fashion about what could have happened to him; but he took the news of his return absentmindedly.

I told him about the recoils that had got stuck, and he thought that was a very funny story; when I said that but for that funny story I would not have come back, he patted me on the back and said, "Come, come, old boy; no need to get gloomy. It's a lot more difficult for inexperienced pupils to hit a target as small as you are with a heavy gun than it is with a light one." I told him that he was talking nonsense, and that it was all right with me if he had lost interest, but I would thank him to keep his bedside manner for his private patients. It wasn't a particularly good joke, but he thought it was awfully funny; he haw-hawed and said, "I must remember to tell that one to Harcourt."

I said I'd prefer him to remind Harcourt of our combined operation. I even went so far as to say that I wouldn't sail next time unless Harcourt was on the spot and we had plotted my course together.

Then Wadlow got angry. It was an Englishman's anger, so it sounded charming. "I somehow don't think that you've got quite the right approach to this business," he said. "The Harcourt setup was a thing I organized off my own bat. I have no authority whatever from Headquarters to bring in Coastal Command, and Harcourt agreed to do it only because we happen to know each other personally. I don't think it's quite the ticket that you should use this more or less private arrangement as the basis for an ultimatum."

I stood for a moment in doubt, then I shrugged my shoulders, and said, "All right, Wadlow; have it your own way," and turned to go. He saw me to the door, assuring me that of course our plan still stood, and that if Harcourt wasn't out on operation he would certainly come and do the job. He had agreed to do it and once he agreed to something he would stick to it; I needn't ever worry that he would not play the game.

Before he shut the door he held out his hand, and for a second I thought he meant to warn me that one of the buttons of my coat was coming off, as we had never shaken hands before. "Chin up, old boy," he said, "and no hard feelings." His hand was small and dry.

As I walked along the pier in the starlight I tried to think about Hasenfratz, for I knew that if I wanted to outwit him now I would have to think fast. But I couldn't be bothered, for I was on my way to Stella. Between now and the next time I should have to sail I would spend at least twenty-four hours with her, and our hours were longer than any hours I had ever lived through. I had often shaken the little clock on the night table, thinking it had stopped, for it had seemed impossible that we should have gone through so much talk and love and happy silence in so short a time. In those hours we had come to know each other as if we had lived together for years. Last time I left I had been looking in the bathroom for the comb, while she was busy in the kitchen cooking the breakfast. I had muttered to myself, "Where is the damn thing?" and she had called, "On the medicine cupboard, darling!" That was indeed where it was, and I combed my hair without giving it a second thought.

Only on the bridge, hours later, when I came across the incident again while remembering the things we had done together this time, did I realize how odd this was, for I had never mentioned the comb. It was a thing one would only expect from an old married couple, and we had known each other for sixteen days. Of those sixteen days I had spent ten at sea and forty-six hours asleep in bed; so all we had really known each other for was ninety-eight hours. It seemed a convincing proof that our idea of time was nonsense.

When I entered the flat I had a big surprise, for Stella was in the kitchen. The table was laid for two and decorated with holly; on a big plate in the center was a cake. When I asked, "What's this?" she put her arms around my neck, said, "Happy Christmas," and kissed me.

I had completely forgotten it was Christmas; I had forgotten that such a thing as Christmas existed. I was very sorry, for I should have thought of it and bought her a present.

She gave me no time to say so; she took me by the hand and led me into the bedroom. A faint light shone through the door, when I stood in the doorway and looked over her shoulder I saw it was candlelight. On the night table stood a little Christmas tree with candles on it and silver balls and little glass birds with colored tails, on top of it was a star. She took me to the tree; underneath it I saw, between the clock and the telephone, a little parcel wrapped in Christmas paper tied with gold thread. I felt miserable because I hadn't got her a present, but I didn't want to spoil this moment for her by saying so for she was watching my face with anxious, expectant eyes. I asked, "Is that for me?" and she nodded with a smile that made me feel worse. I picked up the little parcel and tried to untie the gold thread. It took me some time, for it was knotted very tightly. While I was doing this she sat on the edge of the bed, watching me, and I smiled at her, feeling awful. When I had finally unwrapped the parcel I found a small wooden box.

It was the tiniest box I had ever seen, very nicely carved. I said, "How wonderful," turning it round in my fingers, wondering what on earth I could use it for; it was too small even for a collar stud. Then I opened it, because she still sat looking at me with that heartbreaking expectancy. There must be something inside.

I found a tiny piece of paper, folded neatly. I tried to shake it out on my hand, but it stuck in the box. I tried to prize it out with the nail of my little finger; then I fumbled in the pockets of my greatcoat for a match. I had to sharpen the match by breaking it before I could get it out. When I unfolded it I found it was a tiny strip of ruled notepaper. On it was written "I love you."

I looked at her with surprise, for during all the time we had lived together she had not once said those words to me, and never before had she looked at me like that. I felt embarrassed and at the same time very happy and proud. I didn't know what to say to her; so I said, "I have got nothing for you. I forgot it was Christmas."

She said, "Will you marry me?"

I sat quite still after that. If Dop hadn't whispered to me in the office the night before he was killed, asking me to be his best man, it would have been a wonderful moment; now it seemed as if a U-boat surfaced right behind her. I looked her in the eyes without moving a muscle in my face; during a few seconds I stared at the terrible truth that I was nothing but a link in a chain, that we were both caught in a nightmare of love and death and destruction. De Jong must have been killed after they had agreed to get married, so was Barger, so was Dop.

But when I thought, "So will I," I woke up from that nightmare. Her eyes were so sincere, so gentle, that it just couldn't be true. She meant it, she loved me because of what I was, not just because I had closed the ranks. Even if I had started as just another man with a key, she had given me the little box with its secret message; I was the unknown lover on the distant shore who had found it and replied. I was not just a link in a chain, the other three had led up to me. The other three might have been killed, I wouldn't be, never. I was safe, I was immortal; this time we would make it, it would be I who would break the spell.

I took her hand in mine. It was very cold. I looked at her eyes, tragic with love; her lips, parted in agonizing suspense.

I said, "Yes, Stella."

From that moment on I was walking on clouds. We took the little Christmas tree into the kitchen and put it on the table and switched off the light. While she was heating up the first course at the stove I sat looking at the candles and the little glass birds with a feeling as if I was dreaming. When she put a plate of soup in front of me, I woke up and wanted to start eating; I looked up when she laughed.

"Do you know how you are sitting there?" she asked.

I realized I must be sitting there like an idiot, so I laughed too, and said, "Sorry, I . . ." I forgot what I was going to say, for she looked so beautiful in the candlelight that all I could do was just gaze at her, like a dog.

She said, "Darling, wake up," and stretched out her hand. I thought she wanted me to kiss it, but she took something off my head. It was my cap. I still had my greatcoat on as well. I got up to take it off, knocked the chair over, bent to pick it up and nearly knocked over the Christmas tree. She grabbed it just in time, and I felt a lumbering oaf, for I had spilled soup on the table cloth that she had brought out specially for the occasion.

But all this happened below the clouds, whatever I did and whatever I said: I sat looking at her all the time. I wasn't even thinking any coherent thoughts, and it got worse as the evening went on. The dinner wasn't a success, for when she wanted to bring out the fish dish she had specially prepared for the occasion it was quite raw as she had forgotten to turn the oven on. She nearly cried when she discovered this, but I was secretly delighted for it proved, I thought, that she had been walking on clouds too.

The cake hadn't come off very well either, the top of the outer part was edible, but the center was uncooked and the bottom soggy. She was terribly disappointed, and I tried to laugh it off by saying, "If you had asked me after this meal I would have said no." For some reason this made it worse; perhaps no woman has a sense of humor when it comes to her cooking. Her eyes brimmed over, a fat tear ran down her nose and hung for a moment at the tip, flashing in the candlelight before she wiped it off with the back of her hand. I took her on my lap and said, "Darling, don't be silly, what do I care about the meal? We're going to be married! Even if you had cooked the best dinner I'd ever had, I wouldn't have noticed it."

She felt better after that; she blew her nose in my handkerchief with a very manly sound and sniffed some more and smiled again, and said, "I'm sorry, I know it's silly, but I was so sure it would be all right; they are the two things I do best." I said nonsense, she was a wonderful cook, no girl could be expected to have her mind on her work while she was summing up the courage to propose to a man. That made her laugh, and although I was glad that she was getting over her disappointment, I felt a bit hurt for I had fancied myself as being rather hard to get. "Did you ever consider the possibility of me saying no?" I asked. She said, "Oh, yes, I was terribly nervous," but she obviously meant it as a joke. I didn't think it all that funny and I told her so; but she had only to kiss me to make me lose all sense of dignity and proportion. She could have made me balance an umbrella on my nose that night.

She virtually did: she made me sing the descant to "Come All Ye Faithful" and "Noël, Noël" while we were washing up, after we had some buns with Marmite to replace the fish and the cake. I knew I had not much of a voice except early in the morning, but I barked the descant like a trained seal until the neighbors put a stop to it by hammering on the wall.

When the table was cleared and everything stored away, she suddenly cried, "Oh, no!" I asked her what was the matter; she answered miserably that she had known all through the meal that she had forgotten something, and now only remembered what it was: the wine.

I said, "Well, it's never too late for that. Let's have it now." After protesting for a bit, saying that wine didn't taste nice unless you had it with food, she brought out a bottle; and I started looking through the drawers for a corkscrew to open it with. There was none, and because she looked as if this was the last straw, I said, "I know!" as if I had a brilliant idea, and tried to push the cork inside the bottle with the handle of a wooden spoon. She cried, "Don't! You'll break it!" but I said, "Don't be silly, I've done this hundreds of times," and managed to ram the thing in by using all my strength. As I did so I was hit in the face by a spurt of wine; when I got up and had wiped my eyes, my shirt looked as if it was covered with blood from the waist up. I was ready to laugh it off, but the sight of me made her burst into tears, quite beyond proportion.

This time it took me a lot longer to get her out of it; when at last I had succeeded we were so tired and the whole thing had fallen so flat that

156

there seemed to be little else left to do but to go to bed. The candles had burned down to blue flickering flames; I switched the light on and put them out.

It didn't seem to be one of our lucky nights, for the moment we were in bed, and I took her in my arms, the air raid sirens sounded. It was the first time I had heard them in Westport, but I knew there had been alerts while I was at sea. We got up, but decided not to go down to the shelter until we were sure there was going to be a raid. We opened the curtains and stood looking at the sky for a while; she shivered and I took her inside my dressing gown. There were only a few stars to be seen, the town was very silent. When the first guns started booming behind the horizon I thought: if the star of Bethlehem should rise over us tonight, it would be shot at by ack-ack. I didn't say it, for I wasn't sure how she would take it. We heard planes approaching and decided to go down.

So far I had never seen any of the other tenants living in the house. When we entered the air-raid shelter in the cellar, I was amazed to see how many there were. I didn't count them, but there must have been well over fifty people there, sitting on benches along the wall in dressing gowns and overcoats. Among them was a Rear Admiral in greatcoat and long drawers, with carpet slippers on. I wondered whether I was supposed to do something about him, for I too was wearing my greatcoat over my pyjamas; but he never looked my way. He sat staring gloomily at a cat with a bell round its neck, that had caught a mouse and was playing with it.

We sat down in a corner, on an upturned bath among the bicycles, and waited. Nobody spoke; a baby at the other end of the cellar cried with high screeches, like a sea gull. The ack-ack opened up all round us and we felt the trembling of distant bombs exploding; by then everybody was staring at the cat, who was having a lot of fun with the mouse and stayed in the center all the time, as if she was giving a little floor show. The mouse must have been quite dead by then, but she went on tossing it in the air and batting it with her paw until the Admiral got up, picked it up by the tail and took it to the old janitor who was sitting in the corner. The old janitor was the only one I knew by sight; I had seen him once or twice, going through ritual movements with a broom in the hall or on the stairs, and Stella had told me that he did her shopping for her. He got up when he saw the Admiral approaching and stood at attention; when he took over the mouse he said, "Thank you, sir," and vanished into the coal cellar. By then the ack-ack had died down and there were no more bombs. We heard the sound of engines roaring past; they must be the fire brigade, so the raid was probably over.

It was a long time before the all-clear sounded. We all sat waiting for it, listening to the noises outside. It was a pity that the Admiral had taken the mouse away, for now we had nothing else to look at but one another, and I became aware that people avoided looking at us. It made me feel embarrassed and worried, for I was sure that Stella must be conscious of it too. It certainly wasn't one of her lucky nights, poor kid.

When the all-clear finally sounded everybody got up and started trooping out. As we were sitting near the door, we managed to get up the stairs ahead of everybody. We looked out of the window on the top landing and saw a few fires in the town, but the black mass of the Grand Hotel was still standing, and in the harbor itself there was no sign of anything going on. I considered for a moment ringing up the office to find out if everything was all right, but I thought: the hell with it, if they want me for anything they can ring me.

Perhaps I would have rung them if Stella had not looked so ill. She was very pale as we entered the flat; when we got to the bedroom she fell on the bed, exhausted. I switched off the light in the kitchen and opened the window; then I helped her take off her raincoat and her dressing gown; when I got into bed she seemed to be already asleep. I felt very sorry for her, for everything seemed to have gone wrong that night; yet I was so happy that I almost felt ashamed of it. I was sure that we were going to have a nice life.

An hour later I was woken up by Stella; she whispered, "Darling, there's someone at the door."

I listened, heard a banging noise in the kitchen, and wondered who it could be. Perhaps it was the warden and we were showing a light. I put on my dressing gown and my slippers; as I groped my way to the front door I decided that it couldn't be the warden, for every light in the house was switched off.

It was my Chief Engineer. He said, "Sorry, Skipper, but I'm afraid you'll have to come out. Van Dam is missing."

I said, "What? With the ship?"

"No, no," he said, "just he, himself. And as an S.O.S. came in just now, they sent me over to call you."

I heard Stella come in from the bedroom and turned round. "It's my C.E.," I said. "Do you mind if he comes in? There's something the matter with Van Dam."

She said, "Of course." I switched on the light and let him in. He made an awkward little bow when he saw her, and saluted. "Sorry, ma'am," he said, "but we couldn't get hold of him on the phone; your line must have got out of order during the raid."

I asked him what had happened; he said that the Savage Club had received a direct hit while Van Dam was inside, singing.

"Singing?" I asked, for in connection with Van Dam it sounded grotesque.

"Yes," he said, "didn't you know? He was a member of a male quartet, with a clergyman and two R.A.F. officers. We poked fun at him all last week, for he was rehearsing "Sound the Alarm" in his room; you could hear him bellowing all over the hotel. Tonight was the night of the concert."

I asked him whether they had found his body, but the Chief said they hadn't. The whole place was in such a mess that they hadn't been able to sort it out yet. But he certainly had been inside, for he had left word with Headquarters that if anything came up before midnight, he would be at the Savage Club.

"Well," I said, "in that case I had better go." I hadn't got around to disliking the idea yet, for the news about Van Dam had affected me more than I would have thought. I suddenly realized that I had been fond of the man.

"O.K.," said the Chief. "I don't want to hurry you, but you had better come as quick as you can, for when I left the office the duck was screaming her head off."

I said I'd be there in five minutes; he saluted, bowed to Stella again, tried to go to get out while doing so, and backed into the doorpost. He said, "Sorry," gave a sheepish little laugh and scurried out. He didn't seem to be at ease with girls in dressing gowns.

While he was there, I hadn't looked at Stella; as I turned round to go to the bedroom and get dressed I saw her, and understood why the Chief had been so embarrassed. She was sitting at the table, her dressing gown open, her eyes staring into nothing, her face as white as a sheet. I patted her on the shoulder and said, "Brace up, darling; I know it's bad luck, but there can't be much left that can go wrong tonight." She woke up out of her blank stare as if she had been far away, smiled, and said, "Yes . . ." She obviously hadn't been listening to me.

I said, "Come on, darling, get up and get me another shirt. I said I would be there in five minutes." She said, "Yes, yes," smiling, but she didn't sound as if she was all there yet. I said, "Did you hear what I asked you?" She answered, "Yes, shirt; I'll get it." I wanted to kiss her and make a fuss of her, because she looked so miserable, but there was no time.

I dressed in a hurry. She got me a clean shirt; I didn't pay much attention to her while I was dressing. When I stood in the kitchen with my cap and greatcoat on, I was surprised to see that she was fully dressed. "What's all this?" I asked.

"I'll see you to the ship," she said.

It was a nice thought, but I didn't like it. If I went there alone I could run, and I didn't want her to go back to the flat all by herself at dead of night, there were always a lot of drunken characters about in the boulevard at this hour. But as there wasn't time to explain all this to her, I decided not to top off the evening by refusing to take her. I said, "O.K., let's go," and we went.

We didn't say a word all the way. The boulevard was very crowded, and I liked the idea of her going back by herself less and less. It looked as if after the air raid all the drunks of Westport had crawled into the open; there were so many of them that I couldn't have run even if I had been by myself. She clung to my arm with both hands as we walked; when we got to the bottom of the pier and I said, "Well, darling, let's say good night here," she wouldn't let go of me. She said, "Please, please," in a way that broke my heart but I was firm about it. I didn't want to go up the pier trailing her, and I didn't want her to work her way down again by herself. I said, "No, Stella, I'm not going to take you any farther. Let's kiss good night here and you go home, there's a good girl. I'll be back before you know I've gone."

She must have realized that I couldn't be talked out of it, for she gave in. She looked dead tired. I took her in my arms and kissed her. Her lips were cold and unresponsive. I heard drunks whistling at us, close by; I gave her a furtive hug and hurried away.

I didn't look round, for I knew she would be standing where I had left her, looking after me until I had got out of sight. I felt very sorry for her, for obviously even this last thing of the day had fallen flat, but I was still walking on clouds. I was going to marry her as soon as I came back. I was the happiest man in the world.

When I opened the door of the office, the first thing I noticed was that everyone there was silent, sitting as if they were listening to music. One of the loud-speakers on the wall was twittering frantically; even though my knowledge of Morse was poor I heard it was an S.O.S., followed by what sounded like the markings of a position. I asked, "Who's that?" and the wireless operator answered, "That's your baby."

I said, "Don't be silly," and looked at Wadlow, sitting behind his desk. "Do you mean that this bird has been squeaking all the time?"

Wadlow looked up, shiftily. "I'm afraid so," he said, "the chap obviously forgot to open envelope D."

I said, "Can't be. I've never come across anybody yet who didn't rip open that envelope the minute he gets hit. Doesn't he realize that he is concentrating every U-boat in the region on himself?"

"I wouldn't know," said Wadlow; "you had better go and ask him yourself."

"Don't you think it might have been a good idea if someone had told him?" I asked, in an attempt to be British about it that didn't quite come off, and I pointed at the radio desk. "What else have you got all those blokes lined up for?"

"Take it easy, chum," said the W.O. "We can't do a thing. He has messed up his receiver."

At that moment Goatskin came in, with a wiry little Captain who looked like a jockey. He saw us and noticed there was something wrong; then he too became conscious of the frantic twittering going on all the time. His knowledge of Morse was obviously better than mine, for he listened for a few seconds, then looked at me, and said, "That's nice. Yours?"

"Not yet," I said. "They're still trying to sell it to me."

Wadlow asked what the dickens I meant by that; I told him that I would be damned if I'd sail into what by now must be a concentration of U-boats and a couple of planes thrown in, with a crew that was dead tired, and a gun that couldn't shoot, just because Van Dam had got it into his head to sing "Sound the Alarm" at a concert. I said that I was anybody's dream of a sucker, but that for once I was not going to play the game. I said to Wadlow, "I won't sound the alarm this time; you bloody well put your little manicuring set away and go yourself. I'm sick of being a hero; other people may rejoice in the thought of getting themselves gutted by gunfire for the sake of a donkey who won't even open an envelope and read what is inside, I don't."

"What is it?" asked Goatskin, and Wadlow answered, "Tanker on fire in square 539. American."

"That's the first one, isn't it?" asked Goatskin.

"Yes," said Wadlow. "The first American we've got; I don't know about the other stations."

I said, "I don't care whether it's an American or a Hottentot, I—"

The W.O. called, "Ssh"; and we listened. "They say they are drawing gunfire now," he said. "So whether you go or not that's probably the end of baby."

"Isn't it Van Dam's watch?" asked Goatskin.

"Yes," said Wadlow, "but he got killed in the air raid about an hour ago."

"Oh," said Goatskin, then he looked at me. Since Dop's death we had got on rather well, but this was the same look he had given me twice before. I got angry with him because he made me realize that, sensible as my attitude might be, it had some points against it. I said, "O.K., I'll take her, but, by God, it's the last time. As soon as I come back I'll start kicking up such a stink over this gun business that they'll either come across with them, or lock me up in the asylum. Where is Harcourt?"

Wadlow said, "Where do you think, with this air raid on?"

I said, "O.K., I get it. All the air cover I'll get on this operation will be the angels."

Then the wiry old Captain piped up. So far he had stood quietly in the corner on his bowlegs, his hands behind his back, waiting for his turn; now he said, "Could we get the form business over, gentlemen, please? I don't want to interrupt anything, but I have to get on, you see."

"O.K., Captain," said Goatskin, "sit down, please." The jockey sat down in the empty chair on the other side of the desk, put his cap upside down on it and took off his gloves, which he put inside.

I asked, "Don't tell me old Foghorn was a member of the male quartet too?" for I hadn't registered until then that our red-faced shore Captain wasn't there.

"No," said Wadlow, "he's probably eating a goose somewhere, he's on twenty-four hours' Christmas leave."

We bent over the chart and started plotting my course. The loud-speaker went on twittering all the time, and while we were talking I thought that the W.O. was probably right. This baby couldn't last much longer.

I was wrong. All during the way to square 539 my Sparks came to the bridge at regular intervals to report that the duck was still squeaking. Toward daybreak he came to say that they were being slowly grilled, the ship was burning in a big way and they were under constant gunfire which they tried to hold off with everything they had got.

I said, "Jesus Christ! Don't tell me that fool has been firing back all the time?"

Sparks said, "Sounds like it."

"That's wonderful," I said. "By the time we arrive he'll probably have used up all his ammunition. Do you know anything about American captains? Can't they read?"

Sparks said, "Doesn't sound like it." He was a great talker, that boy.

I said, "O.K., go back and listen some more."

After he had gone I resumed my pacing up and down, worried. I wasn't afraid, for I was sure that we would get through somehow; but it seemed a tricky setup. The only way to tackle it was to follow Van Dam's advice and aim three squares higher, pass the duck for about a square or two, and then sneak up on her from the rear, ready to do some backing business the moment a U-boat spotted us. But even while I planned this I doubted whether it would work. Unless the Unterseebootwaffe Western Approaches was celebrating Christmas in the mess, all the available U-boats must have concentrated on the screaming American by now, and the way the Luftwaffe had chased us out of bed at midnight didn't seem to indicate that they were aglow with the Christmas spirit.

I didn't think about Stella much, but she was at the back of everything I did and thought. If she hadn't asked me to marry her, I would have been creeping up and down that bridge holding on to the rail, instead of running at hiking speed the way I was doing. I held the little box in my pocket and felt safe. I was so certain that I would get through somehow that I could see the whole thing from an objective point of view, almost as if it didn't concern me. It was this objectiveness that had enabled me to say the things I said in the office, if I had been afraid I would have kept my mouth shut so tightly that I should have had trouble to put my pipe in.

I realized that I ought to have felt tired, for I hadn't slept for forty hours, except for the short shut-eye between the all-clear and the moment my Chief started banging the front door; but I felt very vigorous and awake. I kept the boy Waterman walking by my side for miles, nattering at him like a woman for sheer vigor and awakeness. In the end he nearly dropped dead, and I wanted to send him down to his bunk for a snooze before the business started, when we heard a sound in the distance. A sound of heavy gunfire, like faraway thunder.

We listened to it for a while, then the boy Waterman said, "God, this is awful."

I had not noticed before that he was afraid, I had been too busy nattering; now I realized that during all the miles we had tramped side by side he had barely said a word. I said, "I wouldn't worry; we'll be all right."

He gave a little snigger in the darkness, touching in its failing bravery. "I don't quite see how we can be," he said, in a polite little voice, and he added, "frankly."

I said, "It's very simple: the moment I see that it would be suicide to get near that madman, I'll just turn round and go home."

He said, "Oh," in an undecided way, as if he was telling himself that he ought to believe it and couldn't.

I didn't believe it myself.

When we got near the duck I saw it was pointless to try any evading tactics. From whatever angle we approached her, we would be seen as clearly as if it was daylight.

She was burning like a wildfire and listing heavily; we couldn't distinguish her clearly, for she was hidden in red clouds which must be steam. Behind the clouds yellow flames flickered, and although the gunfire thundered on without pause we saw no flashes, so she must be firing over the other side.

I decided to close in, for I assumed that she must be firing at something, and whatever it was, she lay between us and it. I warned the engine room that we were in for it, and whistled all hands. The boy Waterman said, "Well, good luck, Skipper," bravely. Now I could see his face in the sunrise of the distant fire he looked preposterously young; perhaps because he had just had a haircut, his ears looked twice the size.

I had no idea how to tackle the duck, whether to make fast afore or astern, for she was so hidden by steam and smoke that I couldn't even see which side was facing us. There was no wind; the smoke rose perpendicularly into the sky. If there had been wind I could have approached her under her own screen.

But the approach was not the most difficult part of the job. Even if I forgot about the U-boats and tackled this as if it was peacetime, I didn't quite see what we could do to save her. The fire seemed to be out of control; the moment we started towing the speed would fan the fire. I had to find out which end of the ship was least damaged and had most people on it; I would tow her from that end. The people marooned on the other would have to be written off, unless we made them jump and picked them up before we started to travel.

I was working all this out in my mind when I heard the boy Waterman say, "Periscope on starboard, sir." He said it quietly; only the fact that he called me "sir" betrayed how he felt. He pointed and I looked; I saw the periscope silhouetted clearly in the red path the flames made on the water. I dashed toward the engine-room telegraph, put my hand on the handle, but didn't ring it, for I realized there was nothing I could do. Either I must start backing away or carry on, steering clear of it. I pulled the handle on "Slow" and stared at the periscope. It was an unpleasant idea that the periscope must be staring at us too.

We proceeded slowly, and I never took my eyes off it. It seemed to be lying quite still, and it made no attempt at surfacing. One thing was certain: no U-boat would ever waste a torpedo on a tug; so long as it didn't surface to use its gun, we could breathe. As I stood staring at it, wondering why it didn't surface, I noticed something. It moved in an odd way. It could never move like that if it had a whole U-boat underneath it to keep it steady; it moved up and down, like a buoy.

I said to the boy Waterman, "Three starboard three," and he called the order through to the wheel. We swung slowly toward the periscope.

"You—you're heading for it?" he asked, politely.

I said, "Yes. It's not a periscope."

It took him some time to realize that I was right, then he asked, "What do you think it is? A mine?"

"Either that or a decoy."

"Decoy?"

"Yes," I said. "I think I begin to see it all now."

I didn't quite yet, but I was sure I was on to something. If the periscope was a decoy, it must have been sown for some purpose. The only purpose could be to create the impression that there were several U-boats around instead of only one. And the only reason why they should want to create that impression was that a periscope seen from a burning wreck would draw gunfire. If the thing we were now approaching was indeed a decoy, then the American must have been gunning his ammunition away at nothing.

We skimmed the thing so closely that there was no doubt left. It was a decoy all right, and a clumsily made one at that. I considered fishing it, but decided not to; they might have put a booby trap inside just for the hell of it. I saw it turn round in our wake after we passed, and pulled the telegraph on "Full ahead."

While we approached the duck the boy Waterman scanned the sea with his binoculars for other decoys; I just stared at the fire ahead, thinking. The more I thought of it, the more sure I became that I was right: only Hasenfratz could have sown the things. It was a typical lone wolf's ruse: only someone sent out inadequately armed on suicide expeditions would think of a thing like that.

Then I saw it all: Hasenfratz had been detailed to finish off the lame ducks left behind by the convoys just as we had been detailed to pick them up: all by himself, with a gun that was inferior to those the merchant ships carried. He must have felt as much at the wrong end of a shooting gallery as we did, and he had gone on protesting for months, writing petitions for a better gun, just as we had. The difference between us was that he had got his new gun first, but even so it evidently was not strong enough to compete with the artillery he was ordered to meet, so he had hit upon the idea of making the ducks bleed themselves white on a couple of decoys. The moment their guns fell silent he would move in for the kill; this American was what he must have been waiting for, for a long time: a fool, who would let himself be tricked into firing.

I knew now that it could not have been Hasenfratz who had torpedoed the ducks we lost the week before: they must have been bagged by some of his big brothers who still had a cigar to spend on their way home. All he had got to survive with was a bunch of untrained recruits, an inferior gun, and his wits. He and we were in exactly the same boat; if we hadn't been at war we might have been friends.

And then, suddenly, a preposterous thought came to me. I knew it was preposterous the moment I thought it, but I stood there considering it for a long time, for it seemed to explain the last mystery that remained. I had found explanations for everything, except for one undeniable fact: if Hasenfratz had really wanted to, he could have sunk all of us on our first operation. Van Dam had thought that his own cunning maneuvering had saved him; Dop had thought it was his ruse of making a tugboat sail; but I had always known in my heart that their explanations were nonsense. I had dodged Hasenfratz's gun often enough by now to realize that his shooting was exceptionally bad, even for an instructor; no one could tell me any longer that our ruse of backing away from him would not have been spotted by him the first time it happened. A man clever enough to think of using decoys to exhaust the enemy's ammunition could never have fallen for the clumsy device that both Van Dam and I had tried to sell to him at least twenty times. Hasenfratz had decided to let us go scot free.

It was a preposterous thought, and yet it must be true. Daamen and Frankendaal had not been sunk by gunfire. God knew what had happened to them, perhaps they had struck a mine or been bombed by a plane, but they had not been sunk by Hasenfratz.

But as I started circling round the duck to find out what was going on, I realized that this was going to be a situation in which neither Hasenfratz nor I had ever been before. Even if all I thought about him was right, I didn't see how we could get out of this in a friendly way. If I started towing the duck Hasenfratz had to move, whether he liked it or not; if only that silly American had read his instructions from envelope D, this situation would never have occurred.

I put myself in Hasenfratz's place. I assumed that I was the Captain of a U-boat, who just didn't like sinking defenseless tugboats, and had decided to do some gun practicing on them, taking care not to do any damage, and then to let them go. If I was Hasenfratz I would stand there worrying, while scanning the sea through my periscope, how the devil we could get out of this situation, just as I was doing on my bridge. Then I knew. Hasenfratz would let me make fast and start towing; when the duck's guns fell silent he would sink her, for that was his job. But he would let me go.

As we rounded the duck's stern we saw the flashes of her gunfire. I ordered, "Hard starboard hard." The boy Waterman repeated the order to the wheel; then he asked, "Are we making fast?"

I answered, "Yes. Stand by with the line gun." He passed on the order to the bosun on the aftdeck. I made our siren howl: one long blast, which according to envelope D ought to make the duck hold her fire. Frantic people started waving on her poop, but her guns thundered on, crazily. I let the siren howl again; the boy Waterman said, quietly, "That ought to waken the dead."

I knew it would, but I knew also that it wouldn't make any difference to Hasenfratz. He had seen us long ago, and probably said to his second in command, "It's the *Zeeland* tonight." Perhaps he even knew my name as well as I knew his, and had foreseen my coming before I was there, for he must have worked out the schedule of our watches by now.

Then I remembered that this was Van Dam's watch and that he was dead. I was sure that Hasenfratz would be sorry if he heard that the stolid little Dutchman he knew so well had been killed in an air raid while singing at a Christmas concert. If we had had radio contact I would have told him; I thought of flashing the news to him with our Aldis lamp from the bridge, as soon as we caught sight of each other. I wondered where he was.

Wherever he was, he was well within the spray of my fountain of love that night. But for Stella I should have known what would happen.

We didn't see him until after we had made fast and started towing the duck. We towed for quite a way, while she went on firing; then her guns fell silent.

In the silence we heard the roaring of the fire behind us; it was louder than the roaring of our safety valve. It seemed incredible that men could have survived in that hell. Then the boy Waterman said, "There he is."

He surfaced over starboard, about three hundred yards away. I saw the conning tower open and the mannikins come out. I knew he would open

167

fire on the duck, but I decided to play the game. I whistled "lifebelts on," and told the engine room through the blower that we were in for action. I saw the gun being uncovered and felt very sorry for the men on the duck. They had done everything they shouldn't have and so they deserved what they had coming to them, but all the same they had put up one hell of a fight. With a fire like that going on, I myself would have abandoned ship hours before, and taken to the boats before they were burned in the davits. Their very tenacity was foolish; it seemed a pity that they wouldn't live to read the long list of the things they had done wrong. Then I was blown clean off my feet and flung down the length of the bridge, while the world seemed to explode around me.

When I got to my feet again I still didn't believe it; then the second shell came and struck our funnel with a sickening sound of screaming iron. Hasenfratz wasn't aiming at the duck, he was aiming at us.

That was the moment I woke up. In one merciless flash of lightning I saw that the paradise I had lived in for the last weeks was a fool's. I didn't think this, I just knew it, all at once, within one split second, as if I had fallen into icy water. The shock made me act: it wasn't a reflex; it was a short circuit between my instinct for survival and my intelligence. I screamed, "Hard port hard!" ripped the whistle out of the blower, blew, and shouted, "Shut off the safety valve and come on deck in your lifebelts! We're abandoning ship!" The ship swung around sharply; the third shell struck our mast. I whistled the bosun on the aftdeck, and shouted, "Stand by with the hatchets, ready to cut!" The boy Waterman lay on his knees behind the railing, moaning. I asked, "Are you wounded?" When he shook his head I kicked him, and shouted, "Hurry aft! When I call 'cut,' jump!" He scurried away, more terrified by my kick than by the shells. The fifth shell came whining at us and missed; I saw something move on the foredeck, whistled, and shouted, "All hands aft! Hurry!" Then I ran to the wheelhouse, pushed away the man at the wheel, said, "Stay outside and pass on the word when I shout 'cut'; after that, scram." The sixth shell came whining at us and struck something on starboard. The windows of the wheelhouse were blown in. After the racket had died down there was a silence, and I realized that our safety valve had been shut off. The ship started to tremble as the number of revolutions mounted. Within ten minutes the boilers might explode; we lay straining at the leash of our hawser with all our horses lashed into frenzy. Another shell passed very close and missed us. Then I saw Hasenfratz swing into view.

He was very near, his starboard side turned toward us. I righted the wheel and shouted, "Cut!" I heard the sailor outside pass on the command as a scream. I saw a flash spurt from Hasenfratz's gun, heard the whine of a shell soaring at us; then the ship seemed to jump. I was thrown backward against the wall and thought we had received another hit, but we hadn't. We were racing straight at Hasenfratz, at top speed.

I got hold of the wheel again and saw the mannikins scurry away from the gun and scramble into the tower. I thought, "Jesus Christ, the fool!" for I knew he couldn't make it. He ought to have sprinted ahead the moment he realized what I was up to; he had no time for diving, he must have no idea of the speed of my ship. When I felt that she would hold her course I left the wheel and ran outside. I felt in my pocket for Stella's little box. I closed my hand around it just before we struck.

We struck with a blow that sounded like an explosion. I was flung against the rail. What was left of funnel and mast came crashing down; I heard a rumbling noise below and knew it was the boilers torn off their foundations. I knew the ship would blow up; I climbed over the rail and jumped.

When I struck the water I knew this was it. I seemed to go down a long way and had no breath. I felt a scorching heat, realized it was cold, and knew that even if the ship did not blow up and I floated clear of the sinking wrecks I could not survive, but would freeze to death.

I opened my hand and let the little box float away. My last thought was: I love you.

I died in peace.

CHAPTER SIX

I WOKE UP IN A TUGBOAT'S CHARTROOM. IT TOOK ME A LONG TIME BEFORE I realized where I was. First I noticed that I was naked and that people were rubbing me; then I recognized Goatskin. I felt as if only one half of me was there, the other half was dead. I wanted to touch the side of my face that was dead, but Goatskin kept my hand away. I heard his voice, far away, "Leave that alone, we'll see to it in a minute."

I tried to speak, but it was difficult with one half of my face dead. I spoke out of the corner of my mouth. I said, "What . . ."

He said, "Take it easy, you're all right. You've only been in the water for ten minutes."

I wanted to ask him what the hell he was doing here; but all I could say was, "You?"

He said, "I was right behind you all the time. I couldn't let you tackle this setup alone, so I followed you."

I said, "Boys."

"All but three," he said. "Two stokers and your bosun. He looked at me the way Dop had looked at me sometimes. "Would you like anything? Some more brandy, cigarette?"

I said, "Duck?"

"Doing fine," he said. "I took over after your little show. We'll have her home and dry within three hours."

Then I remembered when Dop had looked at me like that. It was just after we had met again. He had grabbed my shoulders, held me at arm's length, and said, "Fancy seeing you here! God, this is wonderful." There was another time he had looked like that, but I couldn't remember.

Goatskin lit a cigarette and held it out to me. "Here," he said. "Can you hold it yourself?"

I put out my hand, which didn't seem to belong to me. I took the cigarette and put it in the live corner of my mouth. I drew in the smoke and felt dizzy. I heard Goatskin say, "Hold it, boys; that'll do. Get a blanket." Then I heard steps and Goatskin's voice again, "And take these bottles to be refilled. Tell cook to make them good and hot." I heard a door open and a gush of sea and wind; then the door shut. I opened my eyes.

Goatskin sat looking at me. "I must say I take my hat off to you," he said. "I don't think I could have done it."

I wondered what he was talking about; then I remembered Hasenfratz. "Sunk?" I asked.

"Both of you," he said. "But his had all the birds inside. We looked for survivors as a matter of manners, but not one. He locked himself in his coffin good and proper."

I felt suddenly sick, and held out my cigarette, my eyes closed. He took it out of my hand; I closed my eyes tighter and for a moment I was nothing but sickness. Then I remembered the other time Dop had looked at me like that: just before he sailed for the last time, when he had whispered to me in the office, "We're going to be married!" Then I remembered Stella.

I had known it, the moment I realized that Hasenfratz wasn't aiming at the duck but at us, and that I would have to kill him to save my life. The moment had been so short that it hadn't done any harm; when I opened my hand to let the little box float away I still felt so close to her that I drowned in happiness. Now the harm happened, slowly. As I lay there on my back, my eyes closed, my body still numb, my thoughts were very clear. I felt no emotion, I just thought, with a cold logic.

Stella had foreseen what would happen; when we kissed she had known it was for the last time. It looked now as if she had been wrong for once, but she hadn't. Even though I was still alive, she had lost me forever; she could never love me any more now I had joined the murderers. As I thought that, I saw Van Dam, his uniform torn, his face covered with blood, staring at me with his pale blue eyes, and it seemed as if I heard him say, "So they got you at last." I tried to chase him away; Goatskin's voice said, "Easy, easy," and I felt his hand on my shoulder. I heard the door opening and a mumbling of voices, then something hot was put under my feet and in my dead side, and something soft and warm was spread on top of me. I remembered how she had covered me with a blanket, and I felt a hollow despair. I was alone again, and would always be, from now on. It wasn't our common fear which had made her love us all as if we were one, it was our innocence. The blood she had seen on me when I pushed the cork into the bottle of wine, and that had made her scream with horror, hadn't been mine.

I wished Goatskin had never fished me. I wished I had never been forced to do what I had done. I wished the bloody American had had the sense to open envelope D. That last wish stuck. My thoughts from that moment onward concentrated on that wish. As I woke up more and more I hated the American with a growing hatred. It was he who had done all this to me. He had made me sail right into Hasenfratz's arms. He had made me scuttle my ship that had served me so faithfully. He had made me kill my bosun, one of the best men who ever sailed, and two stokers who had trusted me blindly. He had yelped with his wireless, squandered his ammunition, bungled the fire on his ship, and now he was being towed home to safety, a victorious hero. My hatred for him grew to such an extent that in the end I realized that I would not be able to face him. When I pictured him, strutting into the office, grinning, I felt like jumping at him and wringing his neck.

I was groggy as I got up, as if I had taken too many sleeping pills. I felt no pain, but I wasn't sure whether I should have if I hadn't been feeling so doped. I felt a dull ache, every time I thought of Stella; I avoided thinking of her, but it was difficult. The only thing stronger than she was my hatred for the American.

I was very calm and composed; I got up, moved about, put on some dry clothes Goatskin gave me; but all the time I was thinking how I would put my hands round the American's neck and tighten my grip and bang his head on the floor. I still knew, secretly, that it was all a reaction, that I was shell-shocked and couldn't be held responsible for what I thought and felt, but that secret knowledge vanished when I saw my face in the mirror. The right hand side was blue and swollen and covered with blood. I had turned into a monster. I could never let Stella see me like this. I had the face of a murderer.

I mumbled, "Christ! How did that happen?"

Goatskin, who seemed to be around all the time, said, "I don't know, it looks like flying glass to me. Don't you remember your windows being blown in, or something?"

I remembered. The sixth shell. It had blown in the windows of the wheelhouse. I didn't remember feeling anything at the time. I said, "The bastard."

Goatskin said, "Well, he's dead now."

I had meant the American.

I got him on the pier, and it was his own fault. When he was brought on board by the British Navy launch I took care to be out of the chartroom before he came in. I went to see the survivors of my crew in the fo'c'sle and in the messroom. All had more or less recovered from lying in the icy water, only the boy Waterman looked bad; he had waited too long before he jumped and been dragged down by the sinking ships, deeper than was good for him. I asked him why the devil he hadn't jumped the moment the hawser was cut, as he had been ordered to do; he answered with a sick little voice, "I was waiting for you, Skipper." Instead of being moved I hated him for it, and said, "So if you kick the bucket it's my fault. Thank you very much."

On my way between the fo'c'sle and the messroom I glanced at the duck being taken over by the channel tugs. She was still burning, but the fire had been pushed back to her midships. I couldn't see what she looked like because it was three o'clock in the morning and pitch dark, but in the glow of what was left of the fire I saw that the superstructure on her poop was a shambles. Her funnel hung over the ruins of her bridge; underneath the bridge was a large ragged hole which looked like a shell wound.

When we moored I stopped Goatskin on his way to the bridge, and asked him to keep the American busy in the chartroom for a couple of minutes while I nipped across to the office to make my report. The moment he came in with the American I would leave. He asked, "Why, for God's sake?" I answered, "I just don't want to set eyes on the bastard, that's all," and hurried away.

The moment our stern touched the quay I jumped. When I came into the office I found Wadlow sitting behind his desk. He looked tired and his eyes were pale, as if he had a hangover. He said, "Well, that was a neat little job you did there." When I asked him how he knew, he answered that the duck had been giving a running commentary of the whole operation over her wireless.

I clenched my teeth, and said, "That's the reason why I'm not going to make a full report until you've put that bugger through the routine. If you don't mind I'll make myself scarce while he is here."

Wadlow said, "Why on earth . . ." but he didn't finish the sentence; the door banged open and in stumbled a giant in a dirty torn uniform, his captain's stripes dangling from his sleeve. It was impossible to make out his age, for his face was covered with soot and he had no eyebrows left; he brought with him a sickening stench of petrol. Goatskin was behind him, and looked as if he had been trying to hold him back. The giant roared, "Where is he? Where is the Goddam son-of-a-gun! I wanta thank him for saving my life!" His voice boomed like a hooter, he sounded shell-shocked too.

The sight of him made me see red. I knew that if I didn't get out fast, there would be accidents. I tried to slip past him toward the door, but he grabbed hold of my sleeve. "Are you the Captain?" he hollered. "Are you the Captain of that Goddam tug?" I snarled, "Let go of me, you big . . ." and tried to tear myself loose, but he swung out his other arm and put a black swollen paw under my nose palm upward. It was covered with dirty open blisters. "Put it there, bud!" he bellowed. "Put it there, you Goddam son-of-bitch! Let me thank you for saving my life!" I got sick with rage at seeing that paw and hearing that voice, I shouted, "Let go, you moron!" and kicked his shin with all my might.

He gave an animal squeal of pain and surprise. His big mouth fell open until he looked like a child, struck in the face by its favorite playmate; but the kick had made him let go of me, and I ran out into the night. I ran in pitch darkness toward the distant dusk of the blacked out lanterns of the esplanade. I couldn't see a hand in front of my face, but I ran on, recklessly, because I heard a voice bellow behind me, "Hey, wait a minute! Hey, come here!" and galloping steps overtook me, as if I was being hunted by an elephant. I heard his breathing pump behind me, then I tripped over something and fell. He tripped over me, and crashed on the pier like a tree.

I lay there for a moment, dazed by the impact, then I was turned on my back and nearly suffocated by a stench of petrol. One of his paws held me down while the other groped for my hand; I struggled but he got hold of my fist and wrung it, shouting, "You Goddam fool! I want to thank you for saving my life!" I screamed, "Get off, you bastard! Get off!" kicking his enormous body with my knees, trying to get away; but he shouted, "I'll thank you if I've got to break your skull! Thank you! Thank you, you Goddam . . ." Then I heard him bark, and he was pulled off me.

I heard sounds of a violent struggle, as if many men were trying to rope a bull. Then the thin beam of a blacked-out torch shone in my face and a hand touched my shoulder. I wanted to fight again, although I felt very weak; then I heard a quiet Cockney voice say, "I'm sorry, sir; but you'd better come quietly."

I gave in and the hand pulled me to my feet. I felt very dizzy; he put his arm round my shoulders to steady me, and asked, "Are you hurt, sir?"

I said, "No; but for God's sake, keep that lunatic away."

He said, "Yes, sir. Very good, sir. Now would you be kind enough to come back to your headquarters with me, sir; a mere formality, but I'm afraid I'll have to ask you to come quietly, sir." I said, "All right, all right; only don't let me set eyes on that maniac again or I'll wring his bloody neck."

He said, "Don't worry, sir, everything will be all right, sir. Take it easy, sir," and we started walking.

We seemed to walk for hours. I saw a faintly lighted doorway in the distance and knew we were going back to the office; it was incredible that I should have run all that distance in so short a time. My face hurt as we walked; I didn't feel any hatred any more, I felt nothing but the pain. The dead side seemed very cold; when I touched it with my hand it was wet. I decided that it must be blood, and the moment I thought so the pain seemed to get much worse, but when I entered the office I forgot it, for the hatred sprang up in me again.

The American was sitting in old Foghorn's chair; he looked horrible. His clothes, that had been torn before, were now ripped to rags. His chest was bare, and among the hair hung a silver dog tag on a chain. The moment he saw me he put out his hand, and tried to struggle to his feet; but Wadlow, who was standing behind him, held him down in his chair. He slumped back like a big doped animal; his eyes filmed over and he muttered, "What's the matter with you folks? All I want is just to shake hands."

Wadlow said, "All right, old chap, all right; we'll get round to that in a minute." He sounded maddeningly British. "Now may I ask what was the cause of this scuffle, please? I'm afraid that I'll have to get at least some notion of it, if you want me to keep you out of the care of the good sergeant here." With that he nodded at the M.P., who was standing uncomfortably at ease between us.

"A mere formality, sir," said the M.P., "you'll understand that."

I felt suddenly cold and very tired. I looked at the clock over the radio desk, and tried to work out how long I hadn't slept, but I gave up when I got to sixty-eight hours. "I'll tell you what was the cause," I said. "He made me kill thirty-three people, and scuttle the best ship I ever had, and . . ." I wanted to add, "And lose the only woman I have ever loved in my life," but I noticed them staring at me in time, so I said, "And hurt me," instead. It sounded very plaintive and feeble, and I began to hate the American again for having made me say such a childish thing. But the hatred was listless and weary; it sank back into tiredness again. I started going through the list of all the things the big clumsy fool had done wrong, but before I had even got to his gunning of decoys until his ammunition had been exhausted, Goatskin said, "He never opened envelope D, because his chartroom was shot away in the first attack. So he couldn't help that."

I said, "He could have used his ears," knowing it was silly while I said it, for I remembered clearly how the W.O. had told me that the duck's receiver wasn't working before I set out. Goatskin told me so, and there was a lot more talk by everybody that I didn't listen to. I sat looking at the American, slumped in his chair; and after a while he began looking at me too. He was young to be a captain of a tanker, he couldn't be much older than I was. He looked at me with sad, hurt eyes and I began to feel sorry for him. Then Wadlow said, "All right, now shake hands, you two. What the whole thing amounts to is that both of you are just dog tired after doing a splendid job; so now shake hands and go to bed."

I got up after a moment's hesitation, because somebody nudged me into it. It must have been Goatskin, who was standing behind me all the time. I went toward the American with a feeling as if I was walking on thin ice, and held out my hand. He lifted his paw with difficulty, as if it weighed a ton, and grabbed mine. We shook hands, and his eyes brimmed over. "Let me show you the people who'll never forget what you did tonight," he said; then he pulled out a wallet from the ruins of his coat and took two snapshots out of it. They had got stuck face to face, probably with the heat. He tried to pull them apart, and when he had done so all he had got to show was two mutilated pictures with a raw white patch in the center, where he had torn the film off. I saw a little naked leg on one, probably a baby's; then he let the things fall out of his hands, said, "Goddam this war. Goddam it," and leaned with his elbows on the desk, his face in his hands.

I suddenly had a feeling of a great difference in age between us, as I realized that his war was only three weeks old.

When we stood in the darkness again, Goatskin said, "O.K., now let me take you to the flat. I have given you your keys and things, haven't I?"

It was the moment that I had known would come all the time, but I had managed to keep my thoughts away from it. Perhaps I had started the fight with the American only to postpone this moment. Now I couldn't evade it any longer. I felt tired and sick; I seemed to move in a cold feelingless clarity. I didn't feel any pain any more, nor hatred. I just knew I should never set eyes on her again.

I said, "No, I'm not going back to the flat. I want you to go there and tell her that I won't come back any more."

Goatskin said, "Don't be silly. You're just . . ."

I said, "Never mind about me. I want you to go to the flat now, and tell her that I won't come back any more. I don't even think that you'll need tell her anything. The moment she sees you after you've opened that door, she'll know."

"Jesus Christ!" said Goatskin. "You're mad."

I said, "I'll give you the key," and started fumbling in my pockets.

"But where are you going to sleep?" he asked. "You can't go back to the hotel, your bunk has been taken by someone else."

"I'll take Waterman's bunk," I said, "or Van Dam's. There'll be plenty of room tonight."

"You're crazy," said Goatskin. "And you ought to see a doctor, you may have glass splinters in your face."

I said, "Never mind my face. Here is the key, and do as I told you."

He sighed when I caught his hand and put the key in it. "O.K.," he said, "now let me take you to the hotel. You won't be able to stand on your feet much longer."

I said, "Oh, I feel fine," but I knew he was right.

When we got to the hotel I said, "All right, now you run along and do as I told you." But he said, "No, let me take you to my bunk first. When I come back I'll take any other that may be going, but I want to see you put up first. I'll take you to a doctor first thing in the morning."

I said, "All right," and he helped me through the swing doors. When we entered the hall the old porter rose from his grave behind the counter with the glass with his dentures in it. Goatskin led me to the stairs without taking any notice of him; the old man called, "Hey, hey, where are you going? That gentleman doesn't live in the hotel!"

176

Goatskin said, "I'm taking him to my bunk. He's wounded."

"That's got nothing to do with me," the old man said, "we are full up, we've got no room for any new ones."

"He isn't a new one," said Goatskin, "he was living here up to three weeks ago."

The old man peered at me, but no look of recognition changed his face. "Don't try to pull that one on me," he said. "People have tried that one before, but they've always been sorry after. Show me his billeting papers."

Goatskin got angry. "Oh, shut up!" he said. "Can't you see he's nearly dropping? His papers must still be in your files. I'll sort them out for you when I come down."

The porter went on calling after us as Goatskin took me up the stairs. He called that he would tell Miss Headland, that we would be sorry for using bad language at him, that he had served in this hotel for forty years but never known such brutes and foul-mouthed bastards as this lot. He was still shouting when we got to the first floor; the last I heard was, "Bloody forcigners."

Goatskin's room was exactly like the one I had slept in before. It had three tiers of three berths each, a cracked wash basin in the corner, a chair heaped with clothes in the center, and drawings on the walls and the ceiling. In every bunk but one lay a sleeper, wheezing and snoring. Goatskin shook one of them by the shoulder, and said, "I've got someone here who is wounded and needs sleep. If the boys start quacking, tell them to shut up. I'll be back later with a doctor." The sleeper grunted. "My second engineer," said Goatskin, "he's all right; if anybody starts making a racket, call him. His name is Henk."

He wanted to help me undress, but I said, "I can manage. Now do as I told you."

He looked at me for a second, the way he had looked at the bottom of the pier after Dop's death. He asked, "Are you sure that's the way you want it?"

I said, "Yes."

Then he said, "I can't blame you," and turned away.

He shut the door behind him, and left me staring at it. I had not remembered it before: he hated Stella's guts. I had seen how he would look at her when she came out of the bedroom with her chalk white face and her bright red mouth. He would not tell her that I was still alive, though dead tired and half mad after killing thirty-three people and sinking two ships. He would tell her nothing, he would just look at her with his cold blue eyes and see her suffer without blinking. He wouldn't believe she cared two hoots whether I was dead or alive, he would eat his beans on toast and sip his coffee and if he felt like it go to bed with her this very night and take her as he would take a tart.

The moment I realized what he was up to I knew I had to stop him at any cost; never mind if it meant that I should have to tell her myself that I would never come back any more, I could not let him do this to her. It wasn't her fault that all of us had been killed one after the other; she had been good to us, she had loved us, truly and sincerely, even if we were all the same man to her; she was a sad, dazed creature from a faraway island with nobody in the whole world to care about her, except a ghost in the desert and me.

The moment I realized what I had done I went after him. I ran down the corridor, stumbled down the stairs, but by the time I got back to the hall I was so dizzy that I had to sit down. I groped my way to one of the chairs and lowered myself into it, cautiously; when I leaned back, I felt very sick. I wanted to get up again, instantly, and run to Stella, but I couldn't. The hall seemed to contract and to expand round me; I saw the counter and the glass with the dentures swim in a faint, eerie light, as if they were reflected in rippling water. The porter's reflection rose from behind the counter and he had something in his hand. "Want a drink, Captain?" he asked. "Canteen price." I remembered how I had been sitting here the night before I went to the flat, how I had to get drunk first before I could summon the courage to face her. I had a ghostly feeling, as if this was the same night and I should have to go through it all again, knowing what would happen. Perhaps the whole thing was a nightmare, perhaps I had never got up after finishing that bottle of hooch, but been sitting here all the time, drunk, dreaming.

I knew it wasn't true, and yet I couldn't convince myself that it wasn't. The dead side of my face was throbbing. I daren't move for fear of vomiting. I was drunker with exhaustion than I had been with hooch that other night. But the thought of what Goatskin would do to her if I didn't prevent him horrified me so that I staggered back to my feet and began to grope my way to the swing doors.

When I lurched out into the night the cold air gave me a short illusion of waking up and feeling strong enough to make it. I steered my way from lantern to lantern, stumbling over lumps of masonry and nearly falling several times. But I managed to remain on my feet, for I knew that if I should fall I would not be able to get up again unless someone helped me and there seemed to be nobody about. A distant hooter boomed in the harbor, and somewhere far away a steam winch was hammering, they were the only sounds of human life in the night.

I had to wait at a lamppost to regain my breath and my strength; my eyes blurred, it seemed as if it was snowing. I lifted up my face to feel if it was true, but it wasn't, my face stayed hot and dry. I staggered on drunkenly; I couldn't think any more, it seemed as if I had forgotten all the words, the only word I could remember was her name. I started whispering, "Stella, Stella, Stella," and that helped me to get to the entrance of Seaview. When I reached the hall, I leaned against the wall, and looked up the first flight of stairs. I could never manage all those flights; the first one alone looked quite impossible, and there were ten of them. Then I took the duplicate key from my pocket, for that gave me the illusion that I was nearly there, and started to climb the stairs.

I don't know how long it took me to get to the top floor. I started to whisper her name again half way up; without that I would not have made it. When at last I pulled myself up at the doorpost I hesitated and listened, but I heard nothing except my own breath. Then I stuck the key in the lock, turned it, and pushed the door open, holding on to the post with my other hand.

I saw Goatskin sitting at the table, a plate in front of him. I saw her, a white death mask with a clown's mouth painted on it, turn round in front of the stove, a plate in her hand. She stared at me for a second with such horror in her eyes that I knew all was lost. Then she dropped the plate and screamed.

It was the most terrible scream I ever heard a living being give; then she seemed to crumple up in front of my eyes. Her face sagged and wrinkled, in one second's time she aged twenty years and turned into an ugly, middle-aged prostitute. Then she crashed into a chair and fell headlong across the table, screaming, "Go away! Go away!"

I turned round and fled. I fell down the stairs, stumbled out of the house, ran into the narrow street round the corner, fleeing from what I had seen happen before my eyes, from what I had done to her. By sending Goatskin and then coming back, I had turned her into a whore; for she had never seen two of us together.

I ended up on Memorial Hill. I wandered among the ruins of the benches in the straggling grass and wanted to sit down several times, but I heard lovers giggling and whispering around me. I climbed to the top, leaned on the parapet, and saw dawn breaking over the notice "Carpet Beating Strictly Forbidden." I was beyond being tired or ill; it was as if my body lay on the map of Africa in front of the door with the inverted "2," and the thing that wandered among the lovers and stood looking at the daybreak was my ghost.

It was quite light when Goatskin found me. I had seen the silhouette of another lonely walker wandering on the hill as the daylight grew, but I had avoided him. When he found me I understood that it had been Goatskin.

He asked, "Where have you been?" and when I answered, "Here," he said, "But I've been here myself for hours, looking for you all the time!" I asked, "What's happened to her?" and he answered, "How should I know? I followed you the moment you ran away. Jesus Christ! Do you think I could stay there after the scream she gave when she saw you? I've never heard anything so terrifying in my life."

The moment I realized that he had left her alone, I started running back to the flat. I don't know how I managed it, I just didn't feel my body any more. I started to run because I suddenly had a horrible vision. I knew she had committed suicide.

Goatskin tried to hold me back at first, running by my side, pulling at my arms to stop me, shouting, "Jesus Christ! Where are you going?" He gave up in the end, and ran with me all the way, panting, muttering, "Jesus Christ!" and "Doctor; I must get a doctor!" It was the first time I had seen him lose his self-control; he ran beside me like a terrified boy.

When we got to the house I jumped up the stairs two steps at a time. We passed the old janitor on one of the landings, a broom in his hands. I pushed him out of my way; he stumbled against the wall, calling, "Captain! Captain!" after me.

The door of the flat stood open. The kitchen was empty, the light still burning, Goatskin's plate still on the table, the mess of the plate she had dropped on the floor.

The bedroom was empty too; the bed hadn't been slept in, the wardrobe stood open, the portrait on top of it was gone.

She wasn't in the bathroom either; when I opened the medicine cupboard I saw that her things had gone.

Then I heard voices in the kitchen, and Goatskin came in, saying, "She has gone to the station. The old man says she asked him to get her a taxi half an hour ago, he carried her bags."

I ran out of the flat and started down the stairs again. Goatskin followed me, shouting, "For Christ's sake! Where are you going this time?"

I didn't answer, I ran out of the house with him at my heels. We ran all the way to the station. When we got there, I barged into the transport office and asked if they had written out a ticket for a girl with blue eyes and long fair hair. The transport officer said, "What do you think we are doing here? Writing out tickets for blondes?"

Goatskin started to explain that I was mad, that I had been wounded in action, that I had rammed a U-boat, had been fished unconscious out of the sea, that I hadn't slept for eighty hours, that my girl had run away; before he had finished going through the list, I was out of the office, running toward the civilian ticket windows.

Only one of them was open, and there was a queue in front of it. I pushed the first man aside; he started protesting, but he shut up when he saw my face. So did the man behind the window. I asked him if he had sold a ticket to a girl with blue eyes and long fair hair; she might have gone back to the Hebrides. He looked at me as if I frightened him, and said, "I sold a ticket to Glasgow to a young lady who asked for one for the Hebrides; I told her I couldn't give her one direct."

I asked, "What time? What platform?" He answered, "The seven-fifteen, platform five."

Goatskin had caught up with me again, and started pulling my sleeve, shouting something, but I didn't listen. I broke away and ran toward platform five. A train stood waiting at the dead end, its big red taillight still burning. The platform was full of steam and the shadows of people; over the steam floated a clock, it was ten past seven.

I was stopped at the barrier by a ticket collector and an M.P. The ticket collector was ready to let me through, but the M.P. was not. He wanted to see my pass. Goatskin caught up with me; he had the transport officer with him. Both of them started talking; I leaned on the barrier, exhausted, the station reeled round me. In that sickening whirl I heard Goatskin's voice. It said, "What in God's name do you want to see her for? Don't you think she's had enough?"

I said, "I want to see if she's all right."

"Jesus Christ!" said Goatskin, with such rage in his voice that I realized he too was cracking up. "You know now that she's all right! She's bought a ticket, she's going home! If you show your crazy mug once more, she'll go to pieces all over again! I know she's a tart; but have a heart, will you!"

I said, "I want to see if she's all right."

Then I heard a voice say, "I'll go and look for you. I'll go through the train, find her, and see how she is. You men look after the Captain in the meantime, he's folding up."

I felt hands grip me under the arms and put me back on my feet. I hadn't noticed that I had started sagging. I opened my eyes and saw the transport officer go through the gate. I heard Goatskin say, "Blue eyes, long hair, blonde, you can't miss her." A porter said, "I know where the lady is, sir. Third class, car number five; I carried her luggage." I saw the transport officer walk away with the porter, and called, "See what she is doing! See if she is all right!" Then they vanished among the shadows in the steam.

I hung over the barrier, supported by the hands under my arms. They seemed to stay away for a long time; I knew something had happened. I felt very weary, very weak, and stared at the red taillight in the steam. It looked like a sun rising, a round red disc in the clouds. I concentrated on that light, for I didn't want to think of what I knew had happened. She was dead, soon I would see them coming out of the steam, carrying a stretcher. I heard voices behind me; one of the hands under my arms was taken away, someone put his arm round my shoulder; I looked up and saw it was Goatskin.

Then the transport officer came back, alone. I wanted him to tell me, instantly, but he passed through the gate first. The ticket collector saluted and he saluted back. Then he came toward me, and the other man who had supported me took his hand away and stepped back. The transport officer took his place and put his hand on my shoulder. He had a little mustache and green eyes. He said, "I have seen her and she's perfectly all right. She's sitting in a corner seat, asleep, with a writing pad on her lap. She must have dozed off after having started her letter. She looked tired, but all right."

I asked, "Letter?" and he said, "Yes. I even took the trouble to take a close look at it. It said: 'Dear Alan, No special news this week.' That was how far she got. Now are you satisfied?"

I said, "Yes."

They wanted to take me away then, but I said I'd like to see the train leave. People talked round me, and I heard the word "Ambulance." Then a whistle sounded and the train left. I saw its red taillight draw away, and vanish in the steam. Then I broke down; the last I heard was Goatskin's voice, saying, "Don't worry, you'll be all right."

The boy Waterman died that night.

Part II PEACE

CHAPTER SEVEN

WHEN I CAME OUT OF HOSPITAL, SOME TWO MONTHS LATER, THINGS HAD changed. The Americans had entered the war good and proper, and after their first convoys made bad crossings they started to deal with the U-boats good and proper. By the time I came back to it, OTWA had become a nice, regular service in which people took baths, cleaned their nails, and went on leave with little suitcases.

I had a hard time picking up, but Goatskin was a help. On his visits to the hospital he looked flashier every fortnight and he turned out to be quite a conversationalist; his talk was mainly about London and how his feet never touched the ground from the moment he came out of Paddington Station until he staggered back into it. He grew a little mustache, collected photographs with "Love and Kisses" written on the back with lipstick, and locks of hair that he pasted in a diary. He said I'd be a different man once he had shown me round the town and introduced me to some of his correspondents. But when I came out, I had hardly adjusted my eyes to the sunlight before I was called to H.Q. and commissioned to the Arctic with the *Vlieland*; we were to sail as a rescue ship with the convoys to Murmansk. I told them there must be a mistake, for the *Vlieland* was commanded by Goatskin. There was no mistake, they said; his had been a temporary promotion, he would sail with me as my mate.

If it had happened to me, I would have been rather relieved; but I knew he would not take it that way. He liked being a captain. At first I thought I'd let him get the news from H.Q. but he would realize I had known all along and not dared to tell him. So I told him myself in the end, over a glass of Coca-Cola in the Social Center. The loud-speakers blared, the short-skirted girls were flung about by jitterbugging Americans, who made the place unsafe to sit in as they kicked like kangaroos. Goatskin was happy, his captain's stripes made him look at the girls with confidence, almost boredom. Then I told him.

He never looked away from the girls, but he remained silent for a long time. Then he said, "Well, that's how it is, I guess."

I said, "I'm sorry."

"To have me as your mate?"

"No."

"That's all right then. When do we sail?"

"Tomorrow at sunrise. Destination Greenock."

"That's what I have against this war," he said, "the Goddam waste of it." Then he hailed a waitress, and we had another bottle of Coca-Cola.

When we sailed the next morning he was wearing his goatskin again, and he had shaved off his little mustache. We would have to grow beards in the Arctic, he said, and he liked the hair to grow evenly all over.

After a day or two it was difficult to believe that things had ever been different, Westport seemed far away. I liked sailing with him better than with the boy Waterman; he was a good mate, quiet, competent, and as brave as they come. We had a hard time with the convoys, but so had a lot of people. Once or twice I thought I'd crack up; so did he, I suppose. The war was ugly up there, the cold made things worse. I often thought of Van Dam and his epidemic of madness. We were lunatics, murdering one another on the brink of nothing, the edge of the world. We only mentioned Stella once, by mistake.

In March, '44, we were directed to London, for orders. This was surprising, as we hadn't been anywhere near London all during the war. Everybody said that this was going to be the Invasion. The Invasion had been in the air for years, and become a matter of faith, like personal survival after death. Either you believed in the invasion, or you didn't; it depended on your religious nature. The Russians, for instance, didn't believe in it, and the people who escaped from occupied Europe did. We neither did nor didn't; we were intellectuals.

It was Goatskin who suggested that we should take up chess. We had to take up something, after we had been lying in Shadwell Basin for a fortnight and it began to dawn on us that we might be lying there for a very long time indeed. The fortnight had been exciting; all the ocean-going tugboats we knew were concentrated in Shadwell Basin, there was a prison ship that gave cocktail parties, and in the West India Dock Road was a Ceylonese restaurant called "The Light of Asia," where curried chicken cost two shillings.

The Light of Asia had become the daily meeting place for the tugboat captains. We were nine in all, five old ones and four young ones, all that was left of our fleet of thirty-two ocean-going tugboats when the war started. Of those thirty-two, six ships had had old captains, the rest youngsters. It was alarming to realize, four years later, that five of the six old captains were still alive and that the sixth had been killed in an air raid ashore. We looked for an explanation of this; we tried to define the magical reason for the survival of the old captains. The reason must be magical, for all five of them were extraordinarily stupid. They were superstitious, bald and fat, with very short sleeves and thick hairy pulses. Their conversation in The Light of Asia was bewildering to hear. "Jews," one of them would say, "dangerous people, Jews. Jewesses are all right, but Jews . . ." Negroes were dangerous too. Old Captain Bakker of the *Texel* told how he had an affair with a Negro woman in Central Africa, who had so terrified him with her size and the blackness of her eyes, that he had nightmares of her for years after. "Perhaps my age had something to do with it," he concluded. "I was thirteen."

The old captains fitted snugly into the atmosphere of The Light of Asia; we did not. We felt ill at ease with the proprietor, a fierce little Ceylonese who was violently anti-British and had the German radio blaring all day as a demonstration. It took us some time to find out that he obviously didn't speak any German himself, for he was tuned in on the German broadcast of the B.B.C. The old captains felt perfectly at home; we had to take up something to defend ourselves. Goatskin thought of chess.

He bought a chessboard and a box of chessmen and we settled down one night in the messroom with the game between us. He shook the pawns in his hands; I chose a fist, and opened the game with white. It was the beginning of a long slow disease, that ended in murderous lunacy. I had never been very good at games because I didn't really care whether I won or not. In Shadwell Basin, during those long nights of March, April, and May, '44, I began to care terribly. I don't know what got into us, but to win a game of chess became a matter of life and death; as we played an average of fifteen games a day we became very tense. I had sailed with Goatskin for almost a year and we had become friends, but in Shadwell Basin we became enemies again. Every time he won a game I felt like breaking his skull; every time I won he looked at me with murder in his eyes. While we had still been friends I had hardly been conscious of his presence; the moment we took up chess I could never forget that he was there. Wherever I went, on ship or ashore, I felt irksome, looking around to see where he was, and he was nearly always there, as he had been for the last year, only I had never noticed it. On my way to The Light of Asia, hearing steps behind me, I would look round, say through clenched teeth, "Can't you go somewhere else?" and he would answer, "Since when do you own this street?" We would march on toward The Light of Asia, our jaws set, our fists in our pockets, to say at the door, "After you," and,

"No, no, after you," and when he went in first I felt like kicking him down the stairs. In the cellar we would find the five old captains, the curried chicken, the anti-British Ceylonese and the German news of the B.B.C. We would sit down at the billiard table, which during the daytime was covered with an oilcloth and served as a communal dining table. The old captains would look at us with their fishlike stare and say at random, "Don't you ever have your tonsils out, for if you drink gin later it may give you heart failure." Goatskin would sit down at the far corner of the table and smile at me and I could taste the hatred on my lips as I licked them. I suppose it was the reaction to the Northeast Passage.

The night before D-day, Goatskin and I played seven games of chess. It worked against the fear we felt; by the end of the seventh game I didn't care any more whether I lived or died, if only I could wring that bastard's neck. Then, at midnight, the news came that there would be no D-day. Operations were postponed because of the gales. It was a pity, because now we got afraid. The second night even our games of chess didn't work. When we finally sailed, we felt awful; I don't think any of us had ever been more afraid in his life. We were ordered to tow the Mulberry harbors to the beaches of Normandy, and we were sure that none of the sections would ever get there.

It turned out to be a walkover. The Germans hardly put up any resistance at all. The sea was more dangerous than they were, for there was a strong wind blowing. The war seemed to be in the bag.

The invasion of the South of France, a few months later, was different. It was much less spectacular, but there the Germans took a heavy toll. It was very hot, the sea was oily, and most of us were suffering from sunburn because we had stripped to the waist, and realized too late how fierce the sun was. We had gone in with the idea that it would be a walkover once more, but when we saw the Liberty ships go down around us one after the other, under the hellishly accurate artillery fire from the mountains, we got panicky. We had been lying in the mothballs for too long. Those months in Shadwell Basin and the peaceful ferrying of lighters and barges across the Channel after D-day, with not an enemy plane or a U-boat in sight, had made us slide back into peacetime. The war wasn't in the bag at all.

Around three o'clock in the afternoon our ship got a direct hit that blew out the engine room, took half of the bridge away and left us a wreck without a funnel, full of howling wounded. Goatskin and the cook were the only ones who came off without a scratch. I got shrapnel in both legs, and screamed like a rabbit. It wasn't so much the pain that made me scream, as the fear that my legs would have to be amputated. We got assistance, were put on stretchers, put on board a landing craft, and taken ashore. Goatskin stayed with us all the time. The Chief Engineer was badly wounded, so was Sparks; the second engineer was dead. Of the crew, only the new bosun and two sailors were left. They went with us in the ambulance to a small hospital among the palm trees.

We were put down, all our stretchers in a row, in an empty room with pink walls, waiting for a doctor. Goatskin had taken the emergency kit with him when we left the ship, and he was messing around with bandages and splints when a girl came in. She was about twenty, had dark hair and dark eyes. She had a nurse's dress on that didn't fit the hips and a cap that had slid off her head and now dangled on her back. We were so sick and frightened and hot that we didn't react to the girl at all. We were just waiting for someone to help us and tell us we would be all right. She had a thermometer in her hand and looked at us very bravely. We must have been quite a sight.

"Do you speak English?" she asked, with a very British accent. Goatskin answered for us, "Yes." We just moaned. "I've come to take your temperatures," she said. Then she went over to the bosun, who was lying in the corner next to me, and said, "Take this in your mouth, please." The bosun obeyed without opening his eyes. He went on moaning with the thing in his mouth.

Goatskin handed her the thermometer from our emergency kit. "This any use to you?" he asked. She said, "Oh, thank you," took the thermometer, and came toward me. "Open your mouth please," she said.

I answered, "Certainly not," for the Dutch take their temperatures in a different way from the English. I had taken many temperatures myself with the thing, whenever a member of my crew imagined he had something the matter with him, so I knew where it had been.

"But you must," she said. "The doctor told me to take your temperatures and he may be here any minute. Please do as I tell you."

I said, "I'm very sorry, but I won't. And that's final."

She began to get flustered; it was obvious that it was her first day as a nurse, and the blood and the wounded began to get her down. I saw her eyes fill with tears and she suppressed a trembling of her lips before she said, "Please, please, open your mouth, for *me* . . ."

I said to Goatskin, "Explain to the young lady why I can't," but he answered, "No, thank you, you tell her yourself."

The moaning had stopped around me. Despite their pain the others were listening. She looked at me with pleading eyes. Then there were steps in the corridor and she looked nervously over her shoulder. "There's the doctor," she said. "Please help me, please take it in your mouth; please —it means so much to me."

I don't know what it was, in her face or in her eyes, but I thought, "If I am going to have my legs cut off, this can't do me much harm." So I took the thing in my mouth. And then the others began to laugh. They were suffering like hell, and terrified and feverish, but the sight of me with that thermometer in my mouth just made them bellow with laughter. When the doctor came in, he looked with his eyebrows raised at the six wounded men on stretchers, splitting their sides. Then he looked at the nurse and said, "Well, Miss Simmons, is this your work?" She stammered, "No, sir, yes, sir," and fled, stumbling over the threshold.

Miss Simmons made my day. She and the information the doctor gave me that he would not have to cut my legs off. There was nothing the matter with them, only a few bits of shrapnel in the bone. We were all very cheered by him. He seemed supremely confident that none of us had anything the matter with him worse than a cold in the nose. One of the sailors died at daybreak.

The next day they operated on my leg. When I woke up, feeling very sick, a girl was standing by my bedside in a state of great emotion. "I'm so awfully sorry," she said. "What can I do to make good? I'm sure you'll never forgive me." A horrible thought reeled through my mind: she was the operating nurse who had cut something off by mistake.

She was Miss Simmons. Somebody had put her wise to the way in which the Dutch took their temperatures. I tried to soothe her but my speech was not very intelligible. Seen on waking up from an ether sleep, she looked very pretty. A vision of beauty and girlish purity. Waking up all the time, I wondered why I hadn't recognized her straight away. Then I realized it was her cap. She wore it on her head today; it made her look like a member of the Dagenham Girl Pipers' Band. She had serious, soft eyes. She seemed to be worried about something. I asked her what it was, and she started to tell me; I must have fallen asleep again, for when I woke up once more she was gone. In her place stood Goatskin, grinning from ear to ear. When he saw me open my eyes, he showed me something: a chessboard. I must have made a noise, for suddenly the room was full of nurses and orderlies and he was taken out backward. I fell asleep for the third time.

When I woke up again, and this time definitely, it was morning. I saw the same room with the pink walls but now there were beds in it. In the one next to me, Sparks was sitting up. His arms were bandaged across his chest in an oriental praying position and he was having his teeth brushed by Miss Simmons. In the bed furthest away, the huge bulk of the Chief lay covered with a sheet. For an awful moment I thought he had died overnight; then I heard his deep rumbling voice give commentaries on Miss Simmons, taking advantage of the fact that Sparks couldn't answer with that brush in his mouth. He was talking in Dutch and I told him to shut up. Miss Simmons was still wearing her Dagenham Girl Pipers' cap, but it was sitting on her forehead now. It seemed to go through phases, like the moon.

After she had finished with Sparks, she came to me. She had a brand-new toothbrush in her hand and a tube of Dr. Pierre's dental cream. When she told me to open my mouth I grinned at her and she began to tell me again how sorry she was. She had a very pretty blush and dimples in her cheeks; I wanted to ask her some questions but she put the brush in my mouth and started scrubbing away like a bosun. She was doing a very thorough job on my gums when the doctor appeared in the doorway and cried, "Miss Simmons! What in the name of Trinity are you doing?" Her cap, by then, was sitting on her eyebrows. The doctor looked exasperated when he pointed out to her that there was no need to brush the teeth of patients who could use their hands. Or had she assumed by any chance that I was in the habit of brushing my teeth with my feet? I felt sorry for the poor girl when she hurried out, leaving me with a mouth full of soap-suds and taking the glass with her. The doctor said, "If any of you gentlemen have the intention of marrying her, please be quick about it." The Chief answered with a colossal, lewd laugh. Whatever was the matter with him, he would live.

Goatskin came back that afternoon, looking shifty. The doctor was around, feeling pulses; while he was there Goatskin told us that the ship had remained afloat and been towed into the harbor but probably would never sail again; he himself was hanging around, waiting for orders. The moment the doctor had turned his back he put his hand in his inside pocket, like a man selling dirty postcards, and brought out a miniature game of chess. I remembered vaguely that he had been thrown out the day before, and, like a sportsman, I had a game with him. I liked it because I won; he went on looking over his shoulder to see whether anyone was coming in. During the second game, Miss Simmons surprised us, her cap on the back of her head once more, carrying a tray with four glasses of milk. Goatskin covered the game with his hand but she had seen it. She was very stern about it, but only to him, not to me. He knew the doctor had forbidden him to excite the wounded, he ought to be ashamed of himself. He tried to look dignified as he put the game back in his pocket. I felt pleased, I had the better of him at last. A week later he was called away, back to London. I didn't set eyes on him again until a year later.

During that year peace had come and I had started to walk again. First on crutches, then with a stick, aided by Miss Simmons. We shuffled around on the clean gravel among the palm trees and sat on a bench looking at the Mediterranean. She told me that she had been in the South of France all during the war and that nobody had ever found out that she was English and so she had remained free. She had joined the Resistance and taken a secret training as a nurse; on the day of the Invasion she had volunteered and we had been her first patients. Before us she had rehearsed with farmers of the Resistance, who had held themselves limp to imitate wounded. She was a nice girl, very English, and I liked her a great deal. Sitting on the bench, playing with the gravel with my stick, listening to her talking, I had my first taste of peace.

It was the only taste, for once I got on my way home to Holland with Sparks, the Chief and the bosun, we soon found out that there was something the matter with the peace. Nothing very serious yet, only nobody seemed quite to believe in it. We went home via Paris and Brussels. The last bit was done in a truck. We said good-by in Amsterdam, and promised to look each other up within a week's time. None of us did.

I found my job with the harbor police in Amsterdam was taken and I was glad of it. I applied for a vacancy on a tugboat but there were very few ships left; all I got offered was a trip to the Dutch East Indies as a mate. I took it and sailed with old Captain Bakker on the *Texel*.

I hadn't seen Captain Bakker again since Shadwell Basin and he didn't remember seeing me. When he asked me for my record and I said, "We lunched together for three months in The Light of Asia," his face changed and he answered, "Oh, were you one of those?" That was all.

The trip was a lesson to me in many ways. I found out, to start with, that if you have once commanded a ship you cannot sail as a second again. Perhaps I also found out the magical reason for the survival of the old captains: they took it easy. Nothing excited old Bakker or got him out of his slow, fishlike train of thought. He spent most of his time in his bunk, half sitting up, playing patience on his thighs with a very small set of cards. At first I thought this meant that he would leave the command of the ship virtually to me, but nothing of the kind. His bunk was right underneath the bridge and every half hour or so he would bellow, "Mate!" through his porthole. I would rush down the bridge steps, break my neck on the threshold of the chartroom, open the communicating door and ask, panting, "Yes, sir?" He would turn over a couple more cards on his thighs, without looking up, and say, "Nothing." I would go back to the bridge, my hands twitching.

It took me a week to realize that he yelled, "Mate!" as soon as he heard my steps stop pacing overhead. I don't know what he thought, perhaps that I had gone to sleep or something. In his eyes, an officer of the watch ought to keep walking the bridge all the time, which was steep for a man who never moved a foot. He took his watches sitting in a deck chair, playing patience on his thighs, outside if there was no wind, in the wheelhouse if there was. I hardly ever saw him stand up. On entering the harbor, he would sit on the helmsman's stool brought out of the wheelhouse, his eyes just over the spray shield, his fat, hairy hand on the handle of the engine-room telegraph. If there was no pilot to bring us in, he'd use the maneuver to frighten the pants off me by heading straight for a rock or a lighthouse, motionless on his stool, until my heart pounded in my ears because it seemed humanly impossible that he should not run the ship aground. The first time this happened I got very nervous, glancing at him all the time, and I was about to make a jump for the engine-room telegraph when he pulled it back and muttered, "Hard port." I yelled the order through to the wheelhouse as if I was sizzling at a stake. He looked up at me with such sleepy disdain in his fish eyes that I blushed to the roots of my hair.

The next time, I didn't play. I just stood stolidly looking over the spray shield with my hands behind my back and didn't shoot him a single glance. Only when perdition seemed inevitable I shut my eyes, and swallowed my saliva. Then he muttered, "Three starboard, three," and I sang the order through with a strained voice that ended in a yodel.

The third time, I was hardened to his treatment. I kept my eyes wide open, stared death in the face without batting an eyelid, and when he pulled the engine-room telegraph on "full astern" in the last split second, I went quietly on breathing, like a cow. This seemed to disturb him, for he looked up and asked, "What?" I answered, "Nothing, sir." It set him frowning, and I am proud to say that during the rest of the trip, although he did his damnedest, he never rattled me again.

He handled his ship as an invalid his wheel chair, that much must be said of him. He could moor her between two ten-thousand-ton merchantmen with only a hand's breadth to spare fore and aft, and he would do so without getting up and without ever raising his voice above a conversational tone. I admired him, but during the three months I sailed with him we never spoke about anything personal at all. Only when we were approaching Ymuiden harbor on our way home, with the pier lights ahead, he asked, "What are you going to do with your life?" I was so taken aback by this sudden interest in my person, that I answered, "Nothing." He nodded and said, "I thought so." That was all.

Back in Amsterdam I found myself in a quandary. During my watches in the course of my trip with Captain Bakker I had been thinking. I hadn't done so for a long time, not since I lost Stella. I had settled down to an unthinking life, saying to myself: first let's get this war over, then think. During my trip with Bakker I took up thinking again. They weren't constructive thoughts; I found out that there was very little positive left in me. The only certainty I could discover was negative: I would never have anything to do with war again. For immediately after this one had been over, the preparations for a new one seemed to have started. People got very excited about the Russians, and there was a lot of indignant talk on platforms and in the papers. I didn't know how my shipmates thought about it, for I hadn't seen them again since the evening we said good-by in the lorry that took us to Amsterdam; but I for one had had my war.

At first, this certainty was rather quiet and vague; it became more aggressive as I saw more of the papers, in Suez, Port Said, Colombo, Billiton, and then Colombo, Port Said, and Suez again. Things seemed to be moving fast. Some German in some meeting had delivered a wonderful speech against the Russians which had been heartily applauded by everybody present, and after the applause he had said, "I have to inform you that the speech I just read has been delivered by Doctor Goebbels three years ago." The paper in which I read that took it as a joke. I thought of the dead, of the second engineer for instance, whose widow I hadn't been to see yet. She would not be very receptive to the joke.

I decided that not only would I have nothing to do with the next war if it came, I would even steer clear of anything that looked like a preparation for it. The tin dredger that old Bakker and I had towed to the Dutch East Indies was part of those preparations. On further reflection practically anything that tugboats towed was part of the preparations. Well, I wouldn't have any of it. I would sooner loaf with a monkey on my shoulder and earn my living with a barrel organ than be connected, however sideways, with World War III. I suppose I wasn't the only one, but I felt that I was. I felt lonely, as if in that lorry I had said good-by to more than just my crew.

So in Amsterdam I handed in my card and announced that I was going to take a holiday. I had decided to make a trip to the past; I wanted to look them up, and see how they felt. The first one I wanted to see was Goatskin, but nobody knew where he was. He had not taken a job with the

Company again after V-J Day, and he had no relatives who could tell me his address. So I moved on to the next one—Sparks. I inquired in the office of Radio Holland, and found out that he was in Paris. The one after that was the Chief. He was in Holland all right; he had bought a little bicycle repair shop somewhere in the New Province—the land that had been reclaimed from the Zuider Zee.

I got there by means of a number of buses, ferries and finally an ex-Army lorry that took passengers along the mud tracks that one day would be roads. When I got out in the village square all I saw was a couple of shacks, the village existed only on paper. One of the shacks was a communal restaurant; the other the Governor's office. Behind them were a number of chicken coops, I was directed toward one of them. I began to like the New Province as I walked along the muddy street. It was the newest part of our planet, there was something creative in the atmosphere. After the ruins of bombed-out Europe, it was nice to see something constructive being born.

When I knocked on the door of No. 16, somebody bellowed. As I opened the door, a little bell tinkled. The Chief roared like a lion when he saw me against the light; the little building quivered as he stamped toward me, threw his arms around my neck, and knocked the breath out of me. He asked me, after he had finished mauling me, "What are you doing here?" I said that I was on my way to the North and had thought this a nice occasion to look him up. "Wonderful!" he said. "You're staying the night, aren't you? I'm just about to go out for choir practice. Come with me." I looked at him agape. All I'd ever heard him sing was "Roll me over in the clover," with a voice as if someone was trying it out on a steam whistle. "Choir?" I asked. "Yes," he said. "I am with the basses. We are rehearsing 'The Messiah.'" I fell silent after that for I remembered Van Dam.

He put on a clean shirt and boots, put his head in the wash basin, combed his hair with the part in the middle, and cleaned his nails with a pen knife, all for "The Messiah." He talked about his little shop, that was very promising but would only get into its full stride once there were roads for people to ride bicycles on; now he was mainly doing repair work on excavators and tractors and the like.

The rehearsal was held in the communal restaurant. There, by the light of two oil lamps, about thirty people were gathered of whom twenty-three were men; once the singing started it became clear that of those twenty-three men twenty were basses. The conductor was an agitated little schoolmaster with spectacles and oddly incongruous mud boots. He asked would the ladies and gentlemen please open their books on page forty-three. "I know that my Redeemer liveth." There was a lot of throat scraping and paper rustling, then the little man raised his baton and a silence fell. The wind had risen outside and moaned through the window cracks. The shack croaked faintly, like a windjammer at sea. The little man struck a tuning fork, sang, "Ah-h!" and the women took up the note. They sallied heroically at the dark mass of waiting basses, but were smothered at once. The basses roared like seals, it was a massacre.

I was sitting alone in the far corner of the empty restaurant and watching the Chief. He was putting all he had into his singing, and could be heard above the rest. I wondered what had come over him; something was changed. I realized what it was when they came to the solo phrase "I know that my Redeemer liveth," for then he looked at the thin soprano singing it, as if she was singing it to him. She was a nondescript creature, with a voice like a parrot, but he glowed with coyness and admiration.

After the Redeemer had been slaughtered five times, and the little man with the glasses had announced that He would rise again next Saturday at the same place, same hour, the Chief came toward me, leading the little soprano by the hand. "This is Miss de Roos," he said. "She would like to meet you." Miss de Roos offered a small, dry hand and fluted, "How do you do, Captain? Benny has told me so much about you," but she looked at me as if she had pins in her mouth. The Chief beamed all over. He offered a round of grenadine and asked whether I'd like a slice of New Province cake with it, it was very good. I had a look at the New Province cake and said I didn't think I would just now, thank you, which was unfortunate, for the Chief continued, "Oh, but you must try it! It's Miss de Roos who makes it." I hurried to make good my mistake, but it was too late. Miss de Roos sat looking at me from that moment onward as if I was a destitute relative.

We took her home after the grenadine. We had to offer her an arm each, for the wind was blowing in its sevens by then and she looked as if she might take off if we didn't keep her down. The Chief went on shouting when we had got outside, but Miss de Roos didn't utter another sound. We dragged her to chicken coop No. 13 where the Chief opened the door for her. She was blown inside the moment we let go of her, and squealed, "Good night!" from the darkness. Then the Chief put his arm round my shoulder and pressed me against him, a thing he hadn't dared do to Miss de Roos. "God!" he said, "it's wonderful to see you." I wished I could believe him.

We went back to No. 16 and he made a cup of tea on a little oil stove that gave a nice homey smell. The wind rattled the windows and smashed against the little house in gusts, like the surf. The Chief sat opposite me at the crude table, beaming in the lamplight, and whatever he talked about, it all led up to Miss de Roos. His whole view on things, past and future, was colored by his love. I couldn't talk to him about the things that bothered me because for him they didn't exist. Nothing existed but Miss de Roos and the wonderful life they would have together. I was jealous.

I didn't sleep much that night. First I thought the building was going to come down, as the wind grew to a gale; then the Chief started snoring. He was one of those alarming snorers, who suddenly break off with a bark and stay for minutes without breathing. I felt very lonely that night.

At six in the morning he brought my heart to my throat by suddenly bursting into song: "I know that my Redeemer liveth!" I looked out of my bunk and saw him standing at the oil stove in long woolen underwear, frying eggs. When he turned round, he beamed and said, "Hello, did you sleep well?" in a tone that made me wait for the word "darling." I said I had slept quite well, thank you. I was getting a bit sick of acting as a substitute for Miss de Roos.

He was miles away; he had even got over the war, because if there had been no war they would never have met. I hurried through breakfast, on the pretext that I had to catch the early lorry toward the north. He took me to it, and when the vehicle started wobbling down the mud track, he stood waving at me for quite a while. She had a good man there.

In the lorry, I became jealous again. Perhaps the sole explanation for my pessimism and my grim principle never to co-operate with any preparation for a new war was that I was lonely. If only I were in love with somebody, peace might really start for me. But I wasn't; and while I had my insides shaken on the mud track through the New Province, I realized that I didn't particularly want to be in love either. There had only been one girl in my life who amounted to anything at all, and after the morning I saw her train pull out of Westport station, I hadn't wanted to be in love again, because I still was. While convalescing in the South, sitting on that bench, playing with the gravel with my stick, I had thought of falling in love with Miss Simmons, for she was certainly as nice a girl as I had ever met. I had even tried to fall in love with her by imagining how nice it would be, the two of us married, with a little house in the country, dogs, chickens, the neighbors to tea, and once a week in our little car to the pictures. But it hadn't worked. One reason was, perhaps, that Miss Simmons was not in love with me. I had tried to hold her hand, sitting on the bench, on the pretext that I had a sudden pain in my leg. But she had not fallen for it. She had said, "Don't be silly, Captain. You go and play some ping-pong with the Colonel." That had put me off. She was supremely sensible, but I didn't like the idea of being sent to play ping-pong with the Colonel, who used the game to express his feelings toward mankind. Yet, if the memory of Stella had not haunted me so, I think I could really have loved Miss Simmons. For in her presence it was impossible to dramatize myself. I had told her long stories of my childhood and the sea and the war, I had even told her about the U-boat we had rammed and how I couldn't get over the thought of the thirty people who had gone down with it. She wouldn't have anything of that; when I started musing about being murderer, she again said, "Don't be silly, Captain," this time in a very grown-up way.

Well, she was probably back in England now, being wooed by a squire with leather on his elbows, and his behind to the fire. He had a good woman there.

On the northern border of the New Province, I got out of the lorry and took a train to a little town in the northwest of Friesland where, so I had been told, Cook had opened a restaurant, called "The Secret of the Seven Seas." I had never liked Cook, although he was the only one with whom I had sailed from the very beginning, when I first arrived in Westport. The name "The Secret of the Seven Seas" sounded just like him. He had been too feminine to my taste, but a very good cook. We had all been proud of him; his reputation stood high in the fleet.

The little town, when I got out of the station, was utterly depressing. I almost smelled the dust of the archives and the baize of the billiard tables. It rained; thick drops dripped from the trees and clattered on the corrugated iron roof of the empty bandstand in the station square. I found the restaurant at once, because it was the only building in the row of gray brick houses that was painted bright yellow. On the windows two mermaids were painted, holding a menu. Outside hung an anchor with a little lantern attached to it.

As I came in, it seemed as if, by an act of magic, I was back in the messroom of my ship. The interior of The Secret of the Seven Seas had nothing to do with this. It was just a restaurant, rather dark, with cane chairs and red and white checkered cloths on the tables. It was the smell that did it. All during the war, our messroom had smelled exactly like this.

There wasn't a client in the place. After a few moments, a door in the back was opened and Cook minced in. When he recognized me he gave a little squeal, and cried, "Captain! Is it you? In the flesh?"

I said it was me in the flesh, and he pumped my arm with both hands. A pimply youth emerged from the shadows with an apron and Cook warbled, "Charles, look who's here! This is the Captain I told you so much about! Sit down, Captain. What will you have? A little apéritif? Luncheon starts in half an hour."

I took the little apéritif, while Cook and his boy hovered around me, talking. The boy first brought a bottle of Cinzano, but Cook snapped, "No, silly, bring the Geneva!" Cook had a little glass with me, glancing nervously at the door, waiting for his first customers. He had quite a nice table d'hôte, he said, with the notary, the chief constable and the headmaster of the Reform School as regular clients, and ever such an interesting crowd of birds of passage. He had got very refined in that year; his hands were washed at last and he wore a ring with a blue stone. He said he was doing very well indeed; a little restaurant like his had been the very thing needed in this charming town.

The first client soon arrived, an irritated little man with a high rubber collar, looking like a surgical contraption for a broken neck. Cook cooed, "Oh, Mr. Notary, how *do* you do?" and went to meet him. The spotty boy hissed a nasty word through his teeth and minced back into the kitchen. I was introduced to Mr. Notary, who couldn't have been less interested, and after that to the chief constable and the headmaster of the Reform School. As I sat watching them, while they were waiting for their meal to be served, I again had a curious sensation of witchery. The three notables, who had come in like personifications of provincial town life, seemed to change in front of my eyes into ship's officers waiting for the first table. They looked like the Chief, Sparks and me, seen in a dream. They sat in the same way, they called the same words to the kitchen, and when Cook came out with the first dish he looked exactly as he had always looked coming down the messroom stairs, angry, but smiling. I got a little dish all my own, and after the first bite the spell was complete. This was exactly the kind of food he had been cooking all through the war. Whatever the ingredients were, it had always had the same, rather rancid taste. It tasted of him.

While I sat eating, I realized for the first time that his grub was awful. I had never realized it during the war; we had told ourselves so often how extraordinarily lucky we were to have such a wonderful cook, that we had hypnotized one another into thinking that what we were eating tasted good. That morning it tasted terrible, and I realized it always had. I wondered why we had been so convinced that he was a wonderful cook; there must have been some truth in it somewhere, for one just can't keep up that self-suggestion for nearly four years. I remembered the trips we had made, the attacks of the U-boats on the Western Approaches, the constant bombing and the frightful cold of the Northeast Passage; and then I discovered why he had, indeed, been a wonderful cook. He had always cooked something, whatever the circumstances. Never had we gone without a meal at the regular hours. During the war he had been a genius; but it hadn't been the way he cooked things. It had been the fact that he had cooked them at all.

While thinking this, I had a feeling I had never had before: a sudden sympathy for him, a contact with him as a human being. He gave me a new sensation that emerged from nothing in particular, but that disturbed me profoundly. For the first time since the guns had stopped firing I felt a nostalgia for the war. I found myself thinking of us, thirteen men on board that small ship, as of something wonderful that was lost. It was a shocking thought.

An hour or so later, after the notables had left and we drank our coffee at my table, I realized that it had been Cook who sent out that thought. While we sat stirring in our cups, talking about the days gone by, with the spotty boy singing in a falsetto while washing the dishes in the kitchen, I discovered that, despite his city manners, he was homesick for the sea. "It's a lovely business," he said. "I've really got a future here. Are you going to sail again?"

I knew that if I said, "Yes" and added, "I'll miss you on board my ship," he would answer, "Oh, I might be able to break away for a trip." I looked at him for a moment in silence and then I answered, "No, I don't think I'll sail again."

He said, "Oh," and he said it in such a pathetic way that I felt more sympathy for him than before. I got up, put out my hand, and said, "Well, Cook, so long."

He remained seated and took my hand. His blue ring gleamed in the rainy light. "So long, Captain," he said. "God bless."

I crossed the square with the bandstand on which the trees still dripped with heavy drops. I sat on the chilly platform of the station for three quarters of an hour, waiting for the train. While sitting there, looking at the rain, the rails and the posters, I thought of going back to that horrible little restaurant, opening the door, and calling, "Cook!" as I had called so often before, when he was late bringing in the grub. And then, when he emerged from the dark kitchen with his smell, I would say, "Come on, let's see if we can find a ship." But those were just the thoughts one has while waiting for a train, on an empty platform. Others imagine they save beautiful women off sinking windjammers, or discover the cure for cancer, or sell the Queen a car. I bought a newspaper to take my mind off it, and read about the tension between the Occupying Powers in Germany.

I went back to Amsterdam, counted my money, and took a third-class ticket to Paris to look up Sparks. He was the last one I could go to apart from the bosun who was at sea, and Goatskin who was lost.

I had wired him from Amsterdam and he met me at the Gare du Nord. He looked different in his civilian clothes: they seemed to bring out the righteousness in his character. He had always been a very calm man, but now his calmness seemed to have acquired a slight edge of disdain.

As we sat sipping coffee on a terrace, opposite the station, he told me that he was the representative of a factory of wireless sets, and building quite a career for himself. But the bit of information that would interest me most, he thought, was that he was engaged to a very nice girl of a very respectable family. French, but not flighty. A really solid piece of work.

We had a meal with the solid piece of work. She was a big-eyed girl, who listened with her mouth open. I soon found out that she probably did so to let the thoughts escape that entered her head through her ears. Sparks was very proud of her; he watched me all through the meal and I nodded several times at him to indicate that he had indeed got something there. She worked in the Galeries Lafayette and told a long story about her floor manager in a very rapid French, full of oh-la-la's. Sparks got quite excited about her story; his eyes lit up and he patted her hand the way I had seen the Chief do sometimes to the dynamo, after he had repaired it and it was ticking over beautifully once more.

We took her home in a taxi. I sat next to the driver and caught an occasional glimpse of them in the little mirror, wrestling on the back seat. After that we walked home to Sparks's boardinghouse, where I would sleep on the couch in his room to save money.

Once I had settled on the couch, and he in his bed, and the lights were out, we talked for the first time the way we had done on board ship. For the first time since peace had started, I spoke aloud the thoughts that bothered me. He listened attentively in the darkness, and when I had finished he said, "I know what's the matter with you, Skipper: you need a girl. You can't settle down to a normal life, after the years we have had, all by yourself. You don't know what meeting Françoise has meant to me; only when I met her was my war really over. I thought you were getting on very nicely with little Simmons a year ago. Haven't you seen her again?"

I said I hadn't, and he started selling her to me. She was just the girl I needed, he said. Sensible, well-educated, sense of humor, healthy. As I lay listening to him, she sounded like a prize cow. I told him so and he rose on his elbows in the darkness and got schoolmastery. "I begin to think you are one of those who cling to their pessimism and make it their one thing in life," he said. "It's all very well to say that the world stinks and that there is another war coming and that you'll be damned if you will have anything to do with it, but are you sure that you aren't secretly longing for it? That you aren't just saying those things because in your heart of hearts you would like to be back in Westport, or in Murmansk, or off the French coast even?"

He took me aback, for I hadn't told him about that part of my thoughts yet. I asked what he thought I should do and he was very definite about it. "First," he said, "for the next day or so, as long as you are staying here, we'll have to find you some company. I think I know somebody—a friend of a friend of Françoise's—a Scottish girl who is spending her holidays in Paris; she comes from the Orkneys, I think. Very nice, big blonde, refined. Her father is something in the Food Office. You play around with her a bit and get a taste back for life. Then you board the London train and go to see little Simmons, and if you still like her as much as you did, you ask her father for her hand."

The hand business spoiled it a bit, but I still thought his advice was sensible. I said, "All right, let's have a look at your big blonde. Good night," and I tried to go to sleep. But I couldn't, for his mentioning the Orkneys had set me thinking of Stella. I thought of Stella for a while, asking myself for at least the hundredth time why I hadn't gone to the Hebrides immediately after the war was over. Well, there were many reasons for it. I hoped the big blonde would be a bit like her.

She was, but on a large scale. She was almost a head taller than I, had long golden hair that hung down on a couple of heavyweight shoulders, and big blue bedroom eyes. But she was refined all right. She told us, over a meal in Montmartre, about the wonderful tea they served at Marshall & Snelgrove's. Sparks looked at me inquiringly, and I nodded approvingly whenever she wasn't looking, which was not often. The one thing that rather attracted me to her were her hands. They were boyish, like Stella's had been, and looked as if they had done a lot of washing up. Perhaps the Marshall & Snelgrove line was just for the holidays.

We took them home in a taxi and she and I sat on the *strapontins* holding hands, looking straight ahead while Sparks and his girl were champing away behind us. When she got out we agreed that we would meet at half-past eleven the next morning under the needle on the Concorde.

When I saw her in daylight she looked a lot nicer. She wore a sensible tweed dress, with a brass bonzo to hold her scarf together, and her smile was very nice and sunny. She called me "skipper," as she had heard Sparks do, and I liked that somehow. The night before, in the dark, I had asked Sparks's advice, as he knew the town a lot better than I did. "Tomorrow, you go to Versailles," he had said. "Show her the waterworks, and the Little Trianon, and play around in the woods a bit. Don't start sparking on all plugs yet, she is a refined girl. Come home in the evening and I'll give you the program for the day after."

I had decided to follow his instructions to the letter. He was a sensible man with a head on his shoulders, and all during the war he had been the image of correctness. So I took her to Versailles, showed her the waterworks and a thing I suppose was the Little Trianon, anyhow they sold tea in it. She didn't mention Marshall & Snelgrove while we were sitting there, watching the sparrows pick crumbs of our cake off the edge of the table. It was a sunny autumn day and there was a nutty smell in the air. The town scemed far away. We didn't say much, we just sat watching the sparrows and I stroked her hand with a feeling of genuine sympathy. She talked a bit about her island and said that most people didn't know that Scapa Flow was pronounced Skeepy Floo.

I was relieved to find out that she was really a nice girl, but it was a pity that she made me think of Stella all the time. After the tea we went into the woods hand in hand and listened to the nightingales and stepped in puddles. We got to one puddle where I had to carry her, and I did so, recklessly, forgetting that the doctor had forbidden me to carry heavy loads. I got her across all right, but it was a bit of a docker's job, without romance. I had a pain in my right leg for the rest of the way, and her bonzo had scratched my nose. At the Metro station we agreed to meet again in the same place, the next morning.

Sparks's instructions that night were businesslike and to the point. "Tomorrow," he said, "you go to the Isle d'Amour, in the Marne. I'll tell you how to get there. It's a very romantic spot full of high reeds and cozy nooks. You are ferried across by an old longshoreman and with three steps you are in the jungle. There you let nature take its course."

I followed his instructions to the dot. We went to the Isle d'Amour, ferried across by an old *batelier*, got into the jungle with three steps, sat down on the soft grass in a little nest of reeds and kissed each other, rather shyly for people of our age. I think we both had the feeling that we were obeying a program that we hadn't made up ourselves; perhaps she had received instructions from Françoise. Anyhow we kissed, and her mouth was soft and warm, and I thought she was very sweet, and then I felt a sudden itch on my ankle and had to scratch whether I liked it or not. We kissed some more and then I had an itch at the back of my knee. As I scratched, I saw out of the corner of my eye that she was scratching too. After a short time we were both scratching ourselves secretly up to the waist. Then she screamed and said, "Look!" and pointed at her ankle. I looked, asked, "What?" and she said, "Fleas!"

She was right. Sparks's little paradise must have been the spawning ground for all the fleas of Paris. We ran back to the jetty and I hollered for the old *batelier*; we went on scratching all the way home. I tried to laugh it off but she didn't think it funny, Marshall & Snelgrove got in the way again.

When I told Sparks that night what had happened, he was very sorry and supposed it must have been the time of the year, for Françoise and he had spent wonderful hours there. But nothing was lost, only a different course of action had to be taken. I was going to meet her again the next afternoon, and he gave me the address of a discreet little hotel somewhere near Gare Montparnasse, where I could get a room for a couple of hours and be quiet and undisturbed in congenial surroundings. Paris was a wonderful city, people never made any fuss about love; all I need do was go to the little hotel, ask for a room, pay, they would give me the number and when I came back with her I could walk straight up without seeing anybody. I should tell her that I had found a little place of my own, with a wonderful view over the roofs of Paris, and would she like to see it, and then show her up there and let nature take its course.

I was a bit worried when I made my preparations according to his instructions, but probably I was fussing too much. He and Françoise had spent wonderful hours there. The hotel was a bit shady and the woman behind the desk looked rather frightening, with the beginnings of a beard and an enormous bust, caught in a net. When I asked her whether by any chance she had a room for a day, she answered, "No, only for a couple of hours. Have you got Madame with you?" I said I hadn't, but that I would come back later and could I pay now. She shrugged her shoulders and said, "If you like." When I gave her the money, she put it in a tin that bore the label "Durant's Baby Powder." I was even more worried when I came out than I had been when I went in, but I decided not to be silly and see it through. After all, one thing about Sparks was undeniable: he was very correct. He and his Françoise would never have gone to a place that wasn't.

She was very gay when I met her at the appointed hour, but somehow a bit strained. Perhaps she too had her apprehensions. I told her about the little place of my own with the view over the roofs of Paris, and she was delighted to come and see it. When we entered the hotel, the old woman was not behind her desk. This was a relief. I took her up the stairs, peering unobtrusively at the room numbers; I had been given number fourteen on the third floor, all I need do was push the door and it would open. I found number fourteen in the end, pushed, and the door did indeed open. I let her go in first, and she stifled a scream.

When I entered after her, I got a shock too. The room was full of mirrors and the walls were covered with murals that left no doubt as to the nature of the establishment. There was no view over the roofs of Paris. She sat down on the bed, sobbing, and I felt sorry for her, but at the same time I had to suppress a hysterical laughter. She sobbed, "Oh, this is hell, hell! Take me out of here!" I tried to soothe her by saying that it wasn't hell at all but just a mistake, and that I was very sorry but that I had never set eyes on the place before, or I wouldn't have taken her here. But she refused to be got out of it, she went all Marshall & Snelgrove again and that was a pity, because I had a feeling that if we had just lain down on that bed and smoked a cigarette and been ourselves we could have talked about something real at last, about the war and what the hell were we to do with our lives. But she didn't feel that way at all; she sobbed that she felt "like one of those awful Parisian women." I had to take her back to the street. I wanted to see her home, but she bolted like a rabbit the moment she sniffed fresh air. I thought of running after her, but didn't.

I wrote her a note on a terrace somewhere, thanking her for the nice time and hoping that we would meet once more. I also wrote to Sparks, saying that I had to leave unexpectedly. I left the notes in his room, collected my stuff and went to the Gare du Nord where I took a ticket to London.

In the blue underwater light of a dimmed-out compartment between Paris and Calais I made the decision. I wouldn't go and see Miss Simmons, there was no point. I had only loved one girl in my life and I still loved her and it was no use trying to shape my future until I had seen her again.

Once I had made that decision the very color of my life seemed to change. I suddenly got hope again and vitality, and the will to do something constructive. I couldn't understand why I hadn't done this long ago. I remembered all the reasons why I hadn't, and I found they were all nonsense because I was sure now that she still loved me too.

I didn't sleep at all that night. I just sat there, dreaming, wide awake, chain smoking, seeing visions of the future. The house, the children, the table, the lamp; the wind in the chimney, the bosun knocking on the door, calling "Captain, S.O.S.!" Why hadn't I thought of it before? That was the one thing I could do with a tugboat that had nothing to do with the preparations for war: the rescue service, to sail to the assistance of ships in distress. It would be the same work we had done in Westport, and I would come back to her after each trip, the way I had done then. What a wonderful life it would be, the only kind of life I was born to, and no other woman would ever understand it the way she would. In London, I bought a ticket to her island. It cost a fortune but it was cheap at the price. I could have stood the whole town a drink, I felt so wonderful. I was sure, in an almost psychic way, that everything would be all right and that we were going to have a wonderful life together.

It took me three days to get to her island. At each station I made up my mind to send her a wire and decided at the last moment not to. I would just go to the door and knock, and when she opened I would say, "Hello, Stella." I missed the last boat and stayed on the mainland for the night in a drafty little hotel, smelling of peat fires.

I arrived on the island by midday the next day. I found her house and knocked and an old woman opened. When I asked whether her daughter was in, her daughter Stella, she said, "But didn't you know? She married a Polish Air Force Officer and is living in Warsaw." I said, "Oh, I'm sorry," and went back to the jetty, just in time to catch the same boat back. The whole thing had lasted less than three minutes.

On that ferry, I spent a nasty hour. I felt completely empty and at a loss. I didn't know where to go. The idea of joining the rescue service had just been a boyish dream. There was no vacancy for captains. Even though eighty per cent of the young ones had been killed, there were still too many of us about, for the old ones were immortal. They had a magic secret, that we would never know.

The sensible thing to do would have been to go back to London, but somehow I couldn't face that idea. I wanted to do something in Scotland just to make myself believe that I had gone there for another reason than just to hear an old woman say, "But didn't you know?" In the station on the other side I saw a poster announcing Highland Games in Pitlochry. I went to Pitlochry, took a room in a hotel that was called "Le Moulin Rouge," and watched giants in kilts throw telegraph poles at each other. They were wildly applauded by the most foreign crowd I ever got lost in, and there came a lucid moment in which I asked myself, quite calmly, what the hell I was doing here. I went back to the hotel, sat down in the hall, picked up a magazine and saw that it was the *International Shipping Information*. It was extraordinary to find it here, but at second thought no more extraordinary than finding a hotel called Le Moulin Rouge in Pitlochry. I leafed through it, smelling nostalgically the distant sea, and then suddenly my heart shot in my throat. I saw the name of my ship.

"Wreck Dutch Tugboat Vlieland, towed to Antwerp Firma Klaassen & Cy, for demolition."

I went to the desk to say that I would leave that night, and could they get me a ticket to Antwerp.

I got to Antwerp a few days later, in the evening. The enormous harbor had always depressed me; that evening it was more depressing than ever. There was a smoky fog hanging over the Scheldt and the town, that occasionally turned into a drizzle. The neon lights of *Dancings* and *Cinemas* flashing on and off in the streets made the skyline look as if the town was burning after an air raid.

It took me several hours before I had located the demolition wharf of the firm Klaassen & Cy. It would have been more sensible to wait until the morning, but this wasn't a sensible expedition anyhow. The wharf was in a far corner of the harbor, called The Church Yard. It wasn't the only one, I found out. There were scores of demolition wharfs, side by side. It was a corner without lights, only some sparsely sown street lamps and an occasional glimmer of candlelight behind the windows of a watchman's hut. The taxi I had taken put me down at the end of the quay; the driver said that his springs couldn't stand the rest of the way. The quay was paved with enormous cobble stones that seemed to have been laid down in waves. Muddy puddles reflected the street lamps.

Klaassen & Cy was at the very end. Behind the gate was a little watchman's hut, and behind the hut the tall masts of a windjammer. I tried to open the gate but found it shut. I called through the bars and my voice echoed back to me from three directions. The drizzle mingled on my forehead with the sweat. After I had stood there calling for quite a while a door in the watchman's hut was opened and an old man came shuffling out with a lantern, muttering. "What do you want?" he called, halfway to the gate.

I said that I would like to visit the wreck of the tugboat *Vlieland*. It made him angry. He said he'd be damned if he'd let any more people on tonight. The sale was tomorrow, and if I wanted to have a look at the inventory, I could come in the morning like everybody else. I said I hadn't come for the sale, just to have a look at the ship; that I had been her captain during the war and had come all the way from Scotland to see her once more before she was broken up. "Tell that to your grandmother!" he shouted. "What do you people take me for? The village idiot? One who pulls that story on me is enough, isn't it? I may be old, but I'm not half-witted yet. Get the hell out of here before I throw a bolt at you." I had no idea what he was talking about and I spoke to him quietly and kindly through the bars, like a doctor.

It took me a quarter of an hour and a hundred Belgian francs. He opened the padlock on the gate with a key he selected from a big rusty bunch, by the light of his lantern. He went on muttering all the time. After the gate had creaked open on rusty hinges, and I had squeezed myself through the gap, he said, "Come to my office before you go out, and I'll search you." I said, "All right, granddad. Where's the ship?" "Alongside the windjammer," he answered. "And if you break your neck on her deck, I'll be delighted." After that nice Christian thought, he retired to his hut, a mole with a lantern.

His wish nearly came true. The windjammer's deck was strewn with rubbish and I had to proceed cautiously, striking matches all the time. When I finally got to her starboard side and looked down over the rail, I saw my ship, and my eyes shot full of tears. I was a little amazed at this for I didn't feel any particular emotion. Perhaps the tears were just a conditioned reflex. She looked very small down there and quite dead. I wouldn't have recognized her if I hadn't known it was she, for I had never seen her after the shelling. When I was carried off for the last time I had been too ill to look. Her funnel was gone, her bridge was a shambles, her radio hut an open grave. That's where the shell had struck and penetrated to the engine room. I found a pilot's ladder hanging down the flank of the windjammer and I lowered myself on board. As I walked cautiously aft, I saw a light shining from the messroom.

It gave me quite a shock. I hadn't seen it from above. I thought it must be another watchman; but when I went down the messroom stairs, the man who sat at the table and looked up gave me another shock. It was Goatskin, very thin and sunburned, in a sailor's outfit. Blue jersey, blue coat, and peaked cap without emblem. "Hello, Skipper," he said. I asked him where he came from, and he said that he had read the news of her demolition in a paper in the South of France. I said, "Well, well," and sat down opposite him.

I had sat down like this so many times that it wasn't as strange a situation to me as I suppose it should have been. It seemed somehow quite normal. The only differences were that the electric light wasn't working, that the table was very dirty and that there was no emblem on his cap. I looked at the oil lantern, wanted to ask him where he had got it from, but recognized it before. It was the bosun's. He must have found it in the fo'c'sle. "Well, well," I said. "And what have you been doing with yourself?"

"Oh, all sorts of things," he answered. "Just now I've got a job in Marseilles."

"As what?"

"As a diver." He smiled, a bit thinly. "There's quite some money in it. We dive down to the decks of the Liberty ships that were sunk during the Invasion, take off the wheels of the jeeps that are still lashed on the decks. The air in the tires makes them float, we collect them, and sell the tires on the black market."

I said, "Well, well. How long have you been doing that for?"

"About three months," he answered. "We've skimmed the easy ones off by now. The next lot is lying too deep for just mask diving. We'll have to get at them with a scaphander or with bottles."

I said, "I see."

He went on for a while about his diving, and I looked at him. He hadn't changed much except for his sunburn, yet there was a difference. I couldn't quite place the difference at first. Last time I had seen him, he had been a quiet, competent boy who didn't worry much about life and the future. He had just been a good sailor and proud of it. Now, he looked much older, and a bit bitter and worried. Perhaps he looked just the way I did, for he returned my stare and smiled his new thin smile and said, "Well, what have you been doing with yourself?"

I said, "Oh, I made one trip as a mate with old Bakker to the East Indies, and after that I loafed a bit and traveled around. I have just come from Scotland."

"So," he said. "What were you doing there?"

When I answered, "I went to look at the Highland Games," he stared, and said, "I see."

There was a silence after that, which became a bit oppressive because he went on looking at me with his blue eyes that seemed a lot bluer now his face was so tanned. Then he opened the drawer in the messroom table, said, "Hey, look what's here!" and took out a chessboard. We looked at each other with a wry smile, yet enjoying it, and he said, casually, "What about a game?"

"Are the chessmen there?" I asked.

He rumbled in a drawer and brought out a pocketknife. It was the second engineer's. I remembered he had been looking for it as far back as Gibraltar. I wanted to say something about it, but I let it pass. "Yes," he said, "here they are. Shall we?"

I hesitated, then I said, "In a minute. Let's look around the ship first."

"I wouldn't if I were you," he said. "You won't like it. Let's have a game and then go and have a drink somewhere. I don't think there's any point in tearing the live skin off your body just for the fun of it."

I said, "All right. Let's play."

He put up the game, took two pawns in his hands, shook them, and held out his fists. I chose one, and opened the game with white.

We played cautiously and with concentration. I was good, but he was better. At the beginning of the game, I felt all mellow and sad inside. The friendship I felt for him was as strong as any emotion I had ever known toward another human being, but as the game went on and it became obvious that he was going to win, my feelings began to change. When there were only half a dozen men left on the board and he had me cornered, I was back in Shadwell Basin with the same sour taste in my mouth and the same itchy feeling in my hands. It was silly, but there was nothing I could do about it.

He sat pondering for a long time before he made his last move. Yet it was very simple, any fool could see it two miles off. If he put my king in check with his castle there was only one place I could go to, and after that it would be his. I sat staring at the board with my arms folded, my jaw set, thinking how lovely it would be to beat the hell out of him at last. Then he looked up with his new smile and said, "All right, Skipper, I give up." I stared at him in amazement, but there was something in the way he looked at me that made me say, "O.K. What about that drink?"

He picked up the lantern and we went out, leaving the game unfinished on the table. There was something gratifying in it, something symbolical, only I had no idea what the symbol stood for. We climbed back on the deck of the windjammer and there he said, "Let's have a look at her. Shall we?" We groped our way through the jungle of rusty iron and old ropes toward her poop, climbed down the stairs to her officer's quarters, and opened a door on which an enameled plate said "Messroom." She must have been a rich ship in her days; everything was made of teak and solid brass, and the benches of her messroom were covered with real leather.

But she was as empty as a shell on the beach. We opened a cupboard and found nothing in it. Only the shelves, covered with newspaper. He lifted the lantern and looked at a newspaper on a shelf and said, "Look at this." It was a newspaper called *Les Annales* of September 15, 1918. It showed a drawing of a fat soldier, kissing a coy, plump girl's hand. The girl was in a factory uniform. Underneath it, it read: *"La Tourneuse d'Obus*—to her murdered little hands he owes his victory." It was extraordinary how comical the drawing looked.

We looked around her quarters a bit more; in her captain's cabin, we found a photograph of her crew, screwed onto the wall in a teak frame. Her officers looked very young; the captain, who sat proudly in the center, couldn't have been more than twenty-five. I said how young they looked, and he said that all crews of the last windjammers had been youngsters. They had been good sailors, he said. The only pity was that they were no good for any other job, once their ships were laid up, when they were about thirty. I asked him, as he seemed to be informed on the subject, what had happened to them, and he answered with a shrug of his shoulders, "God knows."

When we crossed the yard with our lantern, the old watchman came out of his hut, barking like a dog. He wanted to know where we had got that lantern from. When Goatskin said that he had found it on board our ship, the old man ripped it out of his hand and said, "Don't you know there's a sale tomorrow? That everything has been listed? If that lamp is missing, I'll have to pay it out of my own pocket. What else have you got?" We answered, "Nothing," but he wouldn't believe us. He searched our pockets with the light of the lantern swinging beams in the fog like a lighthouse, and our shadows tumbling to and fro. Goatskin gave him a bank note, which he looked at in the light of the lantern before he put it in his pocket. I saw it was a thousand francs. He certainly must have been making money down South.

We had our drink in a tavern on the quay side. An automatic piano jingled German tunes and a couple of lascars were playing billiards in flat clouds of low-hanging cigar smoke, which the light of the lamps over the table cut into cones. He said that any time I wanted a job, all I had to do was to go to Marseilles, Hotel Atlantic, and ask for Maurice. I said I'd think of it and he didn't go on about it. All he said was, "I would, if I were you. There aren't many jobs around for the like of us. I should know, for I've tried them all." Then he finished his beer and said, "Well, I'll have to be off. I've got a girl waiting." I asked him, politely, who she was and he answered with his thin little smile, "Her name is Thalassa."

He was already standing, about to go, when he asked, "Did you see her up there in Scotland?"

I said, "No, she's married. She is living in Warsaw."

He patted my shoulder, said, "Skipper," and went away.

The next morning, when I woke up, I had a very clear picture of the future. I didn't know where I got it from, perhaps I had dreamed it that night. I counted my money; I had to count it several times and do some Chinese calculations before I concluded that I could just make it.

She had given me her address before I left, asking me to write her how I was doing, some time in the future. I never had. Probably she didn't live there any longer. I took the risk: "The Rectory, Woodcliffe, near Oxford" it said, so I went to Oxford. I made the trip in a curious, sleep-walking way. I didn't think about anything; I had a feeling that all thoughts should be postponed until I could speak them aloud in her presence and hear the inevitable answer, "Don't be silly, Captain." I still pictured her in her nurse's dress, straining at the hips, with her Dagenham Girl Pipers' cap around her neck, or on her forehead.

I telephoned her from Oxford station, and only after we had agreed that she'd meet me at the five o'clock bus did it occur to me how extraordinary it was that she should have been there at all. She hadn't sounded surprised on the telephone, and she didn't look surprised when she saw me get out of the bus. She looked different in civilian clothes, younger and a lot prettier than before. She wore a little red pirate's bonnet with a tassel that was perfectly ridiculous. I couldn't help grinning when I saw her, I was glad I had come. She shook me warmly by the hand, said, "How jolly nice of you to come. Have you had tea?" Then we walked briskly up the hill toward a little village of Cotswoldstone houses, with a fat church tower rising above the roofs. "There are some very nice Elizabethan houses here," she said, "that one for instance." She gestured with her head and that sent the tassel flying. As I climbed the steep streets with her I noticed that I was limping, out of habit.

I expected her father to be the rector, but he wasn't. He was a thin man in breeches, who met us in the doorway on his way to let the dog out. "Oh, there you are," he said. "I've been hearing a lot about you. See you in a minute. Have some tea." Gray hairs were growing out of his nose and his ears, and he had bushy eyebrows; the rest of his head was bald. I liked him.

The inside of the rectory was so dark that I didn't see the Elizabethan chest she pointed out to me, but hurt my shin on it, on my way to the dining room. The house seemed to consist entirely of vaults. The dining vault was furnished with heavy Portuguese chairs, a French polished table and a black shiny square in a gilt frame over the mantelpiece, of which she said, "My grandfather." We sat down in a Portuguese chair each and made conversation across the table; the reflection of the lamp in the French polish dazzled me. I started to tell her about my trip with old Captain Bakker; then the words stuck in my throat on hearing what sounded like a streetcar rattling and clanging down the passage.

It was a trolley with tea things, pushed by an old maid who looked exactly like her father with skirts on. "No more butter," said the maid, "and I hope he's brought sugar with him."

"Don't be gloomy, Suzy," said Miss Simmons. "Just leave the trolley, I'll put the things out." The maid shot a steely glance at me, exhaled through her whiskers and clattered off. I realized that her iron-heeled slippers had made part of the noise.

When I looked at Miss Simmons after the door had been slammed shut, she smiled, and I felt very glad I had come. I smiled back at her, and went on telling her about my trip, while she poured out the tea and cut the cake with the tassel dangling in front of her nose. A quarter of an hour later her father came back with the dog and he had some tea too, which he drank noisily during his report on meeting the vicar in the street and arranging a jumble sale for the benefit of the Mothers' Union. I wondered whether she had a mother, and if so where she was.

I met her that night after dinner, after smoking a cigar with her father in the dining room. The first announcement I got of her presence was the plural he used when he said, "Shall we join the ladies?" On entering the sitting vault, I saw an old woman, propped up on a sofa, with a couple of pillows in her back. She looked sweet and gentle and welcomed me with a smile, saying, "So, you are the Flying Dutchman."

It was she who destroyed my hopes, for during the preceding hours I had made up my mind to ask Miss Simmons if she would marry me. It was a bit quick, but I had come to the conclusion that I had been a fool not to have asked her in the South of France; no man could wish himself a better wife. But her mother put a stop to all this. I took her thin hand and pressed it gently. I inquired, politely, but with genuine interest, whether she was seriously ill, and she answered with a radiant smile, "Oh, no, I've got cancer. Isn't it stupid of me?"

That reply put a stop to my lonely man's dreams concerning Miss Simmons. Never before had I felt more alien to the English than at that moment. If I had a cold in the nose, the whole ship had to know it; Cook had to ply me with hot grogs, Goatskin had to come in at least every half hour to inquire how I felt, and I could be heard moaning down in the engine room. I suppose it was unmanly, but that happened to be the way in which I liked my illnesses. If I married Miss Simmons, after the reply the mother gave me, I would have to break a leg and say, "Oh, nothing at all; only my right stilt seems to be a little shorter than the other." Well, I wasn't going to. Not only I couldn't, but I didn't want to, for somehow I felt one couldn't take cancer lightly and treat the war seriously. It was all in the day's work. Miss Simmons' formula, "Don't be silly, Captain," that I had so much longed for, suddenly took on an awesome aspect. From that dazzling height of human sublimation anything I would ever feel or do would be silly.

All the same, she was a charming old lady, with a great sense of humor and an exquisite tact. The way she got the two of us out into the garden was so subtle, that when I found myself hand in hand with Miss Simmons, strolling among the ilexes in the scented darkness, I couldn't for the life of me remember how I'd got there. This should have been the night of the great confession, but as it was I felt obliged to make light of my own problems. Compared with what the old lady was going through, they were chicken feed. I told her about seeing the wreck of my ship again, the game of chess with Goatskin, and she thought it a funny story. I did myself. I laughed with a hawing sound in the darkness, and frightened an owl which, in its turn, frightened me. What a pity, I thought when we strolled back to the house treading on molehills, that I hadn't spoken to her before.

Of course the real reason of this last minute retirement was that I didn't love her. If I had, her mother could have said, "Oh, nothing serious: I'm dead, you know. Isn't it killing?" and it wouldn't have made the slightest difference. She was a very sweet girl and I was sure that we would have been happy together, once we had eased out the national differences; but there was nothing I could do about it: I didn't love her. As for the passion she evoked in me, I might as well have been strolling in that scented summer garden with my aunt.

When we came back to the living vault, her mother was reading *The Farmers' Weekly* and her father was asleep in an armchair, with his head back and his knees wider apart than seemed humanly possible. The gloomy maid on hoofs made us a cup of chocolate and we drank it silently while her father snored away like a fog signal. He woke up when the cups were put together, opened his eyes wide, and said, "No, no, my darling, I'm listening." Then he noticed us two and said, "Oh, sorry, I must have dozed off. Did I?" Miss Simmons answered, "Only for a minute, Daddy," and kissed his forehead. I wished to God at that moment that I loved her. She was a wonderful girl. As it was, I spent a night of nightmares between damp sheets underneath a heavy eiderdown in a four-poster that creaked even when I remained quite still.

In the morning the maid came in with a cup of tea without sugar. I had a little conversation with her about the Government; never had I heard such bloodthirsty talk in my life. We had breakfast in the dining vault; her father wore a corduroy dressing gown and carpet slippers and growled at *The Times*. She went on looking at me all through breakfast with a smile that didn't tally with her eyes, as if there was something that worried her. After she had taken me to the bus stop and we stood waiting in a queue of women with shopping bags, she asked, as the bus horn sounded round the bend, "Are you sure there isn't something you'd like to ask me?"

I looked at her and said, "No, June."

She smiled so widely that it almost became a grin and said, "That's a pity, isn't it?"

I said, "Yes."

I waved back at her from the back window of the bus as it drove away, and I didn't feel happy.

CHAPTER EIGHT

I HAD EXPECTED THE HOTEL ATLANTIC IN MARSEILLES TO BE A SINISTER, shady place, but I had been influenced by the French films. It was a smart establishment with a dancing annex, looking out over the old harbor. It seemed hardly the place to go and ask for Maurice, but as his instructions had been precise, I advanced on the hall porter who looked like a rear admiral, and asked whether Maurice was in. No, he said, he was out on an expedition and wouldn't be home until the day after tomorrow at the earliest. This came as a shock to me, I had so counted on his being there that I had fifty-three francs left in my pocket. I said, "Thank you, I'll be back," and walked out as nonchalantly as I could.

It had never happened to me to find myself in a foreign port without a penny in my pocket, and I was at a loss what to do. There were very few things one could buy for fifty-three francs and, like a fool, I spent them on a glass of *vin rosé* on the terrace of a bistro next door, that looked cheap but wasn't. It was very hot and I was wearing my northern clothes which were all I had. While sipping what was likely to be my last food for a couple of days, I did some thinking. The best plan seemed to be to move as little as possible, so as not to stimulate the appetite, and to find a cozy corner somewhere near the old harbor where I could spend the night.

There weren't many cozy corners to be seen at first glance. The quay was the busiest I had ever known. Old cars and rattling lorries jostled each other in what seemed to be a giant game of Dodgems, and ships and yachts lay so tightly moored side by side with their poops to the quay that I couldn't see the water. I paid for my *vin rosé*, crossed the street leisurely, trying to look rich and carefree, and was knocked down at once by a blow like from a diving board. When I crawled to my knees, after a moment of stupefaction, I saw a fat man get out of a very old car, the back door of which was hanging open. It must have been the door that got me. He was profuse in his apologies, of which I didn't understand a word, and I did a Mrs. Simmons on him by saying, "Oh, it doesn't matter in the least, only my vertebral column broken." He was quick to see his chance, laughed heartily, slapped me on the back, which set me cringing, and drove off with his rattletrap, his back door still open, waiting for the next customer.

I sat down on a bollard with my head in my hands, arrived at the all-time low in my life. The pain in my back robbed me of my sense of humor. I thought of my mother and what she would have thought if she had seen me sitting here: a bum without a penny in his pocket hovering on the brink of anonymity. All the despair, the lack of self-confidence, and the loneliness I had bottled up inside me took possession of me; I sat there, my head in my hands, thinking about suicide. Then I looked up, startled by the sound of a spitfire diving at me. I saw a nun in fluttering gowns streak past on a motor bicycle at eighty miles an hour. She separated a man from a barrel he was rolling across the street, and he stood screaming atheist slogans after her while the barrel quietly wobbled on toward the water, to be stopped by the back of an angler who had managed to worm a fishing rod between two ships. The angler and the barrel man started a row, during which the angler whisked his fishing rod up; the hook caught the shirt of a sailor who was painting a lifebuoy on the poop of one of the ships. This started the angler and the sailor off, who in his turn got involved with another sailor who was hit by the paintbrush as he gesticulated. At that point the row vanished out of my field of vision, but I felt sure that it would ripple all over the Vieux Port and the town of Marseilles until it would stop at the sea.

The nun cured me. It was impossible to see this kind of thing happen in front of my eyes and take myself seriously. After all it was only a matter of three days; if I couldn't get through those in some way or another I wasn't worth my salt. I flung my jacket over my shoulder, got up, and vanished in the crowd.

I led a bum's life for three days, and I discovered to my amazement that it was a delightful existence. I was at complete liberty to do whatever I pleased; I had never suspected that to be rid of money was a liberation. Up till now I had been worrying all the time, counting and recounting my money; I had lain awake at night seeing the darkness of poverty approaching. Now I discovered that poverty wasn't a darkness at all but a sunlit day, the end of all worries and responsibilities. My fellow loafers on the waterfront were charming people, generous and full of fascinating stories. I sat for hours baking in the sun, my cap on my eyebrows, listening to their fairy tales, that sounded as if they came straight out of the *Arabian Nights*. It was an enormous relief, after having spent my entire life in the shackles of Nordic understatement, to be among people who made no secret of their feelings. If a man hurt his toe he yelled the place down, and whenever I came across a crowd around two cars and two screaming drivers, it was always a difference of opinion as to who had crashed into the other with the right of priority. Every person in this town lived in a little universe entirely his own; they were all suns in search of planets. That was perhaps the reason why they made friends so easily.

The first day I had been worrying about food. It turned out to be very easy. If I wanted a meal all I had to do was to go to the gangway of a tramp steamer that didn't look too rich, and holler, "Hey, chum! Anything left for a white man?" I was never refused; the generosity of the sailors regardless of their nationality was astonishing. I suppose they had all been beach-combers themselves in the past and were aware of the fact that they might be once more. As to my sleeping accommodation I had been worrying needlessly too. I had forgotten that Marseilles in the summer is so hot that even the richest people sleep in the open, uncomfortably, in deck chairs on their balconies. I slept underneath a wheelbarrow next door to a police station, on an armful of straw I had pinched off a barge. I woke up every time a singing drunkard was dragged in, or screaming tart; I smoked cigarettes with the constables on duty who sat on kitchen chairs on the pavement, listened to their stories and their jokes, said, "Well, I think I'll turn in again," and crawled back underneath my wheelbarrow. They woke me up in the morning with a cup of coffee; it was a curious town.

When I went back to the Hotel Atlantic at noon on the third day, the hall porter told me that Maurice would come in any minute now. I sat down in a chair in the hall, and waited. I had been wondering during the past week or so who Maurice would be, never suspecting him to be Goatskin himself. He entered the swing doors of the lobby at three o'clock on the dot, dressed in a smart pin-striped suit, wearing a panama hat, and twirling a bamboo cane. He was followed by two tough-looking boys in shorts and a couple of girls on very high heels, who seemed to run in order not to fall on their faces. They were of the brassy blonde type, with a corkscrew curl glued to each forehead. The moment he saw me, Goatskin stopped twirling his cane, cried, "Skipper!" made a dash for me, pulled me out of my chair, threw his arms round my neck, and kissed me on both cheeks. At first I thought that he had become very Mediterranean, but as he kissed me I smelled that he was drunk. The twirling of the cane must have been a gyrostatic device to help him keep upright. After he had embraced me, he shut his eyes, said, "God, I'm tired," and slumped down in my chair with his legs outstretched. He was wearing blue socks with a purple hue that were red on the inside, and suede shoes. He looked young and pathetic, with dark blue rings under his eyes beneath his sunburn. One of the tough boys asked me, gruffly, "Do you know him?" while the other led the giggling blondes to the bar with his arms round their waists. Goatskin answered for me, without opening his eyes, "He's the man I've been waiting for. Buy him a room with a bath and a drink. Make a note of the number." The tough boy said, "O.K." and took me to the desk.

I was given a room with a bath, overlooking the old harbor. A waiter brought up a bottle of whisky and a glass, and went out again without a word. Neither the bath nor the whisky were any good to me as I hadn't got soap or a corkscrew. The room was very luxurious, but a bit depressing, perhaps because there were so many mirrors. Wherever I looked, I saw myself, and I certainly needed a shave. I sat down on the window sill, looking at the old port and the busy quay side, and felt homesick for the world down there that I had come to like so much. I thought of sneaking out of the room, back to the street; I was sure I would find a job somewhere and even if I didn't, lots of people seemed to live quite comfortably without. I got bored, alone in that room, waiting for Goatskin to sleep his alcohol off, or for one of the tough boys to come up to tell me what I was supposed to do. On a little bureau was an inkwell, a pen, and a stack of postcards with a picture of the hotel on them. I thought of someone I could send a postcard to. The only ones I knew were Miss Simmons and the Chief. I didn't feel like sending a postcard to Sparks. I wrote to the Chief first, saying that I was having a wonderful time and asking how "The Messiah" was getting on. I hoped Miss de Roos was feeling well and begged to be remembered to her. When I reread it, it was rather a formal postcard, but I decided to send it anyhow. To Miss Simmons I wrote thanking her for the nice week end; I told her the weather was fine and that I hoped it was the same in England. I sat thinking for a long time, chewing the pen, of something else to write. In the end I added, "I hope to write to you more extensively later. Yours very sincerely, The Flying Dutchman."

I had just finished the postcard when there was a knock on the door and a Chinese girl came in. I was sure she had mistaken my door for somebody else's, and was about to say, "That's quite all right," when she said, "Maurice has sent me."

I said, "Oh, I see. Well?"

She looked at me, a bit amazed, and answered, "Well, here I am."

I again said, "I see," rather embarrassed, because God only knew what the drunk had been up to. She sat down on one of the gilt chairs, at a loss it seemed, tapping on her kneecap with delicate fingers. Then she asked, "Wouldn't you like a bath?" I said I would, but that I hadn't got any soap. That seemed to cheer her up; it gave her something to do. She went to the telephone and ordered a cake of soap—"No, no, not lavender, verbena"—and a big bottle of Eau de Cologne. Then she went into the bathroom and I heard her turn on the taps.

The whole thing had taken me by surprise, and I felt self-conscious about the postcards on the bureau, as if Miss Simmons and the Chief were sitting there, watching me. The urge to get back into the street became stronger. Then there was a knock on the door again and the same silent waiter came in with a cake of soap and a bottle on a silver tray. The Chinese girl emerged from the bathroom and started scolding him because he hadn't brought a corkscrew. He turned silently on his heels and marched out again. After he had gone, she said, "All right, your bath is ready." I said, "Thank you," stood a moment in the middle of the floor, looking silly, and then sauntered into the bathroom. I tried to lock the door from the inside but found that this was not provided for. So I stripped like the wind, plunged into the tub, and started frantically to work up a lather before she should come in, which I was sure she would.

She did, a couple of minutes later. She came in with a corkscrew and a bottle. She pulled the cork out, then went to the washstand, took a glass and filled it. I hadn't realized that it was the whisky bottle she had brought

219

in. She took it to me in the bath and said, "There you are." I hesitated a second, then I filled the rest of the glass with water from the tap, said, "Cheers," and drank it with an air of unconcern. It didn't quite come off, for my first gulp went down the wrong hole and I sat there choking, while she patted my back, soothingly, as to a child. After that I gave up being disconcerted. I said, "Look, I don't know who you are or what the hell you're doing here, but would you mind just sitting outside and look at the view while I have a wash? There's a good girl."

She looked so astonished that she almost convinced me that I had committed a social offense. "Don't you want me to scrub your back for you?" she asked.

I looked at her, the bathroom, the cake of verbena soap, and the bottle of whisky on the washstand and I said, "All right, I don't see why not." I put the glass down at the head of the bath, turned round and said, "Go ahead." Looking at the glass while she gently scrubbed my back, I expected it at any moment to turn into the dial of an alarm clock. Never before had I realized that the platitude "I felt as if I was dreaming" had so much accuracy in it. I had been transplanted in one swoop from a bum's existence into that of Harun El Rashid. Goatskin certainly had things worked out here.

After she had finished with my back, she offered to scrub my front, but that was where I drew the line. I said, "Thank you, I'll see to that myself." She said, "As you like," handed me the brush and the soap, sat down on the stool in the corner, and started filing her nails. Although she seemed entirely uninhibited I got up with my back to her and washed my front in an uncomfortable position. I soon lost my balance and crashed down in the bath with an oath, sending water flying up to the ceiling. That got her out all right. She vanished into the bedroom but left the door open. I finished my washing in at least a moderate privacy.

When I got out of the bath, I found that the towel was a dressing gown and I put it on. I looked at myself in one of the mirrors and woke up. Here I was, Sinbad the Sailor in a Roman outfit, and so far I had behaved like a teetotaler in a wine cellar. Good old Goatskin had prepared a feast for me from the bottom of his generous heart and his wallet; he had given me a rich man's paradise complete with Eau de Cologne and a bathing beauty; if I went on like this, throwing up my hands and saying, Get thee behind me, it was high time I went to see a doctor.

I entered the bedroom full of bad intentions. I was sure that I would find her in the bed or, at least, in the preliminary stages. It came as a surprise when I saw her sitting on the window sill, fully dressed, still filing her nails. I went toward her, put a hand on her shoulder like an uncle, looked at the view, and sighed, "Beautiful." Then I bent over and kissed her on the crown of her head. It was a bit smelly. She looked up, gave me a sweet smile, and continued filing her nails. When I kissed her again, this time like a cousin, she darted away and said, "Come! To bed." I said, "O.K.," strode toward the bed, slipped out of my gown, put my chest out and pulled my stomach in, walked round the bed once to impress her with my torso, and lay down.

The moment I lay down I felt dizzy. It was a long time since I had a bed under me. I looked up when I felt something on my forehead and saw it was her hand. She stood by my bedside like a nurse, and said, "Ssh—sleep."

I said, "Sleep? Are you mad? It's four o'clock."

"Oh," she said, "everybody here sleeps in the afternoon. We never eat before ten at night."

"That may be," I said, "but I won't." Then I put my arm round her and gave her a solid kiss. I might as well have kissed the back of my own hand for all the response I got. She calmly took my arm away and said, "Sorry. That's not included."

It made me angry, for in that case the way I was lying there was perfectly ridiculous. "You could have told me," I said. "I'm sorry if I frightened you, but if a girl puts me in a bath, scrubs my back for me, and offers to do the front too, it puts ideas into my head."

She looked at me with dim amazement. "Maurice told me to go and see if you had everything you wanted," she said.

"All right," I said, "in that case I tell him you have bungled it." I was furious, and felt like taking her across my knee. I shut my eyes tight and the moment I did so I felt dizzy again.

She put her hand on my forehead once more. I tried to stay furious but I couldn't. I found that I was very tired; it must have been the whisky. Her hand stroking my forehead was soothing.

I said, slowly, "Two postcards. On the desk. Post them."

"Ssh," she whispered, "sleep."

I did.

When I woke up, it was dark. I saw her silhouetted against a deep blue sky, sitting on the window sill. I got up, put the bathrobe around my shoulders and joined her on the window sill.

She smiled at me and said, "You certainly slept well."

221

"Did I?"

"Maurice came in and wanted to talk to you. You didn't answer. You didn't even wake up when he shook you by the shoulder."

I said, "Fancy that."

"Would you like a glass of whisky?" she asked.

"You people seem to have a whisky complex," I said.

She shrugged her shoulders. "It's Maurice. He never drinks anything else, so he never wants anyone to drink something else either."

"That's curious," I said. "When I knew him, he detested the stuff. I wonder what gave him this passion for it."

She shrugged her shoulders again with a little laugh that wasn't gay. "I suppose he likes it because it's expensive," she said.

We sat looking for a while at the illuminated terraces, the yellow lamp-lit window squares in the dark row of houses across the harbor, and the sweep of the lighthouse beam, scything the slender shadows of the masts. We sat a yard apart, but I felt close to her. For the first time there was something real about her, something human.

"You sailed with him, didn't you?" she asked suddenly.

"Yes."

"What was he like during the war?"

"A very good sailor, and a good friend."

"How long is it since you saw him last?"

"About a month ago."

"Here, in the South of France?"

"No, in Antwerp."

"What was he doing there?"

"We went to see the wreck of our ship, before it was broken up."

"Oh," she said. And then, after a silence, "So that's where he went."

It sounded mysterious, but I let it pass, waiting for her to tell me some more.

She didn't. She sat looking at the masts and the stars; accordion-music came from a distance in waves with the wind. It was growing darker. I could hardly distinguish her face and her arms any more, as if she was slowly vanishing out of the white shell of her dress. Then she asked, "Has he always been such a liar?"

It took me aback. I didn't answer straight away; I looked back in the past, but I couldn't remember a single instance in which he had lied, to my knowledge. He had always been a rather tense, dry sort of chap, not at all the imaginative type. "No," I said, "I don't think so. Is he now?"

She laughed again, without gaiety. "He's very sweet," she said. "But he doesn't know the difference between reality and his imagination any more. You were his captain, weren't you?"

"Yes, once. But he is a captain himself."

"He talked a lot about you, nights, after dinner, when he was a bit drunk. He said you were a pirate; one of the toughest men he had ever known, and that you took women like other people took a cigarette."

I said, "Well, well," and felt like laughing. But I didn't, because at second thought I rather liked that picture of myself. The fact that she had told me this as a proof of what a liar he was didn't please me altogether; I must have given her the impression of one of Snow White's dwarfs. As it was dark, the rich blue darkness of the South, and as I was still trailing the last wisps of the dream of Sinbad the Sailor, I asked, "What makes you think that it isn't the truth?"

She didn't answer. She must have looked at me in the darkness, for suddenly she bent forward, and kissed me. Then she got up and I saw her ghost vanish in the blackness of the bedroom.

I knew I was behaving like a boy, but I couldn't help asking, "Honestly, what makes you think that there isn't some truth in that?"

Her voice answered from the darkness, "I saw you asleep."

For some reason that irritated me. I said, "All right, put the light on. Let's have something to eat."

She put the light on and I saw her again as she really was: a thin Chinese girl, with a tired face and straight hair. She seemed a quite different person from the one that had talked to me in the darkness.

I was dressing when the door was opened without a knock. It was Goatskin, in his pin-striped suit but without his cane and his hat. He looked like a provincial boy on Sunday. "All right," he said to the Chinese girl, "scram."

I wanted to say something pompous, like: "The lady is my guest now," but I let it pass. For one thing, she was out of the room too soon, she flitted out like a cat. Goatskin kicked the door shut behind her, pulled out a long, chromium cigarette case, snapped it open, and held it out to me. I said, "No, thanks"; he stuck one in his mouth and struck a match on the sole of his shoe. As it was crepe, it didn't work; so he struck it on the table, making a scratch on the polish. I watched his performance, curiously. He looked as if he was acting a gangster in an amateur show. Perhaps I would have fallen for it if I hadn't known him so long and so well. To me he was just Goatskin putting on an act. Perhaps he put it on a bit thick for my benefit.

"Well," he said. "So there you are. I told you you would come." I couldn't remember him telling me, but I let it pass. "Is she to your liking?" he asked.

There were various answers to this; I stood a moment in doubt which line to take. Then the memory of him when I was lying on the couch in his chartroom got the upper hand. I said, "Are you sure you want me here?"

He looked at me, amazed at first, then suspicious. "Why?"

"Because I'm not going to take that act from you," I said. "I don't mind if you want the rest of the world to believe that you're a baby Al Capone; to me you're just my mate with a hat on and pansy socks. And the hell with Maurice."

At first I thought he was going to be nasty. Then he suddenly deflated, fell down on the bed, stretched his arms over his head, and said, "Jesus, what a life." I smelled another act coming on; this time the lonely ring leader, a victim of circumstances. But I wasn't sure yet, so I decided to let him swim on for a bit. "Suppose you tell me something about that life," I said, "and stop throwing Chinese girls at me and filling my bath with whisky. What are you doing here, apart from throwing your weight around?"

"I told you," he said. "Tires, and cut the captain business because here it's me who is the boss."

I said, "Get the idea out of your head that everybody is acting a role. I'm asking you a straight question. If you prefer to make rings around me, tell me so and I'll be off."

"All right," he said. "Keep your shirt on." He had got a lot weaker in the meantime. I wondered why. In Antwerp he had still seemed his old tough self. Perhaps he was better off the stage.

I tried my best to get him off the stage. It took about half an hour of bootlegger's wisecracks before, at last, he sat up on the bed, forgetting his pin-striped suit and the gaudy bedroom. For the first time, sincerity flickered in his eyes. "All right," he said. "I'll give you the full case history. After I left you in that hospital, I went to Holland. Only the South had been liberated by then. I got a ride on a lorry from Brussels to Antwerp. There were Dutch girls in the lorry, who worked in Headquarters in Brussels and were on their way home for the holidays, because it was Christmas. One of them got out in Antwerp to buy something—a present for her mother. You'll ask what this has to do with me; I'm getting to it. She came back after a few minutes, radiant, with a leather handbag. She was a very nice girl. The kind of girl I had been dreaming about all during the war, while laying the United Nations. 'I had a lovely stroke of luck,' she said. 'The old woman charged me five hundred francs for this thing and although it was much too dear, I decided to take it. I gave her a thousand franc note, and what do you think she did? She gave me two thousand in return.' All the other girls in that lorry laughed their heads off. And I looked at them and felt—Jesus, I don't know how I felt. Only it was that girl that started me off."

"On what?" I asked.

"On the road that led to—here," he said. "It was only the beginning, perhaps I got mixed up with the wrong crowd. When I came to Holland all the girls were like that. They had no sense of honesty, of decency. As far as they are concerned, we lost the war. Well, after that, I began to look around for signs of rot, and I found plenty, let me tell you. When the North was liberated, I thought things would be different there. The people had suffered a lot. There had been famine and what they call heroism. But when I walked through the Vondel Park in Amsterdam, a few days after the Liberation, I broke my neck over copulating couples at every three steps: the Canadians had arrived. And then those boys of the Resistance— I didn't like the sight of them either. I may be mistaken, but I had the feeling that most of them were profiteers, who had joined at the last minute. The real ones had been shot or beaten to death in concentration camps. I know that all this doesn't seem to add up to anything, and I can't very well talk about it. It's the first time I'm telling anybody and it doesn't sound convincing, now I hear it. It must have been the outcome of all sorts of little things, things I can't remember now. But the general effect was to give me the feeling that Dop had died, and Waterman and Van Dam and the rest, for nothing, for a mystification. That I'd been living in a fool's paradise all during the war, thinking that I was defending something which was true and real and worth dying for, to leave it to the children, even if they weren't your own. Oh well . . ." He fell back on the bed and stretched his arms over his head again. "I suppose it was just one man's fate—what happened to me. Perhaps the same would have happened if I'd found our country full of angels, playing harps. Perhaps all I'm doing and have been doing for the last year is just trying to find a justification for my going to hell. Because I suppose that's what this is." He made a vague gesture round the room. "Hell."

I felt he was getting onto the stage once more, and I tried to drag him off again by saying, "A very pleasant hell, if you ask me. I wouldn't take yourself too seriously, you know. It clouds the issue."

"All right," he said. "I'll give it to you straight, without commentary. I tried at first to do a decent job, but for many reasons I couldn't stick it anywhere. For one thing people just didn't want to see the facts as they were; they talked and thought in preposterous platitudes about liberty and the Queen and national honor and those filthy Germans, and at the same time they all voted for the annexation of a bit of German territory along the border—'Straightening out the frontier,' they called it. Nobody seemed to remember that what got us into trouble in the first place was Mr. Hitler wanting to straighten out some frontiers too. And then they all read the papers, and yet they didn't see the headlines I saw. "Market Declines as Peace Scare Widens," for instance. They didn't see the advertisement of a big steel factory, saying, "What does your country sell to Bethlehem?" Perhaps I was already on my road to here and unconsciously looking for justifications. But I made a collection of those headlines and articles and advertisements and speeches, I became quite a collector. In the end those things stopped making me feel indignant or miserable. On the contrary, they delighted me. I felt a sort of collector's joy every time I found a new beauty to stick in my album. So I was one of the few people, I think, who saw this next war coming even before the last one was quite over. And when I was offered a lucrative job by a casual friend whom I met in a bar in Brussels, I took it because I didn't feel under the moral obligation to be a nice, clean, honest citizen any more."

"What kind of job was that?" I asked.

"Smuggling," he said. "Cognac and spirits and other stuff to England. It was quite a foolproof scheme. We had two identical tank landing craft, both called *Crazy Lady*. The name was painted on their sterns in exactly the same lettering. One of them was lying in a harbor in the South of England with a crew of jolly young camping people; the other in a harbor in Normandy with another crew, including me as the skipper. We played around with those craft for about a month, chugging in and out of our harbors, staying within the three-mile limit, until the customs came to know us quite well and started waving at us from their launches when we came in from a trip, without bothering to search us any more. After that, the operations started. The *Crazy Lady* from the South of England and we, from Normandy, sailed for the open at exactly the same hour. But this time we were loaded with stuff. We met our partners that night half-way across the Channel. And there we changed crews. So the *Crazy Lady* from the South of England, at whom the customs waved the next morning, was really the *Crazy Lady* from Normandy. We kept that up for almost half a year."

"Whose idea was that?" I asked.

He laughed. "Not mine. I'm not a brain, just a sucker. In all these games, there are brains and suckers. The brains sit somewhere quite safe, in London or Paris or Brussels, smoking cigars and taking their ladies out, just like during the war."

"Were you found out in the end?"

"I wasn't," he said. "I left in time, when I thought they were getting too confident of themselves. They were caught a month later. After that I came here. The tire racket seemed quite a wholesome job compared to the smuggling. Easy money too. And I liked the crowd. You will too, once you get to know them. No, what happened to me here was different. The sea got me."

I thought he was play acting again. But he wasn't. He sat up on the bed once more, put his arms round his knees, and looked at me with eyes that were completely sincere. He was old Goatskin again, the boy with whom I shared so many memories neither of us had ever spoken about. "When I dived for the first time," he said, "something happened to me. I can't describe to you what. I can only compare it to something: to dive for the first time with a mask and to see the world under water is like making love to a woman for the first time in your life. It is a shock, a birth, being torn loose from everything you have known before. Once you get underneath the mirror of the sea, you are cut off from everything, even your own personality. You're like the first man on the moon, completely alone, and you change into something, I don't know, a superhuman being, with a tremendous feeling of power. A hunter in a jungle where no man has ever been. I suppose you don't believe me. You think I'm exaggerating. Well, wait till you get there yourself. Perhaps it won't work on you the way it did on me, but then you'll be an exception. When you meet my crowd, Pierre and Bernard and Jacques and the little Russian, you'll meet four people who live in a dream as long as they are ashore, who don't care a damn about what they do above the water or what people do to them. They begin to live only when they've got their masks on and their frogman's feet, and their tubes in their mouths. You'll see."

I waited for him to go on but he fell silent. He looked at his hands. I looked too and noticed for the first time how wrinkled they were. The skin seemed loose, as if he had just got out of a bath. "And this spiv's setup," I asked, "how does that fit in?"

He looked at me, not understanding at first. Then he said, "Oh, this you mean," including the room, the rumpled bed, the socks, the whisky. "This is just a way of killing time ashore. We are all a bit frightened, you know, of the spell the sea has thrown over us. And that's why we try to make our life above the water as attractive as possible. I, for one, like a lot of girls and good food and drinks and a lot of loose money. I like to throw parties and swagger around a bit, because once I am back among other human beings, back from my prehistoric jungle, there is one thing I want to forget: the war. The rottenness of men. The exploitation of sentiments that were decent and noble once. The lies, the speeches, the steel of Bethlehem, the concentration camps in our own country. Because, now, I have a feeling that I would go on like this for ever, living the life of a male mermaid, loving the girls, loving my friends, feeling one with the whole of humanity, gay and carefree and hopeful. But there is one thing that might mess all that up, and that's the new war they are preparing. I want to forget that. To forget it like hell."

I said, "Suppose you did something about it. Opened your mouth, for instance, instead of getting blind drunk or hiding with the fish."

He shrugged his shoulders and looked at me with a smile that made me feel slightly ill at ease, for it was a smile of indulgence. "Good old Skipper," he said. "Let's go and eat."

I took my jacket over my arm and went to the door. He got up from the bed and followed me; one of his trouser legs stuck halfway up his calf. When I was about to open the door, he put his hand on my shoulder and said, "I'm glad you came. I like you a lot, after all."

I said, "Straighten your trousers," and we went down the carpeted stairs to the lobby, where the hall porter saluted when he saw us, and the blondes came tottering out of the bar, cackling like chickens. "Where are we going?" they cried.

"To Ginette's," he said. "Call the crowd."

We had dinner in a very nice restaurant, full of jolly people, in candlelight, at a long table heaped with food, on which the bottles were changed all the time and a little cat gingerly trod its way across the remains of bouillabaisse and empty oyster shells. I was introduced to over a dozen people and called "Skipper"; their names escaped me. At first I felt rather out of it, but the Chinese girl appeared after a while and sat down by my side and started telling me which ones out of the crowd I should remember. There were the two boys with whom Maurice had come in when I was waiting for him in the hotel lobby, the tall one was Bernard and the fat one Jacques. They were deep-sea hunters and very nice; both had been in the Resistance. The small fat man with the child's face, sitting between the blondes at the other end of the table, was Pjotr, who acted as a cook on board, but all he ever cooked was the fish he caught himself. He was an underwater hunter too, he worked with a mask and a harpoon gun.

The rest were just charming people having a free meal. She hadn't the faintest idea who they were.

We drank a lot of *vin rosé* and all of us got very gay. Goatskin sat, flushed, between two candles at the head of the table, holding the hand of a gorgeous creature who was quite bored, for he told long stories in what he obviously thought was excellent French. I listened to him with amazement; he told about his adventures during the war and practically every word he uttered was a lie with an accent. I looked at the Chinese girl by my side, and wondered what had happened to make such a liar out of this boy, whom I had always known as a wonderful guy.

After the meal we went to a "dancing." On our way there, Goatskin and the three boys that had been pointed out to me took me in their midst, and Goatskin told me incoherently what I was supposed to do on board their ship. I wouldn't have to dive, I could try if I liked but it wasn't necessary because it wasn't a diver they wanted. The schooner with which they sailed didn't belong to them, but to a Captain, who was very old and nearly blind and a very bad sailor. What they really wanted me for was to keep an eye on the navigation, and replace the Captain as much as possible without hurting his feelings. I said I'd do my best, but that it seemed a tricky proposition. The captains I had sailed with so far wouldn't let themselves be replaced; not even Captain Goatskin of the old *Vlieland.*

The dancing was in a cellar bursting with the most hellish noise I had ever heard musical instruments make. There was a snarling trumpet that pierced the eardrums and a percussion battery that gave me palpitations by the sheer volume of its thunder. The dancing that was going on in the couple of square yards among the tables was of the postwar kind. Men in zoot suits tugged with girls with horse tails on their heads and flung them over their shoulders; I thought I couldn't stand much of this.

But after a while the injections of sound jabbed into me had a vitalizing effect; also there was a lot of whisky going. I got so above myself that I ventured to dance with the Chinese girl, but the space between the tables was too small for me. First I cleared the floor by swirling round like a dervish, then I knocked over a table full of glasses. I had a great success with this and sat down amidst generous applause. Goatskin had tears streaming down his face, and I heard him say, "You haven't seen anything yet, wait till he gets going properly." I was too drunk to mind by then. He was a wonderful guy, he could lie as much as he liked.

When at last I got back to the hotel, the room behaved as if there were a heavy swell going. I fell on the bed as into the sea, and fell asleep like a sinking plate.

I woke up in a pink morning. By my bedside stood the Chinese girl with a cup of coffee and a croissant. When she saw me open my eyes she dipped the croissant in the coffee and held it out to me, which was rather messy but made me feel luxurious and oriental. "Good morning," I said, and tried to manage the croissant. I found I had to eat it like a chicken drinking. I wanted to sip my coffee, when I suddenly remembered with alarm that we had been supposed to sail this morning at five o'clock. When I said this she smiled and said, "My friend, you are in the South of France now. If people say here that they'll sail at five o'clock in the morning, you'll be lucky if everybody is on board by midnight." I thought how sweet she would be, and how I would like her, if only her eyes weren't so black. I couldn't see anything at all in them, just two black discs the size of a farthing. I liked her ears, though; they were very delicate despite their size. "Tell me something about yourself," I said. "Where do you fit in?"

She smiled and looked at me for a while before she answered. I got a bit uneasy under that look; it was as if she was searching my eyes through dark glasses. "I was a student," she said. "And when the Liberation came, I was very enthusiastic. I thought that, after the war, there would be no more racial prejudices and a new unity of men. When I found out that I was wrong, I decided to have a good time."

I said, "I see," instead of the other things I felt like saying. "Do you sail with us?" I asked.

"No," she said.

"Well," I said, "I suppose I had better get up and have a look at that ship. Or doesn't it exist after all?"

"Oh, yes," she said. "It exists all right. And it's quite a sight. You'll see."

She was right. When I had finally located the ship in a far corner of the bombed-out harbor, I stood looking at it, musing, for quite a while. She was called *Euridice*, had the body of a barge and the rigging of a two-masted schooner. Her sails were lying on the beams like heaps of laundry, hastily ripped off the line, her deck was littered with a multitude of things in wild confusion: diving masks, frogmen's feet, bathing trunks, deck chairs, harpoon guns, respirators, rubber dingies, a motor bicycle, folding tables and two wine barrels. The center piece of this sailor's nightmare was an old upright piano, lashed to the back of the midships, where I supposed the galley was.

She looked quite deserted and was moored in a way that made me think her crew had fled in a panic. She lay, with her stern to the quay, at anchor. She was attached to the quay by a solitary mooring rope, the size of a flag line.

I went on board, trod my way cautiously through the litter on her deck, opened the lid of the piano, to find out if it was true. It was. I advanced slowly toward her foredeck and ended up at the anchor winch. There I saw that they had paid out the full chain, so any time there might be a breeze that wasn't right on, she'd break her flag line and start sailing.

As I stood contemplating this, I heard a sound behind me: snoring. It came from the wheelhouse, which was midships. I looked through the dirty window, saw two bunks, one above the other against the back wall. From the top bunk dangled a thin, white leg. The interior of the wheelhouse, as far as I could see it, was worse than her deck. Every square inch of horizontal space was covered with objects; on the walls hung yet another rash of diving masks, respiration tubes, dirty towels, long underwear and a hunting horn.

I felt like giving up and thumbing a lift on the road toward the North as fast as I could. But when I strolled back to the hotel in the very hot sunlight, I felt a laziness overcome me, a sleepy desire to get into the shadow, and an indifference toward life and all its problems that was new to me. After all, I had nowhere to go to, nobody was waiting for me anywhere on this earth, so who the hell was I to feel a moral indignation at the presence of an upright piano on the deck of a seagoing ship? I found the Chinese girl, sitting on the terrace in front of the hotel, in the company of Pjotr and the tall Bernard. They were having a Pernod and so I had a Pernod too. It did its work quickly and pleasantly. After one glass I began to like the idea of the piano. After the second I asked myself why nobody had ever thought of it before. It would make no end of difference to seafaring life if one could sit down at odd moments to tinkle: "Tiptoe through the Tulips with Me." And then a revolutionary thought dawned on me, as I was sitting there enjoying the taste of aniseed and feeling an agreeable morning mist rise in my brain. For three thousand years people had taken the art of navigation much too seriously. All of us, young, ambitious sailors, dreaming of being master mariners, were the victims of several hundred generations of impostors. I didn't think of giving up any more. I couldn't wait for the moment when I would see the helmsman leave the wheel to play the piano.

After my second glass, as I began to grin in anticipation of our first cruise, I had the impression that the Chinese girl was watching me. I couldn't make sure, for she was indeed wearing dark glasses now. I looked at her eyeless skull and said, "By the way, sweetheart, what's your name? Thalassa?"

She smiled without gaiety. "No," she said, "Nicole. What did you say the other was?"

I said, "Never mind," and raised my glass. "Here's luck."

She looked at me, expressionless, while I drank.

We sailed at eleven o'clock that evening. It was a very hot night, full of stars and harmonica music, and the drunks could be heard yodeling blocks away. The drunks weren't our crew; they were all brand sober and very agitated. I didn't quite grasp the number of them, because there were many people about and I wasn't sure who was intended to sail with us. I sat on a bollard, in a corner, and listened with amazement to the rows.

The whole ship seemed to be full of rows. Everybody was screaming at somebody else, and every few minutes or so there was the same furious exclamation that rose above the rest: "All right, in that case we can't sail!" At first I tried to follow the arguments, but I discovered that this exclamation was traditional, and did not really mean what it said. For, while everybody was screaming that we couldn't sail, some absent-minded shadows on the fo'c'sle were weighing anchor. Then came the moment which I had seen coming for the last ten minutes, when the strain of the anchor chain being pulled taut became too much for the flag line on the poop, so it snapped and the ship started sailing.

There were wild cries of "Stop, stop!" and "I have got to go ashore!" and "Hey, who is that at the anchor winch?" A crowd of dark silhouettes gathered on the poop, gesticulating, throwing ropes at the beachcombers ashore, that fell far short and splashed into the water. Somebody yelled, "Full speed astern!" which was a wish rather than a command, for the engine wasn't running. The chorus on the back started chanting "Full speed astern!" until somebody realized that the engine hadn't been started yet. That brought forth another chorus: "Captain!"

The crowd surged from the poop to the midships where they gathered round the wheelhouse. Two silhouettes opened the door, from the inside came shouts and curses, and after a few moments a white ghost was dragged out, struggling: an old man in pyjamas. Before he was forced down the hatch to the engine room, he too yelled the war cry, "In that case we can't sail!" Then he vanished. The ship, in the meantime, was slowly drifting out and started swinging round. There were sounds of blows and a clanking of iron from the engine room, then a loud explosion, and blue smoke poured from the hatch through the lamplight. The lamp had been brought by somebody from somewhere and put on the piano. After the explosion the engine started running, full astern. But as the ship's stern was not pointing at the quay any longer, the crowd started shouting, "Ahead, ahead!" The ghost in pyjamas emerged from the engine room hatch, put his hand over his eyes, looked around and asked, "Where is the shore?"

At that moment I began to giggle, one of those nervous giggles that are so difficult to get out of. I sat in the darkness, giggling helplessly, while the crowd argued on the deck and the ship made the full tour of the compass until, for some reason, it ended up with its stern toward the quay once more. I was just getting over my giggles, when suddenly, above the general noise, I heard a flapping sound and saw the little fat Russian advance on me in bathing trunks and with frogman's feet on. I expected him to sit down and start playing the piano, but he touched my shoulder, said, "Sorry, old man, would you mind shifting? I want that rope." I got up, laughing again; the little fat man took the rope between his teeth and dived overboard with a splash. Then he swam to the shore, while about seven people were paying out the rope after him, climbed the quay, and handed it to the beachcombers, who fastened it to a mooring ring. There were more shouts of "full speed astern!" until somebody remembered that the anchor chain had been shortened. Then some people rushed toward the winch and the chain thundered out again.

A quarter of an hour later we were back where we had been an hour before. Half of the crowd filed ashore as soon as the gangplank was put down, and the little fat man with the frogman's feet flapped back on board. Somebody hollered, "Let go!" and the beachcombers were loosening the rope, when somebody else cried, "Maurice! Maurice isn't back yet!" So the chorus chanted, "Maurice!" and, "Make fast!" then, at last, peace descended.

I was delighted to see the little man with the frogman's feet roll a wine barrel toward the piano, sit down on top of it, open the piano's lid and start playing a *berceuse* by Chopin. Somebody asked me from the darkness, "Well, Skipper? Happy?"

I said, "Yes." I had never said it more sincerely.

Goatskin was brought on board several hours later, dead drunk, carried on a stretcher by two gay people and followed by the staggering blondes. When I saw the small cortege approaching it chilled me; as a boy, in South Shields, I had seen a drowned sailor carried on board and the picture of his boots with his dead feet inside was still very clear, I had forgotten his face. When I saw them carry Goatskin on board I thought he was dead.

I was the only one who felt a moment's alarm, the others took the spectacle as a matter of course. He was gently lowered down the steep ladder to the fo'c'sle, where we all had our bunks, and laid out on the couch after the usual heap of dirty clothes, bathing trunks, shoes, and empty bottles had been swept onto the floor. Once he lay there the ship left.

I didn't go on deck, but I knew what happened by the noises. I wasn't worried, yet I felt ill at ease, sitting by Goatskin's side, listening to his sick breathing, that seemed louder than the rattle of the anchor winch, the frantic shouts and curses outside. I looked at his face in the yellow light of the oil lamp, and again the memory of that night I woke up on the couch in his chartroom came back to me. He must have sat looking at me the way I sat looking at him now, and he must have felt the same.

He woke up after a quarter of an hour or so, opened his eyes, and looked at me with a drunken dazedness.

"Cigarette?" I asked.

The words took a long time reaching him, then he nodded, with difficulty. I lit one and stuck it in his mouth. He puffed at it, then it fell from his lips onto his collar. I took it away.

He wanted to say something, I couldn't make out what. Then he put out his hand; only after he had groped for a while I realized he was groping for mine. It was a strange moment; I suddenly thought of Dop and Barger and the boy Waterman and the poem on the wall in room 77 in the Grand Hotel. It was the first time I realized that all of our old friends were now on that distant shore; he and I were the only ones left this side.

Then the others came down and Pjotr opened a bottle of Pernod. We had many Pernods, so many that I don't quite remember when we went to bed. I remember lying on my back at a given moment under a very low ceiling, hearing the creaking of the rigging, the slow swish of waves, and an old man's voice singing in the distance *"Le joli printemps des roses."* It struck me, because I realized in a slow, serious way that there were no roses in the spring. But then I remembered that I was in the South of France, where everything was different, and I fell asleep with a lovely glow of happiness and peace and love for everybody, alive or dead, for there wasn't any real difference, the only difference was time.

CHAPTER NINE

THE FOLLOWING NIGHT, TOWARD SUNSET, WE ARRIVED AT A LITTLE ISLAND off the coast. I remembered it from the Invasion; that hot day in August,

'44, seemed far away. The island looked innocent now. It hadn't been then. I remembered the armada of ships, the flashes of gunfire from the mountains, the explosions, the fires, the frantic birds, the thousands of dead fish coming to the surface after each explosion. Now it was beautiful and still; the sea was like a mirror, gently rocking and distorting the reflection of the island. I stood looking at it, leaning on the rail at the foremost spot of the ship. Then I heard the sound of flapping steps behind me and saw the four boys come out of the fo'c'sle with their frogman's feet on, their masks on their heads, their respiration tubes and their harpoon guns in their hands. "We'll see whether we can get some dinner," Bernard said. "Would you like to join us?" I said I'd rather wait and see; I'd never swum with a mask and a respirator.

That morning I had got a first notion of what terrific swimmers they were. Contrary to all the rules imbued in me since my childhood, they had all had a swim immediately after breakfast and no one had gone down with a cramp. As the ship had been making no speed at all, they had splashed around lustily and I had watched them as if I were standing on the beach. Then the Captain had come out of the wheelhouse in his pyjamas, vanished down the hatch to the engine room, and started explosions. As the engine started running full speed, the bathers yelled from the sea. Luckily I heard them. The Captain, arising with the smoke from the inside of the ship, became furious when I said there were four people in the sea, being left behind. He said that if he stopped the engine now, it would take another hour to start it up again for the fuel pump would be drowned. I said that he had to make up his mind as to whom he preferred to be drowned; he muttered, "All right. Next trip I retire. I'm sick of this," but he went down the engine hatch again and stopped the thing with a reverberating explosion. It had taken the bathers about twenty minutes to catch up with us; but when they finally climbed on board, they hadn't seemed to be tired in the least.

That evening I understood why. After they had put their masks in front of their faces and stuck their tubes in their mouths, they went down the pilot's ladder and swam round the ship several times before striking out toward the island. It was a curious sight, for just the four tubes stuck out above the water, and they could be heard breathing for many yards away. They all breathed in a different way: Bernard with slow deep sighs, Jacques with short puffs; Goatskin and Pjotr breathed like whales, with a little spout of water spurting from their tubes at every exhalation, and were the first to be off, at terrific speed. As it was near sunset, the sea got slightly hazy and they vanished soon from sight.

The moment they were off, everybody on board ship went to sleep. I remained alone on the deck, waiting for them, until it became dark. That was three hours later, and they still hadn't come home. I began to get worried and called the captain. He half woke up when I shook him and said that the swimmers had been away for over three hours and that it was getting dark. "Don't worry," he mumbled. "They never come back within four hours," and turned over on his other side.

"But it's getting dark," I said. "They may not be able to find us."

"Put out a light," he mumbled, "if you're nervous. Now let me sleep."

I lit the lantern on the piano and sat waiting for them, like an anxious mother, peering overboard at every splash I heard. I heard many splashes as the night got darker, and discovered that they were fish jumping at the light. In the end I got so bored and worried that I sat down at the piano, opened the lid, and stared at the yellow teeth of the keyboard, thinking that if a fairy came to say that I could make a wish and it would be granted, I'd wish to play the piano like Rachmaninoff. As it was, I tried out, "Ye Banks and Braes," with one finger. I remembered Stella, humming it in our little flat, that morning, long ago. I lit a cigarette, leaned back with my feet on the piano, and thought about Stella, but she seemed far away. Not only because she was married now and living in Warsaw, of all places, but because I could no longer take myself and her and our love and the war quite as seriously as I'd been doing. It was difficult to take anything seriously in these surroundings, not even the fact that four people had probably just drowned. If it pleased them to get drowned they were at perfect liberty to do so; everybody was at perfect liberty to do whatever he pleased in this world of the Mediterranean. I felt at peace, sitting there, smoking, looking at the first stars and the hazy silhouette of the grim little island, wreathed in memories. I felt that nobody could hurt me very much, because they couldn't get in touch with me any more. I remembered how on the quays of Marseilles everybody had seemed to live in a little universe all his own. The same thing was happening to me; it was rather a pleasant state. I felt entirely rid of all responsibility, even toward my own life. Then they came home.

The first I heard was a soft, puffing sound, rapidly approaching, as of a little engine. It was Pjotr's staccato breathing. He climbed the pilot's ladder, with the sound of a sea lion emerging from the water. His feet flapped on the deck like flippers. From his belt dangled three loops of steel wire, full of fish, still alive, twitching their tails and gaping. Their gold eyes glittered in the lamplight. "I saw liches," he said, "as big as a man. Over there, in that wreck. Golly, if we had only had the boat!

Maurice and Bernard got one of them, but I don't think they managed to tow it over here. And I saw a lovely ray, as big as an eagle. Tomorrow morning you come, with the boat. Follow us. Ray with butter. Wonderful!" He flapped toward the galley, loosening his belt with the fish. "Didn't you get cold?" I asked. "Of course," he said, "I'm frozen. Let's have a drink."

I went to get a drink from the fo'c'sle; when I came back the others had arrived. They were standing in the lamplight, on the poop, their masks on their heads, all of them with huge bunches of twitching fish dangling from their belts. Goatskin looked quite different from the way I'd ever seen him; his blue eyes were lighter than ever and his face thin and beaky, his wet hair matted on his forehead. He looked almost mad. "I'm sure there are jeeps in the holds of that wreck," he said. "And even if there aren't, I'm going to have a look tomorrow."

"With luck, you might find a nice nest of conger eels," Pjotr said. "The holds are shut. They like the dark."

"But how could they have got in," I asked, "if the holds are shut?"

They laughed and Bernard said, "Why do you think that ship sank? Through lack of breath? There must be a hole in its side the size of a house. Let's have a drink."

They had their drinks by lantern light, with towels round their shoulders. The fish they had caught made little flapping noises on the deck and glistened in the darkness. They glistened like fish themselves. When I sat looking at them and saw them laugh in the lantern light, I thought how voracious their teeth looked and how cruelly excited were their eyes. I felt as if I were having a drink with beings from another world. The kind, gay people of the days before seemed to have shed their magic cloaks that made them look like human beings; now they looked like deep-sea monsters. I was very romantic that night.

Pjotr cooked the fish. It smelled delicious when I passed the galley, but three quarters of their catch lay still twitching on the deck. When I asked Bernard what they were going to do with those, he said, "Oh, I don't know, throw them away." As I had never been a hunter, I thought it was rather gruesome, this happy passion for slaughter for slaughter's sake. When the fish was served, I didn't enjoy it the way I had thought I would. The soft flapping noises in the corner spoiled my appetite. I knew I was being sentimental but I was living in my own universe now and could be as sentimental as I damn well pleased.

After the meal, when they had put on jerseys and trousers, we sat on the aft deck of the idly drifting ship and talked about hunting and fish and the deep sea. I asked them what was the attraction of killing animals under water, just for the sake of killing? I found out that they all were as tenderhearted as spinsters so long as it concerned nice woolly things ashore, like bunnies and foxes and the defenseless grouse. But under water it was different, they said. Fish were different from other animals. They didn't have the same sensations of pain and fear, they were cold-blooded and they didn't scream. Rays, for instance, were evil monsters; once I'd seen a ray advance on me, slowly flapping its wings like an evil bird, I'd feel how different fish were from other animals. I was very interested in their arguments, and I thought of the German officer I had talked to at the beginning of the war who had said practically the same things about Jews, compared to other people.

Pjotr got quite lyrical in his descriptions of underwater hunting. He said it was vital, beautiful, ferocious, a world that had remained unchanged for millions of years, where man entered like a terror that fell from the sky. I asked what was the attraction of feeling like a terror that fell from the sky; he looked at me in amazement and said, "Why, it's beautiful!" In the past, in pubs and Nissen bars in the outposts of the war, I had often tried to trick bomber pilots into that very same confession, but they had never fallen into the trap, however drunk they were. It was odd that an innocent Russian boy, on the deck of an idly floating ship under the diamond sky of the Mediterranean, should speak for them at last. It gave me, somehow, a grim satisfaction.

Goatskin looked at me with the thin smile I remembered from our meeting on board the wreck of our ship. "That's right, Skipper," he said. "Feel fine and righteous while there's still time. For this is your last chance, you know. Tomorrow we'll throw you in the water with a mask on and you'll have your first look at what you have been sailing on top of all your life. You've been crawling on the skin of a monster ever since you were little. Tomorrow you'll see the X-ray. Have you ever been in one of those modern shoe shops in England, where you try on a new pair and they put your foot in a little box and you look through a slot and you see the bones of your feet wriggling inside, and then a nice girl asks you, 'You see how it fits, sir?' That's nothing, Skipper, compared to what you'll see tomorrow. It will frighten the pants off you."

"Don't be ridiculous," said Pjotr. "It's the most wonderful sight you have ever seen. He doesn't know what beauty is until he has seen a wonderful light rock with sea urchins and sea stars, and thousands of little fish that come toward him and peer in his mask. It's the most beautiful thing in the world."

238

"I'm not going to show him the sea urchins and the little fish," Goatskin said. "I'm going to show him the wreck."

I asked, "Why? Is this a special treatment?"

He smiled again and looked at me with his cruel blue eyes. I didn't like him then. "Yes," he said. "I want you to remember a U-boat with a captain called Hasenfratz. When you see the wreck tomorrow, remember that somewhere off the coast of England, he is lying just like that, among the sea urchins and the little fish. He, and your first ship."

I said, "That's a pretty nasty thing to say. Why?"

He looked at me, still smiling, and answered, "Because you are too damned snooty. You think that you are the only one with beautiful thoughts and refined sentiments. You think little Pjotr is a bloodthirsty animal of prey, because he harpoons rays and fights with congers. It'll do you good to remember that when it comes to killing fish, you out of the lot of us have killed the biggest one."

I looked at him, trying to see in his eyes whether that was the truth or whether there was something else. But I could see nothing in them. He looked at me without expression, like the sea.

The next morning at sunrise I followed them down the pilot's ladder with frogman's feet on, a respirator in my hand, and a mask on my head. The longboat had been lowered; in it sat Goatskin, with a diving apparatus on his back. It consisted of two bottles of compressed air and two rubber tubes that came together in a mouthpiece. He also had a mask on his head, and a belt with lead weights round his waist and a knife with a cork handle stuck in the belt. It was the so-called Cousteau apparatus, a French invention with which it was possible to dive down to a hundred meters without being bothered by a diving suit with its ropes and tubes. He was going to investigate the holds of the wreck.

While we were still rowing to the spot he looked like a boy with bottles on his back and a mask on his head; the moment Pjotr said, "Here we are," after looking through the mask he held in the water, Goatskin put his mask in front of his face, the mouthpiece underneath his lips, and became entirely inhuman, an evil robot with a dagger in his hands. As he breathed, the apparatus gave a soft, whistling sound in the nape of his neck. When he gently lowered himself over the edge of the boat and sunk below the surface, bursts of bubbles rose on the spot where he had vanished.

"All right," said Pjotr. "Now you have a look. Take your mask off." I obeyed. "Now, spit in it. That's right. Now rub the saliva over the surface of the glass. Good. Now rinse it with sea water." I obeyed. "That's right. Now put it in front of your face. No, no, your nose inside. Blow through your nose." I blew and the air escaped from the mask with an unpleasant sound. "Now suck. No, no, through your nose." I breathed in through my nose and the mask flattened itself against my face. "All right, that fits. Now stick the tube underneath the strap of your mask on the left side of your head. No, no, in front of your ear. That's it. Now take the mouthpiece in your mouth." The mouthpiece was a surgical looking rubber flange, with a hole in the middle to let the air from the tube through and two little warts that fitted behind my teeth. I took the thing in my mouth, put my lips over it and clenched my teeth over the warts. As I breathed through the mouth, the tube made a hollow, hornlike sound. It felt uncomfortable.

"All right," said Pjotr. "Go ahead. Float face downward. Don't dive yet. Just look and breathe slowly, regularly. Don't get into a panic and pull your mouthpiece out, or you'll get into trouble. If you want to dive, fold yourself double, your hands touching your feet, and you'll go down like a stone. Don't go too deep at first. If you get a pain in your ears, come back. And don't forget to blow the water out of your tube first thing when you come back to the surface. You'll find there'll be a good tumblerful of water in there. Blow and it will spurt out. Then breathe again. All right?"

I said, "All right," but could not form the word with the tube in my mouth.

"Are your frogman's feet comfortable?" he asked.

They weren't, for I had put them on much too soon and sat in the sun with them. Now they pinched my feet. I said, "Yes."

"All right," he said. "Off you go."

I lowered myself slowly over the edge of the boat. The water was very warm. When I first put my face in the water, breathing crampily through the tube, my heart nearly stopped, for I saw a giant orange hand gesture in front of me. It was my own. I let go of the boat, tried to breathe regularly with my eyes closed, lying face downward in the water. When I felt that I would float, I opened my eyes.

The sight I saw made me forget whether I breathed or not. I saw, in a curious blue light, a fantastic landscape of hills and rocks, overgrown with curious dreamlike shrubs and long waving grass. I saw hundreds of little fish, hovering like birds, and lower down, on the grass that stretched out from horizon to horizon like a prairie, big dark animals, like cows seen from above, that seemed to be quietly grazing. It was a world of absolute silence; I heard nothing but a faint crackling noise in my ears, like fire heard from a distance. Then, suddenly, there was a sound, a sharp, metallic clank, that seemed to come from very close by, on my left hand side. I paddled with my feet, and swerved round much faster than I had foreseen. Then I saw it.

Below me, half submerged in a blue ground mist in which the prairie vanished, lay a ship. It seemed enormous. It was lying half on its side, and looked real and new as if it had sunk only a couple of days ago. I saw its funnel, its masts, its bridge. Everything looked quite normal, though quite deserted. What gave it the sinister spell of a nightmare was that its boats were floating upside down above their davits.

I was staring at the ship, not feeling anything but a blank amazement, when suddenly I noticed something moving. Along the foremast a small orange creature descended slowly, not like a bird, nor like a thing sinking, it was a movement unlike any I had ever seen. A slow spurt of silver bubbles came from its neck in regular bursts, rose all the way to the surface like a little flight of soap bubbles, glittering in the sun, until they vanished in the golden mist of the sky. The creature moved its feet slowly, the frogman's fins had come to an eerie, undulating life, as if they were a part of the living body.

I saw him gently descend on the bridge and open the door to the wheelhouse. At that moment there seemed to be a soundless explosion. In one split second, thousands of little silver fish burst from the windows and the door, in a blinding, scattering flash. Then I saw the orange creature go blue, as he vanished through the shadow into the inside. The little bursts of bubbles went on floating playfully upwards through the open door, although I couldn't see him any more. I heard again the curious clanking noise that seemed very near; and suddenly the bubbles stopped. Nothing rose from the door any more, and I lay staring at it, my heart pounding. Then, a dark streak changing into white, something shot out of the door, a huge bat, flapping its wings, twisting and turning in the air. The bubbles burst from the doorway again, the creature shot out, changed from blue to orange, and chased the bat at an astonishing speed.

The bat was a ray, one of the biggest I had ever seen. It winged toward the surface, twisting and turning, and I saw something like thin, brown smoke trail behind it. It spurted from a spot in the white of its belly, where a thick handle stuck out. It was Goatskin's knife. Then, suddenly, as the ray came closer, and I already had begun paddling backward in fright, a second creature shot down toward it. It was Pjotr; a long blue harpoon gun, stretched out along his right arm, glistened on his shoulder. The ray didn't see him coming. He shot straight down at it, the gun pointing. At a yard he pressed the trigger. I heard the loud clank of the report, saw the arrow flash out and pierce the ray.

The ray struggled with colossal force. It winged downward, trailing him by the line of his harpoon. Then he released the gun, and rose back to the surface.

The orange creature went after the ray, swooping and turning, and grabbed the gun. There followed a struggle that was horrible to watch. The orange creature and the huge, dark bat seemed to sink toward the blue, in a struggling embrace. Then I saw them rise again, struggling, straight toward me. I turned round to flee, lifted my head out of the water to see where the boat was, and instantly I suffocated, my mouth full of sea water. I got into a panic, pulled the mouthpiece out, and gasped for air. I had the horrible feeling that I was drowning, the moment I wasn't breathing through the tube any more. I felt as if I were sinking. I managed to reach the boat, kicking with my frogman's feet that suddenly seemed to suck me down, hoisted myself over the edge and tumbled inside, hurting my knees. I was very cold.

Pjotr was the first whose hands I saw, grabbing the edge. He pulled himself up, spouted water through his tube, swung a fat leg over the edge and pulled off his mask. "Have you seen that?" he asked, breathlessly. "I had to let him go, for I was bursting. God, what a beauty! Ray and butter tonight, old boy!" He slapped my naked shoulder with such force that it hurt. Then I heard the sound of bubbles, and a hand grabbed the edge. Then another hand appeared, waving, holding the gun that seemed to be twitching and pulling. Pjotr bent over the side and got hold of it. "Pull!" he called to me. "Quick, or he'll get stung!" I grabbed hold of the gun with him and felt a terrific force, pulling at it in wild jerks. The sound of bubbles went round the boat to the other side. Then the boat heeled sharply as Goatskin heaved himself in, with his heavy diving apparatus.

It took a quarter of an hour before the ray was finally pulled into the boat. When it fell on the floor between the benches, flapping its wings wildly, it looked much smaller than it had seemed in the water. On its back a little tail stuck out, quivering. It ended in a point as sharp as a needle. "Don't touch it!" Pjotr said, panting. "If you are stung, you'll get blood poisoning." Then he pulled a knife out of his belt and jabbed the head of the ray several times. With the last jab, he nailed the head to the floor.

I sat looking at the black, slimy animal in horror. For it breathed; its fleshy wings lay quivering on the floor. Despite the knife through its body, the knife through its head, and the harpoon that had pierced it, it went on breathing and twitching its wings, that slapped in the blood.

Pjotr rowed back to the ship. The ray went on breathing all the time. It still breathed after it had been hoisted on board with a hook and pinned to the deck in front of the galley. It went on breathing all through the day. Every time I passed it, I thought it looked dead, but it wasn't. Its little eyes, on stalks on its square head, remained open and staring, and its wings quivered all the time. I asked, after three hours of this torture, why he didn't kill it. He answered, "Are you mad? We won't eat it until tonight, and the moment it's dead it goes bad in the sun."

Bernard and Jacques came back, loaded with fish. It would have been enough for a crew of twenty. The fish were thrown on their steel wire loops by the side of the twitching ray; but they didn't last as long. That night there were delicious smells from the kitchen again and fragrant blue smoke rose from the open door toward the stars. There was an hors d'oeuvre of small fish, braised, and then delicious ray in butter. They all had a gorgeous time; the *vin rosé* in the glasses gleamed like rubies in the lantern light. When Jacques asked why I wasn't eating I said I wasn't hungry.

After the meal was over the old sailor made coffee, and Bernard sang Spanish songs that sounded very fierce and nostalgic in the moonlight. The crew, a little group of dark shadows on the lower deck, murmured "Olé, olé" after every phrase of the songs. The dead fish glistened, coldly, behind the piano.

The next day Goatskin went down to the wreck again with his diving apparatus and started looking for tires in the holds. His bottles had been recharged with compressed air, by means of a little engine on the deck, that I hadn't discovered so far because it was carefully wrapped up in a tarpaulin. It was the only thing on board that got some care, for on it depended their existence. If the little engine should get out of order, they would have to go to Nice or Cannes to have their bottles recharged. Every charge lasted for about twenty minutes per bottle, at a depth down to twenty meters. If they went down lower they used more air.

I watched Goatskin dive again through my mask. The sight of the wreck gave me that curious dreamlike sensation once more, that was unlike anything I had ever felt; my mind seemed to be undecided yet how to react to that vision: with horror or delight. I thought of Hasenfratz this time, and pictured our two ships lying on the sandy soil of the Western Approaches. It wasn't the ship that gave me a feeling of coldness, it was the thought of those inside. The two stokers: white skeletons in the dusk of the engine room, between the still, dead pistons and the little iron staircase, through which little fish would be swimming, catching the faint light from above. As I was looking down at the wreck and saw the little orange creature slowly descend toward its deck, I suddenly thought of the fairy tale about the man left alone in an empty house with the key to one room that he was forbidden to open. He opened it and saw a vision of delight and wonder that ended in some nightmarish horror, from which only a miracle of love would rescue him. I felt as if I hadn't quite opened that door yet, but was peeping through the keyhole. As I saw the little orange creature, with the small swarms of silver bubbles slowly rising from its neck, tear the tarpaulin covering the holds and open up the hatch, my heart started pounding again and I had a sudden feeling of deep insecurity. The miracle of love spun idly around in my thoughts, and brought forth two faces, hazily. They were faint and helpless and faraway: Nicole and June Simmons. I knew that if I were ever to penetrate into that world of silence, I would need someone as strong as Stella to hold the slowly unwinding life line that I would trail into the darkness. Odd, fairy-tale thoughts; the orange creature had opened two hatches now and vanished in the black, square hole as in a grave.

No fish came bursting from the darkness this time; only the bubbles rose, playfully, in little silver bursts to the golden mist of the surface. Everything was peaceful; little fish hung watching, motionlessly, in the still water. My breath made a soft, hollow sound in the tube at every exhalation; there still was the crackling sound as of a distant fire in my ears. Then, suddenly, one of the hatches was pushed upward by a colossal blow from below and a dark thing shot up from the darkness. Only as it rose into the sunlight, swirling, I saw it was a wheel. The bubbles went on rising from the hatch, irregularly by now; the wheels floated upward in a steady succession. I counted ten, before the little orange creature came floating out of the grave again and slowly swam toward the midships. As he entered the wheelhouse once more, there was again the explosion of thousands of silver fish, scattering from the windows. After that nothing happened. The bubbles went on rising now from the door, then from a window; then the orange creature appeared again, swam past the funnel and the upturned boats and descended in front of the radio hut. He seemed to have difficulty opening the door; he succeeded only by pulling with all his strength, with his feet against the wall, and he fell over backward when it opened. He made a slow, graceful somersault, trailing a stream of silver bubbles; then he swam back to the door and vanished inside. The bubbles went on rising from the doorway; something gray came sneaking out of the door, at the top, and rose slowly to the surface, turning. It was a tropical helmet. The bubbles stopped. I knew this meant something. The orange creature was holding its breath. Then it shot out of the doorway, feet first, fighting something, in a cloud. It was a dark cloud, almost black; I saw snakelike arms and something that looked like a bald skull. Then there was another sudden cloud, in which the orange creature vanished, struggling; then I saw a whole set of entrails sink down from the cloud; silver guts gleamed in the sunlight, between the upturned boats, curling, as if still alive. I lifted my head and got my mouth full of sea water again as I breathed; this time I blew it out and I swam back to the boat as quick as I could. Bernard was floating alongside it, one hand on the edge, looking down.

I touched his shoulder and he looked up. I took the mouthpiece out and asked, "What is that? What's happening?"

He took out his mouthpiece as well, said, "He's caught an octopus," and wanted to put it back again.

"But what were those entrails?" I asked. "Whose were they?"

He laughed and answered, "The animal's, what did you think? He turned its bag inside out." Then he stuck the mouthpiece back and went on looking.

Goatskin surfaced shortly afterward. On his left shoulder sat the horrible bald skull. Its tentacles groped round his neck, his arms, and his chest. He took his mouthpiece out and shouted, "Cut it off! It's sucking like hell! Isn't it a beauty?" Bernard started carving away at the thing with his knife. As he pulled it off Goatskin's shoulder it made a sucking sound, and I saw that the tentacles around his arms, although cut off, went on twisting and groping. It took quite some time to get them all off.

"Are you going down again?" Bernard asked.

"No," said Goatskin. "I've only got about ten minutes' air left. It isn't worth the trouble. Take off my bottles, will you?"

Bernard, while unstrapping the harness, asked, "Didn't you come up a bit quick from that hold? How deep were you?"

"Oh," said Goatskin, "only twenty meters or so. Perhaps twenty-five. Nothing to worry about."

But Bernard wasn't satisfied. After he had helped him into the boat, he said, "You're too damned reckless. You were at thirty-five at least. If you get the illness it will be your own fault."

Goatskin said, "Ah, shut up," and pointed at the octopus, slithering in the boat with the bilge water. "There's a nice dinner," he said. "Ever eaten that, Skipper?"

I said, "No."

He laughed. "Getting used to it?" he asked. "Tomorrow you go down with the Cousteau. This floating on the surface is nothing."

I said I didn't think I'd care to go down here, I'd rather try it out somewhere neutral. He chuckled. "Hasenfratz, eh? Yes, my boy, your sins come back to you." I wanted to say something, but let it pass.

That night we had lovely cooked octopus with tomato sauce. I was getting rather hungry but I stuck to the small fry Pjotr and Jacques had brought home. We drank lots of wine again and this time there was community singing around the piano, mostly scabrous French sea chanteys that sounded very nostalgic. Goatskin and I sang Dutch children's songs, the only ones we both knew. "A little cart drove down a sandy road" and "Two mice in a cornfield, peep, peep, peep." Pjotr played the *berceuse* by Chopin again and "Teddybear's Wedding March."

Goatskin got drunk; when we finally went to the fo'c'sle to sleep, he said, "Skipper, come here a moment." I was about to go down the ladder and asked, "What?" He beckoned me toward the stacks of wheels piled up out front. "I want to talk to you," he said. "God, I'm dizzy."

He sat down on the deck and I leaned against the tires. The night was very still, the reflection of the stars quivered on the sea. "I'm probably a fool to tell you," he said thickly, "but do you know why I said those things about that U-boat? About Hasenfratz? Do you? You don't."

I said, "I don't."

"Well," he said. "I'll tell you. Because I like you. Because I'm loyal. Do you hear? Loyal." He shook his finger at me, drunkenly.

I remembered him as he had been: a quiet figure in a goatskin coat on the bridge, a friend. I hated him for letting himself be changed into this. I said, "Don't be a fool. Stop play acting."

He looked up and sniggered. "So I'm play acting, eh?" he said. "So you are still little skipper God Almighty? Composed and unrattled, and so snooty that I could knock your teeth out."

I said, "Go ahead. It will be a pleasure."

He sat looking at me from below. I couldn't see his eyes but I could imagine what they were like. Then he said, "It may come to that, you know. One day I may grab you by that self-satisfied throat of yours and bang your snooty skull on the deck."

"You're talking nonsense," I said, and went toward the hatch. "Go to sleep."

246

He wheedled after me, "Don't you want to hear the secret, little Hasenfratz?"

I don't know what made me do it; perhaps the fact that I kicked against the bucket on my way to the hatch. I took it to the rail, threw it in the sea, heaved it up full of water and threw it in his face.

He remained quite still. The water could be heard dripping off his body on to the deck. Then he said, "Would you believe that that did me a lot of good? Thank you, old boy." And he got to his feet. His fist caught me unawares, it hit me on the jaw. I felt a blind rage spring up inside me, and I shut my eyes. I said, "You'd better go down now, before I break your neck." Then he hit me again.

It was Pjotr who pulled us apart. I had been whacking into him, cursing, possessed by a dark brutality that was utterly frightening. I hadn't known Pjotr was that strong; he held my arms pinned on my back like a vice. "Come, come," he said. "That's not the way we like things on board here." I felt suddenly very silly, and very much alone. I said, "I'm sorry." Goatskin got shakily to his feet. "All right, Pjotr," he said. "It was my fault. I asked for it." Bernard's head came out of the hatch. "What's going on?" he asked. "Nothing," said Pjotr. "The Dutchmen have beaten each other up." Bernard asked, "Why?"

"Because of the Chinese whore," said Goatskin.

That made me see red again. I shook Pjotr off and grabbed his neck and said, "If you say that again, I'll kill you." It sounded very adolescent. The whole thing became preposterous and embarrassing.

He said, "O.K. I'm sorry. I'm drunk."

"Let's all go down and talk it over," said Pjotr, "and have a drink."

We went down; I didn't want to talk anything over, but I didn't mind the drink. The others were very interested. They seemed to think it quite normal that two lifelong friends should beat the sparks off each other because of a girl neither of them cared about. When I lay on my bunk, my jaw hurt and I had a headache. My hands clenched to fists all the time, automatically, like the octopus' tentacles after they had been cut off. I asked myself why we had done this; whether it was indeed because of the Chinese girl. He had sent her to me in the first place, so he could not be very interested, and I didn't feel any tenderness toward her, nor desire. Remembering her gave me a feeling of distant comradeship, as if we had a lot in common but wouldn't ever be able to express it, because we were worlds apart. I was nearly asleep when suddenly a head appeared by my side. It was Pjotr.

"Something to eat?" he whispered.

I said, "God, no," and turned away.

Before I fell asleep I remembered that I should take nothing seriously, least of all myself. It was quite a relief, that thought, and I fell asleep smiling, thinking of the Chief, Miss de Roos, and New Province cake.

CHAPTER TEN

I FOUND I COULDN'T TAKE A FIGHT LIKE A BIT OF HORSEPLAY ANY MORE; I took it as a proof that I was growing up. I had hated the fight with Goatskin when it happened, hated the anger and the brutality it had released in me. Somewhere inside me was an aggressive animal, whose existence I had only felt once before: during my fight with the American after I had sunk Hasenfratz.

The fight with Goatskin had an odd effect. It made me see the crew and the ship in another light. I didn't think they were so funny any more. Their daily slaughter revolted me; their constant drinking became a bore, and the piano got on my nerves. The crew, whom at first I had thought so picturesque and French, became a pain in the neck; the dear old Captain in his pyjamas wasn't funny any more either. I found out that he was asleep most of the time because he drank himself to a standstill; as the boys refused to give him alcohol, he had to buy it himself and to that end he sold, this trip, the ship's bell, in an island called Port Cros. Before my fight with Goatskin I would have thought it amusing; now I couldn't help thinking what would happen if we should find ourselves in a fog. The only solution seemed to be to line up the crew along the rail and make them shout "Boo" every two seconds, for there wasn't a foghorn either. There weren't a lot of things. There was no sextant, no chronometer, no log, no logbook, no parallel rules, no table of logarithms, the charts were of 1916 and the nautical instructions of 1920, the bilge pump didn't work and the compasses in the wheelhouse and on the poop disagreed seven degrees. As I was supposed to occupy myself with the navigation, I made a list of things that were missing and showed it to Goatskin. He was airy about it and said we should buy those things in Marseilles. Bernard asked, "With what?" There was no answer.

Yet all this didn't depress me, nor give me the wish to be off. I had been diving again every day; I called "diving" floating on the surface and looking down at the world under the sea. I had actually dived a couple of times down to about three meters, but choked. It had been more a matter of pride than of interest, for I saw things much better from above. The underwater world was fascinating, and looking at it had a soothing effect. It seemed to take the edge off everything that happened elsewhere. When I floated above the dream landscape, with the blue mist in the valleys, the dark fish grazing on the plains, the banks of flowers, the deserts of sand with sea urchins and dark, sausagelike things—I didn't know whether they were plants or animals—I felt far away from it all.

We crawled on along the coast and I saw different landscapes of breathtaking beauty, lit by slanting sunbeams that fell through the water, and in which dust seemed to be dancing, as in a cathedral. Slowly the world below seemed to open up for me, I saw more every day. I began to know the fish, of which only the smallest and silliest paid any attention to me; I saw columns of yellow and black striped ones parade and knew that the solitary one in front was the leader, for if he came to an obstacle he turned smartly round and the others followed his command in a single, hundredfold movement, like Prussians. I began to know the rays, dark, melancholy bats of the depth, that were entirely inoffensive, and seemed to be looking for something lost, absent-mindedly. I began to know the *mérous*, monsters to look at, but who never did anybody any harm. I began to know the little octopi, who seemed to be the most intelligent down there, and who changed colors like a chameleon according to their background as soon as they spotted me and wanted to hide themselves. The better I came to know that world, the less dreamlike it seemed; the dream seemed to shift toward the other world: the ship. Occasionally, at night, when they were drinking and playing games in the fo'c'sle I watched them with a feeling as if this was a dream, and not that million-year-old world we were floating on. I knew I was indulging in a kind of dope, like opium; I couldn't say that I hadn't been warned in advance. But it seemed a harmless dope.

What struck me most about the underwater world was its harmlessness. The only things terrible under the sea were either man-made or man himself. Off the island of Port Cros, when floating over what seemed to be a magic summer garden, full of golden little fish and blue and pink flowers, I saw something white, swam toward it and saw it was a newspaper with a headline about the Civil War in Greece. Another time I came across a twisted horror of steel girders and torn aluminum sheets, a weird animal with its back broken and twisted wings: the wreck of a plane. Inside its cockpit a little dome of plexiglass, I saw something white that was, even before I had recognized it, terrifying. It was a skeleton with a leather cap on its skull. But these things were exceptions, strange phenomena that stuck out from the landscape like things utterly alien. Occasionally, as I lay contemplating the silent life below and its graceful gentleness, an orange monster would soar down on a fish grazing, or an octopus playing with colors, and there would be the sharp clank of a gun's spring and the harpoon would pierce the flesh and an agonizing struggle would start as the terrified animal was dragged up toward its death, trailing the thin smoke of blood. I hated the hunters in those moments, and began to understand why I had fought with Goatskin that night. It hadn't been because of the Chinese girl, nor anything else to do with the world of men. It had been because of the ray and the octopus and the bunches of gaping fish, glistening in the dark behind the piano. I was offered daily to try out the diving apparatus and go for a walk on the bottom of the sea. But I didn't feel like it yet; so far I hadn't seen anything down below that had given me the wish to change my bird's life for that of a pedestrian.

We pottered around the small islands for a week or so, without finding anything that justified the expedition economically. Goatskin searched three more wrecks, none of which I saw at close quarters because they were lying too deep. The sea was light as the day down to twenty meters; there the blue started, followed by the purple at fifty meters; and at eighty meters it was dark. The wrecks were lying in the purple; all I saw, of one of them, were two mastheads, sticking out of the blue. Of the others I saw nothing.

I watched him diving, though. The little, orange creature descended slowly, like an autumn leaf falling, into the mist, trailing a line to which at every five meters a rag had been attached. When he went down deeper than thirty meters he had to come up slowly, to avoid the diver's illness: *le mal de caisson*. Bernard explained it to me at great length, full of medical and chemical terms. As far as I understood it the nitrogen in the air, which commonly wasn't absorbed by the blood of the human being but passed out of the lungs again as it came in, became absorbed by the blood if the body was exposed to a heavy pressure. If the pressure was lifted too quickly, the nitrogen turned into gas in the blood, and the result was that the blood vessels became full of little gas bubbles. If those bubbles reached the heart or the brain the consequences could be madness, paralysis, stroke, or blindness. So a diver, once he went down into the purple, had to take his time rising to the surface again. At every five meters of his ascent, he had to hover for periods that varied in length with the depths, so as to adapt his body to the diminishing pressure and give the nitrogen a chance to get worked out of his blood without having turned into gas.

It was an eerie sight to see Goatskin rise out of the mist. He would stop at the next rag, his hand to the line, and hover like a hawk, his frogman's feet slowly flapping. The underwater world became as still and deserted as a rabbit warren with a hawk hovering over it, only the smallest fish would stay to watch. The moment he vanished in the sky, after a couple more periods of hovering at a higher level, life would come back. The melancholy ray would wing out of the dusk again; the *mérou* would run busily along, like an ugly old woman continuing her shopping, the gentle calves would start grazing again on the grassy slope of the hill that rose from the mist, and the octopi would continue their elflike dance and play with colors when they saw me. The fact that the animals reappeared the moment the orange creature was gone gave me a certain satisfaction, for it seemed to prove that they weren't afraid of me. They seemed to have understood that I wasn't a bird of prey, hovering over them to kill, but just a fat, pink bird of contemplation.

Toward the end of the trip, the atmosphere on board became gloomy. There were long conversations about money. All they had to show for their catch were ten tires, much the worse for having been submerged in salt water for so long, for the canvas inside had rotted. Bernard had no more money, all they had to rely on now was Goatskin's luck at roulette. He was very confident about this, for he had a system. He explained the system, but I didn't understand it; all I understood was that he had to spend days at the Casino before it worked.

We went to Cannes, and had quite a time entering the port. There weren't nearly as many yachts moored at the quay as there had been before the war, but we managed to bang into practically all of them. After the fourth collision Goatskin dragged the old Captain to the rail and wanted to drown him. Even taking into account the Mediterranean passion for exaggeration, it seemed a strong measure. Pjotr and Jacques prevented it; the old bosun started dropping the anchor while everybody's back was turned. During the altercation a boy with a red cyclist's cap sat at the wheel, knitting.

In the end we were moored by the harbor master's launch; he wanted to see the Captain's papers and got a drink instead, which seemed to satisfy him. When, finally, the gangplank was out Goatskin said, flustered, "Honestly, Skipper, next time you must take over command. This is ridiculous." He was wearing his pin-striped suit again and his purple socks. His hat and his cane had remained behind in Marseilles.

For two days running he stayed away from noon till midnight, and labored in the Casino. But this time his system didn't work. When he came back, dejected, at one o'clock in the morning of the fourth day, he had on him exactly the same amount of money with which he had left three days ago. They had got wise to his system, he said, those crooks had fiddled with the roulette table. Every time he had put a bet on the red, black had come up. There was nothing to do but to leave for Marseilles; to carry on under these circumstances would be folly.

That night we left, and I took command of the maneuver. I had expected it to be an ugly moment when I told the old Captain that I would take her out; I put it as tactfully as I could, in a little speech I had been rehearsing. I said I would so love to do some maneuvering once more, after all these years, and would he please let me and watch me closely and tell me honestly if I did something wrong. It wasn't at all necessary; the moment he understood that he could go back to bed, he did.

I came to the harrowing conclusion that what we had taken to be the Captain's incompetence was in reality the character of the ship. She was mad. If I put the rudder to port, with her engine running ahead, she started traveling astern; and when I put it to starboard there came an explosion like a detonating mine from the engine room, followed by a pall of black smoke, and the engine stopped. I tried to make it run again, but didn't succeed. In the meantime we had kissed three yachts moored at the quay; when I came back on deck, black in the face with tears running down my cheeks from the stinging smoke, Goatskin watched me coldly, but didn't say a word.

There was a slight breeze blowing from the shore, so I decided to sail her out. This was a fatal decision, for once the sails had been set, after a lot of slapstick comedy, the ship would only travel sideways. We were approaching a new cluster of yachts at an alarming speed, when I got an inspiration. If she wanted to travel sideways she should be allowed to do so, in the direction in which I wanted her to travel stern first. After all, who said that ships shouldn't travel sideways? Just another silly tradition, kept up to make navigation an esoteric trade. So I steered point blank at the yachts, on which shivering little crowds in pyjamas and dressing gowns stood screaming in panic, and we drifted out to sea like a crab. In the open, as I went into the wheelhouse to look at the chart, wiping the sweat off my brow, a toothless voice said from the upper bunk, "Very good, young man. You haven't forgotten a thing. Next time don't ask me, I'll be happy to let you handle her." I said, "Thank you, sir," and he said, "You're welcome."

The idea was that we should go to Marseilles, but the ship wanted to go to Saint Tropez. I tried everything to stop her from drifting there, but in the end I had to give up. Like the old captain, I found myself forced to think up an excuse for her, like a mother for an idiot child. I said that reasons of navigation made it necessary for us to go to Saint Tropez: we had a rope in our propeller. It was a stupid excuse, I hadn't had time to think of a better one and I realized too late that this was probably the one ship on earth where a rope in the propeller was the easiest thing to remedy. Pjotr jumped into the sea at once with his mask on, dived under her poop and came back with the message that there was no rope. I said, lamely, "Fancy. The tide must have washed it out," forgetting that the Mediterranean was the only sea on earth where there was no tide. In the end I gave up finding an excuse. I just said, "We'll go to Saint Tropez, and that's final." They didn't argue, but from that moment onward I lived under a cloud.

Our entry into the harbor of Saint Tropez was something that would have delighted a connoisseur of medieval harlequinade. We entered the port backward. When our stern rammed the quay, the deck was full of silent figures, sitting with their heads in their hands. The harbor master came on board and the first thing he said was, "Good Lord, that was a lovely piece of seamanship. How did you manage, captain? Ships have been swinging on their anchors in this damn port for nine centuries; you hadn't got your engine running, had you?" At first I thought it was heavy irony, but when I looked at his innocent dark eyes I realized, with a feeling of nausea, that he was sincere. I looked round, like a man waking up from a nightmare, and realized that Saint Tropez was indeed a hell of a port to get into for any normal ship. I hadn't noticed it before, I had been too occupied with the fit of epileptics our *Euridice* had got into between the pier heads. Saint Tropez obviously was the place she wanted to go to, and I began to wonder whether she could ever be made to leave it again.

As we had no money left worth speaking of, the days of whisky and Grand Hotels were over. We stayed on board. Only Goatskin took a room in a boardinghouse, because it was necessary for the plans he had made for our future. It was very simple, he said; the tire racket was obviously no good any more and so he had had to think of something else. Well, he had found it. This place was full of tired businessmen on holiday, who wanted fresh air, healthy food and relaxation. They wouldn't find those sitting on the terraces of bistros, sipping Pernods, and ogling the girls, so we would organize a cruise for them, show them lovely underwater sights, teach them to hunt, eat glorious seafood, listen to jolly yarns on the poop at night and sing chanteys at the piano. That was the reason why he had come to Saint Tropez. I thought we had come to Saint Tropez because of circumstances beyond our control, but I let it pass, as it lifted the cloud a bit under which I had been living.

I must say, to his credit, that he worked his ropes fast. He tore into the ruminating herd of tired businessmen like a lassoing cowboy. By nightfall of the first day he had caught three; at the end of the week sixteen. It was fascinating to watch the catch mounting nightly, but when we passed half a dozen I began to get worried. Everybody had become so excited over the game, that they seemed to forget about having to put all these people up. They couldn't be shoved into the fo'c'sle in layers, like loaves into an oven. Once Goatskin had reached the number of sixteen, which seemed to have something to do with his gambling system and hence appeared to satisfy him, he started making his preparations for the cruise. The businessmen had all paid in advance, which seemed unbusinesslike but said a great deal for his power of persuasion. So we were rich once more, and the first preparation he made was to telephone to Marseilles for his cane, his hat, the blondes, and the Chinese girl.

She arrived at a critical moment, carrying the cane and the hat. We were sitting in the fo'c'sle, trying to work out the geometrical problem of putting sixteen businessmen up, when she appeared at the top of the ladder, said, "Hello, boys," and came down, her slender legs moving into the lamplight. Goatskin asked boorishly, "Are you alone?" and she answered, "Yes, the others could not come." He muttered something, turned his back on her, and continued tackling the geometrical problem.

She asked, "Where do you want your cane and hat?"

He answered, without looking, "On my bunk. Now boys, how far have we got? Two in the double bunk, seven in the singles, five on the floor, and if we take the door out of that cupboard, that would mean one more. It leaves us with. . . ." While he counted on his fingers, she smiled at me and put out her hand. I shook it secretly and whispered, "Drink?" She nodded, and we sneaked out.

Goatskin cried, "Fifteen! Where the hell are we going to put the odd one?"

I didn't hear the answer, for we were out.

We had a Pastis on one of the terraces facing the harbor, underneath a blue parasol that made her look green. I hoped she would take off her sunglasses in the shade, but she didn't.

After I had ordered our drinks, she said, "I've got some mail for you," opened her bag, and took two letters out.

I had no idea whom they could be from, until I saw that they were addressed to Hotel Atlantic in Marseilles and remembered the postcards. I said, "Thank you" and put them in my pocket. I felt so excited that my mind was not on the conversation for a while. She asked what the trip had been like and I began to tell her, but I gave up because the adjectives failed me.

"Have you dived?" she asked.

I said I had.

"Liked it?"

"I like to look. I don't think I'll ever be a hunter."

"You didn't go down with the Cousteau yet?"

"No, but I've had my first spell of the deep, if that's what you are trying to find out."

"I am not trying to find out anything," she said, smiling. "I'm just making conversation."

I realized that I had been thinking about her a good deal. I wished she would take those glasses off. "I had a fight with Maurice," I said.

"So?" She took it very calmly. "What about?"

"About you."

"How did it happen?"

"We were drunk," I said. And then, to change the subject; "Would you mind taking your glasses off? I'd like to see you."

She said "Sorry" and took them off. It didn't make much difference; I had forgotten about that. "Are you going to sail with us next time?" I asked.

"No," she said, "I've got a hotel room booked. I'll stay here and wait for your return. What's this new plan Maurice has?"

I told her about the businessmen and tried to be witty about it, but it petered out. It was difficult to take up contact with her again, probably my imagination had been at work at sea and I had started shaping her into somebody different. We sat watching the passers-by for a while; they were dressed in miniature shorts and the women wore a ribbon around the chest. They showed burns in various grades and glistened with oil in the sunlight.

"You might like to call on me tonight," she said, getting up. "The hotel is called 'Majestic.' Thanks for the drink."

I said, "You're welcome," and watched her as she walked away. She looked slim and dressed among the nudists. The moment she had turned the corner, I took the letters from my pocket.

I opened the one from the Chief first. He wrote with ill-spelled exuberation about the joy he had experienced upon getting my postcard, and then went on about Miss de Roos. He gave me a description of her qualities as a housewife, cook, comrade, and soprano and said that she had accepted him as her future husband. They were going to be married as soon as the temporary church was finished, which would be a month from now, God willing. As either of their little houses was too small for a couple, they were thinking of taking one of them apart and joining it to the other. They hadn't decided yet which one. Yours sincerely.

June Simmons had written four pages. The size of her letter alarmed me a bit; my postcard had sprung entirely from boredom and hardly merited such an extensive reply. Her letter was amusing and very English; she wrote about nothing at all, except at the very end. "I have been thinking about you a lot. There is something that worries me, but probably I'm imagining things. Take care of yourself and don't get depressed. You have got friends. Yours ever."

I ordered another Pastis and sat thoughtless in the sun with my eyes closed, like a cat. Then Goatskin descended on me, full of pep. "I've got it!" he cried. "Hammocks!"

I failed him.

I went to see her that night. I had decided not to, but then I had thought of her, alone in that hotel room. I didn't want to get involved, but there was no harm in being kind.

I shaved first. While I was doing so Goatskin and the boys were putting up hammocks in the fo'c'sle. It had a depressing effect on me, I imagined the businessmen inside them, swinging. When Goatskin saw me leave he asked where I was going and I said I was going for a walk. As I mounted the ladder, he called after me, "Give the bitch my love!"

She looked pretty and composed in a thin, pink dressing gown. The room was frightful, with a cracked ceiling, roses on the wallpaper, and a dark grease stain above the head of the bed; but it had a nice view on the masts and the night sky.

She asked if I would like a drink and when I said I wouldn't she put out the light and sat down on the window sill, trying to recapture Marseilles. It didn't work; in Marseilles there had been a comradeship between us, now there was nothing. I gave her Goatskin's message, verbally; only after I had said it I realized that there had been no need to.

She took it very calmly. "I don't know why," she said after a while, "but there must be something in me that makes men want to hurt me."

She was right. I hadn't deliberately wanted to hurt her, but I had. I sat looking at her silhouette, wanting to feel something, some warmth, some contact. "All right," I said, suddenly tired. "I don't care a damn what that lunatic is obsessed by. Let's go to bed."

She obeyed at once, without saying a word. I remembered how promptly she had obeyed all my wishes in Marseilles, and it irritated me. I said, "I'm

256

sorry, I didn't want to order you about. I'll sit and smoke a cigarette for a minute."

I sat in the window and lit a cigarette. It tasted foul; after a few puffs I shot it into the darkness, got up and went toward her, a dark patch on the white bed. I sat down, found her hand, felt a sudden tenderness toward her, and said, "I've been thinking about you a lot." Then I remembered that June Simmons had written the same words to me, and it was over.

"Well?" she asked, as I remained silent.

Just to say something nice, I said, "I love you, Nicole"; and then she threw her arms round my neck and hid her head on my shoulder, sobbing. She gave me quite a shock, I didn't like this. But I put my arms around her and stroked her hair and said, "come, come," and "don't" and "sweetheart." She recovered, said, "I'm sorry," and lay down again. I lay down with her, feeling uncomfortable.

"Aren't you frightfully hot?" she asked.

I said, "No."

We lay rigidly in silence, listening to the babbling of the little waves against the ships in the harbor and somebody whistling "Trees." I wished I were at sea at sunrise; I would put on my mask and my frogman's feet and go to have a look at the world under water, which was very pretty early in the morning. The sunlight didn't quite penetrate the waves yet; the landscape was covered by a golden mist. Then, as the sun rose, slanting beams of light would start quivering in the mist, and catch the flicker of silver fish, with long shadows. Still later the hills would emerge, the white rocks, the plains of seaweed with the dark animals lazily grazing, and there wouldn't be a danger nor an enemy in sight, and I'd feel far away and happy.

When I woke up it was a hot morning and she was brushing her teeth. I opened my eyes and looked at her. She had a lovely figure. I shut my eyes again; then I heard a soft stroking sound that brought a memory: Stella brushing her hair in the silent bedroom while I sat waiting in the kitchen with the message of Dop's death. I opened my eyes and saw her start plucking her eyebrows, her face very close to the mirror. I thought how odd it was, this complete intimacy between us, without us having made love. If she hadn't been Chinese, she could have been my sister.

She saw me look at her in the mirror and smiled and asked, "Slept well?"

I said, "Fine."

"Are you going to sail today, do you think?"

"I don't know."

257

"I wonder what will happen to those businessmen."

"What worries me is what will happen to us, once we are in the open and they find out."

There was a silence, and then she said, "I know he's awful, but I can't help feeling sorry for him."

I said, "H'm."

"Was he a good captain during the war?"

"You have put me that question once before, and the answer was yes."

She went on plucking her eyebrows and I lay looking at her and then the door was opened without a knock and Goatskin came in. He looked at her, then at me, said, "Sorry," and went out again, slamming the door.

"Well," I said. "That's that."

She didn't say anything. She sat down on the window sill, her back to the quay, the tweezers in her hand. Her face didn't express anything, but the way she sat there did. I said, "Would you remember that you are naked? It might attract a crowd."

She said, "Sorry," came to the bed and sat down.

I asked, "You are in love with him, aren't you?"

"No," she said. "I've never been in love with anybody. All I have ever felt was pity."

"That's grim," I said. "I'm not sure I feel flattered."

"With you it's different," she said. "With you I feel that we have a lot in common, but . . ."

"But that we are worlds apart," I completed, smiling.

"That's it," she said.

I shut my eyes. I didn't want to get involved. All I wanted was to get back to sea. Yet I wanted to talk to her about the war, and our life, and the newspaper between the sea urchins, and the wreck of the plane, and the hopelessness of it all, and the beauty of the slanting sunbeams in the water. But it was all too blurred, too much a feeling, not thoughts. I said, "I love you, Nicole."

"I know," she said. "I love you too."

I knew it was not true, but that she had felt the same thing, wanting to talk about the war and the students and the hope and the disillusion and the whisky and the blondes and us all going to hell. I wanted to kiss her, but I didn't. I didn't want to get involved. I asked, "What about breakfast?"

She said, "All right. On the terrace?"

I said, "Let's."

She dressed and we went down and had breakfast on the terrace.

258

CHAPTER ELEVEN

THE CRUISE WITH THE BUSINESSMEN WAS A FAILURE, AS EVERYBODY HAD known it would be. Yet it was extraordinary how much they took, before they stopped being amused.

The moment they got on board they became very hearty and jocular, started calling each other "tu" and loved their hammocks and the confusion of shoes and shirts in the fo'c'sle. They loved everything, even the poisonous smoke that poured through the partition as soon as the engine started running; they were determined to recapture their boyhood and be scouts again; the fo'c'sle looked like a messy tent. The blankets were greasy with sun oil, they hit their heads on the deck every time they sat up, they twisted their ankles on the ladder and kicked each other in the stomach coming down, but it was all part of a wonderful memory, of youth revived.

Pjotr did it. The idea had been to show them lovely underwater landscapes and open up for them the beauty of the sea. None of them had bathed with a mask yet and they were all looking forward to it tremendously. Pjotr, who was to cook for the lot, got very worried about the fish. There had been too much hunting going on along the coast, the fish had hidden in some stark, terrifying precipices where the rocky coast sank perpendicularly into the blue and where the sun hardly ever penetrated. So, for their first swim, he flung them into the water at this spot. The first view they got of the beauty of the underwater world was a vision of a dark hell. It was a psychological mistake, that might have been remedied if Pjotr, Bernard, and Jacques hadn't left them to their fate and shot off like sharks to hunt the dinner. And they had taken the longboat with them.

I watched the floating businessmen through the captain's binoculars from the deck of the ship. They stayed together at first; then some of them splashed toward the shore and hoisted themselves on a rock, hurting their legs, their behinds full of sea urchins' needles. They stood there, shivering, flailing their arms, and hollered, "Ahoy!" at the vanishing longboat. The braver ones remained in the water, spread out above the precipice, staring down, fascinated by the horror of it. I saw one of them, who was floating quite by himself, swim slowly round; then another one overtook him, touched his foot and they both nearly drowned, one from fright, the other from laughter. They reached the shore with difficulty and climbed a rock on the other side.

There were still three left in the water when Pjotr's voice hollered from the distance, "A shark! A shark!" It was not a warning of danger, just a call to Jacques and Bernard to join him with their guns to harpoon the prize; but the remaining businessmen swam to the shore in panic. I could see the blood on their knees after they had scrambled up the rock, much too fast. I thought of attracting Pjotr's attention but, like a coward, I wanted to postpone Judgment Day as long as I could.

When the marooned bathers were finally collected, it was nearly night. Pjotr and the others had caught the shark and it was lying in the boat; at least, I couldn't think of any other reason why the businessmen did not want to enter it. Pjotr didn't throw the shark's corpse back into the sea, which would have been the reasonable thing to do, for he couldn't cook it. But the fool was so proud of his catch that he couldn't let go of it, and rowed back all the way to the ship to have it hauled on board first, before he went back to collect the businessmen. It was a very small shark, still gaping, although he had broken its back. It hung upside down from one of the davits, dripping blood.

When the businessmen came back on board it was obvious that the thing was over. They were scouts no longer. They clamored angrily for iodine and adhesive tape and drinks and a hot meal; we only had drinks, and they finished the lot during a powwow in the fo'c'sle. After half an hour two of them came on deck, called for Goatskin, and told him that they wanted to return to port at once. He passed the order on to me, angrily. He repeated, "At once," and said that there was no point in continuing the cruise with a lot of unsporting, spoiled, foul-mouthed night-club characters. There was no room at sea for those; let them go back to their smoky joints and pinch bottoms. "At once, do you hear?" This conversation took place in the wheelhouse. The old Captain chuckled in his bunk.

I did what I could, but it took us three days. In the end they went ashore in La Ciotat, which seemed to be the ship's port of preference this time. La Ciotat wasn't a holiday resort, it was an industrial town with shipyards and factories and looked like Grimstadt in Norway. After the businessmen had left, without saying good-by, we watched them being taken ashore in the longboat, for I hadn't managed to get to the quay. We lay anchored in the middle of the harbor.

Pjotr and the old bosun rowed, and Pjotr lost his oar. It took them a quarter of an hour to paddle back to the spot where the oar drifted. The businessmen sat in solid rows on the benches, their suitcases and their brand new kit bags on their knees. It was all rather sad, for they had been so happy in the beginning that I had hoped against reason that it would end well.

Goatskin went to Cannes from La Ciotat and stayed away for three days. He came back very excited; when he stood hollering on the shore for the longboat, we all thought he had broken the bank. He had lost every penny he had on him, but he had something else: a job for us. A very nice old antiquarian had chartered the ship to go to Greece, and he wanted us to dive for some antiques that were submerged off one of the little islands. He would come on board himself in Saint Tropez, with perhaps one or two guests, and we would leave at once because the whole thing had to be over in eight weeks' time.

The others were delighted, but the word "Greece" made me gloomy. I was sure the ship didn't dream of going to Greece. I was getting superstitious about her; I didn't mention the word "Greece" in our conversations, out of some half-witted fear that she might prick up her ears and make up her mind. Yet I had come to like her; like the old Captain I felt that I could do a lot with patience and kindness and a poker face. When I told the old Captain that we were going to Greece, he said, "Oh, that's all right. She has been there." For some reason this relieved me.

The antiquarian had paid some money in advance; but not to Goatskin. He had written out a cheque to a shop in Sainte Maxime for a second Cousteau apparatus. "We'll have to do a lot of diving," Goatskin said. "You'd better start to get used to the thing, for I think it will be us two who'll have to bring up the loot. If I let Pjotr or the others do it, they'll be off the moment they see a fish and forget all about the antiques." I said I was willing to try.

I tried that same afternoon, in the harbor of La Ciotat. Goatskin put the bottles on my back and adjusted the straps; the thing seemed to weigh a ton. He put the mouthpiece in my mouth and I breathed the compressed air. It tasted stale and gassy. The mouthpiece was much bigger than the one on my respirator, and I felt slightly sick after having had it in my mouth for a minute. "You're too fat," Goatskin said, "for my ballast belt. We'll have to add some lead. Four kilos in all, I think." He added two blocks of lead to the belt that I had seen him wear; when he put it round my waist my knees nearly gave in.

"Surely, this is too much?" I asked. "I'll go down like a stone."

But he said, "Nonsense. You'll find when you are in the water that you have no weight at all. Now listen carefully. This is very easy, but there are a few simple rules. First: you must breathe as little as possible, for the air is precious. If you take it in gulps, the bottles will be finished much too soon. Inhale not to the full, but half, wait three seconds, then exhale. You'll find that after a while you'll do that automatically. Then: don't splash around on the surface but dive; fold yourself double, hands to your toes, and down you go. When you feel a pain in your ears, rise again for about one meter and swallow your saliva. You'll find that it relieves the pressure. Fold double again and go down to the next stage, which is about five meters deeper, where you'll feel a pain again in your ears. Do the same thing: rise one meter, swallow your saliva until the pain stops, go down five meters more. As you go deeper, you'll meet fish that aren't afraid of you because they never have seen a man at their depth. They are curious, and they'll come for you, to look. Don't get panicky; they won't do you any harm, and don't forget that under water they look twice their size. You won't meet anything interesting down here, in this harbor, perhaps a liche or two. They are very big and look alarming but they are harmless. If you want to chase them away for some reason, flap your feet. In case you should meet a shark, which is practically impossible, but you never know: take your knife and tap on your bottles. It'll go away. If it comes back, it'll come very close because they are myopic and anything white attracts them. Then just prick it gently with your knife and it'll go away. Don't stab, just give a little push, like this," and he prodded my side with his finger. "Got it?"

I said, "Yes." My mouth was very dry.

"One more thing," he said. "These bottles have a little spare tank. The opener is on the left-hand side, at the bottom, just on your hip. If your air gives out, open it and you'll have ten minutes left." Then he asked the bosun to sound the harbor. It was twenty-five meters. "In that case, don't quite go to the bottom," he said. "Stay at twenty meters."

"But how do I know that I am at twenty meters?" I asked.

"That's very simple," he answered. "You get a pain in your ears and have to make a ceiling the way I told you every five meters. So if you do that three times, you'll be between fifteen and twenty meters. In you go."

I put on my mask, but I had forgotten to spit in it. It filmed over. I took it off and spat. "Bring a potato," Goatskin said to Pjotr. "This spitting business is not enough." Pjotr brought a potato, Goatskin cut it in half and rubbed the inside of my mask with it. "You'd better rinse it under the tap," he said. "Then you needn't do it in the harbor."

I wanted to go to the galley, but found I had to walk bent forward because of the heavy load on my back. My feet seemed to have swollen under the weight. My frogman's feet hurt badly. "Don't bother," said Goatskin. "I'll do it for you."

He took my mask to the galley and rinsed it. After I had put it on and inhaled through the nose to see whether it was well closed, he said, "One more thing. When you go lower down, you may find that your mask gets pressed against your nose and hurts. Breathe out through your nose, and you'll be all right again. That's all."

Before I went down the pilot's ladder, I looked at the water. It wasn't very clean. I said, like a child at the dentist's, "Don't you think we'd better wait a bit?"

"Wait?" he asked. "What for?"

"Well, the water seems rather dirty."

"Don't be silly. Hurry up."

I climbed down the pilot's ladder. I had to use all the strength in my hands, for the load pulled me backward. I couldn't look down because of it. When my foot first touched water, it felt cold.

"Hey!" Goatskin called from above. "What about putting your mouthpiece in?"

I said, "Sorry," feeling very nervous, and let go with one hand to put the mouthpiece in. The ladder swung round; I hit the side of the ship with a bang and hurt myself. I was shaken now. The bottles on my back had shifted. I called up to him, "They've shifted!"

He called back, "What?"

"The bottles!"

He called, "Go down, you fool, or I'll cut the ladder!"

I said, "O.K., O.K." and put the mouthpiece in my mouth. It seemed bigger than before, and hurt on the inside of my lip underneath my nose. The air hissed through the tubes with a mechanical noise. I descended a few more steps, swallowing. Then one more step and my foot groped in vain. There were no more steps. This was it. I tried to hover on the last step with my knee, thinking of some excuse for climbing back on board that wouldn't sound too silly. Then Goatskin cried, "Hey!" and shook the ladder. I lost my balance and fell into the water backward.

I went down a couple of meters, breathing like a stag, and I was terrified out of my wits when I heard the sound of a double horn, like a Paris fire engine: "tee-ta, tee-ta," very loud. It was a nightmare: drowning in what seemed to be liquid mud, chased by a fire engine. I got back to the surface so short of breath that I had only one urge: to take my mouthpiece out. I heard Goatskin's voice, shouting, "If you take it out, you'll drown! Lie flat on your face! Breathe!"

It seemed to be the last voice in the universe. I surrendered myself to it, trying to master my panic. Turn on your face—I did. Breathe—I breathed, in long, greedy gulps. I couldn't remember what else he had called, but I remembered him saying "breathe slowly, not full, three seconds." I tried, and it worked. I calmed down a bit. At every exhalation there was a loud bubbling noise in my neck. I didn't hear the horn any more.

Then I looked, for the first time consciously. The water was very dirty, a dull green. I saw nothing at all; my vision was limited to about two meters. At first I thought I'd be damned if I'd dive into that; I thought of the sharks I had to prod gently with my knife, and groped for it on my back. Doing so made me turn over and slide down, head first, toward the depth. I heard the horn again: tee-ta, tee-ta, at every breath. Then I thought what a fool I was making of myself. There was no place safer than La Ciotat harbor. Yet I daren't dive into that ugly green, like a blind man groping. I needed something to hold onto, something solid and reliable in this fog. I thought of the anchor chain. I lifted my head out of the water, with bubbles spluttering from my neck, saw that I was very near it, and swam. I saw it emerge from the fog at close quarters, took hold of it with one hand, breathed quietly, shut my eyes and folded double.

I had to let go of the anchor chain to dive, for it made me turn round again. I tried once more, feeling grim and indifferent. If I had to drown, all right. I shut my eyes again, bent double, groping for my feet, and slid down into the silence. The horn sounded its two notes loudly in my ears; they began to hurt, and I heard the crackling of fire again, louder than ever. I opened my eyes, saw nothing at all, only the green fog, pushed myself upward and swallowed my saliva.

The crackling of fire died down. I felt the bottles float on my back. I didn't weigh anything; even the square lead weights on my belt seemed to float, for they didn't hurt me any more. I looked round for the anchor chain, but couldn't find it. The horn sounded softer now, as if it was further away. I bent double again and slid down deeper, the bottles moving on my back. I heard again the crackling in my ears, mounting, and the pain started. Ten meters. The height of a house. I swallowed my saliva, not only to relieve the pressure on my ears. I swallowed it several times. I hovered for a while, my arms spread out in the fog, looking for the anchor chain. It was nowhere. Then I bent double again, feeling cold and disinterested, and I slid down once more. I was just thinking that I was not doing badly, that I might get used to this after a couple of times and be a little orange creature myself, descending into the silent summer garden like a falling leaf, when, suddenly, I saw something. An enormous crab, with two horns, very close by. My heart pounded, I thought I'd die. Then I recognized it. It was an old bicycle. It made me laugh. The horn sounded in my ears in rapid succession. Then I felt something soft and slimy on my leg, pulled it in like a flash, and realized it must have been mud. I rose a couple of meters, back in the fog again, seeing nothing. And then a huge, silent shadow slid past. A fish. It looked enormous, and was about to vanish in the fog when I saw it flip its tail sharply, and turn round to approach me from the back.

Then I got into a panic. I jerked myself upright and pushed with my legs. I hit the bicycle with my right foot. It must have been the bicycle, for it was sharp and stung me. I shot up toward the surface, holding my breath.

My ears hurt again and the crackling of fire rose to the sound of splintering wood. I swallowed several times, but I had no saliva left. Something stung in my eyes and my vision became blurred. I realized that water had got into my mask. I gasped for breath, inhaled through the nose, sucked up the water and choked.

Then my head rose above the water. I saw the anchor chain, very close to, grabbed it, pulled myself up, ripped off my mask, pulled out the mouthpiece, and shouted, with my last breath, "Help!"

He was there, right overhead. His voice sounded calm, I hadn't heard it like this since the war. "Don't worry," he said. "You're all right. Hang on for a bit. I'll put the boat out."

I shut my eyes and felt sick. My mouth tasted acid and sickly. His voice said, quietly, overhead, "Don't worry, it's always like that the first time. You did very well. I didn't think you would go down that deep. Good old Skipper, well done."

I heard the splashing of oars and voices and then I felt the coolness of the shadow of the boat. "Take off his bottles," he said, in French. I hadn't realized that he had been talking Dutch to me. "Take his mask," he said. "It's about to fall off." They helped me out of my harness and then his voice said, "All right, Skipper, get into the boat. You're home and dry now."

I climbed into the boat, shivering, suddenly cold. The world seemed a very light place to come back to; it dazzled me. I still had the sickly taste in my mouth of locked-up air and rubber.

When I climbed the pilot's ladder again, he came towards me and patted my shoulder. "Sorry to have thrown you into this soup," he said, "but you've had the worst now. You'll see, next time it's wonderful."

I tried to laugh and said, "I wonder. I don't think I'm any good at this."

"Don't be silly," he said. "You're a born diver." Then he lit a cigarette and gave it to me. The war had come very close.

He patted my shoulder again and left his hand there. "Sorry about the other things," he said. "We'll be all right now. Now, you're one of us." Then he turned round and went to the fo'c'sle.

That night, on a marble table of a bistro, I wrote a letter to June Simmons. When I started it I didn't know why I had suddenly felt the need to write to her; I discovered it only when I wrote. I told her about the diving and Goatskin, and when I arrived at where he had said, "Now you're one of us," I stopped. It was this remark that had set me writing. I ordered another drink and continued the letter. "You said that there was something that worried you. I should like to know what it is. I am taking care of myself and am not getting depressed at all. I know I have got friends. Yours ever."

As I sat there, watching the crowd of workmen and their girls stroll along the quay, laughing and kissing, I thought it was nonsense to think of Goatskin and Pjotr and the others as belonging to another world of which, from now on, I would be part. It was very tempting to consider my first dive with the Cousteau as a sort of baptism, but one could go too far in being romantic.

I thought it would be a good idea to take a stroll myself, and I walked along the quay and the shipyards. It was hard to believe that this was the South of France. It looked more like Brest or Le Havre. A thin fog came from the harbor, and the street lamps made cones in it through which lovers and cats slid silently.

There was a stale smell of welding in the cul-de-sac where I ended up; behind the wooden hoarding I heard the bubbling sound of vats of carbide. I turned round and walked back to the harbor. Now my eyes were accustomed to the darkness I saw sleeping bums at the bottom of the hoarding.

On the quay I called for the longboat. It was Goatskin who came to fetch me. When he stepped ashore he said, "Let's have one more drink," so we went back to the bistro. It was odd the way he had changed since that afternoon. We were sitting in the bistro like we had so often sat in the Social Center.

It was he who started talking about Nicole. He said she was a nice girl, but that occasionally he felt like kicking her up the stairs. Perhaps because she was so damn even tempered. Had I noticed that?

I said I had, but that it didn't bother me.

He lit a cigarette. "Well, you wait. If you tell her that you have dived, you're in for it. She's got a thing about diving, some oriental twist in her mind, I suppose. Hasn't she told you yet that the dividing line between life and death is the mirror of the sea, and that what we are doing is penetrating in the realm of death?"

I said she hadn't and he laughed, stubbing out the cigarette he had just lit. "Well, you'll get it, don't worry," he said. "It's her favorite topic. And there is something else I should tell you."

I asked, "What?" because he didn't go on.

"I know it's none of my business," he said, "but just as a matter of interest: have you been to bed with her yet?" Before I could answer he continued, "Well, whether you have or haven't, you'll see that from now on, that's finished. She won't let you touch her any more once you've started going down with the Cousteau, until the day you give it up." He snorted. "The cheek of it! Girls—you never know what they'll think of next."

I wanted to ask him several things, but I sat there silently, thinking of Stella. She had loved us all, so long as we had been innocent and defenseless. The moment we had killed our first enemy it had been all over. "Yes," I said, "women are odd. I don't think we'll ever know what motivates them. Maybe she has got something there."

"Of course," he said. "But what's the use?"

I didn't quite get what he meant, but I left it at that. While we finished our drinks we talked about the trip to Greece and wondered what the old antiquarian expected us to bring up for him. I asked what he was like.

"Oh, a charmer," Goatskin said.

He was his new self again.

The charmer arrived within the hour of our arrival in Saint Tropez. He was called Mr. Astanasia, and for once Goatskin had been right. He was indeed a charming old man. He looked delicate and cultured, had steely gray hair and dark eyes, and his smile was very winning. We all liked him at first sight.

He had a crook with him on crutches, who looked so much like a musical-comedy pirate that the one thing lacking was a screaming parrot on his shoulder. He was introduced by Mr. Astanasia as a Greek sea captain; his name was very Greek and nobody quite got it. He was tentatively called Captain Perpendiculous, and as he didn't seem to find anything wrong with that we must have been pretty close.

Captain Perpendiculous was obviously looking for trouble. He whispered in Mr. Astanasia's ear all the time while they made the tour of the ship, guided by Goatskin. He was obviously telling him the truth about the ship, but Mr. Astanasia wasn't in the least impressed. He loved the ship, was delighted to see the old Captain in the wheelhouse, peering out of his bunk like a suspicious cat; he muttered "charming" all the time. We all felt greatly heartened and Pjotr said, "There goes a wonderful man." Mr. Astanasia was delighted also with the little cabin he got underneath the piano; Captain Perpendiculous was not as pleased with his, although it was exactly the same only on the starboard side. He said it was a death trap and that the mattress stank and asked whether engine fumes ever penetrated into it. Goatskin said, "No, no," on the sound principle that once we had got him at sea he wouldn't be able to get off.

The only one who wasn't delighted with Mr. Astanasia was the old Captain. He called me with a conspiratory "Psst!" as I passed the wheelhouse on my way to the fo'c'sle. He asked whether the little man with the gray hair was going to sail with us. I said he was.

"Is he the one who's paying for the trip?"

"Yes."

"In that case," said the Captain, "we can't sail."

I asked him why not, but he just went on doggedly repeating the classic phrase. At first I thought he had one of his usual tempers, but later on I heard the sounds of a colossal row in the wheelhouse. When I came back on deck I saw Goatskin, beside himself, in a curious position, half bent over the chart table, as if he was kneading dough. He was busy strangling the Captain. As I came in the old man was on the edge of a fit; he screamed that the ship was his, that he would have us taken off by the police and put in jail; that this was France, the country of justice, where no bloody foreigner could go too far. We could stand on our heads, or plate him with gold, if that man was sailing with us, we must find another ship! That was final, final! I was afraid it was indeed, because at that moment he clutched his chest, rumpling his pyjamas, and sat down in the lower bunk gasping for breath. It was the worst row we had had so far; but I still wasn't acclimatized to the South of France entirely yet. An hour later it seemed as if nothing had happened; only the old Captain had gone ashore with a handsome banknote in his pocket to take a rest in a hotel while we were away. His nerves were overstrained and he had agreed that as I had been sailing the ship for several weeks now, I knew her well enough and if anything happened to her the insurance would pay. I asked Goatskin where he had got the banknote from; he said that Mr. Astanasia had advanced it when he heard of the trouble.

Mr. Astanasia came to see me when I was shifting my bed sheets and my clothes from the fo'c'sle to the wheelhouse. He said that he was very pleased to know that I would command the ship and that if he was in my way at all at any given moment I shouldn't hesitate to say so. Captain Perpendiculous swung into view behind him on his crutches, shot me a Long John Silver glance, and whispered something in his ear; Mr. Astanasia laughed and said, "Nonsense, Captain." I didn't know what Captain

Perpendiculous had said, but judging from the look he gave me his remark must have expressed a doubt as to my abilities.

We would leave as soon as the new Cousteau apparatus had been delivered. After I had finished clearing out the wheelhouse I started looking among the charts for the Greek Archipelago. It wasn't there. I told Goatskin, and said that if we hadn't got those charts we couldn't sail. Only after the words had left my mouth I realized that I had taken over the classic phrase. Goatskin sighed and said, through clenched teeth, "One of these days I'm going to settle everybody." He must have gone to tell Mr. Astanasia about it, for a few minutes later the old gentleman appeared in the wheelhouse with a roll of paper under his arm. "I forgot to tell you, Captain," he said, "that I've got a complete set of charts with me."

I said, "Thank you, sir. Could we have a look at the route now or would you prefer to do that later?"

He laughed and said, patting me on the shoulder, "We'll have plenty of time for that, Captain, on our way to Corsica. Your first point of reference is Cap Corse."

That sounded fair enough. I began to like the old man. He was at least sensible, and seemed to take a lot of things in his stride.

While waiting for the new Cousteau we had a drink on a terrace, Goatskin and I. He was quite his new self again. He babbled on without interruption about how splendid things were and how rich we would be in four weeks' time. As we were sitting there, a quiet girl's voice said, "Hello. Mind if I sit down with you?" It was Nicole, very pretty, in a black dress with a plunging neckline and with her sun glasses on. Goatskin didn't answer, just made a vague gesture at a chair.

She asked what the trip with the businessmen had been like, and I began to tell her, but Goatskin interrupted by saying, "Oh, for God's sake, shut up! We've had that now. No, this time we've got something much better." And he went on telling her about the wonderful Mr. Astanasia and the Greek treasure. He hadn't finished singing the praises of Mr. Astanasia yet, when the old gentleman passed our table, spotted us, and came toward us, smiling. I introduced him to Nicole whom I called "Miss Nicole" because that was all I knew. He was very charming and old-world to her and ordered expensive drinks for all of us. Nicole sat looking at him through her dark glasses, smiling.

Mr. Astanasia was really an exquisitely mannered man, for he finished his drink quickly and left us before a silence had fallen in the conversation. He said he was going to do some last minute shopping, and we saw him disappear in a *parfumerie*, which bore a notice saying "Have yourself perfumed before you leave."

Then Nicole put her staggering suggestion to us. She said, calmly, "What if I went with you this time?"

We both looked at her with our mouths open; before we answered she went on, saying that although the old gentleman was very charming, he shouldn't be left to the cares of Pjotr and the old bosun as far as his food and the cleaning of his cabin was concerned. If we wanted him to remain charming it would be a good idea if we took somebody on board to look after these little things. Well, she was willing to come if we thought she might be any use.

Goatskin had recovered from his amazement by then and become boorish once more. He shrugged his shoulders and said, nodding at me, "Ask him. Not only is he the Captain, but you're his moll now." I swallowed a lot of things; then I said that I would be delighted. She said, "Thank you, Skipper."

After that there was a long silence which got strained to breaking point; then, luckily, a little van stopped at the gangway of our ship. "Ah," said Goatskin, jumping up. "That must be the new Cousteau! Excuse me," and he ran across the quay to welcome his new toy.

"Another diving set?" she asked.

I said, "Yes."

"Whom for?"

"Me."

"Are you going to work as a diver?"

"Yes."

"I see." We were silent for a while; then she got up. "Well, I suppose I had better pack my things now. Are we leaving soon?"

"In about twenty minutes."

"All right," she said, "I'll be there," and she went away.

As I crossed the quay to go to the ship I saw Captain Perpendiculous swing along, causing quite a sensation among the population. He looked like a sandwich man in a fancy costume, looking for his board with the advertisement of Jamaica Rum. As I mounted the gangway I saw him enter the perfumer's. They certainly had a handful coming.

Goatskin put her in the lower bunk in the wheelhouse.

I was on the poop taking the watch, after we had left the harbor on our way to Corsica, so I didn't see her go in there. I found her in the bunk when I entered the wheelhouse after he had taken over.

I asked, "What are you doing here?" stupidly, and she said, "This is the bed I've been given."

I felt like going back to the poop and having it out with him, once and for all; but I thought of Mr. Astanasia underneath, with his portholes open, and decided to let the lunatic get away with it once more. What made me see red was the deliberate callousness of it toward her. She must be a strong girl indeed to lie there, smiling, understanding it all and letting it pass. I asked, "Wouldn't you rather have a cabin? Here there will be people in and out all the time."

"Oh, no," she said. "I'm quite happy. If we leave the doors open it will be nice and fresh at night and I may not get seasick."

As it was going to be my watch again in four hours' time I wanted to get some sleep, so I just said, "As you like. Good night," and she said, "Good night, Skipper. Thank you."

"For what?" I asked, halfway up the ladder to my bunk.

"You know," she said. "Good night."

I wasn't sure I did know, but I shrugged my shoulders and climbed into my bunk.

Although I had changed the sheets and aired the mattress, it still smelled of the old captain. At the head of the bunk there was a little bookshelf, with an edge to it to prevent the books from falling out with the rolling of the ship. It looked empty, but when I put down my pack of cigarettes on it I noticed there was one book left, lying flat. It was a cheap edition of Negro spirituals, very battered and torn. I looked through it. One of the songs was marked with a heavy penciled cross and two exclamation marks. It ran:

> Sometimes I feel like a motherless child
> Sometimes I feel like a motherless child
> Sometimes I feel like a motherless child
> Far away from ho-o-ome
> Far away from home.

I looked at the flyleaf and saw it belonged to the old Captain. I put it back on the shelf, blew out the light, and went to sleep.

CHAPTER TWELVE

THE TRIP TO CAP CORSE WENT WELL. I HAD LOOKED FORWARD WITH apprehension to the moment when we would lose the land, for not only were the compasses suspect, but no Mediterranean helmsman could be made to stick to his course. The old bosun and the boy with the red cyclist's cap would greet each other at the changing of the watch like long lost friends after years of separation, embrace one another, kiss on both cheeks, and ask what their health was like, to arrive at the mentioning of the course only after at least five minutes, during which the wheel spun to and fro at every wave. Once the next man had taken the wheel he began to sing or, in case of the boy, to knit. Every time I checked the course we were at least five degrees out.

The second night I got sick of this, and I told the old bosun what I thought of his steering without mincing my words. An airplane was coming over low at that moment, and it drowned my little speech with the drone of its engine. "But, *mon commandant,* what are you worrying about?" the old bosun asked, sincerely amazed. "We are on the right course. There goes the plane to Corsica." After that I gave up.

The other one who worried about the course was Captain Perpendiculous; but then, he was worrying about everything. We never exchanged a word, he didn't seem to be talkative. He just appeared on the poop at irregular times and glowered at the compass, the sails, and the dozing helmsman. To see him emerge from the hatch was an eerie sight. First he threw his crutches onto the deck from below, then he mounted the stairs on his knees, collected his crutches, put them up, and hoisted himself to his one foot. The only proof of his experience as a sailor was that the moment he got on board he had taken the rubber caps off the butts of his crutches and driven a nail into each of them to prevent them from slipping. Within twenty-four hours the poop deck was already getting pockmarked with holes.

We saw the snow on the mountains of Corsica in the sky a full day before we arrived. At first I thought they were thin white clouds. I had no idea at what point we were going to hit the island, so when toward sunset a mistral started I got worried, it was blowing right on the beam. I had never come across the mistral before. It rose within five minutes from zero to seven, and after half an hour it was a gale. I had all sails taken in except the jib, and never had I known *Euridice* to run faster. I insisted on steering north-northeast when the mistral hit us, although this made the ship roll like a barrel, I didn't want to run smack into Corsica. The old bosun shrugged his shoulders and sighed. At nightfall, when the lighthouses began to wink on the horizon, I saw to my astonishment that we had been heading straight for Cap Corse, without knowing it. So I brought the ship back on her course and we lunged heavily toward the flashing light. As

Goatskin took over my watch and I went to the wheelhouse I found Nicole lying dead still in her bunk with her eyes closed, moaning softly. I asked, "Seasick?" and she nodded without opening her eyes. I said, "You'd better get up and come out on deck with me for a minute. It'll make you feel better." She tried to get up but was too weak. I wrapped her in a blanket, carried her out, and put her down on a wine barrel in the shelter of the wheelhouse. I sat down beside her, my arm around her shoulders, and she leaned against me, breathing heavily. I stroked her arm, the way Goatskin had done when I lay on the bridge wounded after the shelling of our ship. It had been very comforting, and it seemed to work on her too. After a while she relaxed a bit and her breathing became normal. "Better?" I asked. I felt her nod. We sat there for at least an hour, and I had dozed off when a torch shone in our faces. I blinked and asked, "Who's that?" The torch flicked out, and a shadow said, "Sorry." It was Goatskin.

I carried her back to the wheelhouse, put her down on her bunk, and covered her with a blanket. She wasn't feeling all right yet, for when I wanted to stand up and climb in my bunk she held on to my hand, squeezing it hard. I sat down on the edge of her bunk, her hand in mine, waiting until she would go to sleep.

I went to sleep first; when I woke up because the old bosun called, "*Commandant!* Cap Corse on the green!" I was lying on her bunk with my head on her shoulder.

The gale had freshened. When I came out on the deck I was nearly blown off my feet. As I reached the poop I saw Captain Perpendiculous stand behind the helmsman in the compass light, his crutches spread out, looking like a spider. Goatskin was there too, trying to light a pipe. I said, "I think we'd better take shelter behind the peninsula, don't you think so?" He answered, "Can't you make love if the ship's rolling?" I said: "All right, if you want it that way," called the bosun and told him we'd round the cape and try to enter the port of Macinaggio. He said we drew too much water for that, but we could anchor in the roads. He knew the corner, there was quite a nice little bay there.

When we dropped anchor off Macinaggio we were alone, and I was worried that it wasn't such a healthy corner after all. But within a matter of hours three other ships lay anchored with us, and by noon the next day our number had grown to nine. It was funny to think that these old Mediterranean salts had followed our example, trusting our appearance. We looked indeed very experienced; we had covered the piano with a tarpaulin when the gale started.

We lay anchored off Macinaggio for two days, waiting for the mistral to blow itself out. Goatskin suggested that I should try out the Cousteau once more.

I knew instantly why he suggested this, because he was watching Nicole while he said it. She was wearing her dark glasses and didn't react. She looked as if she wasn't listening.

As I was putting on the diving set Mr. Astanasia was very interested. He had never seen this before, he said, and while Goatskin was adjusting the straps of my harness he put intelligent questions about the thing. What seemed to interest him most was how deep we could go with it, and how long the bottles lasted. The answer seemed to satisfy him. I wasn't surprised, for Goatskin said that he could go down to a hundred and twenty meters at least and that the bottles lasted an hour and a half. As a matter of fact they lasted about an hour, and the record depth for the Cousteau, so Pjotr had told me, was a hundred and twenty-four meters; but when the diver came back to the surface he was dead.

The whole crew stood watching me as I went down the pilot's ladder. On the poop I saw the pirate, trying to look disinterested but watching like a hawk. Nicole was the only one who wasn't there. As I put my foot in the water it was very cold, much colder than it had been in La Ciotat. The mistral had cooled it off. This time I dived straight away, for the water was so crystal clear that I could see everything: our anchor buried in the seaweed, the yellow plate Pjotr had broken the day before and thrown overboard, the little fish flitting over a beautiful, white rocky bottom. I couldn't see any big fish from above, the mistral must have chased them away. As I slid down deeper I heard the two-toned horn again and the crackling in my ears. When the pain started I rose for a meter, swallowed, and dived deeper. I knew we were lying at fifteen meters, and the rocky soil looked very clean and inviting, so after having made a ceiling once more I went down to the bottom and stood up.

It was the most curious sensation I had ever had. I hadn't thought that the difference between floating and standing upright on the bottom of the sea was so striking. I had difficulty in remaining upright, for there was a slow ground swell that lifted me off the ground and gently put me down again. I tried to walk, but the moment I advanced, my feet were lifted off the ground and I came back to a horizontal position once more. It was my frogman's feet that did it, and after a short hesitation I took them off, feeling reckless. It did indeed make a difference. Once I had them in my hands I could walk. It wasn't normal walking, it was a slow, graceful dancing, like an athlete jumping on a slow motion film. It gave me an extraordinary sensation of joy and power; I touched the weeds with my hands and felt they were real. This was, at last, the heart of the dream; for in my dreams, ever since childhood, whenever I had stretched out my hand toward something, first a little cake and later a girl, I had woken up the moment before my fingers touched. The underwater world had looked like that from above; when I lay floating on the surface and looked down at the landscape with its waving shrubs, its flowers and its grassy plains, it had looked as if it would vanish at the touch of my big orange hand.

Now I was there, and touched it. I let go of the piece of seaweed, and as it floated away I caught it again, and I felt such a joy that I jumped like a child and rose five meters in the air. It wasn't water any longer; it was air. The clumsy mouthpiece, the sound of the horn, the staleness of the air I breathed, they all vanished the moment I stood upright with that bit of seaweed in my hand. The garden was mine.

I danced through the garden until I suddenly felt I was choking. I realized that my bottles had run out and opened the spare tank on my back. I had ten minutes left and I looked up to see where the ship was.

I saw it float above me, among the others, very small, like a model. I saw its propeller, and its rudder and the anchor chain going down. Now I had opened my spare tank it was high time I went back. I was about to rise when I saw a little flower of an extraordinary transparent blue in a little nest of seaweed. I danced toward it, and it was so beautiful that I couldn't resist the temptation to take it with me. I bent down, my feet rose in the air and I picked it, hovering like a humming bird. Then I rose back to the surface.

As I climbed the pilot's ladder I saw them all standing there, looking down at me, the orange creature coming back from the depth with a little flower in his hand. Goatskin asked, "Where the hell are your frogman's feet?" He gave me a shock, I had forgotten about them. They must be lying somewhere below in the garden. I thought of going back, but I remembered my air was finished so I climbed the rest of the ladder and was helped over the rail by many hands. I took the mouthpiece out and said, "I've left them below. I'll go and get them later."

Mr. Astanasia patted me on the shoulder as I was taking off my mask. "My hearty respect, Captain," he said. "What a wonderful diver you are. Could you have stayed down there longer?" I said, "No, sorry." Goatskin got angry and said, "Nonsense! He had at least three quarters of an hour left." When I told him that I had to open my spare tank he looked at me furiously and said, "In the first place your bottles weren't full; second, you're a bloody amateur. I watched your bubbles. You breathe much too fast." I said, "Give me a chance will you?" and went into the wheelhouse to look for a towel.

Nicole was sitting on her bunk, doing nothing. When I came in, she looked up. I said, "I've got something for you," and gave her the little flower. She said, "Oh, thank you. That's very nice of you," and looked at it, a bit startled, I thought. When I saw it in her hand I couldn't believe my eyes. The little flower that had looked so beautiful below was now a limp, leathery thing without any color at all, just a slimy piece of muck.

I said, "I'm so sorry, it looked ravishing below."

She put her arms round my neck, kissed me and said, "I'm sure it did, darling."

I was very disappointed, but her kiss made it good.

Mr. Astanasia told us our destination, at last, on the evening of the day we sailed from Macinaggio. He came to the poop in a white dressing gown, the sleeves rolled up to the elbows, looking like a Roman senator, carrying a lantern. He had his roll of charts with him and asked the bosun to call Goatskin, who had just gone down to sleep. After Goatskin had joined us he unrolled one of his charts and pointed at a little island in the farthest southwest of the Cyclades. "This is where we are going," he said. "Just here, at my finger, are the ruins of a Greek temple, submerged three thousand years ago after a landslide. I want you two to dive for it and have a look at what's inside. Probably nothing, but I thought it would be amusing to find out."

"How deep is it?" Goatskin asked.

"That's the point: I don't know. I got my information from the Greek gentleman who is with me, and who had a little sponge fishing business with a couple of divers. His fisherman found a wreck on one of their expeditions: an old three-master that was shipwrecked there about eighty years ago. They wanted to search the wreck, but it was lying too deep for them. They could see it quite clearly though; it seemed to rest on a curious scaffolding of white pillars. The news spread in the bistros ashore and got to some official, who passed it on to the Historical Institute in Athens, and there somebody came to the conclusion that the white scaffolding must be the ruins of a temple of Pallas Athene which they knew had been submerged three thousand years ago, only nobody knew exactly where. All this happened during the war. They kept the news a secret, for fear that the Germans would organize an expedition and pilfer the temple. They were about to organize an expedition after the war themselves, when their civil war started."

"Did they tell you about this?" Goatskin asked, boyishly.

Mr. Astanasia smiled in the lantern light. "No," he said; and then, after a silence in which Goatskin looked foolish, he added, "And I'd appreciate it if you young gentlemen could be as discreet as possible when you go down with your diving apparatus. I think that the best solution is that you go down on the side that is turned away from the shore. Although at the moment they have other things to do, there may be people looking at us through binoculars. Let's keep this little expedition private."

After that he asked me how long I thought it would take us to get there, and we discussed the route, and had a glass of wine together. He offered us one of his long, fragrant cigarettes, and was very charming and aristocratic.

When I told Nicole about the temple, she sat thinking for a while and then she asked, "Did he mention what he expected to find in there?"

I said he hadn't mentioned it, but that I remembered that some famous statue which was now in the Louvre had been found under water. She said it was called "The Victory of Samothrace." "Well," I said, "I suppose he hopes for yet another Victory." And then I remembered the newspaper in the cupboard on the dead windjammer in Antwerp, the picture of the soldier kissing the fat girl's hand. "To her murdered little hands, he owes his Victory." I realized for the first time what I had found under the sea. It was peace.

When we reached our Treasure Island, one starry night, the whole thing became too romantic for words, for Long John Silver came into action. He threw his crutches onto the deck from below, climbed the stairs on his knees, crawled over the threshold, and spread out a piece of paper on the deck. We knelt around him; Mr. Astanasia put down the lantern and we saw on the paper a crude, handmade map: the map of an island. It was scribbled full of Greek, which made it look even more picturesque; off the southeast coast was a rock, and at that rock was drawn a cross. He put a finger the size of a banana on the cross and said, "There." No actor in Hollywood could have said it better.

We were all very impressed and excited; this was what we had been reading about with glowing ears very long ago, when somebody had angrily said, "If you don't put that book down at once and go to bed, I'll take it away for good."

After we had got over our boyhood we started investigating the depths on the official chart. The soundings were from five to seven hundred meters within half a mile off the coast; so, unless the temple was sitting on a plateau with a precipice going down right in front of it, there either was no temple or we would need a bathyscope. We tried to get out of Captain Perpendiculous what exactly he had seen, and he gave a long flowery description of which the first six words were French and the rest Greek. Mr. Astanasia translated it for us; the upshot seemed to be that he had seen the wreck very clearly and that the white pillars had loomed in the blue. If that was true the temple must be at thirty or forty meters at the utmost, which was nothing. Anyhow, we would soon know. Goatskin and I would go down together first thing in the morning.

The next morning, when we stood ready with our bottles on in the wheelhouse, where we had put ourselves so as not to be seen from the shore, Mr. Astanasia came to wish us luck and said that in case a warship or a patrol from the shore hailed us we should say we were hunting. Goatskin said that it had all been arranged; Pjotr, Bernard, and Jacques would get into the water first with their respirators and their guns, to make the whole thing look natural. Captain Perpendiculous came swinging to the door and said something excitedly in Greek. Mr. Astanasia remained calm and aristocratic, but he took out a cigarette, which he forgot to light. "He says we're there," he said, "so perhaps you two might care to go down and have a look."

I called to the bosun to stop the engine, for we had approached the rock under power as there was no wind. The Greek coast showed blue and hazy in the distance; the little island seemed to be entirely uninhabited. There wasn't even a lighthouse on it, and no ships were in sight. Goatskin explained to Mr. Astanasia that Pjotr and the others would go first to see whether we were overhead, it would be a pity if we wasted our air on searching. If the Greek Captain had indeed seen it from the surface, then the boys would too.

Pjotr, Jacques, and Bernard went down the ladder and splashed into the water. They had hardly been in it three minutes when Bernard cried, "Here!" at about fifty yards distance from the ship. "All right," said Goatskin. "Let's go, Skipper. Good luck." Before he put in his mouthpiece he added, "Let's stay close together this time; if anything should happen that we don't want to happen, tap on your bottles. I'll do the same." I said, "O.K.," and we went down.

He got in first. When I followed him I felt the water was much warmer than it had been off the French coast. When I looked down, before I dived, I saw a sight so breath-taking that I lay floating on the surface blowing spluttering bubbles from my neck for minutes on end.

The rock near which we had descended was stark and bare above the water, but as soon as it vanished under the sea it turned into a mountain slope full of flowers of such unearthly colors that I stared at them in amazement and wonder. They were all shades of blue and pink and silver, and yellow and turquoise green; among them flitted millions of little fish of dazzling colors themselves, like butterflies. The flowered slope went down almost perpendicularly into the blue, but ahead of me I saw something dark jut out of it. I swam slowly toward it, after I had gone down my first five meters, and I saw the stern of a ship emerge from the blue. The first thing I recognized was a broken steering wheel, overgrown with weeds. Then, as I swam further, I recognized stumps of masts and the dark holes of holds. She must have been lying there for a very long time, for she was entirely overgrown; garlands of flowers hung down her sides and vanished in the blue.

I saw Goatskin pass underneath me and swim over her deck. When he reached the other side he stopped. He stayed motionless for about a minute. Then he suddenly turned round, looked, and I saw him pull his knife and tap on the bottles; it sounded as if he was just by my side. I went down five meters deeper, made my ceiling and swam toward him, crossing the wreck at about three meters above her deck.

On the other side the water was green and full of quivering, slanting beams of sunlight. At first I couldn't make out what it was, then I recognized a rectangular pattern, like the foundation of a house, but it was all overgrown with weeds and there were thousands of fish of all sizes who obscured the view.

I saw Goatskin go down, and I followed him. I made one more ceiling, and then another, and then yet another. I was now at thirty meters, in the green dusk of the depth. Then I touched ground and stood upright.

Again I had the curious sensation of a complete change, the moment I stood on my feet. I stood in what seemed to be the courtyard of a ruin. Huge pillars were lying among the weeds, broken in round discs. Only where the wreck was some of them stood upright. The wreck was resting on what must have been a roof three thousand years ago. She was silhouetted darkly against the blue and the silver of the sea, and sunlight slanted through the pillars. We stood looking at it, motionless, and saw the shadow of fish pass behind the pillars like birds against the deep blue of an evening sky. It was so fantastic and beautiful and unreal that we took a long time before we started dancing from pillar to pillar with long slow steps, looking. I had forgotten about Goatskin and he about me; yet we stayed close to one another instinctively, like geese.

We were sitting side by side on one of the sections of a fallen pillar in the courtyard when I saw it: a long dark silhouette, which slid silently past behind the standing pillars.

I had never seen one that size. It looked enormous, the triangular fin on its back stood out like a sail. I put out my hand and touched Goatskin's arm. It was the first time I touched a living body under water, it felt very cold.

We saw the shark pass from gap to gap, until it vanished in the blue behind the wreck's curved stem. From the stem a bowsprit hung down, broken; there were still ropes attached to it, garlands of weeds. Then we saw a round dark shape come toward us.

It was the shark again, heading for us. I didn't feel afraid, but I couldn't let go of Goatskin's arm. He had to shake me off to pull his knife. I pulled mine too, but I didn't intend to use it. I was very calm and not afraid of the shark attacking me; I was afraid of Goatskin attacking the shark.

It came gliding toward us silently, then it swerved and passed at five yards distance in front of us. I saw its white belly with three little fish hanging from it, sucked to its skin. I saw its small myopic eyes and its huge blue body beautifully shaped, and its tail, that moved gently but gave the impression of colossal strength. I turned round, following it with my eyes, and tried to see us as seen by him: two little orange creatures, sitting side by side on a pillar covered with seaweed, silver bubbles rising from their necks, that floated upward in little twin clusters, glistening in the sun. I would come and have a closer look if I was a shark; I would be much too amazed to think about eating straight away. I wouldn't believe my eyes; the shark did nothing that wasn't natural.

It made a circle around us, and then another much closer; and then Goatskin rose to his feet and waved his arms, but he didn't make any impression. He only made us more interesting to look at, two thin orange tentacles, waving, with something glistening in one. I got to my feet too, slipped on the seaweed and made a slow somersault backward. For a second I lost my sense of direction, then I saw Goatskin rise, and the long blue shape slide past below him, and then the shark rose perpendicularly too, and I saw it and Goatskin side by side for a moment, which gave me a feeling of nausea, for it was twice as tall as he.

Goatskin rose about five meters higher, became horizontal again, and hovered. I thought I had seen enough; as I rose past him I pointed upward, indicating that I was going to the surface. I looked up at the silver mist of the sky as I rose, then suddenly something gripped my right leg. I choked with fright, lost control of my breath, for one terrible moment I knew I was drowning. Then I looked down and saw it was Goatskin who had gripped me. He tugged at my leg angrily, and tapped his forehead. Then I remembered: we had been at thirty meters. If I went to the surface without hovering first at an intermediate level I would go blind, or paralyzed, or mad, or get a stroke. So I hovered, shaking, looking for the shark.

I had lost it from sight and thought it had gone away, but then the huge blue thing slid past again, turning. Goatskin's frogman's feet moved slowly by the side of my head; he had put himself like this so that we would be looking both ways, without need to turn round the clock as the shark circled around us. He came closer and closer, and I gripped my knife with failing courage, ready to give him the gentle prod Goatskin had told me about. I hoped that if any prodding had to be done he would do it first, but most of all I hoped and prayed that there would be no prodding at all.

My prayer was not granted. I knew something was about to happen when I saw his frogman's feet flap rapidly and vanish. I turned round and saw the shark's white belly pass right overhead at about an arm's length. I saw the little sucking fish very close by, they seemed to be dragged across my mask. Then Goatskin shot up beside me, his right arm with the knife stretched out, and he stabbed the white belly as it slid past again.

At that moment something seemed to explode. I turned over several times in a whirlpool of violent currents; when I had found my sense of direction again Goatskin was circling underneath me, and the shark was nowhere to be seen. What hit me must have been the backwash of its tail, when it fled at the sting of the knife.

I had no idea any more at what height we were, but I hovered on, my heart pounding and my knees trembling, until Goatskin joined me. We floated hand in hand over the ruins, the wreck, and the flowers; two children in a dream. Then, at last, he nudged me, and pointed upward, and we rose.

When we climbed back on board and told Mr. Astanasia what we had seen, he was very pleased and offered us a drink which we took in the sunlight, shivering, while our harnesses were taken off. Although the water had been warm, we were very cold now. We told about the shark too, and Goatskin sounded very confident about it. Just a big dumb animal, he said. Nobody had ever been attacked by a shark in the Mediterranean. They were the harmless kind, only very curious. I said I was quite willing to believe that, but hoped he wouldn't be there next time. "No hope," said

Goatskin, "we have aroused his curiosity, now he'll be there every time we go down."

I said, "I see."

We didn't go down again that day. Mr. Astanasia thought it better not to hang around the spot too long. We sailed back into the open and lay in the sun and slept, while Bernard and Jacques and Pjotr went out to hunt the dinner.

That night, after everybody had gone to bed, I chatted with the old bosun. We were just idly drifting, so for once he could forget about the wheel and talk. When we came to our diving he said, "Yes, that temple is a lovely sight, with that old wreck on top. I saw it when I was a boy."

I thought that was extraordinary, and told him so. But he laughed. "I think every sailor boy in the Mediterranean has seen it," he said. "Whenever we were around these corners we always went to have a look, through a little glass case, you know, that we held outside the boat in the water. The number of people that have been going down there with masks and diving bells and scaphanders, my, they must have been at it for centuries. That wreck has been picked as clean as a skeleton in the desert."

I thought at first that this was just another Mediterranean fantasy; but as I thought about it, looking at the stars, I found a lot of sense in his story. The wreck and the ruins were so close to the surface, and could so easily be seen, that it seemed unlikely that nobody had ever bothered to go down before. Mr. Astanasia's expedition became a bit of a mystery.

"What did the old gent come here for?" the bosun asked. "To take photographs or something?"

I thought there was no harm in telling him the truth. "No, he's looking for antiques," I said.

The old man laughed. "Antiques?" he asked. "The only antiques left to take away down there will be those stone wheels. I wonder who sold him that idea. The Greek?" I said I didn't know.

When I went to call Goatskin for the changing of the watch I told him about the bosun's story, and, for once, he reacted reasonably. He too must have realized that the ruins were much too close to the surface to have remained untouched for three thousand years.

"Well," he said. "I don't know. Either the old boy has been sold a dud by Captain Perpendiculous, or he's looking for something else that he hasn't told us yet. We'll soon know."

Four hours later, toward sunrise, when I had just come back to the poop after my four hours' sleep and Goatskin was about to go down, Mr.

Astanasia rose silently from the hatch in his Roman senator's gown, smoking one of his long cigarettes. He said, "Good morning," and "Well, this looks like the beginning of another glorious day," and then, with a smile at the old bosun, "Surely there is no need to keep the crew out of their beds? We are just drifting, aren't we?" I could take a hint, so I told the bosun to go back to his bunk. He was delighted.

When we were alone on the poop Mr. Astanasia offered us a cigarette each, and after he had even lit them for us with an aristocratic hand, he said, "I think it's time, gentlemen, that we had a little talk in private."

Goatskin, who never looked before he jumped, said, "Yes, I think so. We heard—"

Mr. Astanasia lifted his hand, a cultured gesture of interruption. "There's no need to tell me what you heard," he said. "My portholes were open."

"Right," said Goatskin. "Well then, what are we looking for?"

"For something that may be found one plateau lower down," Mr. Astanasia replied. "And if it isn't there, you may have to go down one step deeper."

"How deep will that be?" I asked.

"A hundred and forty meters."

"So we can forget about the second step," Goatskin said.

Mr. Astanasia smiled and shrugged his shoulders. "If you prefer," he said. Goatskin was about to say something hearty; I put my hand on his arm before he shot his mouth off. I wanted to know what the dear old gentleman was up to. "Then what are we looking for?" I asked, and Mr. Astanasia answered, "You'll see when you find it."

"What do you want us to do if we find it?" Goatskin asked.

"We'll cross that bridge when we get to it," the old gentleman said, tersely. "You find it first. Good night."

As he turned and went down the stairs Goatskin said, "Good morning." Then he grinned at me in the blue light that preceded sunrise. "For our next private conversation," he said loudly, "we'll climb the foremast." I beckoned him to follow me, and we went along the deck as far forward as we could go. Then we leaned over the rail, and looked at the bow of our ship, slowly rising and sinking in the limpid water with the long, slow swell. We talked about the mysterious order and agreed that it was all very fishy and were sure it was gold he was after, or bags of diamonds, or something, and that the temple business had been a device to get us out here without a share in the profit. Goatskin said we should insist on a share before we started risking our necks by going down deeper; I was in favor of locating the mystery thing first if we could, there was no need to kick up a row before his appetite had been whetted.

As we stood there, whispering, we had our backs to the ship, so we didn't see her coming. When she said, "So, sweet old Mr. Astanasia has shed his mask?" she gave us quite a shock.

Goatskin didn't even bother to look round. I said, "Good morning. Yes, he has. Did you know him, by any chance?" She was wearing the thin pink dressing gown and, although there was no sunlight yet, her dark glasses.

"No," she said. "I'd never seen him in my life, before he sat down with us on the terrace."

"So when you offered to come with us it was only a pretext, your saying that you wanted to look after him?" I asked.

"That's right," she said. "I didn't like the look of him. I wanted to be around."

Goatskin snorted, with his back to her. "I never thought I'd sink so deep," he said, "that one day I would set out for a diving expedition with a body-guard of whores."

I said, "What if you went to bed?"

"Want to pick another fight?" he asked. "I'm your man, you know."

I said, "Go to bed."

He stood up, stretched, and yawned; then he said, "If you want to be a sucker, I don't suppose anyone can stop you. But if I may give you a piece of sound advice as a friend, put her—there." At that he pointed overboard, walked away, and went down the ladder to the fo'c'sle.

We had become used to this, so I wasn't amazed any more that she should take it so calmly. She took his place by my side, and we leaned over the rail again, looking at the sea and the orange clouds of sunrise.

"It looks as if you and the old Captain were the only ones the old crook didn't take in," I said.

She shrugged her shoulders. "He is quite a common type on the coast. If you had been living in the South of France as long as I have, you would have seen through him too."

"Well," I said. "I don't think there is anything seriously wrong. I only hope that that bloody fool won't get one of his fits of bragging and go down to a hundred meters or worse."

"So do I," she said. "That's why I came."

It was the closest she got to the confession that she was in love with him since I had first met her. I wanted to say something, but I didn't. "It isn't so much the danger of going down," I said. "I think that theoretically we can go down as deep as we like with those bottles. It's the danger of coming up. I had a look at the list of depths and hovering times. With two bottles we can go down to ninety meters, cast one look round and then we have to start coming back. By the time we arrive at our last decompression stage we'll have to open our spare tanks. So if the thing is lying at eighty or below, we might as well forget about it, for we won't have the time to do any work on it."

"I don't like this," she said. "I hope there will be nothing."

I said, "So do I," and then, after a silence, "There's something else I don't like, and that's the sharks. Not so much because they frighten me, but because I'll have to frighten them, and that will make me use my air too fast. If we go down deeper, we'll have to sink as quietly as we can, hardly moving, to eke out our air; the moment a shark turns up, you start breathing like a steam engine."

"What about those anti-shark tablets?" she asked. "Somebody told me they existed."

I said, "Yes, we had them during the war in our lifebelts. 'Shark chasers,' they were called. Big tablets, the size of a cigarette box, sown into the linen. If you found yourself afloat in the tropics you ripped them out and they dissolved in the water and made a black cloud around you like an octopus. They are no good under water. You can't take that cloud with you as you move."

"I thought there were other ones," she said. "An American invention, tablets that when they dissolve give off the smell of a decomposing shark's corpse. It seems they stay away from that."

"Maybe," I said. "But I've never heard of them. And even if they exist, we haven't got them on board. No, all we can hope for is that our friend stays away."

"He won't," she said. "Everybody says so. He'll stay around here for weeks now he has seen you."

I said, "So I gather."

It had become lighter, the sun was about to rise, the world looked very beautiful. I felt far away from everything; I didn't worry about today, this morning was lovely. I said, "He told me in La Ciotat that you had some oriental theory about the mirror of the sea being the dividing line between life and death. Is that true?"

"Yes," she said.

"He also said that once he had dived with the Cousteau you wouldn't let him touch you any more. Is that true too?"

She answered, after a silence, "I never let him touch me, not even before he dived."

I don't know what it was, perhaps the peace of the sunrise, the beauty of the sea, but it was as if I could hear her thoughts whisper in the silence. I said, "There is no need to lie to me about him. We have got beyond the point where he matters. If you don't want to talk about him, say so, but don't lie. It spoils things."

"All right," she said, "I don't want to talk about him."

I said, "That's fair enough," and we stood silently looking at the sun rising until it blinded us.

As we stood by the wheelhouse with our harnesses on, Goatskin said, "I think the best plan is that we dive together until we get into the blue. As soon as you feel that you have gone deep enough, stay where you are and wait for me. Don't think you're God's brother-in-law, the dark is pretty frightening, and I don't expect you to go down with me all the way. If you get into a panic at a depth of eighty, we'd find ourselves in an awkward situation."

I said, "All right. I'll put my safety before my honor."

"But I think it's more likely," he said, "that you'll have to stay at a pretty low depth anyhow, because of the shark. If it turns up again, I'll leave it to you. You stay at the depth where we meet it, and play around with it a bit. Then I can sneak into the purple without it following me. There's no need to be frightened."

I said, "I suppose there isn't, but I am."

It irritated him. "Don't be silly," he said. "You know now that they aren't dangerous, just curious. If you meet it again today, you'll see it looks like an old friend."

I said, "I know it won't attack me, but yesterday I was knocked for six by just the backwash of its tail. I hate to think what would happen if it gave me a wallop with that thing while we are playing."

"Then take a harpoon with you," he said. "It's six times as long as your knife and you can keep at a safe distance while prodding."

I said, "All right. Let's go and see."

We went down the pilot's ladder and dived. Mr. Astanasia was not standing at the rail this time to wish us good luck. He was standing on the poop, with the spider. The others shouted jocular greetings as we clumsily lowered ourselves into the water. The bosun called, "Daddy, bring back a little monkey for me!" It wasn't funny, but under the circumstances it

286

made me laugh—hysterically. I had difficulty checking myself by remembering that I was using precious air with this nonsense.

We were slightly farther away from the wreck and the temple than we had been yesterday; we descended in a slant and didn't catch sight of the flowery mountain slope until we were at about twenty meters. After we had made our fourth ceiling, we swam horizontally toward the wreck until we found ourselves in about the same spot where the shark had been when we first saw it slide past behind the pillars. I looked round for it, but it wasn't there. Only swarms of smaller fish, of wonderful colors, who hovered round us in a glittering cloud.

Once we had reached the pillars underneath the wreck, we went down deeper into the blue, descending along them. It was the first time I had entered the blue and although it was very beautiful, like floating in an evening sky, I didn't like it, it restricted my field of vision to about six meters. It began to remind me of La Ciotat harbor.

We went down deeper still. I followed Goatskin and saw his color change below me from orange to brown, then from brown to dark green. Beyond him, the blue became purplish; there was nothing else in view. We had passed the base of the pillars now and slid down sideways along what seemed to be steps. The steps continued down into the blue, darker and darker, until I saw a vague dividing line, quite straight, that seemed to be the edge of a precipice. Goatskin got darker and darker, although I stayed very close to him. The blue changed to deep purple. I didn't like the sight of that purple; the gathering darkness began to terrify me. And then, quite suddenly, as I went deeper with my hand stretched out, I felt something cold, as if I had dipped my hand into the water from a boat.

I slid into the coldness, then I stopped. This was too much for me. I hovered for a moment, getting very cold, and I saw Goatskin's shadow vanish in the darkness below. Only his bubbles went on rising past me in little clusters, joining and separating, big round ones into myriads of small ones, glistening like foam. I rose a couple of meters and when I rose I slid into the warmth again, like stepping out of the shadow on a hot summer's day. The bubbles went on floating past me, glistening, and I rose higher to get back to the light. As I rose, I felt very confident. I timed my periods of hovering with a feeling of familiarity. I was an expert now. I thought I must be at fifty meters, so I had to wait a long time before I went higher up. It was a pity I hadn't got a waterproof wristwatch, for I wasn't sure whether I had the right idea of time. Goatskin's bubbles rose slowly, regularly. I counted the periods between them. Three seconds one time, four the next, then four and a half, then three again. It was no use counting them. I just had to trust my common sense.

I thought I had hovered on the edge of the steps for at least a quarter of an hour and decided to rise to the next ceiling. It got lighter as I rose, I could make out the steps again. As I had nothing to do but to hang around until this decompression period was over, I got closer to the steps to see what they were made of. They were thickly overgrown with weeds and a sort of moss, and full of little animals, crawling, flitting, and jumping. I thought I saw a sea star and prodded it gently with my harpoon. It shot up and vanished in the dusk with a few spasmodic movements.

Now I was hovering, the crowd of fish around me got thicker. There were a few that were almost as big as I was, and they came very close. I knew there was no reason to be afraid, they were just curious; but then I saw an eye staring at me, luminous like a cat's at night when it catches a light. I didn't like that; I waved at it with my harpoon. The eye blinked and vanished. I thought there would be no harm now in going up to my next stage, for the dusk didn't get lighter as I hung on. It seemed to darken.

I rose another five meters or so, and all the fish rose with me. I began to get irritated by their silent curiosity. I did silly things in my lonely boredom: I pointed at one and followed it with my finger, I shook my fist and blew a burst of angry bubbles by calling "Boo." As a particularly stupid one advanced on me, stopped at about a yard's distance from my mask, and gaped like a village idiot, I put my thumbs on my temples and twiddled my fingers. His face was so stupid that I burst out laughing. I had to stop that, the air was much too precious. I tried to put my mind off what I had done, for every time my thoughts skirted it, I began to giggle again. So I began to hum. At first I just hummed, while breathing out. It sounded deep and sonorous, like a church organ. I had a beautiful voice under water. I started playing a tune on the organ with one finger, "Sometimes I feel like a motherless child." It sounded so beautiful and sad that it brought tears to my eyes, which would run down my cheeks and start filling my mask if I went on humming this heart-breaking tune. I had to find something gayer. I tried "Daisy," but that sounded out of place. I suddenly became conscious of the situation: an orange creature hovering on the steps of a temple no human feet had trod on for three thousand years, humming "Daisy." Goatskin's bubbles were still rising from the depth, but they didn't rise like soap suds any more. They rose like puffs of foam. He must be very deep. I began to get worried. It was high time that he was on his way back. I wondered whether he had lost his sense of depth, or perhaps he had got stuck down there. I decided that I must put my mind off thoughts like those, for they set my heart pounding and that made me breathe too quickly. I rose another ten meters, back into the light.

I was halfway up the pillars now, the wreck rested somewhere above me. I wanted to look up but thought I had better not turn on my back, every unnecessary movement was a waste. The crowd of fish had followed me; there must be hundreds of thousands of them around me by now, and as they caught the sunlight they began to glitter and get color, and I floated, dazed, in a whirlpool of diamonds and rubies. They were the most beautiful creatures I had ever seen; and now that I remained so still for so long they came closer and closer, throngs of them, swerving around and below me, changing from silver to green and from blue to gold in whole sheets, like starlings swarming. Goatskin's bubbles rose through them, clusters of silver dust blown up, and whole swarms of little fish rose with them. Then suddenly, as if swept away by a gust of wind, they vanished, all of them, blown into the blue. I looked round, alarmed, and felt a shadow pass over me. Then I saw the shadow pass, a slanting tunnel into the blue. I turned on my back and saw the shark, the three suckling fish hanging limply from his belly.

I thought, "Well, here we go again," and giggled, and my knees started trembling. Goatskin's bubbles were still rising, but they had got bigger now. They weren't silver foam any longer; little round suds glistened in the sunlight, changing color as they rose. The shark turned round in the distance and came back. I rose another five meters; I wanted to have a clear view and so I hovered at the level of the wreck's deck. It was at about six meters to my left. The shark came straight at me and I pointed at it with my harpoon, like an old lady with an umbrella. That thought made me giggle again, and I prayed, with a feeling of panic, "God, don't let me giggle, don't let me giggle, dear God."

I thought the shark with its myopic eyes was going to run into my harpoon and I dived again, foolishly, and turned on my back once more; my bubbles rose in two bursts by the side of my face. The shark passed overhead and dropped something. It was as big as a horse's, and I darted aside to avoid it. Then I saw that something had attracted its attention.

It had turned around, looking for me, and was suddenly distracted by something else: Goatskin's bubbles. It seemed to be fascinated by them. It advanced on a little cluster, rose with it, as if it were sniffing, then it dived again, circled, and advanced on the next lot. At the fourth cluster of bubbles it did something that set my heart pounding. It sniffed, made a full swerve very fast, during which it turned on its back. I saw it open its mouth, which was much bigger than I had thought, and flash through the cluster of bubbles, catching them.

I suppose it was all part of the play, but I didn't like it. I wanted to get back to the surface, before it should start playing with my bubbles and follow them down to their source. But it had forgotten me; it stuck to Goatskin's bubbles, playing with them again and again, swerving round, turning on its back, opening its mouth, swallowing them. And then, abruptly, it hung quite still in the air, as if listening to something, seemed to be shaken by a convulsion and I saw a spurt of bubbles burst out of its mouth. I heard a deep rumbling sound. It shot backward and flashed away at high speed. As it vanished in the blue, I understood that it had belched. Its own belch had terrified it out of its wits. It must have been the first.

I didn't know how much time passed before I saw Goatskin emerge again, but practically the instant I saw him hover below me, my air stopped and I had to open my spare tank. I was alarmed, because at the depth where he was now, he couldn't come up straight away. I rose almost to the surface and watched him for awhile; then I had to go to the ship. My air gave out at two meters' distance from the pilot's ladder.

He didn't come up until a quarter of an hour later. I felt a bit ashamed. I had breathed very regularly and sparingly, I thought, and he had been down much deeper; yet I had used my air a lot quicker than he. When he came up the pilot's ladder I got a shock. His mask seemed rusty inside, I could hardly see his face. As he took out his mouthpiece he spat angrily, and his spittle was red. "Ugh!" he said. "What a mess! I'll have to wash those damn tubes out before I use them again." Then he took his mask off and I saw that underneath it his face was covered with blood. It looked horrible. "Christ," I said. "What happened?" He answered, "Nothing. My nose started bleeding. I pushed up my mask against my nostrils to block them. Then I had to swallow the blood and kept on blowing it into the tube. Give me a drink quick. I'm as sick as a cat."

Pjotr hurried to get him a drink and Bernard washed his face. While he sat on a wine barrel, shivering, having his face washed, he asked, "Seen the shark at all?"

I told him about the shark chasing the bubbles, as he sat sipping his drink. When I told him that it had swallowed them and been chased by its own belch he looked up. I said it had been very funny and he said, "Yes, it must have been," and then suddenly he went to the rail and vomited. Nicole was by his side in a flash and wanted to put her hand on his forehead but he snarled, "Bugger off, you Goddam bitch," and hung over the rail, retching. I led her away.

She was very calm and composed, but she trembled. Although I was getting cold despite the sun, I didn't want to leave her to get a towel. I took her to the foredeck where we sat down on the bowsprit. She looked as if she would break down any moment. Her face had gone a curious green, the color it had been as she sat underneath the blue parasol in Saint Tropez. Then I had thought it had been the blue shadow, now I realized it must have been something else. "I don't think it's anything serious," I said. "It's swallowing the blood that made him sick."

She looked at me and smiled. "You're sweet," she said. "But would you mind just leaving me alone for a bit?"

I said, "Sorry," and went down to get my towel. I was very chilled and felt rather lonely, which I hadn't for some time. I wondered how deep he had been and if he had seen something.

When I came back on deck after having put on some clothes she was still sitting in the same place. I wanted to go to the midships but she called me. I went back to her, smiling formally, like a nurse.

"Sorry," she said. "It wasn't because of you. It was because I—I didn't feel well."

I said, "I see."

"Sharks aren't dangerous until they smell blood," she said. "If you hadn't frightened it away, he would never have come back."

I felt my cheeks go cold. "It wasn't me who frightened it away," I said. "It was the sound it made itself."

"I know," she said. "I . . ." and then she covered her face with her hands.

I thought of putting my hand on her shoulder but then I didn't. I said, "Don't worry, I'll see to it that he doesn't go down again." Then I went to the poop.

Goatskin was lying in the sun, a rolled up blanket under his head, smoking a long cigarette. I sat down beside him and asked, "Feeling better?"

He said, "Yes."

"Seen anything?"

"No."

I looked at him. His eyes were closed and his face was pale, but his thin lips seemed to be smiling. I didn't like that smile and I didn't like that cigarette. I knew he had seen something. I sat by his side for a while but we didn't talk. The bosun sang *Les jeunes filles de Camaret se disent toutes vierges.* I jumped when there was a loud clatter behind my back;

two crutches had been thrown out of the hatch. Captain Perpendiculous' head appeared above the threshold as he climbed the stairs on his knees. When he saw me he grinned and said, "Good morning, Captain!"

Then I knew for certain that Goatskin had seen something. The pirate had never greeted me before.

CHAPTER THIRTEEN

THAT NIGHT I TRIED TO KEEP HIM FROM DIVING AGAIN THE NEXT DAY. I didn't ask what he had seen, I didn't mention the purpose of his diving at all. I just talked about the shark, saying that if he went down again as deep as he had done, his nose would certainly start bleeding again and this time the shark might not frighten itself away.

He listened to me calmly, his thin lips smiling, and when I had finished, he asked, "Are you by any chance speaking on behalf of Nicole?"

"I'm speaking on behalf of every sane person on board this ship."

He laughed. It was an unpleasant little laugh. So far I had thought he wanted to go down again to get what he had seen; after that little laugh I began to suspect that he was back on the stage once more in the role of a tight-lipped, cynical desperado, at the end of his tether, about to commit suicide in a daring exploit that would end his life with a flourish. It made me angry. I suddenly realized that both Nicole and I had been playing up to him by our worrying, and now I was again acting the perfect stooge. "All right," I said, "if that's the way you want it, go and have yourself torn to pieces by a shark. But I can tell you this much: even if you had found Aladdin's cave in the purple, I am not coming with you tomorrow. Let your Mr. Astanasia put on the Cousteau and have a romp with the shark himself. I'm through."

"I am glad you have realized at last that you won't get anywhere with that Chinese whore while I'm alive," he said.

I said nothing. I told myself that it was unfair to slap the face of a man who was recovering from a bleeding nose.

"If I told you what I found, would that make any difference?" he asked, with his stage voice.

I said, "No."

He put his hand in his trouser pocket, brought out a smart oblong box, opened it and selected a cigarette. He had never selected a cigarette before, on the sound principle that they were all the same. This conception of smartness came straight out of English detective novels, the only place where people selected cigarettes. I knew for certain now that he was play acting. I knew for certain too that, whatever he had found, Mr. Astanasia had been very pleased with him.

"Want one?" he asked.

I said, "No, thanks," and then, "I must say things have changed. I never would have thought, when we sailed the Northeast Passage together, that the time would come when some night-club crook would make you feel pleased with yourself by giving you a box of cigarettes for risking your neck." It was quite a little speech. It sounded as if I was getting onto the stage too.

He answered, "That's right, Skipper. Things have changed. If I don't come back tomorrow that will be the logical ending to a lot of things."

I suppose he expected me to oblige him with some more, but I didn't. I said, "Good night, Hamlet," and went to the wheelhouse.

Nicole was lying on her bunk, I thought she was asleep, and I started undressing quietly so as not to wake her up. She asked from the darkness, "Did you talk to him?"

"Yes."

"Any good?"

"No."

I went on undressing. Then I lit a cigarette and sat down on the chart table and looked at my shadow, moving on the ceiling in the faint light of the compass.

"So you are going down tomorrow?" she asked.

I said, "He is, but I am not. I won't do any good, and I hate to see a human being torn to shreds by a shark."

"Don't talk like that," she said, "please."

I sat smoking for a while in silence, feeling rotten. I knew he would go and I would go, and I wished it was all over. I stubbed out my cigarette, said, "Good night," and climbed into my bunk. I lay awake for a long time, waiting for her voice to call softly, "Skipper," and then I'd go down and lie down beside her and she'd put her head on my shoulder and tell me everything: that she loved him and he loved her, that she had seen him go to hell and known he would commit suicide one day if he went on diving, that she had feebly tried to wake him up from the spell the sea had thrown over him by refusing to let him touch her unless he gave up diving. She must have been torn between her love and her urge for self-preservation until she was frantic. I thought I understood it all now, and I was sure I could help her, if only she opened her mouth and called me.

But she didn't. I lay awake, waiting, until the bosun came to call me for the day watch.

The next morning, after he had put on his bottles, his frogman's feet, and his mask, he stood ready to go down in the wheelhouse and saw me fully dressed. He said, "Well, Skipper, it's been nice knowing you."

I said, "Don't be a Goddamned fool. Kick that old bastard in the arse and be your age."

He smiled his maddening smile and said, "I've only got one thing to ask you. Either I come back or I don't, either way suits me, but I don't want to come back as a cripple. Do you understand?"

I said, "No."

"I am serious," he said, "it's the last favor I ask you for old times' sake. You have made up your mind to stay where you are, all right, stick it. If for some reason you find that I got into trouble, don't act the little hero and pull me out. I'd rather drown than spend the rest of my life in a wheelchair, babbling nonsense."

He was so completely in his role that I couldn't think of anything to say that would sound real. In the end I said, "Don't worry, I'm through with you," and turned to go. As I heard him laugh behind me I couldn't help looking round. He stood grinning at me, his blue eyes were cruel and mad. "Don't think," he said, "that you'll ever be alone in bed with her. There will be a ghost between you."

I said, "Jesus, you make me sick," and went away.

As I went to the fo'c'sle I heard a voice ask, "Captain?" and saw Mr. Astanasia in his Roman bathrobe advance on me. "Aren't you going down?" he asked.

I said, "No sir."

His old-world politeness waned as he said, "This is a surprise. I thought we had agreed that both of you would do your best to make this expedition worth while for me. I am afraid I must insist that you go."

Suddenly all my pent-up rage concentrated on the old man. "Sir," I said, "I don't know what you are after and I don't care, but I warn you: if anything should happen to that boy you'll be sorry for a long, long time. Understand?"

His face hardened until it looked as if it had been cast in bronze. He looked at me like a sphinx, who had been watching the vermin at its feet for over three thousand years, and was resigned to watch some more. "I have never been impressed by threats, young man," he said in a bored voice; then he turned on his heels and went away.

I had decided not to be on deck when he dived. I was going to lie in my bunk in the fo'c'sle and read. But while looking for a book in the mess behind Bernard's bunk I couldn't help glancing out of the porthole.

I could not see him go down without putting my head out, but I heard him. I heard the crunching of the rungs of the ladder as he descended, the spluttering of the bubbles as he put his head under water; then I saw an orange patch slide past below me and I followed the trail of the bubbles with my eyes as he swam away. We were very near the wreck, he went almost straight down. The bubbles went on rising in the same spot after a while. Then the ship slowly swung round on the swell, and I lost sight of the spot. I went to the wheelhouse.

Nicole was still lying on her bunk, her eyes closed. I took the old captain's binoculars and watched the spot. The bubbles went on rising, regularly. I glanced at the clock, it was a quarter to eight. He had been in the water for five minutes; he should be well into the blue by now, making his seventh ceiling. I went on watching the bubbles and saw them change gradually to patches of milky foam. He must be at about eighty meters now, the bubbles would go on coming up like foam even if he went down to a hundred or more. I looked at Nicole; she hadn't moved but her face had the same greenish paleness that I had seen twice before. It was the only thing she couldn't control with her will.

The ship was very silent. I looked at the deck and saw them all lined up at the rail, watching the bubbles. I also saw my bottles, my mask and my frogman's feet, lying ready beside the wheelhouse. I wondered who had put them there.

He had been under water for nearly half an hour now; at the depth where he was his bottles would not last longer than an hour. He should be on his way back, but the foam still rose in milk-white patches. I counted the periods between them. Three seconds. Four and a half. Three. Four. Three. I had hardly let them out of my sight since the moment he had gone down; they had been coming up regularly like this for over half an hour. This meant he was either still going down or searching in the purple. He had not worked yet, or I would have seen it. The periods between the bubbles would have been a lot shorter if he had.

My mouth was very dry. I realized it as I swallowed. If he was still at his lowest depth by this time, without having done anything, it meant that he was very late rising. He should have been on his way back, but I was sure he wasn't. I fumbled in my pockets and took out a crumpled pack of cigarettes. Without looking away from the bubbles I put one in my mouth, searched my pockets for my lighter, counting the periods all the time.

Three. Three. Three and a half. And then suddenly: One. One. A half. One. . . . This was it.

I couldn't stick it in that wheelhouse, I went outside, stood beside Pjotr at the rail, staring at the bubbles. One. A half. A half. Three. Five. Five. . . . I felt something hot on my arm; it was Pjotr's hand, squeezing. One. A half. A half. Five. And then the bubbles changed. They rose to the surface differently, much weaker, as if he was breathing very little. One and a half. One and a half. One. One. One. I said, "All right."

Pjotr jumped at my bottles, and not he alone. Jacques, Bernard, the old bosun, all the men who had stood leaning on the rail, staring at the bubbles, rushed toward my diving set at that one word. They put the bottles on me in a matter of seconds. I put on my frogman's feet while they were adjusting the harness and strapping the ballast belt round my waist. I put them on the wrong feet, but left them as they were; I went down the pilot's ladder without blowing in my mask to try it. I had wanted to jump into the water from the deck, but checked myself in time. If I had, the mask would have been ripped off at the impact. I remembered to blow in my mask when my feet were already dangling. There was an air leak on the left hand side. While I was adjusting it a voice called, "Look!"

I saw a great commotion in the water on the spot where the bubbles had risen, bits of seaweed came to the surface, and then a limp, round thing. I thought, feeling suddenly sick, that it was he. I dived and swam toward it. The moment I was under water I saw it was dust and bits of seaweed. There was no living fish in sight. The brown thing was an old lifebelt.

I dived; as soon as I saw the wreck and the pillars I went down seven or eight meters, then I had to make a ceiling because of the pain in my ears. I was looking for his bubbles rising, and I thought I saw them, very faintly, floating up, with the dirt that went on rising in clouds. I had my harpoon with me; as it flickered in the sunlight I thought it was something else and started breathing faster, fear tightened the skin on my thighs. I dived again until the pain forced me to make a new ceiling, and then I heard a weak tapping sound, very close.

This tapping gave me a sudden courage. Perhaps it wasn't courage but something else. It just made me realize that he knew I was there, and was calling me. I forgot about the shark, I forgot about the terror of the purple, I went down deeper and deeper in reckless plunges, making ceilings only when I had to bite in my mouthpiece for excruciating pain. Then, on the verge of the darkness, I saw him.

He was rising slowly out of the night. Weak foam spiraled out of his neck. His arms hung limply by his side. But what gave me that feeling of sickness again was that the foam coming from his neck was red. As I got to him I saw his mask had turned into a dark, opaque disc.

He was rising limply, on his side. I thought he had lost consciousness, but when I touched his shoulder he threw his arms around my waist and tightened them, desperately. I knew I had to get him back to the surface as quickly as I could, but if we rose straight without hovering it would be suicide. I had to decide for him, and I knew there was only one decision I could make: to stick to our decompression periods, even if he died with his arms around me. I rose back to seventy meters, trailing him as the shark had trailed the little fish hanging from its belly. When I thought of the shark I realized that I had lost my harpoon.

In the heart of the blue, at fifty meters, I saw the faint red foam that rose from his neck stop. I thought he was dead, but his arms that were still round my waist suddenly tightened in spasmodic convulsions. I groped hastily for the gauge of his spare tank and opened it. The foam started rising again. He was still alive, but he had only got ten minutes left. I rose to forty; it was much too soon, but I had to risk it. The blue got lighter, I saw the flowered slope again and somewhere above us on the left the dark shadow of the wreck on the pillars. Then I saw it move. It wasn't the wreck, but another shadow, circling.

I didn't know what to do. We were at forty meters. We needed at least one more hovering period, at twenty-five. Then my air stopped and I opened my spare tank. Only as my hand went toward it I discovered that all the time I had been stroking his arm, the way he had done to me after the shelling. For some reason this decided it. I took a deep breath, pushed down my feet like a frog, and we shot upward, out of the blue, toward the sky.

I saw the white belly of the shark streak over us and gripped his arm tightly and shut my eyes, while my ears began to hammer and scream. I swallowed my saliva to release the pressure and the thought flickered through my mind how futile this was. Then, just as my eardrums had recovered, I heard the sharp click of a report, and then two more, in rapid succession. I recognized that sound. Harpoon guns, discharging.

I opened my eyes, saw we were very close to the surface, saw three orange creatures with diving respirators swim above me, blue guns gleamed along their outstretched arms. I saw the harpoons dangle at the end of the lines, grazed off the shark's skin that was as hard as armor. I saw the shark speed toward them, back from a swerve into the blue, its mouth open, its teeth glistening in the slanting sunlight. Then I reached the surface.

We were all pulled into the longboat, one by one, by frantic people.

The moment we were out of the water, I took off his mask. Blood fell out of it like a soggy cake. He was horrible to see; his skin was blue, his legs were scratched, he felt stone cold and didn't seem to breathe any more. Pjotr was weeping in the boat with long heaving sobs; Jacques comforted him mechanically and went on staring at the sea. Bernard sat quietly smiling, but he shivered all the time. I felt numb and dizzy, and sat sick and motionless with Goatskin in my arms, while the bosun and the boy rowed us back to the ship. He was hauled on board in the boat and lifted out of it when it was on the level of the deck.

I had only one wish: to lie down on my back in the sun and sleep and forget it all, but I couldn't. I had to make decisions, arrange for him to be taken to a hospital, make a report of what had happened and have it signed by witnesses. I would get into no end of trouble once we arrived in the civilized world; everything the old Captain had forgotten would now fall back on me: there was no logbook on board and they would certainly ask for it, I should have written my report in it. Goatskin was carried into the wheelhouse and put on Nicole's bunk. She washed him and nursed him, covered him with blankets and hot water bottles and tried to make him drink cognac; if someone else wanted to get near him she almost snarled.

I woke up out of my dazedness because Mr. Astanasia asked me where we were going, after I had started the engine and given the bosun the course. When I said we were going to Athens he became very nasty. He said he could under no circumstances agree to that, he commanded me to proceed to an Italian port. I said Goatskin was dying and I was going to take him to the nearest hospital that was any good, and that was Athens. He dropped all his old-world charm as he screamed that he would not let me, that he commanded me to go to an Italian port, that I was responsible for the consequences; Captain Perpendiculous threw his crutches onto the deck when he heard the row and joined in, shaking his fists, hollering Greek curses. I called Pjotr and Jacques and told them to take these people away and lock them up in their cabins. When Mr. Astanasia heard this he changed his tune; he started wheedling and wringing his hands. He said that if we went to Greece he would get into the most terrible trouble, would I please, please go to an Italian port. I said that if we met a fishing smack we would hail it and perhaps they would take him and his Greek on board and sail them to an Italian port at a price. He tried to make it Goatskin who would be taken to Athens by a fishing smack, but he didn't succeed. He sat on the foredeck for hours in the hot sun in his white bathrobe, smoking one long cigarette after the other, watching the horizon. Captain Perpendiculous watched the horizon too, pacing up and down on the poop on his crutches, pockmarking the deck.

We met a small fishing smack toward four o'clock and I hailed it. There was a long conversation in Greek between the Skipper and the two passengers. In the end they hurried down the stairs and got their luggage. When he wanted to leave I said I'd like some money. He went mad and started hissing foul language. I said, "You are wasting your time. I want some money, and I won't let you off the ship until I have got it." He looked as if he was going to strike me, then the Skipper of the fishing smack called from below, and he pulled out a wallet and took out some banknotes and threw them on the deck; the bosun had to jump on all fours to prevent them being blown away. When I counted them I saw it was quite a lot, but I didn't know the value of Greek money. When we arrived in Piraeus the next morning I found out that it would just pay our mooring charge and a thousand liters of water.

In Piraeus Goatskin was carried off the ship on a stretcher by two orderlies, who had come with the ambulance. The ambulance looked clean and white in the dark confusion of the quay. Military and police swarmed over the deck, I had forgotten that in Greece the war was still on. It took a long time to fend off all those wasps; then I went with Pjotr and Jacques to the French consul. There, in a cool office with antiblast strips pasted to the window, I made my report and signed the declarations. We had agreed to leave Mr. Astanasia out of it, so as not to complicate things. If indeed he was wanted by the police here it would mean that we wouldn't get out of this place for weeks, answering questions.

We lay in Piraeus for weeks all the same, waiting for Goatskin to die. Nicole had gone with him to the hospital and she stayed with him all the time. She wasn't allowed to see him for more than two half hours per day, but she sat on the bench in the hall all day, and when she was put outside at night she sat on a bench in the courtyard. We brought her food and a blanket, when she didn't want to come back to the ship; we agreed that we would take watches by her side at night. We could not let her sit there alone.

During a fortnight, when it still seemed a matter of hours before Goatskin should die, she didn't say a word all night. She just sat, the blanket round her knees, and occasionally she dozed, her head on the shoulder of whoever was sitting beside her. Then, the message came that he would live, but the left side of his body would remain paralyzed. When Nicole heard this she broke down and cried. I led her away with my arm round her shoulders to the bench in the courtyard, where we sat down in the sun. I talked to her, and so did Pjotr and Jacques and Bernard, but she wouldn't listen, she just cried. We didn't quite know why, whether from joy or horror, or just exhaustion. We all said to each other how lucky he was to have pulled through, but we lied. Every one of us knew that this was the worst that could have happened, and not only to him, to all of us. That was the curious thing. We took it as a matter of course that we should stay with him and nurse him and look after him. I only realized this when I was allowed to see him for the first time, that night we were told that he would live. He was lying in a small white room; his face and his hands were dark patches in the gathering dusk. He could hardly move his lips. We talked only for a few minutes. I didn't understand all he said, but I gathered that he was telling me what had happened. He talked about the wreck of a plane at the depth of a hundred meters, of a steel box on the lap of a skeleton, and how the plane had suddenly started moving and slid off the edge on which it was resting, and sunk into the darkness. He seemed to think it was funny, for he laughed; then I realized that the gasping sound he was making wasn't laughter. He gabbled, "Skipper," and "old times" and "living corpse" and "don't leave me alone" and wept. I said, "Don't worry, old boy, we'll stay with you." Then a nurse touched my shoulder and gestured that I had to go. He waved at me weakly with his left hand as she opened the door to let me out.

A week later he and Nicole went to Nice by plane. The consul paid for the tickets, saying he would get the money back from the insurance. The insurance seemed indeed to be well arranged, the old Captain had done it. He had insured the crew against accidents, and this meant that Goatskin would probably have a pension for the rest of his life. If that old Captain hadn't been there, I hate to think of what would have happened. I thought of the many times Goatskin had wanted to strangle or drown him or lash him to the mast. Now, he owed his living to him.

On the first night of our homeward trip I remained on deck to keep an eye on the navigation, as the Cyclades were a tricky water. I hadn't been able to think clearly ashore, but now we were sailing slowly under the stars, heeling in a soft night breeze, a fog seemed to lift in my brain. It was the first time that I remembered clearly what had happened, from the moment that I lay on my bunk, awake, waiting for Nicole to call me, the night before he dived to his death. For the first time I realized how odd it had been, us two, lying one above the other, staring in the darkness, waiting for what we knew would happen and not making a move to prevent it. Not only we, the hunters too, the crew, everybody: all of us had waited, without doing anything, for the drama to take its course. We had all dumbly accepted as inevitable that he should go down the second time, as if we had been taking part in a tragedy of Fate. But it had not been a tragedy of Fate at all, just a desperate boy imagining things. If, the next morning, I had knocked him down I would have saved him. And if he had wanted to go down all the same, even after he had woken up, I should have broken his leg or locked him up in a cabin; but whatever I should have done, I hadn't done it. I had just said theatrically, "I won't go," and lain on my bunk, staring in the darkness, knowing that he would go and that I would go after him, a victim of forces stronger than I, and I hadn't woken up to reality before it was too late.

And then I thought of Nicole, who had made a mess of things too. She should have got up, quietly gone to the deck and thrown the bottles overboard, then we would have sailed back to the South of France the way we had left, a jolly crowd of youngsters on a crazy ship, with a piano on the poop.

I leaned on the rail and looked down at the dark mirror of the sea. Occasionally a shimmer of luminous green rippled past from the bow of the ship. I thought of the dream landscape lying below, and hated Goatskin for taking me away from it. For now we would have to nurse him and stay around him and feel guilty and let ourselves be insulted and pestered by this cripple, who had never had such power before, who was the only one among us whose philosophy of life had remained unchallenged: that we were jetsam washed ashore by the war, a few useless creatures left over from the massacre of youth that was World War II.

And suddenly, as I thought this, I knew it wasn't true. This conception of ourselves as a lost generation was false, a mystification that had sprung from Goatskin's warped mind. I had been lost and lonely for a while after the war, but that was only natural. Everybody who had gone through it needed a period of readjustment. He had imposed that conception upon me; it had started in Antwerp. I had known he was play acting all the time, and yet he had convinced me. And not only me, but Jacques and Pjotr and Bernard too.

When I thought this I had a curious feeling. A spell was taken away from me in those moments, a spell that had started long ago, when I had lain awake on my bunk in room 77 in the Grand Hotel in Westport, and listened to the others wheezing and snoring around me, and read the poem on the wall. All of them were now on that distant shore, except me. Even Goatskin was there, and I suddenly knew that he had always been.

Suddenly I understood what had bound us together and at the same time made me hate him: he lived with the dead, and he had wanted me to live with them too. To him the distant shore was the jungle under water, the bottom of the sea, where they all were.

It was a romantic thought, but it liberated me. When the sun rose over the Cyclades I felt as if I had conquered the terrible pull of the dead, of the war.

I wanted to do something that would save us, something that would liberate us from the war and make us take up a new life, in peace. Only, I had no idea what.

CHAPTER FOURTEEN

IT WAS JUNE SIMMONS WHO MADE ME THINK OF IT. IN SAINT TROPEZ I found her letter. It had been waiting for me at the harbor master's office for over a month. She wrote a lot of amusing nonsense but again at the very end of her letter she almost blushingly wrote in a hurry a few serious lines: "You said that you didn't know what to do with yourself because there is no room for you with any of the tugboat companies. Surely there is always room for a rescue tug somewhere, and surely there are lots of old war-surplus tugboats around. Couldn't you try to interest somebody with a little money in manning a tugboat with an ex-war crew, and get a fair chance of a good profit in the gale season? I hope all this doesn't sound too amateurish, but you told me so much about ocean-going tugboats when we were sitting on that bench under the palm trees that I feel a bit of an expert now. If it is silly what I have said, don't judge me too harshly. It is so nice to think about you and the sea in an English vicarage garden."

I thought the plan over for a while, then I decided to tell Goatskin.

He had recovered as far as he probably ever would recover. He was a plump pink body in a wheel chair with one side of his face still and re-signed in a weird half-smiling melancholy. The other side, that was alive, was devilish. He could form words with only half a mouth but whatever he said was destructive. Nicole, who pushed his chair, fed him, washed him, put him to bed and helped him on the toilet, got the worst of it. His entire mumbled conversation to her consisted of insults. He called her "Chinese whore" several times an hour, urged her to bugger off, to leave him alone instead of using him to attain holiness, why the hell didn't she go to a nunnery and do some useful work if that was the way she felt, instead of wasting her time on a useless piece of meat that had been kept alive against his will by a lot of sadists and good-for-nothings? He knew

302

why we had fished him and nursed him past the death he had longed for: to profit from the insurance. If not, could we please tell him what money we were living on? He was just a paralyzed pig, being fattened by a lot of bums who made hay with the money he earned by having turned into a cripple. His metaphors got mixed up whenever he talked about himself, and he exaggerated so shamelessly that no one among us took it seriously and told him to shut up. Yet in all this exaggeration there was a core of truth that went on secretly nagging our consciences: we were all guilty, because we had let ourselves be paralyzed into inactivity by his one-man drama until it was too late.

When I told him about our plan he was sitting in the sun, his eyes closed, sweating. Toward the end of my story he opened his evil eye and the live half of his mouth started grinning. When I had finished he said, "Charming. So you want to drag me onto the bridge of a tugboat now and lash my chair to the rail. Well, well! Aren't you afraid that one day you might kill the pig that lays the golden eggs?" I wanted to argue with him but Nicole, who stood behind him with her sunglasses on, shook her head. She had grown very thin of late; the shape of her skull had become marked in her face which made her look alien and oriental and a bit frightening. Goatskin saw me sigh and turn away. He said, "Don't worry, Skipper, I'm your man. Lash my chair to that rail. I want to see you make a mess of it." I couldn't quite remember what the moral arguments were against slapping the face of a cripple. I got up, said, "You're having quite a time, aren't you?" and went away.

If I wanted to put our plan into practice I would have to go to Le Havre or Brest, the only places where a rescue tug had a chance in the gale season. The sad thing was that the money to pay for this trip had to come from his insurance. I tried to forget about that, but I couldn't. His crooked half-smile traveled with me as I went North.

The pianist was really mad. He had a red face, bulging eyes, bat ears, and his chin stuck out. He played tinny dance tunes of the twenties, kicking the piano, slamming the lid up and down, and he sang with a breath-less falsetto to his own accompaniment, "I love my mummy, my mummy loves me, I am only twenty, and she's twenty-three."

He was the only excited person in the café; the rest were stolid, silent tugboat captains, staring at him, their big hands asleep on the marble by the side of their little glasses. They looked exactly like the old captains in Shadwell Basin, nationality didn't seem to make any difference. Only their berets were French, otherwise they looked like Captain Bakker done by different cartoonists.

I had told the landlord that I was looking for Captain Perseil of the tugboat *Jeanne,* the owner of the ship *Brighton Belle,* and he had said he hadn't arrived yet, but he would point him out to me when he came. I sat listening to the mad pianist screaming, banging the piano, making obscene noises with his lips, whispering filthy language between two crashing chords. Then, after an hour or so, the landlord called, "Psst!" and pointed at a man coming in.

He was very tall but looked stocky because his shoulders were as wide as a bull's. He walked with the gait of the sea. On the back of his head was a peaked cap with a dirty white cover. He sat down at one of the marble tables and I got up.

"Monsieur Perseil?"

He looked up. His face was very large; his small black eyes looked at me without interest.

"Are you the owner of the *Brighton Belle?*"

He looked at me for almost a minute. Then he said, "So what?"

I told him I had seen the ship, lying in a dead arm of the harbor. I had asked whom it belonged to, they had given me his name, and said that I probably would meet him if I went to the Café de la Marine around ten o'clock.

"So what?" he asked, after another long silence.

I told him I was looking for a laid-up tugboat, and wanted to interest the owner in putting the ship into the rescue service with a crew of war veterans, who would ask only a very small salary and take the rest in a percentage of the prize money if they brought in a ship.

"I have no money," he said. Then he looked away for the first time and called, "Calva!" at the counter. I thought he would continue the conversation, but he didn't. He sat waiting for his Calvados, staring at the counter. The mad pianist hammered and screamed. Captain Perseil seemed to have forgotten I was there.

A fortnight ago I would have left it at that, but this was our last chance. I had seen scores of old tugboats all along the Channel coast, but either the owners hadn't been interested or the ships weren't seaworthy anymore. The *Brighton Belle,* which I had discovered that afternoon in Le Havre, was a wooden ship, but I had been on board and seen that she was in a fair condition with her engines still in and a full equipment. Beachcombers had told me she belonged to the Captain of the tugboat *Jeanne,* who was

304

very rich but very hard to deal with. As to the second definition they had certainly been right.

I went on telling him about our proposition, shouting down the mad pianist, but he didn't listen. He was waiting for his Calvados; when it came he thanked the landlord with a nod and a smile, as if he was quite alone and tried to establish some human contact.

I told him about our experience as a crew, about the Western Approaches, the Northeast Passage, D-day, and the Invasion of the South of France. I thought he had forgotten me altogether and was about to go away, when he asked, "When did you sail the last time?"

I thought the game was lost anyhow, so there was no harm in telling him the truth. "The last time I sailed as a mate on the Dutch tugboat *Texel*," I said, "to the Far East."

He looked at me for the first time with something like interest. "Captain Bakker?" he asked.

"Yes."

"All right," he said, "come back here tomorrow morning at eleven. Good night."

I said, "Good night, sir," and went back to my table. The mad pianist was in a frenzy. He spat between his legs, turned on his stool, glowered at the motionless sea captains with his bulging eyes, and mumbled, "Bombs. Air raids. Sirens. Blood. God damn it, give me sensation. What the hell am I doing here, in this fish pond?" Then he turned round again and played a boogy-woogy version of "Silent Night, Holy Night," kicking the piano, howling blood-curdling screams, ramming his elbows down on the keys. I thought he was going to have a fit; to see all those stolid faces gaze at him without mercy became a revolting spectacle. Then, as he began to get hoarse in a paroxysm of obscenities, they got up, one after another, put money underneath their empty glasses and filed out.

After they had gone the landlord patted the pianist on the shoulder and said, "All right, all right, stop it." The pianist couldn't stop, he went on playing, sniggering madly. The landlord slapped his hands and slammed the lid shut. "Go home," he said. "Tell Celina to give you an injection." The pianist got up, mumbling about blood and air raids, and shuffled out.

"Wonderful boy," the landlord said to me, as he was stacking the chairs. "The best barometer in town. If he carries on like that you can be sure there's a gale brewing."

I said, "How extraordinary."

"Haven't you seen them run?" the landlord asked. "They've all gone to rake their fires and round up their crews. He is a full six hours ahead of the meteorological office, and he has never been wrong yet. Where are you from?"

I told him that I was a Dutchman, and that I came from the South of France, to look for a ship.

"Tugboat?"

"Yes."

He asked me what my rank was, and when I told him that I was a captain with a crew who wanted to sail on the rescue service he understood that I was after the *Brighton Belle*. A lovely ship, a pity she was made of wood. Wartime job. He had seen Captain Perseil talk to me, so he must be very interested. "If you can sail for him," he said, "you'll find he is as straight as a die and as hard as nails. His yes is yes, but if he says no, not even an earthquake will rattle him. Are you staying in a hotel? You can have a room upstairs, if you like. It's small, but the sheets are dry."

The room was indeed very small. I had to bend down to get through the door, and to undress stooping. But the sheets were dry; they seemed to be the only dry things in the world as I lay listening to the rain lashing the little window, and sweeping the roof in waves.

I wished June Simmons were here, for I felt so homesick for the sea and the jungle of silence that it frightened me.

The next morning at eleven o'clock a gale was rattling the windows of Café de la Marine. Every time a customer opened the door a whirl of sawdust was blown up from the floor, and those inside put their hands over their glasses to protect them.

Captain Perseil wasn't there; when I told the landlord that I was waiting for him he said, "In that case you might as well go for a walk. He left at three o'clock last night for an S.O.S." I asked him where the S.O.S. had come from, but he didn't know. He was proud of the gale because of his pianist. "What did I tell you last night?" he asked. "Not a cloud in the sky there was, not a breeze, and now listen to it."

The wind whined under the door and hurled itself against the façade in shuddering bursts, like blast. I sat in the Café de la Marine sipping sour red wine for the rest of the morning, and talked about the war with the landlord. He said Le Havre had been badly bombed; I had seen that for myself when I arrived. Never in my life had I set eyes on a town that looked more desolate, even Westport had been gay compared to this. We also talked about Perseil and the other captains who came to the Café de la Marine each night. He told me that the *Jeanne* was the only ocean-going tug on rescue service; the others were harbor tugs that would meet incoming vessels in a gale but never ventured beyond the pierheads if the wind got above its nines. The only other rescue tug between the Scheldt and Cherbourg was the *Texel* in Flushing; Perseil and Bakker were constantly in each other's hair if there was an S.O.S. between them.

I hadn't known Bakker was in rescue service this season; for some reason I liked the idea. I walked along the quays that night, my pipe upside down in my mouth against the rain, leaning against the wind that occasionally knocked the breath out of me. As I staggered along the barges crunching against their poles, in the wild light of arc lamps swinging with a sound of iron, I imagined how gratifying it would be to meet old Bakker in a gale and snatch a wreck from under his nose, the old bastard. I wondered whether Captain Perseil hoped I'd know some of the old man's tricks, to beat him with his own weapons.

As I had nothing to do I went to see the *Brighton Belle* once more. The wind had risen to such fury that it blew the spray off the surface of the harbor and sent it careering through the rain; I had to clutch a lamppost occasionally not to be blown off the crown of the dike. The *Brighton Belle* lay tugging at her moorings and I had some difficulty getting on board for she veered away from the quay all the time. After a gust had pushed her stern in I jumped, and as I landed on her wooden deck I was surprised at the softness of the impact. Water spurted up my trouser legs as my heels struck the wood; it was so rotten that it had become spongy. I hadn't noticed this when I had my quick look at her yesterday; the weather had been dry.

It was the first of a series of alarming things I came to notice during my second visit. As I slowly made the round through her insides, striking matches, I saw how old she was and how tired, although she was only five years old. Like all wartime vessels she had been intended to last four years only and been constructed like an M.T.B. or an M.L.; two layers of wood diagonally put, with linen between them. Now her outer skin had cracked, water had soaked between the linen and the wood and set it rotting. As I stood on deck once more, my back to the rain, and looked at her, I knew that we would be lucky if she didn't spring a major leak the first time we ventured out with her in a gale.

That was the reason why I wasn't so delighted with Captain Perseil's acceptance of my offer as I had expected. He had come in the morning after, towing a Finn with a list of twenty degrees and the splintered remains of a deckload of timber. He looked pleased when he entered the Café de la Marine: he greeted me almost jocularly, called me *mon gars* and offered me a Calvados. Then he said, "I have considered your offer and I'm interested. Tell me the details."

I told him all the details. I said I hadn't got a crew yet, apart from a mate, but that I was sure I would have a first class one together within a fortnight if he gave the word. They would all be war veterans used to the rescue service; we had been doing nothing else for over a year on the Western Approaches. What he was interested in most, I found, was whether I knew Bakker well. He put me some leading questions about what I would do under certain circumstances with a wreck in a strong gale. My answers seemed to satisfy him. When I told him that I had sailed as opposite number on the same boat with Captain Van Dam during the war, he seemed quite delighted, this obviously settled it. It was clear that he wanted to beat the Dutch with one of their own pupils; old Bakker must have kept him awake nights. "All right," he said, "it's a deal. I'll fit out the ship and I'll advance you some money to pay your crew a week's salary each. How much do they get?"

I made the calculations in the margin of a newspaper. Each salary he halved, without listening to reason. I tried to stick my ground but I might as well have tried to haggle with a statue. He wouldn't pay more than half of whatever I suggested; when I arrived at the mate's salary and my own I doubled the amount I had in mind, but he didn't fall for it. "Nonsense," he said, "I'll pay you a quarter of that." He certainly knew what he was talking about.

I expected him to be as stingy when I came to my calculations for fitting out the ship, but I was mistaken. He was so generous with the hawsers, the overhaul of the engines, and the paint that I dared to say I had the impression she was rotting. "Of course," he said. "What do you think? That I'd have left her lying there with a hood on her funnel if she wasn't? In that case I would have manned her with an A-one crew long ago, instead of with a lot of bums." I tried to be a little gentleman and said, "Thank you, sir," but he wasn't impressed. He was a realist.

That same afternoon I wired to Saint Tropez for Goatskin and Nicole to come, and I telephoned Sparks in his Paris office. They told me he was no longer with the company, but they gave me his address. I sent him a wire, saying that I had found a ship for the season to be stationed in Le Havre in rescue service, and would he be interested in a post as a wireless operator on a co-operative basis. I had little hope that he would, but it was worth spending money on trying. In the rescue service the wireless operator is the most important member of the crew, if he is a bungler you might as well stay at the quay.

To my surprise he sent back a wire: ARRIVE LE HAVRE NINETEEN FIFTEEN PLEASE MEET. It seemed I had caught him at the right moment. When he got out of the train I saw at first glance that he hadn't been doing well. He acted breezy and confident, but his clothes were shabby. I told him about our plan, on our way to the Café de la Marine. He had difficulty with the wind on corners with his cardboard suitcase. At first he tried to be choosy and aloof about the whole thing, but when we went on board to have a look at the transmitter toward nightfall he dropped all pretense. He inspected the set in the dark cubicle, striking matches all the time, and giving soft whistles of admiration. It was a lovely wartime job, he said, full of gadgets to play with. The only thing that would take a lot of money to get repaired was the radar set, which had been half dismantled.

We had a meal in the Café de la Marine. He ate ravenously and gulped down the red wine, with his Adam's apple sliding up and down his scraggy neck. I asked how Françoise was; he shrugged his shoulders and said he had got bored with her, but he was obviously lying. She must have left him when his luck gave out. I suspected he had slept under the bridges for quite a while with that cardboard suitcase.

Later on, when the wine had done its work and mellowed the months between us, it felt as if we had come closer to one another than ever since the war, closer than last time in Paris. I was happy to have him with us, for he was a wonderful wireless operator, one of the best.

Goatskin arrived three days later. I went to meet him with Sparks at the station. Sparks was very good at mastering his surprise when he saw him sit in a corner seat of a third-class compartment, grinning half-wittedly behind the steamed window. He talked with him quite normally, while we were waiting for the wheel chair to be taken out of the van. Nicole was looking after that. He said, "Well, well," and "How are you, old scoundrel," and made a move to slap his knee, but his hand stopped in midair. Goatskin was obviously very pleased to see him, but he couldn't help being nasty. He gabbled, "You look very rich and healthy. How's your millionaire's daughter?" Sparks was casual and airy about it, but I saw him blush.

Nicole came trotting along the platform with the chair on its squeaking little wheels; we lifted Goatskin out of the compartment and put him in it. The gale was still blowing, Nicole wrapped him up in his coat and his muffler, he was wheeled to the Café de la Marine like a sack of potatoes. My heart sank as I saw this; I imagined what he would be like on the bridge in that chair, with the spray coming over in torrents.

When we arrived at the café and Nicole unwrapped him he was dazed and shaken. He sat blinking with his one live eye and had difficulty breathing. When he got a glass of red wine he spilled half of it down his shirt and snarled at Nicole when she wanted to mop it up with her handkerchief. The landlord did it with a towel.

After we had carried him to his room, Sparks looked at me, horrified, and asked, "God, how did that happen?" I told him; he listened shaking his head and muttering "God" all the time. I was surprised to find that he reacted to the idea of diving as to a horrible, unnatural thing. I didn't try to tell him; I didn't want to get more homesick than I was.

When Goatskin came down again for dinner he had picked up. At first he was cross and silent, but after several glasses of red wine he became lively; when the mad pianist started kicking and slamming the piano he became gay for the first time. It was the first time I saw him forget that he was a wreck now, the live half of his body seemed to have conquered the other at last. He laughed and babbled and began to sweat; if I had held up my hand and looked at him with one eye shut, covering his right half, I could have believed the old days had come back.

He seemed to believe it. After he had sent Nicole to bed, he put his hand on Sparks's, and said, "Good old Sparks! God, am I glad we came through it alive." He sighed a sick man's happy sigh, then he looked at me like old Goatskin again, for the first time since the last morning he dived. "All right, Skipper," he said, "tell us about the ship you found."

I told him, but I wasn't thinking of what I was saying. I was looking at his happy face, his broken youth, and felt like crying. If ever there was a motherless child, far away from home, it was he.

To get a crew we put a small advertisement in a Dutch weekly: "Tugboat company wants experienced officers and crew, ex-war, for ship in rescue service, one season only." We had decided on the advertisement because to travel to Holland and round them up would have cost much more. We hoped we would get some replies but doubted it.

Within a week we received over a hundred letters. We had never suspected there were so many of us left. We had a choice of mates, engineers, wireless operators, and cooks; our old cook was among them. He wrote a flowery letter on yellow stationery, with the name of his restaurant printed on it in glossy lettering. He gave a truthful report of his experience during the war, but exaggerated the size of his restaurant shamelessly. I had hoped that the Chief would reply, but there was no letter from him among the hundred. I wrote him specially, and he answered that he would have loved to come but that his wife was expecting a baby and that his shop was getting into its stride at last, so he couldn't, but he knew of a very good first engineer who had nothing to do, a man called Baas who had sailed with him as a second. Baas was among the letters, so we asked him to come. He arrived with Cook, a second engineer, a bosun, and three sailors. They had joined forces in Amsterdam at Sparks's suggestion, and taken an excursion ticket together.

When we met them at the station we found that we knew them all, but during the war we hadn't known their names. They were all delighted to find that they knew us too and our first communal meal in Café de la Marine was happy and quite like old times.

Goatskin was delighted to see them. As long as he was in a room without a draft, where he could remain seated like everybody else, he seemed almost normal apart from the stillness of half his face and the fact that he couldn't use his right hand. He had become very adroit eating with his left hand. After the first few glasses of wine nobody seemed to remember that there was something the matter with him.

It was extraordinary how little time we needed to recapture the old wartime atmosphere; by the time the coffee was served it seemed as if we had not been separated at all. Cook still wore his blue ring, but he lost his peacetime refinement when we started singing. The only one who liked our singing was the mad pianist. He jumped up and down like a frog, clawing the piano and screaming high mad squeals of brotherhood. Every night he had been mumbling about air raids and blood and sensation and wished the war would come; now he seemed to think that it had indeed come, that we had brought it with us; he wasn't bright enough to realize it wasn't the new one yet but the old one revived. Cook was drunk first. He started singing New Year's Eve psalms that were very gloomy, about man being like grass and our footsteps being wiped out by the wind of time. We sat listening to his sentimental tenor with a feeling of drunken sadness. Then Goatskin began to tell stories. He was quite drunk too, but his words came easier than when he was sober. He would have talked exactly like this if he had just been drunk and not half paralyzed. He told us about the most wonderful woman he had ever met, the woman of his life. She was much older than he, much older than any of us, but yet eternally young. Five thousand years ago a Greek had seen her, after climbing a sand dune, and he had stretched out his arms toward her and cried, "Thalassa!" Millions of men had tried to possess her since, but he had been one of the few who had succeeded. Perhaps it was because we were all drunk, but when he told his story of love with Thalassa, the sea, we listened with a feeling of beauty and wonder; even the mad pianist, who didn't understand a word of Dutch, sat watching him spellbound. Nicole was sitting behind him. She couldn't know what he was talking about, I thought, but I had forgotten that she knew Greek; she had told me about the Victory of Samothrace, so she probably knew what Thalassa stood for. As I was listening to Goatskin's drunken fairy tale of love I began to understand that she had always known this. She had refused to let him touch her as long as he made love to that other woman, the sea, and although he would never make love to that other woman again, she still would never get him back.

Goatskin told the listening crew about the world under water for hours on end, and he gave the sea a curious bewitching personality, calling her Thalassa all the time. It was the story I had thought of when I had looked down on the magic jungle for the second time: the forbidden door, the opening of it, the land of dazzling beauty and mystery, the ending in a nightmare of horror. "That's why," he said, suddenly, "I suggest that we change the ship's name." He took his glass in his shaky left hand, lifted it solemnly, and his live eye glistened when he said, "I christen her Thalassa."

The mad pianist understood him. He raised his glass too, and said, "Thalassa, à-Dieu-vat."

When he looked round our circle and asked, "Agreed, boys, dear boys?" we mumbled, "Yes," and drank to her.

Looking at it from Captain Perseil's point of view I couldn't blame him. He was an unimaginative man, a black-eyed Bakker. When we told him the next morning that we wanted to rechristen the ship, he was angry. "Nonsense," he said, "the ship has been registered under her proper name and I'm certainly not going to the trouble of having it changed. And who the hell do you think you are? The ship is mine, you are just a crew of bums whom I want to give a chance. I begin to regret it."

He was right. Every sailor knows that it brings bad luck to change a ship's name; we had aroused his suspicions. So far he had left us entirely alone, now he began to ask for our licenses, because of the insurance, he said. He took our licenses with him and came back with the message that the mate and the second engineer had been turned down by the insurance. The mate because he was a cripple, the second engineer because he had no license at all. When the war started he had been a donkeyman who had been promoted after the second engineer on his ship had been killed in action. As the tugboat captains had a complete freedom of action during the war his Captain had promoted him without bothering about examinations. It was a nasty shock to us, mainly because of Goatskin. We had all, without talking about it, behaved as if there was nothing the matter with him; I had planned to take the bosun on the bridge to take the watch with him, and if we went into action I would be there myself anyhow. Now I was forced to find an official mate. I decided to talk it over with him first, before I sent for another one.

When I told him the live half of his face remained calm and smiling. I had expected him to get one of his fits of rage; for once he would have been justified. But he listened as quietly as when I had told him I was to take over the command of his ship in Westport. When I had finished he said, "I can't blame him. I know I am finished and I don't mind. When I dived that last time I knew what I was doing. My only regret is that you didn't do what I asked you to do."

"If you had really wanted that," I asked, "why did you tap for help? I heard you."

"Weakness," he said, "a last fear, which I suppose is natural. But I was quite ready to go. I had been playing with the idea for a long time. You should have let me."

I didn't say anything. He frightened me a bit, he sat there so calmly. I knew there was something coming.

"If this tugboat plan should fail," he said, "I want you to do something for me. If you promise me that, the whole thing will be bearable, a last mad adventure. Even if we fail I'll like it, for I like mad adventures. But what I don't like is that desert in front of me. I can't spend the rest of my life in this wheel chair. Skipper, I just can't. You must promise."

"What?"

"If we fail you must come back with me to Saint Tropez. There we'll take a twenty-foot cutter, one of those little fishing smacks, and go, the two of us, to the Bay of Port Cros. There, one morning, you'll put the Cousteau on me and one frogman's foot. One is enough, because under water I can walk on one leg. I'll walk among the white rocks, the banks of flowers, past the wood that you have seen, near the wreck we went to on the first day. In it I know a little open space, where the bottom is almost blue. It is full of sea stars and anemones, and there's a little cave with a colony of *mérous* that I have never disturbed. It's the only spot under the sea where I have never felt the urge to hunt. I have sat there often, watching the *mérous* at play, and one day, just before I went to Antwerp, I went there again and lay on my back in the sunlight. I must have fallen asleep, for I woke up because my air gave out. I woke up with an odd feeling of drunk-

313

enness, and I wanted to stay there. It cost me a tremendous effort to open my spare tank, and surface. For days after I had to fight the urge to go back there and lie down again in the sunlight and fall asleep. That's why I went to Antwerp. I wanted to see whether I could still get away. When I left you that night, after that game of chess we left unfinished, I told you I had to go back because there was a girl waiting for me. You asked me who she was, and I told you. Do you remember?"

I did.

I got a proper mate, who was rather young but had very good references. His name was Middag. I met him at the station and explained the situation to him: he would be the mate only in name, the moment we left the harbor he would be third officer. He understood it all without much explanation and when he met Goatskin he called him "sir," which was clever and put our minds at ease. The new second engineer was in reality a chief; Chief Baas and he got on well, after the first day when they turned round each other like suspicious dogs.

Just before we made our trial run with the *Brighton Belle* Sparks received a letter from Flushing. It was from a friend of his who was now the wireless operator on the *Texel*. He wrote that the news had reached Flushing; everybody had been tickled by it except Captain Bakker; he had taken the news grimly and said that it was shocking because we were undermining the reputation of the Dutch tugboat service. He had called us "bloody amateurs" and "warm water sailors with megalomania" so we shouldn't expect any help or mercy from him, if ever we found ourselves fighting over a wreck.

When Sparks read the letter aloud everybody laughed and said silly things about old Bakker, but I didn't like it. God knew I didn't worship the man, but I had sailed with him and one thing nobody could deny: he was about the best tugboat captain alive. When I said this, Goatskin made a little speech: "The trouble with you, Skipper," he said, "is that you have no self-confidence. You have been like that ever since you came to Westport; any old man who told you that you were an amateur always had you on his side. I think it's about time you got out of that. You won't be much good in the rescue service if you don't."

I thought about this and found that he was right. It had started in Westport, before I sailed on my first operation. When I went to see Van Dam he had regarded me as an amateur and I had felt he had reason to. I had quickly taken up the routine of our work on the Western Approaches, but I had never quite rid myself of the notion that I was a wartime emergency. Probably I was wrong, for I hadn't done badly since, but the feeling was still there, and it became acute on hearing that letter.

Our trial run was successful; the ship was old but she held the sea well and her speed was really something. When I tried her it was a choppy day; she rolled a lot cross-seas, but the moment I turned her in the wind she took the waves like a race horse. If we were lucky we would get our first S.O.S. from a direction in the wind, head on she could take anything and would remain very fast, much faster than the old *Texel*, who was forced to slow down to half speed sailing head on as soon as the seas became steep.

When we came back from our trial run we were very pleased with ourselves and with the ship, but Captain Perseil, who had been watching us on the pierhead through a pair of binoculars, looked gloomy when he came on board after we had moored. He didn't say anything about our maneuvering; he just looked gloomy and said he wanted a word with me. I took him to the chartroom, and there he put down an unexpected ultimatum. "I've been watching you boys," he said, "and I want to tell you something. I'll give you one chance, a fair one. If we get a gale with a lot of S.O.S.'s I'll take the one that is farthest away. You needn't sail unless there's something near home, the kind of thing your compatriot from Flushing will jump on. If you bring that in I'll give you a contract for the season. If you lose it to him, you're through."

I wanted to argue with him at first, but he wasn't the man to argue with, and I also couldn't help thinking that his point was reasonable. The others didn't agree with me; there was a lot of bad language in the messroom addressed at Captain Perseil. Goatskin and I didn't take part in the general slandering. We sat smoking in silence, listening to the boys, and then he looked at me with his live eye, and smiled.

CHAPTER FIFTEEN

OUR FIRST GALE CAME THREE WEEKS LATER. WE HAD BEEN WAITING FOR IT nervously, congregating in the Café de la Marine every night around nine o'clock to listen to the weather forecast on the radio and the mad pianist, like the other captains. The mad pianist was indeed six hours ahead of the meteorological office with his forecast. That night he screamed and kicked the piano and spat between his knees and slammed the lid up and down, howling like a banshee and hissing obscenities; I was embarrassed because June Simmons was there.

She had arrived that afternoon, and I had met her at the station. I hadn't arranged her coming. She had just written me a postcard saying that she had a week's holiday and taken her ticket. When I stood on the draughty platform, waiting for the train to arrive, I was worried. Our crowd wasn't very wholesome for an English girl to mix with; the wartime vocabulary had come back, and after it the wartime habits, our table manners had dwindled with the rest of our social graces and by now we were as we had been on the Northeast Passage: a bunch of pirates whose entire conversation was made up of curses and anatomical discussions about the female body. But when I saw her get out of the train with the same red bonnet on, I was unexpectedly delighted. She had stayed exactly the same, as if it was only yesterday that we had said good-by and she had gone on waving until the bus turned the corner. She said, "Hello, Skipper, how are you?" and shook me by the hand. I carried her suitcase on my shoulder to the Café de la Marine, leaning against the wind, and she chatted all the time, with her tassel fluttering behind her. The boys were waiting in the café; Sparks kissed her on both cheeks in a very French fashion. I had forgotten that he knew her from the Invasion. She also knew Goatskin, of course, and said, "Well, well, how's chess?" He grinned, looking very pleased, and said, "How are you, nurse?" She was introduced to the others as "Nurse Simmons" and she sat down with us for a meal, chatting all the time and laughing. It was miraculous to see how well mannered everybody got in her presence, a bit hard on Nicole who hadn't been able to keep us decent during the past weeks. She and Nicole hardly exchanged a word, but whenever someone else was talking they sat secretly watching each other and smiled politely whenever their glances crossed. I wondered how they would get on.

The evening seemed to be a great success until the mad pianist went berserk. Of course June Simmons knew perfect French, after the years she had spent in the Midi, so there was no hope that the nature of the lunatic's screams would remain hidden to her. She didn't betray with a single remark, or even as much as a silence, that she understood what he was hollering. It was we who were embarrassed. Sparks explained to her that the man was a human barometer, trying to make it a joke; but never before had I heard the madman go so far in his frenzy. As the other captains began to get up and leave it was a relief that I could do the same. I told her that I'd be back after the ship had been put ready, and she said, "All right, Skipper, I'll wait for you." Then she smiled at me, and that was the moment in which I realized what I should have known months before.

It was quite a discovery, and I thought about it on our way to the ship, pushing Goatskin's wheel chair against the strong gusty wind together with Sparks and the boy Middag. I had been full of apprehension for this gale that had come at last; it was odd how this apprehension had been taken away from me by her smile. It was all still very indistinct, just a feeling of warmth and a boyish happiness, but I didn't mind sailing into the teeth of old Captain Bakker any longer, now she was there to come back to.

We made the ship ready for sailing. Sparks sat down at his receiver and it was agreed that if anything came up I'd be sent for at the Café de la Marine. I suggested, rather feebly, that I should stay on board, but Sparks patted my shoulder and said, "Off you go, Skipper, and good luck." When I opened the door and let in a whirl of wind he called after me, "I'll do my damnedest to hold them off until the morning!"

When I came back to the café the landlord was stacking the chairs; as I opened the door I sent a cloud of sawdust spiraling off the floor and Nicole, who was used to this by now, quickly covered her glass with her hand. June didn't; when I got to their table she was busy fishing sawdust out of her wine. They seemed to have broken the ice; Nicole got up after quickly finishing her wine and said, "Good night, June, see you in the morning. I'll give you a knock at eight." Then she went away.

I felt ill at ease hanging on downstairs because of the landlord, but being French he loved the situation. He brought us a new bottle of wine and asked, "You are sitting up for an S.O.S., I suppose?" I said, "Yes, I don't think I'll go to bed." He stuck a candle in a bottle, lit it, and put it on our table. Then he said, "Good night, *Commandant, bonne chance,*" turned out the lights and left us alone.

I had looked forward to this, but now we found ourselves alone in the empty café with the rain lashing the dark windows, the candle flame fluttering in the draft, and the shadows of the stacked chairs dancing on the walls, I felt uncomfortable, at a loss what to say. She looked at me in the candlelight with her dark eyes, the silly tassel hanging over one ear, and smiled and said, "Well, here we are."

I said, "Yes."

"I am glad you came north," she said, after a silence, "I didn't like your letters from the South of France."

"So?" I said. "What was wrong with them?"

"I didn't like your descriptions of the diving."

"Why not?"

"You said it was like a dream, and I could quite see it was. I thought that to go to sleep and dream is all right as long as you wake up in the morning, refreshed. I had a feeling you didn't."

"I can hear you have been talking to Nicole," I said.

"I have," she answered. "But I have known it for a long time. When I sat looking at your friend tonight, I couldn't help thinking how lucky I was that it wasn't you."

I didn't say anything to that. I sat looking at the candle flame, fluttering in the draft. It was courageous of her to say so frankly that she was in love with me. She had done it before, when we stood waiting for the bus. Yet, this time like the other, I felt uneasy. The warmth and the happiness after her smile an hour ago began to wane. Perhaps I had been imagining things. I had been lonely ever since Stella. It was only natural that I should have been looking for someone to fall in love with. It was a pity she had said that; it gave me the feeling that she was after me. I wanted to take the initiative myself.

She must have felt this, for she said, "I know it's bad tactics to throw myself at you, but I think that we owe it to each other to be frank. I'm in love with you, and if you are not with me that's just too bad. But I think you are. Only there is something else. Someone else, if you like."

I couldn't help smiling, for she had said it so solemnly.

"Thalassa, I suppose?"

She met my smile without flinching. Her dark eyes were kind and full of understanding, but very strong. It was a gentle strength, that gave me a feeling of warmth and happiness once more, faintly, like a first hint of sunrise.

"You don't know it yourself," she said, "but you are further gone than you think." Then she sat watching the candle flame too; the wind hurled itself against the windowpanes and set the reflection of the candle flame trembling. "Nicole is worried, in case this tugboat venture should not come off," she said. "He asked you to help him to commit suicide, didn't he?"

I didn't know what to answer. In the end I said, "Yes."

Then she put her hand on mine. We sat looking at the candle flame, not saying anything, when a ghost appeared behind the glass door and banged on it. I got up to open, the wind blew out the candle. It was the boy Middag. "S.O.S., Captain," he said.

I wanted to turn round to tell her, but she was by my side. "Good luck," she said, and then she put her arms round my neck and we kissed. It was as if the gentle strength she had quietly radiated during all these years went inside me during that kiss. Then she said, "Good-by."

While I had been sitting in the candlelight, things had been moving fast outside. The boy Middag tried to tell me, shouting, on our way to the ship; when I came on board Sparks was very excited. Lots of S.O.S.'s had come in, one from a Dutchman in the Gulf of Biscay for whom Captain Perseil with the *Jeanne* had left an hour ago. Now he had contact with a Greek, who had lost his rudder due west of Ostende; he had already arranged with him that we would come to his assistance and we had better be quick about it, for his signals were getting very weak. Obviously his transmitter was folding up. While he was telling me this, his right hand went on nervously tapping a calling-up signal; I thought it was the Greek, but suddenly he said, "Hush, there he is," stopped tapping away, then he listened, intently. I watched the words his right hand pieced together, "Leaving—this—minute—for—Greek—Ostende—sorry—no—more—old—man —watching."

"Who was that?" I asked.

"The *Texel*," he said.

He gave me the markings of the Greek's position and the boy Middag and I set out the course. Goatskin wasn't with us in the chartroom, he had already been lashed to the bridge rail in his bath chair. I found him when I came up; he was wrapped in a tarpaulin as if he was a piece of cargo made sea-fast, with ropes crosswise across the parcel. He was wearing a southwester, tied up under his chin; I could scarcely hear him when he shouted, "Good luck, Skipper!" from underneath his wrappings.

We sailed at once. The wind had livened to fury. When we stuck our head into the outer harbor and passed the shelter of the quay, we heeled sharply under the impact and I had to give ten degrees of rudder to keep her on her course. When we cast off I had still felt confident and calm, the whole thing seemed an exciting adventure. But the moment the wind got us not only my breath was knocked out of me, but my self-confidence too. It was incredible that I had never realized it before: this was the first full-scale gale into which I sailed as a captain. On the Western Approaches, whenever the wind had got over eight, we had stayed in port enjoying a well-earned rest, for if the weather was bad, there were no planes or U-boats; the convoys could sail at their ease. On the Northeast Passage we had known a gale or two, but then all I had to do was to follow the tail-light of the merchantman ahead of us. The only gale I had ever sailed into with a ship under my command had been the one on D-day, but that had only been a half-grown one, and the ships had been so thick on the sea that my main worry had been not to crash into my neighbor. Now, for the first time in my life, I was sailing into the open, asking to have the hell beaten out of me, with no one to rely on but myself. It was only a moment, I dismissed the thought as soon as it came up; but during that moment I knew the truth.

When the full force of the gale hit us smack on the nose as we swung out of the harbor, the *Brighton Belle* rammed her head in with such force that the spray flew above her funnel and I had to duck behind the shield to protect myself, as the water clattered down and lashed the windows of the wheelhouse with a sound of hail. I was worried because of Goatskin, but he had ducked inside his tarpaulin like a turtle.

The beating the *Brighton Belle* took from the sea was terrifying. Like an old bird, out for the first time in years, her feathers were sent flying in all directions. First we lost the starboard navigation light; it was swept clean off its brackets. Then the tarpaulin covering of the starboard boat was sent flying, an hour later the starboard boat itself. The rail of our foredeck caved in after an hour and a half; then the boy Middag came running up, drowning in the spray, and hollered in my ear that the door to the chartroom had been ripped off and the water was playing inside, washing things away. I decided to keep her head on the course; while I stood on the bridge trying to see a landmark, a horizon, a star in the swirling darkness ahead of us, I realized that this indeed was our last chance and I was grimly determined to take it or drown.

What the crew did during that trip was impressive. Others would have abandoned the effort within an hour after we had left the harbor, for the ship was obviously breaking up. She, like we, had not been intended to outlast the war. During the six hours we were ploughing away toward the Greek I expected, at almost every white horse that came storming toward us out of the total darkness, that she would stick her head in never to rise again.

But she didn't. Every time she rose, foam streaming from her nostrils, and every time she rammed her head in again, sending up explosions of spray, her propeller turning wild, setting her whole ramshackle body aquiver. I had no idea what speed we were making, but even if we made only five or six knots we should be very near the spot where the Greek had sent his last signal. Sparks came to the bridge several times and said he went on calling him, but that there was no answer. I asked him if he had heard any of Bakker's signals but he hadn't. The *Texel* had been as silent as a grave.

I knew the *Texel*, I knew her better than my own ship. She was sturdy and would remain afloat under any circumstances short of the great flood, riding the waves like a duck, but she couldn't make any speed. Even though she had the wind on her hind quarters right now, it would take old

Bakker at least three more hours to reach the spot of the Greek's last position. He was ours, only in this turmoil of heaving darkness and crashing avalanches of water I couldn't see a thing, so I told Sparks to send out a last signal to the Greek, hoping his receiver was still working although his transmitter had packed up; a signal asking him to send up a flare to mark his position. During a quarter of an hour after Sparks had palmed himself hand over hand back to his cubicle to transmit the signal, the boy Middag and I stood peering in the darkness, due north, waiting. Then suddenly, far away, a faint red light shot up into the sky and we slapped each other's shoulders and cursed with joy and I hollered when Sparks appeared, "Make answer! We have seen your flare and will change our course accordingly!"

The flare had been very far away, much farther north than I had expected, but I didn't know the *Brighton Belle* yet. I didn't know how much she would drift in a wind like this. I changed our course and we lunged ahead, the waves came in over our portside now and started stripping the last of the feathers off her. I had forgotten about Goatskin until I suddenly heard a scream and jumped aside just in time to avoid a dark object being hurled at me from the darkness down the slope of the heeling bridge. It was the wheel chair. The sea had smashed the port rail of the bridge. If we heeled over the other side the bath-chair would roll back and vanish overboard.

It happened. The boy Middag and I both threw ourselves onto the dark parcel hurtling down at us, its little wheels screeching. We were dragged all the way down the bridge but we wouldn't let go. We wouldn't have let go of it even it it had meant that we would have been washed overboard; but when we were nearing the dark edge of nothing, the ship heeled over once more and we were hurled back to starboard, dragged by the chair, our boots scratching the planking, vainly trying to get hold of it. The chair crashed into the starboard rail with a sickening thud and a howl of pain. Then it started rolling down the glistening slope toward the open portside once more. But the helmsman jumped out of the wheelhouse and managed to throw a rope under the wheels that acted as a brake. It took us a long time, wrestling, panting in the darkness, lashed by the spray, but we managed to get hold of the thing and to fasten it to the front rail. I tried to look under the tarpaulin, shining into it with a torch. All I saw was a pale still face hanging limp, its eyes closed. I shouted, "Are you all right?!" but he didn't answer. He had passed out. I wanted to take him down and put him on the bunk, but the chartroom was open to the wind and the waves and it wouldn't be long before the communicating door to the cabin would cave in as well. There was no other solution than to leave him where he was. I called the Cook and asked for brandy; Cook tried to pour it into his mouth, but he wouldn't take it. At first I thought he was dead, but he moaned and tried to lift his hand. He couldn't. He tried some more; in the end he took a gulp of brandy and there was no other solution than to leave him like that. The ordeal would soon be over.

It should have been. After we had been sailing on our new course for four hours I began to worry. I had the bosun standing by at the line gun for over three hours now, ready to shoot the hawser line over the Greek's deck the moment we spotted him. But wherever we peered in the darkness we saw nothing. In the end I asked Sparks to send a new message asking for one more flare, hoping his receiver would still be working.

We waited for Sparks to come back; he took a long time. I went down to his cubicle myself. He sat cramped in his chair, lashed to the table, listening. When I came in I was flung against the bunk and held on to its side with all my strength. The ship rolled as I had never known a ship to roll before. "Any answer?" I shouted, and he made a gesture silencing me. I saw his right hand scribble; I let go of the bunk, slid down to his chair and grabbed it, my legs spread out. Then I read over his shoulder: "Sorry— tried—to—warn—you—but—the—bastard—was—sitting—in—my—cabin— watching—me—stop—we—got—hold—of—the—Greek—one—hour—ago— after—you—changed—your—course—because—of—flare—which—Bakker— let—off—himself—stop—the—old—crook—you—break—his—skull—when— we—meet—in—Le—Havre—where—we—are—towing—this—duck—stop—I —wish—sorry—there—he—is—again."

Sparks turned round in his chair and looked up at me. There were tears in his eyes. "Well," he said, "there goes our future."

I went to the bridge and wheeled her round for home.

When we entered the harbor in the dull gray light of the storm-swept morning, the *Texel* was mooring her Greek at the main quay. All the boys were on deck and looked at her. All of them had only one thought: to get hold of that old bastard's neck and wring it. To have let off that flare, making us believe it was the Greek, was such a callous miserable deed that the only revenge could be physical violence. No words could express that depth of mean play. He had known it was our last chance, he had known that if this time we failed there would be no hope left for us ever to come back in the tugboat service, unless we signed as sailors and stokers. Yet he had done it. He had snatched that Greek away from us, who had been so near, and he had snatched him away not because of his superior seamanship but by means of a dirty trick.

The only one who thought it funny was Goatskin. When we unwrapped him so soon as we entered the calm water between the piers, he was dizzy and very pale but conscious. "What happened?" he asked, and when I told him he laughed. He laughed so much that the tears ran down his cheeks. I thought, with an odd feeling of disgust, that the only thing his dead eye could still do was weep.

When we moored in our home berth the two girls stood waiting on the quay. They must have seen us come in and ran round the harbor to meet us as we moored. They came on board the moment the gangplank was out. Nicole climbed the bridge, panting, and when she saw Goatskin she gave a curious animal sound, fell on her knees beside him and hid her face in the tarpaulin that covered his legs. I felt very tense and clenched my fists to keep down the blind rage that urged me to go ashore and run round the harbor to the *Texel* and jump on board and rip open that communicating door and go for Bakker with all the violence of the seven arid years that surged behind me.

I met June at the bottom of the bridge steps. She looked very pale. "God," she said, "what happened to the ship?" The old *Brighton Belle* was indeed a gruesome sight. Even without Captain Perseil's ultimatum we would never have sailed her again, for to get her repaired would cost several months in dock.

I said, "Yes, we took quite a beating." Then I saw the faces of my crew, silently staring at me almost in reproach. I said, "Don't worry, boys, that's exactly where I am going now," brushed past June and went ashore.

She caught up with me when I was walking round the harbor, very fast, cursing under my breath. "Where are you going?" she asked. I said, "I am going to settle an account." "No," she said, trying to hold me back by my arm, "no, please." I pulled myself free, and said, "Leave me alone," but she went on running beside me, imploring me not to do anything silly. I had my whole life before me, I was a wonderful sailor, there was nothing wrong with me, the ship had been old and rotten, please, please, darling, don't do it, please. I stopped at the *Texel's* gangway. June looked quite haggard; she had lost her red bonnet and her hair was blown across her face. She grabbed my arms with both hands and looked at me with such despair in her eyes that I felt my rage sink down, like a wave retiring. I said, "Sorry, I didn't mean to be rude."

She looked at me and I saw her face change. She managed a smile, then she said, "All right, darling, go ahead," and she turned me round herself until I faced that gangway.

When I crossed it I tried to recapture the fury I had felt since Sparks and I had looked at each other after that message about the flare. But I couldn't any more. I felt tired and hopeless, when I stepped down on the deck and went to the chartroom that I knew so well. I stood for a moment in doubt, my hand on the doorknob. Then I turned it and went in without knocking.

The old man was sitting at the table, writing in his log. When I saw the back of his bald head, his fleshy neck, his short sleeves, his hairy pulses, the rage came back all right. I said, "Captain, I want to talk to you," and my voice was not steady. He looked up. When I saw his blue fish eyes stare at me without any feeling, any expression at all but a cruel, merciless stupidity, I felt like smashing his teeth in. I thought of the twenty-nine young tugboat captains out of the thirty-five that had died during the war, of Dop and Barger and Frankendaal and Daamen, and then of the five fat old men out of six who had come through alive, and of whom this bastard was the worst. In Shadwell Basin we had asked ourselves timidly what had been the magic secret of their survival; now, looking at that stupid cruel mug, I asked myself what had been the curse on us.

"Well?" he asked.

I said, "That flare you let off when you heard us asking the Greek was a dirty trick. I ought to beat the daylight out of you, you Goddam old swindler." He rose slowly to his feet, menacing like a bull, and my voice rose in fury when I said, "You knew it was our last chance. We have sailed this whole Goddam war together and yet you rubbed our face in the shit."

"Yes," he said, and his voice growled deeper than I had ever heard it. "And do you want to know why, young man? Because if our country wants to get back on its feet after the beating we took, we have to give the best we have got. As long as I can help it, the tugboat business shall not fall into the hands of a lot of amateurs, like you and your beachcombers."

At that moment I knew I was going to strike him. I talked on only to postpone the blow that I felt quivering in my fists. "You call us amateurs, but you needed a dirty trick to get ahead of us!" I cried.

He gave a deep sigh through the nose, and looked at me almost with pity when he said, "You go somewhere quiet and think out the answer to this question: how come that I have found that Greek in the dark, whereas you have not?"

Then he sat down and continued his writing.

324

When I came off the ship, dazed, June was there. She didn't ask any questions, she just put her arm through mine. We walked along the quay, down the pier, until we sat down on a bollard behind the fishing smacks, because we couldn't go any further.

I hadn't noticed where I was going. I had been trying to recover from the blow, but there was no recovery possible unless I accepted the truth that stared me in the face. At last I had discovered the magic secret of the old captains: they had known their job.

As I sat there, staring at the ships and the harbor, I forgot about her, until she asked, "Well?"

I put my hand on hers and said, "Well, I have just heard the verdict." Then I looked at her and tried to smile. But I felt at the end of my tether.

"And what is that?" she asked.

I bit my lip, for my eyes went hot, and said, "I am no good. Old Bakker found that Greek in the dark. I didn't. God knows how he found him, but there you are."

"He must be a wonderful captain," she said calmly, almost cheerfully. I felt very alien to her. She couldn't know what this meant to me. I think that that moment, sitting close to her on that bollard, hand in hand, was the loneliest moment in my life.

"There was a time when I thought I was a wonderful captain too," I said, trying to make it sound like a joke.

She pressed my hand. "And I thought I was a wonderful nurse."

I looked at her, smiling at me, at her dark eyes full of gentleness and understanding. I remembered her with her Dagenham Girl Pipers' cap on her eyebrows, sticking that thermometer in my mouth. "Well," I said, "you weren't."

I looked at the masts again, the ragged clouds blown low across the sky, and I felt nothing, I felt empty. But she went on quietly talking as if all this was quite normal, as if we were as common as the sparrows on the quay.

"I think that we all have to learn a lesson after this war," she said. "Whatever we may think we have done in the emergency isn't solid. If we really want to start the peace we have to pick up our life at the point where we left it when the war started, because peace isn't just the fact that the guns have stopped firing, it is something in ourselves."

"That sounds lovely," I said, "but what the hell am I to do with myself, if I am not a good captain?"

She pressed my hand again, smiling. "Could it be that you are a very good mate?" she asked.

I looked at her, with a song rising inside me, and then I kissed her, her head in my hands. I kissed her like mad, my eyes tightly closed, with the song thundering in my ears like the surf, and then I said, "God, June! You are right!"

We got up and walked back to the city.

When I told Goatskin that I was going to look for a post as a mate on a tugboat again, he didn't look surprised. He just asked quietly, "Why?" and I said, "Because I want to learn the job."

He looked at me with his one live eye as he had looked only once before: on the deck of our schooner, in the harbor of La Ciotat, after I had come up, shaken, from my first dive with the Cousteau. Then he said, "You lucky bugger," and called for a bottle of wine.

Our farewell dinner was very gay, if one took into consideration that to all of us except to me this meant the end, and perhaps to me too. But I didn't care any more; it wasn't my future I had been worrying about, but my past. We raised our glasses for the last time and the mad pianist played "Auld Lang Syne." Goatskin was very cheerful, and that was a lucky thing; if he had been depressed we would all have been.

After the others had left, Nicole and June hung on. Goatskin said, "What if you girls went to bed? I would like to have a word with the Skipper." They were very good; they finished their glasses and went, arm in arm.

"Well," he said, after they had left, "now tell me what happened."

I told him, all of it. Never before had I felt so close to him. It was as if I was talking to myself. I told him how I had gone to the *Texel* to break old Bakker's skull, how he had put me that question in the nick of time, how I had ended up at the end of the quay with June and sat down on that bollard, and what she had said. "The funny thing is," I said, "that I don't mind not being a captain. I always felt like an impostor, ever since I first sailed with the *Zeeland* in Westport with old Van Dam as my opposite number. He was a professional all right. If he hadn't been killed in that air raid he'd still be sailing, like the others."

"Good old Skipper," said Goatskin, and then he drained his glass and looked at me sentimentally with his live eye. He looked as if he was getting drunk. "Self-confidence has never been one of your vices."

"Take it easy," I said. "As a mate, I don't think anybody could wish himself a better one than I."

"Hear, hear," he said, and then he poured out another glass. He sat with it in his hand looking at the sparkle of the light in the wine when he asked, "So you won't come with me in that twenty-foot cutter, will you?"

I said, "No," and when he smiled, I added, "I am sorry."

After that we sat in silence. There were so many things we wanted to say, so much feeling that waited to be expressed, that we just sat and looked at the landlord stacking the chairs. Then he said, "O.K., Skipper, take me upstairs."

I lifted him out of his wheel chair and carried him up the stairs. The landlord wanted to help but I said I could manage. Nicole heard us come up and she opened the door. June was there. I put him down on the bed.

"Good night," I said. "Good night, Nicole."

Nicole said good night, and then he asked, "Are you leaving in the morning?"

I said, "Yes."

"All right," he said. "God bless, Skipper. See you on that distant shore." June took my hand on the dark landing.

CHAPTER SIXTEEN

I TRIED TO FIND A JOB AS A MATE DURING THE REST OF THAT WINTER. NO-body wanted me, mates came thirteen to a dozen. I would have given up after a fortnight, if June hadn't been there. I found odd jobs ashore to keep going; none of them lasted longer than a couple of weeks. Then one night in early spring I heard in a pub on the Amsterdam harbor that old Captain Bakker was looking for a mate. He had fired three in rapid succession and there were no applications any more, because those three had told stories that made your hair stand on end.

June came with me when I went to Flushing. The *Texel* lay riding on her moorings, the tide was strong. As we approached the ship, that lay quite alone at the empty quay, I heard the old man bellow curses to his bosun, ordering him to slacken the mooring ropes, telling him he was a Goddam bungler who ought to be drowned with his head in a bucket of his own blood. June mumbled, "Charming," and kissed me and said, "All right, darling, this is it. Here comes the best mate of the fleet."

When I appeared on the quayside I saw him standing in the doorway of the chartroom. He said: "Jesus Christ, there he is again. Haven't you stopped following me about, you bungler?"

I said, "No, sir," and went on board. When I entered the chartroom he glowered at me as if we were still facing each other, that morning in Le Havre. "What do you want?" he growled.

"I heard you are looking for a mate," I said.

He stared at me, and I saw something dawn on his face that I had never expected I would see there: incredulity. "You want to sail as a mate?" he asked.

I said, "Yes, sir."

"With me?"

"Yes, sir."

The incredulity changed into suspicion as he went on staring at me, narrowing his fish eyes. "Why?" he asked.

And then I said, with a feeling as if it were the marriage vow, "Because I want to learn the job."

He looked at me a few seconds longer. Then he said, "High time too," and turned away.

"Does that mean that I am accepted?" I asked.

"Yes," he said, "one bloody bungler or the other, it's all the same to me. We sail at six, to Hammerfest, so you'd better get some warm underwear."

I said, "Yes, sir," and turned away to go.

His voice stopped me in the doorway. "But I warn you!" he cried. "On board my ship the war is over!"

I said, "Yes, sir"; and after stepping over the threshold onto the deck I turned round once more and said, "Thank you, sir." But by that time he had vanished in his cabin.

June stood waiting on the quay. I said: "Yes. We leave at six for Hammerfest."

"Congratulations," she said, "Mate."

We walked along the quay in silence. Then I said, "You'd better take a hotel room if you want to see me off."

"I will," she said.

We walked some more. Then I said, "I don't think we can marry until I'm a captain."

Then she laughed and kissed me in full view of everybody, which was very un-English, and said, "But darling, that may be never!"

I said, "You're right," and we walked arm in arm to the station restaurant where we ordered the full menu.

Later that night, in her hotel, we spent our last money on a whim. We rang up Saint Tropez to tell Goatskin and Nicole that we were going to be married when I came back from this trip.

I rang up the harbor master and when I asked him to call Maurice to the phone the old man shouted that I was two days too late. Maurice and the Chinese girl had left for a cruise in a cutter they had hired, just the two of them. When I asked whether by any chance he knew their destination, he answered that he wasn't sure, but that he had heard them mention the island of Port Cros.

A Sailor's Life

SOME TIME AGO I RECEIVED A LETTER FROM A BOY IN GERMANY. HE AD-
dressed me as "Highly Honoured Sir Captain" which flattered me considerably, and wrote that he had decided to go to sea, flying in the face of
his father, after reading a novel of mine. In view of his decision and my
responsibility for it, he requested of me a few hints about what every
young sailor should know before setting out for his first voyage, and he
enclosed a postage stamp for my reply. As I mulled over his request, I
jotted down the subjects on which, in my experience, a young sailor should
be advised. The total amounted to two hundred and twenty. This obviously
was too hefty a volume to be covered by the postage stamp.

During the weeks that followed, the sea was exceptionally lenient, the
sunset red and promising, the dawns still and dove-grey. Looking at the
water-colour world through which we were sailing like a black beetle on
the palette of a very young god, one wondered why mankind had to wait
for Columbus before America was discovered, and why the Flying Dutchman sold his soul for a day of calm. The German boy's decision seemed a
sensible one.

So I started a collection of small hints meant for a young sailor, and
called it *A Young Sailor's Companion*. When the book was finished, I
discovered to my dismay that, instead of giving the young sailor a book of
reference, I had provided him with a portrait of the author as a middle-
aged man. My publisher obviously came to the same conclusion, as he
changed the title from *A Young Sailor's Companion* to *A Sailor's Life*.

The purpose of this preface is to reassure the general reader that this
book is neither technical nor nautical. It might as well be called *Navigation for the Housewife* or *A Fireside Pilot*. It serves no purpose whatso-

ever; my only hope is that, when all is said, the image may linger of a late summer's view of the sea, a ship, the men who sail her and the gulls that circle over her wake.

J. DE H.

Ship *Rival*, at sea

1954–1955

Part I LIFE AT SEA *(Outward Bound)*

BOYHOOD DREAMS

ONE WOULD EXPECT THAT DREAMING ABOUT THE SEA IS RESTRICTED TO young boys living near it. Yet the commanding officer of any naval college will tell you that half of his pupils come from far inland and have never set eyes on the silver horizon.

What makes a boy dream about the sea is as mysterious as what makes him dream at all. Somewhere, sometime towards dawn, a seed is carried through the stillness to alight in an unconscious child's mind. When bacon spluttering in the kitchen wakes him up for a new day, he will wonder what those thousands of white birds were, wheeling over a great water, gackering and mewing. That morning, he will walk slowly along the road to school, musing about the land beyond the hills among which he was born.

Later, he may read a book, see a picture, or listen to the story of an old pedlar resting on a milestone; after that nothing will keep him from going to sea. He will be obsessed, like the early Christians who left father and mother, brother and sister, wife and children, to learn the news. His family will worry about him in the oil-light and search among those who went before for a sailor, a cranky aunt or the unknown lover that came and went one spring day a century ago. The difference between the boyhood visions of the young sailor and other boys' fantasies is that they have nothing to do with excitement, uniforms, roaring about in bright red fire-engines or screaming through the midsummer's night in a jet fighter. They have to do with the other side of the moon of childhood: dreams. They are homing-pigeons who winged across uncharted seas from the mystic island whence the great questions come, like: "Has God got a deep voice?" It is useless to try to make the boy-sailor who has never set eyes on the sea forget about it and become a doctor or an accountant. The result will only be that he will be a bad doctor or a hen-pecked accountant, forever messing about with boats. Parents who instinctively feel that to become a sailor is as bad as getting into debt or marrying one's aunt should realise that life at sea is about the sanest life a man can lead under present-day circumstances. If a boy wants to go to sea, let him, for if you don't, he will be a stranger at your table.

Boys born near the sea have an easier time, yet they are up against a lesser evil: their parents' perpetual fear that they will drown before their time. "Don't play near the water" or "If I see you once more with those boys in that rickety boat" are almost as bad as the "I never heard of such a thing" and "Whatever next?" of the landsman of the interior.

The thing to do is to teach them to swim and let them fall in the water as early as possible. For to warn them away from the water is to warn them away from life.

ON PACKING

THIS MAY BE DIFFICULT, BUT THE YOUNG SAILOR MUST LET HIS MOTHER PUT anything she likes into his luggage, or he'll be sorry later. Not because he'll miss the articles she suggests, but because he'll be homesick and indulge in remorse for hurting her on the eve of his departure. He should not forget that, to her, it is the final act of motherhood, to help him pack for his first voyage. In a mother's opinion, a son sails away forever, even if he only leaves for a three-week trip.

The young sailor had better be prepared for chocolate, warm slippers, frilly bags to hold his sponge, and a pillowcase with some endearment written on it in pencil. He must be warned that his cabin companion, if at all experienced, will watch him like a hawk as he unpacks, ready to pounce on bars of whole-milk chocolate self-consciously tossed aside. The thing to do is to pack the bottom layers of one's bag oneself, and to tell one's mother that her contributions should go on top, where they will be least squashed. The first thing to do on board ship is to fill one's private cupboard with the top layer. So don't prevent her from putting things in, but stop her putting in surprises. I'll never forget a young apprentice's face when he unpacked in my presence, full of manly banter, and brought out a banana.

Now, what should the young sailor take out to sea and how should he pack it? There are obvious things to avoid, hardly worth mentioning, like tennis rackets and barometers, which I have actually seen carried on board by self-conscious novices. Other things to avoid are all garments that suggest seafaring to be in any way related to mountain-climbing or going on safari. Ski-shoes, double-barrelled shot-guns and stained-glass mittens sold to tobogganers by aborigines of the Alps should never be taken on board ship; sunhelmets tend to provoke mortifying hilarity before being carried off by the first tropical squall. This caution does not apply to Balaclavas, which are sensible if the trip is going to be really cold. There should be, unless regulations insist on formal dress, two ordinary seaman's jerseys, which don't show the dirt and are waterproof into the bargain. As to underwear, two sets will do. The thing to remember is that, if the ship is on the small side, there will be very little space for personal effects and it is better to have some to spare for presents brought aboard, or you'll crowd yourself out of your bunk.

Trousers should be of the uniform type for daily wear on watches, and two pairs of blue jeans for working in. Things to remember are: a second comb as the first will get broken, a sewing kit, shoe-polish kit, and a brief-case. The apprentice is sure to be sent ashore to the company's agent or ship-chandler with papers, and he will feel conspicuous if he has to carry these about in a big envelope.

The actual packing is not so very important, as the stuff is taken out the moment the young sailor gets on board his ship, at least it should be. His first action on board should be to unpack. In this connection it may be useful to remember that the kit-bag is not a folksy tradition but a sensible solution to the problem of space, as it can be rolled up and stored away when empty. Most small ships provide no room for suitcases in their junior officers' cabins.

As to caps: take one with a removable top instead of two caps, one white and one blue. If the cap has a lining, take it out. You will find it too hot in any circumstance unless you are bald.

Things to avoid: sweaters with Rugby team initials, and duffel coats with hearts painted on them or jocular remarks like "If you can read this you are too damn close." Witty garments become unwitty when looked at by a captain. Also to be avoided: perfumed hair lotion, powder unless hermetically packed, brown shoes and electric razors. I suppose there is no need to talk about dressing-gowns, unless the young sailor is a wireless-operator, in which case a flowered bathrobe will be expected of him as a part of his uniform. It may be necessary to assure the young sailor that he will need pyjamas; sleeping in the nude puts one at a disadvantage when the messroom-boy rips open the curtain, calling, "Quarter hour!" Also, to change into pyjamas after a watch induces sleep, because man, like the dog, is governed by conditioned reflexes.

The portrait of one's mother should be small. Portraits grow to three times their size when pinned up in a bunk. One's sweetheart, whatever her size, should be fully clothed.

The label you attach to your kit-bag should mention your name, your ship and its home port, not your rank. You are not in the Navy.

DEPARTURES, EXCEPT WHEN THE SHIP IS RUNNING ON A REGULAR FERRY service, are always depressing. Everyone is full of the worries or the joys of his shore-life; women weep, children are a nuisance, the lavatories are full of dirty water and some sailors are always missing up to the last minute when they are carried on board blind drunk by the man-trader. The only ones who enjoy all this are those members of the crew who have no home and who have been waiting eagerly for the reunion. Nobody likes them until at sea, so tension is a common feature of every departure.

First departures, so the young sailor will find, are unforgettable in their bleak nausea. Ships always leave either at dead of night or at dawn; to say good-bye to one's family on a dark quayside amidst the rails, the cranes and the slack heaps feels like dying.

There are a few ways of lightening the burden of departure but they are only stop-gaps; they cannot cure the heart of the matter. Rule number one is: say good-bye to your family at home and forbid them to accompany you to the quayside. Otherwise they will stand shivering in the icy dawn underneath the most dismal light in the world, a naked electric bulb high up on a crane. They will want to wave, but the ship leaves so cumbersomely that they neither know when to start nor when to stop. On board, every departure is a chaos, so the last thing the young sailor will feel like is waving. Another unforeseen element is that every apprentice feels embarrassed about his family and their handkerchiefs. If your family wants to see the ship, show it to them the day before leaving when there are only a couple of watchmen on board and an engineer who loves being introduced as "Chief." The best person to put your mother and even your father at ease is the wireless-operator, who will make the coming voyage sound like a sight-seeing tour in a streamlined bus; but he is rarely there unless he is engaged, in which case he takes his fiancée on board and is not in a position to act as guide at short notice.

Rule number two is: bring your luggage on board and arrange your belongings for the trip in their cupboards well in advance. To face the turmoil of the departure with a dismal cabin full of unpacked bags makes everything seem worse than it is. The best time for bringing your luggage is two days beforehand. It will give you a chance to wander about the ship alone and get acquainted with its lay-out. If in the pitch darkness of the night of departure the first mate orders you to get his oilskins from the airing-cupboard, you will at least have some notion of where to run.

Rule number three, and to my mind the most important, is: see to it that you come on board well rested and relaxed. The first two rules will help you to achieve this but they are not enough. Get plenty of sleep during the week before you sail, say good-bye to distant relatives in good time and in small doses, and don't leave anything until the last minutes. An old captain I knew, who was a paragon of calm and patient cheerfulness during any departure, told me his secret: he forbade his wife and his family to see him off and told them the ship would leave two days before it actually did. Those two days he spent on his back in a hotel, reading women's magazines, doing crossword puzzles and harmlessly drowning his homesickness in beer.

SEASICKNESS

UNTIL RECENTLY, SEASICKNESS WAS THE YOUNG SAILOR'S CURSE. NOWADAYS, drugs may lead him to think he need not worry.

Perhaps he needn't. The best chance of suppressing seasickness with a drug is to take the pills well before the movement starts. Yet the young sailor will not be protected by pills, for if the seasickness doesn't catch up with him on leaving, it will later.

Seasickness is one of those diseases that are popular with non-sufferers as it bolsters their ego. I have rarely met an old lady passenger who did not tell me that on her last trip she sailed through such a terrible storm that only the captain and she sat down to dinner. So the first consolation I can tender to the seasick young sailor is that he'll be richly rewarded by a feeling of superiority once he is no longer seasick but someone else is. Not to be seasick is as pleasant as to be seasick is depressing. But for the moment, he is, and the first question that will loom largely in his mind is why he did not listen to those wise old people who warned him not to go to sea. Yet after a fortnight at sea, the young sailor will smile at the memory and tear out the pages he wrote in his diary at the time. Seasickness and homesickness go together, and they produce embarrassing outpourings in longhand.

There are a few simple rules to observe, which will help you over the seasickness. First of all, keep warm. Then find something to do, preferably in the open. Inactivity is your worst enemy. Liquids should not be taken, although cooks insist on telling young sailors that a cup of coffee will put them right. Fatty foods and starchy foods should also be avoided, for everything that gives the stomach work will aggravate your condition. It is, however, important that you eat something because the real hellish state

341

of seasickness begins when you want to throw up on an empty stomach. Another hint is to look as little as possible at the sea or the horizon. You will be amazed how you can keep seasickness at bay as long as you don't become conscious of the horizon rising and falling. It is a well-known phenomenon, which was used to the crew's advantage on board the hospital-church-ship on which I sailed as a boy. There the sea-chaplain insisted on celebrating evensong every day, which was too often. The sail-maker soon found out that if he left the little doors of the companion-way open so that the parson could see the horizon from where he sat, the service would be short.

Lying down on your bunk will give you momentary relief but only postpone the execution. You'll get into a state where you will feel more or less all right as long as you are in bed, but seasick the moment you get up. So don't consider senior officers who rout you out as being cruel; they are wise.

One thing seasickness should teach you: sympathy with future sufferers. Sadly, this rarely is the case.

HOMESICKNESS

NO SUFFERING MAKES A MAN FEEL MORE HELPLESS AND LOST AT SEA. THE homesickness will centre, like regret after a beloved's demise, on things one neglected while one still had them. The cup of tea mother used to bring in in the morning, the sound of the church-bells at dawn on Sunday, the smell of cooking from the kitchen and the thump of the newspaper at the door. If the young sailor is in love, or should discover he is after leaving, the homesickness becomes not only unbearable but dangerous. One can write long incoherent letters bewailing the separation only to one's mother and father, without influencing one's future beyond repair.

So perhaps it is not the young sailor who should be warned or helped. He'll be homesick and he will get over it. His girl-friend, who receives the fruits of his homesickness when it is probably long past, is the true victim. There it is, in black and white: "The upshot of all this, my darling, is, of course, that I love you. I love you more than any other human being alive, for to be away from you is such agony as I never thought a man could endure. Think of the day I'll come home. . . ."

Then he comes home, looking sheepish, with the infuriating smile and the baby-voice of endearment, and wards off embraces with excited talk and sighs of how lovely it is to be home. "Let me have a look round first, darling. . . ." Once he is put on the spot in the twilight, he says, "I don't love you in that way," and tries to sell it as a compliment.

No young sailor will ever understand why a girl, who once shrank from passionate embraces, should rise in fury when he suggests she is indeed too special for that kind of thing. It is not that she wants it; she wants him to writhe and fume and stammer in a frenzy of frustration. She will instantly know the truth, which is that since he wrote that letter he has been cured of his homesickness, and is now homesick for the sea.

So don't write letters at the height of your suffering. Keep a diary.

DIARY

EVERY APPRENTICE SHOULD KEEP A DIARY. IF HE DOESN'T, HE MAY ACTUALLY give the scathing answers he has thought of while lying hot-eyed on his bunk after the first unjustified reprimand from a senior officer. If he writes them down in his diary, with a full word-picture of the foul-mouthed brute's coarseness, he will face him afterwards with a sense of shame, which is as it should be. For to be an apprentice means to suffer from injustice all day long, for months on end; the result is homesickness, brooding, and doubt about life at sea. The diary changes all this into delightful souvenirs, which become useful once he is a mate himself and called upon to deal with apprentices.

What the young sailor cannot possibly realise at present is that he would be a lot more unjust in the mate's place. There is something about pimples, dirty fingernails and solemnity gazing from underneath a new peaked cap that calls forth exasperation instead of sympathy. Diaries turn every frustrating or bewildering experience into something positive: a written page. The sufferer will be amazed at the difference it makes to feel that everything happening to him serves a purpose.

The diary is the great confessional of youth, for the only one really interested in the young sailor's struggles, hopes, joys, desires and despair is the young sailor. A diary is a lone youth's trail on a wet beach at low tide. Letters should be summaries of diaries; the letter-writer will discover that the summary of the fifteen blackest pages of his diary will run, ". . . and so we sailed on, every day much the same as every other, until we sighted Sandy Hook."

Diaries also help to explore and formulate vague feelings, a thing the apprentice will be expected to do in connection with others the moment he becomes an officer. No one who has not kept a diary has the means of knowing what worries the seaman who morosely complains about the food. Only by discovering within one's own soul that lack of appetite stands for homesickness can one make him eat again. A secondary but very important function of the diary is that it will encourage the young sailor to use big unfamiliar words with satisfaction.

It may well be that the youngster who carries his brand-new kit-bag on board, dumps it in the triangular cabin, and looks around him apprehensively is going to outdazzle Joseph Conrad's star. The road to literary brilliance will lead via his diary. The moment the apprentice can capture the mood of the moon rising at sea in words, he has arrived at that great bliss of creation which the French painter Renoir defined as "Correcting nature." The boy with the diary is stronger than the man with the grudge. It is David's pebble.

THE WATCHES

THE WATCHES ON BOARD SHIP WILL REGULATE THE YOUNG SAILOR'S LIFE from now on. Even after he has become a captain and thus watchless, the striking of the ship's bell will mean more to him than the neighbouring church clock ashore.

At sea, the day begins at noon, for it divides time rather than that it regulates the ebb and flow of activity. At sea, there are always people about and people asleep; to those about, it is day and to the others, night. The watches last four hours each, except the dog-watch which is split into two to make sure that everyone takes his turn and no one shall be condemned to take the middle watch, which lasts from 4 A.M. to 8 A.M., every night for the rest of the trip.

The first watch is called the Afternoon Watch and lasts from twelve to four. It is a pleasant watch to take, for those officers who might come on the bridge to check will be asleep. The young sailor will feel more at ease during this watch than during any of the others, including the night. First mates get up at regular hours at dead of night to go to the toilet, and make a detour either via the bridge itself or halfway up the steps. During the hours of siesta, the ship is peaceful; noisy activities are banned, and to see a sailor polishing the brass or doing a bit of painting is a pleasant homely sight, seen from above. Nobody is homesick during the Afternoon Watch.

From 4 P.M. to 6 P.M. is the first dog-watch, and the next two hours up to 8 P.M. the second. Both are pleasant, because they are short and supper falls in them. If you have the first dog-watch, you may have to wait a bit

344

longer for your meal but you'll have the consolation that any errors in the cook's produce of the day will have been corrected as a result of the first table. If you have the second watch, you won't go hungry. In Northern climes, sunset falls in the second dog-watch so it is tinged with beauty, a poetic mood and somebody singing on the foredeck. Sunset is larking time to the foc'sle, as if it were fortifying itself for the coming darkness. You'll find the sound of laughter coming from for'ard very cheering. The sunset also has a softening effect on senior officers. The first mate will be up to check and teach you how to shoot a star as if you were a human being. He may also enquire after your love-life, which should be taken as a sign that he feels in need of a monologue; tell him very briefly, so that he may sally forth with his human and manly counsel as soon as possible. You must be brief, for, unlike you, he has eaten, and he will feel offended if hunger shows on your face while he gives you the benefit of his experience.

From 8 p.m. to midnight is called the First Watch for no apparent reason. It is a good second to the ones that went before, but has a tendency to drag. It should not be used for private efforts at celestial observation, for they won't be private. This is the favourite inspection-time for captains who, like owls, see better in the twilight. So make sure you have shaved and don't be lulled into a false sense of security by the gathering darkness and doze while standing up. If there is a lunatic on board, this is the time he will sing or howl. If there is no lunatic, the ship's dog will sound off. The highlight of the First Watch is the tea which, as the messroom-boy has turned in, will be fetched from the galley by the sailor at the wheel; so for five minutes at least, you can steer the ship yourself. When the tea comes, and the sailor at the wheel takes his place once more, you will feel tempted, while sipping the hot sweet beverage, to talk with him about love. This should be kept for the next watch; the captain may arrive at any moment now; old-age heartburn takes about two hours after dinner to manifest itself.

Some people hate the next four hours, called the Middle Watch, as they are the longest of all and are spent in total darkness. True, the circumstances are uninspiring, but the sense of intimacy between the officer and the man at the wheel largely compensates for them. These are the hours of stories and confessions, and although there is nothing to see outside, the apprentice will take with him vivid images of an unknown world when it is over. It is the ideal time to get acquainted with the crew individually; the sailors don't have a second dog-watch, and the man at the wheel will be different each time. The only time for caution is between three and four, when the senior officers go to the lavatory and may check. Be sure

345

that you are on the bridge and out in the drizzle by then. You will be rewarded, even if no one turns up, by the sunrise.

From four to eight, the Morning Watch, is the worst but one. Sunrise may fall in it and you are lucky if it does, for just afterwards come the bleary hours. If this is your first trip, you will be very sleepy towards the end of the watch, your eyes will feel boiled and you will wonder whether life at sea is really what you want. Take these worries in your stride and deal with them as best you can. The coffee is tepid and tastes bitter because it has been sitting on the galley-stove all night, and every single person appearing on deck will yawn infectiously. Officers get up and may be forced to fetch their own hot water as they all want it at the same time; this makes them short-tempered and their furry tongues will lash out. The main thing to remember is that you should be very quiet during this watch as the captain, just below, is stirring in half-sleep and may roar like a lion if you are not careful. There is nothing more unnerving than the question, "Who is that?" bellowed through a skylight while you are trying to warm your feet. The answer, "Me, sir," should be avoided.

The less said about the Forenoon Watch, the better. It is the messiest, most harassed and longest of the lot. The deck is scrubbed under your very feet; the compass polished; and both scrubber and polisher will sing in Italian, which, for some reason, a tired man feels in his eyeballs. If you want to know how you'll feel during the Forenoon Watch, ask your mother what morning sickness is.

SLEEP

ONE OF THE MOST PROFOUND CHANGES THE YOUNG SAILOR WILL GO THROUGH is concerned with sleeping. The younger you are, the more difficult you will find it to adjust yourself to a sailor's life in the beginning. You will be called upon to sleep at any hour and under any conditions. In the tropics, you will swelter and see blood on closing your eyes. In the Northern winter you will either pile all your belongings on top of you or lie stark-naked bathing in your own sweat with a parched throat because the captain felt chilly and ordered the Chief to push the central heating. Captain's cabins, being high up, should be warmer than others if you ask any central heating expert, but if you ask any captain you will hear they are colder. It is one of those mysteries the young sailor will have to accept unquestioningly until he becomes a captain himself.

There are a few things to keep in mind with regard to sleep on board

346

ship. The first is that no sedative should be taken. They work, but go on working after the sleeper has been awakened, as no pill is adjusted to three hours' rest only. If you sail on a small ship like a tugboat or a coaster, you'll be four hours on and four hours off, and it will turn out to be the best training you can possibly have for your future at sea. To take nine hours' rest in twenty-four, by periods of three hours at a time, is the very reverse of what your mother thinks it is. Babies thrive on it and many a hollow-eyed business man would feel better rested if, instead of snoring in an arctic climate with the windows open for seven hours at a stretch, he were forced into the open sea air after three hours of suffocation in an airless cabin. The great thing to master is how to fall asleep and, silly as they may sound, the old home remedies are the best. Counting sheep may make you feel silly and defeat its purpose. I found the best image to induce sleep was that of a cornfield waving in the wind under a summer sky. This may be a personal preference, but I haven't heard of a better one yet. Sheep never jump across hedges at all, let alone in their hundreds; the undulating cornfield is a much more real and relaxing image.

Another important detail is that your feet should be warm. They are much more important than the rest of your body in that respect. You'll find that no cook will provide a hot-water bottle, but as there is always hot water on the galley-stove, you'll be wise to include a rubber hot-water bottle in your kit. Yet the warming of the feet will take some precious time which will rapidly make the cornfield give way to its association: the sea, which is the reverse of relaxing. So, the best advice I can tender is to wear wooden-soled short sea-boots when on watch.

After you have finally lived up to the challenge of sleeping at all hours and under any noises for short periods, you come home and have to start all over again. This is not as difficult as it may seem, for to wake up in a ship buzzing with life is a different thing from finding oneself alone in a dark, still house full of sleeping people.

One more thing connected with sleep the young sailor should know is that if one immerses a sleeper's dangling hand cautiously in a bowl of tepid water, he will wet his bunk. I don't expect the young sailor to do this to anyone, but someone might do it to him.

HYGIENE

OF ALL THE THINGS THE YOUNG SAILOR HAS TO GET ACCUSTOMED TO, personal cleanliness is the most important. Gone are the days of the weekly bath, mother reminding one that one's toenails need cutting and Sis sniffing disgustedly and saying, "Oof poof!" Gone also is the routine of going to bed at night, taking one's turn in the bathroom, and getting up in the morning to face the crowds with plastered hair, clean fingernails and a clean shave. The moment the young sailor turns from a young man about town into an exhausted, puff-eyed sleep-walker, he will be tempted to let his personal hygiene slide.

His cabin is as small as a compartment in a third-class sleeper; the wash-basin, apart from being almost impossible to get at, is placed very high after long experience with lazy ship's officers who don't want to go to the toilet. The newcomer will face the sanitary arrangements in his new world with dismay and after a long and dejected study, sitting on the edge of his bunk, he will come to the conclusion that he should have a good wash all over but will wait for an opportune moment. He may be told here and now that the opportune moment will never come. Either he gets up, undresses and does it, or the morning is near when he'll be looked over by the captain's icy stare and hear the mortifying words, "Mr. Er, I don't approve of your appearance." Even captains rarely use the word "smell."

Every young sailor in history has been surprised in his time at the smell of his companion, to discover that the offender was himself. My first effort in the field of literature was written on board a freighter at the age of sixteen; it was a short story, entitled "Satan's Breath," about a young man with a delicate sense of olfaction who murdered seven people because they stank, discovered in the end that it had been himself all the time, and committed suicide.

To wash on board ship is one of those things one has to teach oneself, or else. Once the young sailor has washed all over every day for three years, he will, if not like it, be convinced of the inevitability of the operation. Washing on board ship can, like all complicated technical achievements, be simplified. Two basic restrictions have to be faced: lack of water and lack of space. One has to wash oneself thoroughly from head to foot with a pint and a half of water, in cupboard space.

The first thing to do is to strip completely, whatever the temperature and whatever the comments of the cynic watching you from the upper bunk with his chin on his hands. The difficult moment is the moment of nakedness. You may bring yourself with an effort to take off your under-wear; you will be tempted to hastily pull on your pyjamas instead of facing the bird's bath, nailed at chin-height in the corner behind the door. The thing to do is to forget the cynic and tell yourself that you will tingle all over with delicious warmth after vigorous rubbing. Now run half a pint into the wash-basin and wash as far down as possible, beginning with the face. Ears are better cleaned with a wet than with a dry towel. After washing as far down as possible, run the water out, rinsing the basin, run a quarter of a pint, and wash Possible. For the lower half of the body, jam yourself into a sea-worthy position before lifting a foot. Don't try to put your foot in the wash-basin, for not only is it too high, it will give the cynic a view that inspires mortifying comments. After washing the feet, run out the water once more, and wash the basin.

Teeth should be brushed last and, if they are false, not put in a glass on a shelf to soak, for although taken out after you have drawn your bunk curtains, you may be called while asleep and answer unwittingly with the voice of the turtle. Anyhow, the messroom-boy is sure to see them when he rips open the curtains to say, "Quarter hour!" Artificial teeth should be kept secret, otherwise you are sure to regret them later, ashore, when the battle for supremacy starts in the dance-hall. They should be brushed in private with the latch on the door; or, better still, have two sets made which can alternate and be hidden in a cavity cut in a volume of Pastor Newman's sermons, to soak at their ease.

OILSKINS

HERE A PITFALL AWAITS THE UNSUSPECTING YOUNG SAILOR. THE BUYING of his first oilskins and sou'wester will be one of his most pleasurable experiences; to try them on in front of his family will be his most humiliating. Sou'westers make girls laugh, whether it be his sister or his girlfriend, as they remind them of advertisements for cod liver oil. Many a young sailor's first oilskins have been ruined in a gale of giggles.

Apart from this, oilskins will give a feeling of satisfaction in a man's world. There is something exhilarating about being waterproof that makes one ignore the fact that the water the garments keep out is compensated by the moisture they collect within. So far man has not invented a garment that will give his body air while protecting it against water. In this respect long oilskins are the least offensive, but they can only be worn by sailors who don't move about, like captains and first-class passengers. Others are better served with the short coat and trousers that should be worn over the sea-boots and not inside them.

The trouble about oilskins is that they need a lot of care and attention. They should be hung airily when not in use and inspected frequently, or they will stick together into a solid gluey mass. Of course, they should never be rolled up or folded. In bad weather, a towel should be worn underneath the collar to catch the water running down.

As to sou'westers, every young sailor will eventually find his own way of wearing them. He will certainly spend some time in the privacy of his bedroom trying out angles, and come to the erroneous conclusion that they are most practical when worn back to front. To help him out: they should be worn as they are grabbed. Don't forget to tie the chin-straps.

RUST

UNTIL THE NOT SO DISTANT DAY ON WHICH STAINLESS STEEL SHIPS WILL flash on the horizon, rust will remain the sailor's number-one enemy. Nobody on board is spared the consequences of rust. Even the captain, alone in his lofty cabin, is occasionally driven to ripping open his porthole and screaming, "Stop!" at the unrelenting rattle of the rust-pickers' hammers.

Rust-picking has taken the place of holy-stoning the deck in the glorious days of sail. As far as the men who do it are concerned, it is an improvement. The holy-stoners were naturals for early Russian films to personify the slavery of the masses. There they were, the stone lashed to their feet, scootering away like children in hell without ever getting any further. But they suffered without the satisfaction of driving everybody else crazy.

Rust-pickers have received this precious gift from a democratic god: they can express their opinion about their superiors while obeying orders. I have often listened to the staccato song of the rust-hammers with misgiving. As long as their rhythm was leisurely and constant, all was well. The moment they started rattling away like infuriated woodpeckers, trouble was ahead; when the hammers tapped out rhythms like the leitmotif of Berlioz' *Damnation of Faust*, somebody was saying something that would have landed him in irons if uttered.

The rust-hammer is the tom-tom of the ship. Experienced pickers can warn a thieving messroom-boy that the first mate is on his way to his cabin, insult the cook and make the stokers down below burst out laughing. It is the most jealously guarded secret of the foc'sle; no use in idling up to them as they lie on their knees on the deck, tap-tapping away, and asking, "Now, tell me, old man, just how do you convey messages?" The only answer will be a blank stare and a cretinous "Uh?" from parted lips.

I don't know who started this secret code of the sea; it must have been an ex-gaol bird at the dawn of the age of steel who had been taught the prison telegraph. Yet the code is different; it differs from ship to ship.

Its simplest form is the humorous "rattaratattattattat." Its most complicated are the five minutes' rattling that once made a cook I knew stop the recital of his operation, listen open-mouthed and rush out to look through the captain's porthole. Being a messroom-boy at the time I was allowed to look through the captain's porthole too, and saw him in front of his mirror conducting "Belle of the Ball" that was playing on his gramophone. This incident greatly increased the crew's sympathy for the captain, who was a notorious sour-puss. The pay-off came when, weeks later, he harangued the crew about personal hygiene in a martial fashion, and got carried away to the point where he began waving his arms. At that moment, some innocent in the back row started to whistle "Belle of the Ball." The result was gratifying. The captain froze like Lot's wife, one arm in the air, said, "The hell with the lot of you," in a movingly human tone, and the ship sailed happily ever after with dirty sailors.

If ever the stainless steel ship should make rust-picking redundant, the loss of the tom-tom will be felt by the foc'sles of the world. But not for long; man's adaptability is the marvel of life on our planet.

BOOKS

OF COURSE, THE YOUNG SAILOR WILL HAVE TAKEN BOOKS WITH HIM ON HIS first voyage: Shakespeare, *War and Peace,* five detective novels, a couple of text books, a pocket atlas and the Bible.

Of all these, the Bible will turn out the best choice, for there is something about it that goes with the sea, certainly if it is the old translation. As to the others: Shakespeare you'll sniff at, *War and Peace* will send you to sleep the moment the fifth Russian count with a name of seven syllables turns up, which is on page 3, and the detective novels are like cigarettes: they go with the land-bound nervousness. No officer or sailor, except the captain and the cook, feels like lying awake for two out of three hours of sleep before his next watch, reading by insufficient light until his eyeballs glow, his ears throb and his right buttock goes numb, only to discover that it was the butler.

I think the best reading matter at sea is Jack London, but this may be a personal preference. When I was a messroom-boy, the cook was in charge of the reading bag for the foc'sle. He kept it in his bunk, which was over mine, and never read a line; but he kept books printed on thin, soft paper for his own use, tearing the leaves out from back to front. At that time, a thin-paper edition of Jack London's works was a favourite among the reading bags for the Merchant Navy. I read *The Sea-Wolf*, *Martin Eden*, and *The Cruise of the Snark* in sharp competition with cook's digestion; owing to the fact that he tore out about fifty pages per book, I rarely managed to catch up with their endings. I was thus spared Jack London's women, who come in at the end of his books and spoil them; so perhaps the best advice I can give the young sailor is to read Jack London and use him at the same time from the end inward.

Another favourite of mine is a volume of three hundred and ninety pages jam-packed with information called *The News Chronicle Housewives' Handy Book*, subtitled "A complete library of information for every practical home-lover." I don't think that there is another book in the world's library that could give me so much joy, good cheer and information. I am by now an expert on stitchcraft made easy, dressmaking in the twenties, cooking bloaters and Australian groper, rewebbing a chair seat, how to prevent electricity leaking, buying in joint names, the law about pets, money-making at home with the angora rabbit, Your Place in the Stars, which contains intimate and accurate descriptions of all my friends and relations, Beauty and the Housewife, which hasn't lost its fascination since I bought the book in 1933, and the Home Garden for Women, which kept me at sea.

You will find that the best books to read on board ship are the incongruous ones. Conrad, who may be the instigator of your naval career, will be found to talk about a different sea on a different planet, for he stood with one foot in the glorious age of sail and the other on Queen Victoria; *Two Years before the Mast*, which one is forced to read in naval college, will last a great deal longer than two years, and funny sea-stories are for some reason no longer funny.

Until you become a captain, you will find that novels are difficult to cope with anyhow, because they either send one to sleep or keep one awake. If you must do something about literature for your ego, make it cheap and light. Pocket books are ideal, for they are a messroom-boy's favourite bait at the end of the trip. Speaking about messroom-boys, there is one book you must have or you'll be sorry. It must be the last word in forbidding boredom, like a treatise on the laws of licensing hours or any diplomat's memoirs. It is meant to hold your love letters. I must warn you however that you may take to be boring what a messroom-boy finds fascinating. My errors were called *With Rod and Gun through Mysterious Tibet*, by the Reverend J. B. Bangma, and *Nitchewo, or Why Russia Will Never Go Communist*, by Prince Danieloff. The messroom-boy went for them at once and read them from cover to cover, taking several highly personal communications in his stride. Once the damage was done, I followed his example, to discover that he had a keener eye for literary delight than I.

AUTHORITY

ONE HAS REALLY ACHIEVED AUTHORITY THE MOMENT ONE FORGETS ABOUT it. Stern captains and unbending officers may manage to have themselves obeyed, yet they have no authority. The most authoritative person I knew was the captain of a tugboat who, to the uninitiated observer, behaved exactly like a fat woman. He had two characteristics commonly regarded as drawbacks to those who think about authority: he could not be alone and he couldn't keep his mouth shut. He would trundle onto the bridge or into the galley at odd moments, carrying a mug of tea or a miniature glass of Geneva, to tell somebody about his inner life. Whenever he thought he was doing something sly or subtle, he became as conspicuous as an elephant trying to hide behind a palm tree. He committed all the sins I have warned the young sailor against, and will go on warning him against, as regards authority. He went back on his decisions, he asked his subordinate's opinion, he was frequently afraid and showed it, and whenever he as much as pricked his finger he screamed the place down. Yet he inspired not only complete trust but devotion. I have never since known a captain for whom I would forgo my salary, keep double watches, or walk miles in a strange city to get a bottle of cleansing powder for his false teeth. Under his command I felt quite content at the idea of being a mate forever. The secret may have been that he made a happy ship.

As the young sailor will find out in due course, happy ships are rare. They become so only through the influence of their captains. Whenever the young sailor sails on one, he will find out that his captain is not worried about authority. If I were asked on what their authority is based, there is only one definition I can think of: the ship is their world, and in it they are content. Their worries concern the ship and their health exclusively; ashore they either lead a clumsy double life or go to the pictures.

Contrary to the Army, authority at sea has to do with sympathy. A captain holds such absolute powers that he cannot refer to a higher authority or hide behind it. A major has always a colonel handy in the cupboard, a sea-captain has nobody but God. A good example of the kind of authority I mean is a recent conflict that arose on board the liner *Queen Mary*.

She carried a crew of over a thousand, and a captain five feet high. When the Queen Mother of Great Britain was about to visit America, the company replaced the tiny captain with a commodore in her honour. The result was mutiny. It was a British mutiny, so everything was handled in a civil spirit; the fact remains that the crew refused to sail unless their Little Man was on the bridge. It is possible that the commodore was more impressive, and certainly sterner, yet the tiny captain had infinitely more authority. Had the *Queen Mary* flown any flag but the Union Jack, the Queen Mother would have had to stay put. Being British, the crew accepted the commodore in the end, after their point was made. The commodore never betrayed how uncomfortable he felt.

Until he becomes a captain, the young sailor need worry little about his authority. Officers are rarely called upon to make decisions, they only execute them. So it will depend on the apprentice's captain whether he has any authority or not; yet one thing the novice should know: the only way to handle crews on board cargoes is to forget about the Navy.

NAVIGATIONAL AIDS

THE THING TO REMEMBER ABOUT NAVIGATIONAL AIDS, IF YOU WANT TO remain their master, is that they are aids. The navigation itself is done by man and will always be, even if one day, heaven forbid, the wireless-operator and his little dials take over the running of the ship. Any wireless-operator will tell you airily that it is only a matter of time before the deck officers become redundant, the engineers pre-fabricated robots and the captain an animated figurehead, presiding at table.

So, if you value your future, rid yourself with determination of the dominance of your navigational aids. Caressing a sextant while mumbling a prayer that this time the sun may be taken true amounts to the same thing as caressing a hare's foot. Yet the sextant is the most domesticated of the navigational aids, once one has mastered it. Barometers harbour sly surprises, like the one that awaits you in a high canal; no naval college teaches its pupils what happens to the barometer when a ship is at a thousand feet altitude. The log is to be watched too, as its propeller can easily be fouled by weeds, the blades get out of line after hitting a piece of driftwood, or can be swallowed wholesale by a shark.

Worst of all, however, are the navigational tables with their hundreds of thousands of little figures in the smallest print known to man. The composers of navigational tables never take into account that the light-generator may have failed, that water may drip down the navigator's nose or that he may be cross-eyed with exhaustion. Following the columns down with the finger soon obscures the figures with a brownish smog. So, although modern tables simplify celestial observation considerably, they should, in addition to the height of eye of the observer as taken from the sea-surface, include a height of eye as from the printed page, which will be found to be about an inch and a half. Unless the apprentice has some experience of engraving the Lord's Prayer on a pea, he had better include a magnifying glass in his kit.

The most useful navigational aid for the apprentice I can think of is an alarm clock, as junior officers of the watch are either the first or the last to be called by the messroom-boy or the look-out. In both cases, they will be late; either because they think they have a few minutes to spare or because they haven't got a second. To be called by your own alarm clock makes for independence, until it is doctored by your cabin companion. But by that time, routine has taken over.

CHARTS

THE TROUBLE ABOUT CHARTS IS THAT THEY BECOME REDUNDANT THE moment they leave the hydrographer's office. The caution printed on them that the Admiralty Notices to Mariners of "The latest date" have to be consulted before use will not inspire confidence in the young sailor. But then, charts are not meant to inspire confidence, but to frighten him. The essential contrast between a land-map and a sea-chart is that whereas a land-map coaxes the wanderer onto its brightly coloured roads towards delicately shaded woods and hills full of promise, the sea-chart seems to spell disaster to anyone reckless enough to leave the safety of the harbour. Everything is a warning wrapped in a caution, and the small print at the bottom does nothing to put the young navigator at his ease.

All charts state blandly, "Compiled from the latest Admiralty and Foreign Government Surveys, by Rear Admiral A. Mostyn-Field, F.R.S., Hydrographer, 1906." Not only does the word "Foreign" relieve the Admiralty of all responsibility, the mere thought of having to consult all the notices to mariners since 1906 is disturbing. As if this were not enough, the dubious value of the chart is underlined by the smallest print of all that says, "Owing to the small scale of this chart, numerous wrecks are omitted to avoid overcrowding in congested areas."

The idea of the chart is that the apprentice shall pencil out the ship's course in a thin line across a field of numbers. In order to do this, the compass direction of the ship has to be decided upon. There are compass roses printed in convenient places to help the apprentice draw his line. Nothing could be simpler in principle, but there are two compass roses, one inside the other, of which one is true in a geographical sense—which means useless—and another true in a magnetic sense—which would be useful if its date as marked were not five years old and subject to variation. In short, none of the compass roses on the sea-chart can be used unless the navigator applies a correction. Once he has made this calculation, he is only half-way through his troubles, for the compass on board his ship isn't true either.

Despite Rear Admiral A. Mostyn-Field, F.R.S., I would advise the young sailor to ignore everything on his chart except the buoys and the lights and proceed from there. The moment he finds that something on the chart is true, it may be the seed for future confidence. Ten to one, however, that the next buoy he waits for has been either washed away, replaced by a temporary one or preceded by an addition. The most important thing about the chart, as far as the young sailor is concerned, is to behave with complete ease when a senior officer is looking over his shoulder. The only thing to remember is that the miles are measured on the side of the chart and not at the bottom. The little drawings or silhouettes found on charts of distant shores are romantic, but taken from the direction in which your ship is not approaching the coast. As there are only a few basic patterns for mountain groups and headlands, the danger is obvious.

The best use for charts to the young sailor is to give them to his sweetheart, who will pin them on the wall. You will be comforted to find the snapshot of Uncle Bill and his dog over the West Pit, the Devil's Reef or Sandettie Bank. When you come home from your next trip it will be worked into a lampshade, and no one who has not experienced it can imagine the satisfaction of seeing Rear Admiral A. Mostyn-Field, F.R.S., watch over grandma's knitting and hear his grim warnings called "cosy."

CHRONOMETER

THE CHRONOMETER IS A WONDERFUL INSTRUMENT, AND THOUGH SHIPS HAVE come to rely less on them—now time signals can be picked up many times a day by radio—the chronometer is still the heart of the ship. In the old days, the captain would take the chronometer to the Institute for oiling and correction himself. It was as important as the ship's papers.

The apprentice may be called upon to wind the chronometer and, if he forgets to do so, he will feel that his sea-days have come to an end. I cannot think of a graver omission, nor can his captain. To make him realise the full portent of his crime, the young sailor will be told that the chronometer is now practically useless for the rest of the voyage; for it is a well-known fact that no chronometer should be adjusted by a layman. The wireless-operator will be called in and, on hearing that the chronometer has stopped, his face will take on a grave expression. He will receive the holy box with reverent hands and carry it to his cubicle like an old butler a bottle of age-old wine.

A young sailor who has sailed on a passenger ship may know what happens to age-old wine before it is gently carried to the first-class table in its cradle. He may have reflected upon the fact that no passenger ever realises that his wine is shaken to hell by the sheer rolling of the ship anyhow, so that the cradle business is sheer hocus-pocus. If the apprentice has omitted to wind the chronometer and feels that now he has no future left, I may tell him what the wireless-operator does after he has closed the steel door of his cubicle behind him with a last grim look directed at the culprit. If the chronometer has stopped at, say, thirteen hours three minutes and twenty seconds, the wireless-operator will put the thing on his desk, between the ashtin and the glass nude, and forget about it until the time signal at noon the following day. At the pip of noon, he presses the button of a stop-watch, puts it on top of the chronometer and, if he remembers, he will open the chronometer's lid when the stop-watch has ticked away one hour. Then he will put his hand on the winding knob of the chronometer and start winding the moment the stop-watch reaches one hour three minutes twenty seconds. As he starts winding, the chronometer starts ticking away, and chances are that, after this, it is more correct than before. At the messroom table, the wireless-operator will say, "I'll thank you not to forget it again, young man. I've been sitting up with your damned chronometer for the better part of the night."

In small ships, chronometers are either watches or alarm clocks and, considering that small ships get to their destinations as frequently as bigger ones, the case for the chronometer is perhaps largely a mystical one by now. Its discovery had such momentous consequences for navigation that it became the Holy Grail of the ship. So, the young sailor had better treat it with the respect due to its worthy past, but realise, at the same time, that what once was a mortal sin, has, by the grace of God, become a peccadillo.

OF ALL THE BOOKS ON BOARD, THE NAUTICAL ALMANAC IS THE MOST IMPOR-
tant. Not only for its useful information, but also because it makes enter-
taining reading for those who are supposed to clean the chart-room. To the
young English sailor, Brown's *Nautical Almanac* offers highly coloured
pages in which unromantic instruments like "Echo Fishing with the Fish
Finder," "Marine Log Type SAL 24," "Pneumercator Tank Gauges" and
"Ralston Stability and Trim Indicators" look more attractive than the toys
of one's boyhood. There are glossy photographs of gentlemen in tropical
shorts peering through a Double Marine Sextant with one-minute microm-
etre, or pouring a liquid from a glass container into a copper pot with a
bartender's leer, in which case they are salinometring. There are three-
coloured pages of compasses called names like "The Happy Bridler" or
"Faithful Freddy" in a coy attempt to make light of their prices, which
equal that of a racing car. There are advertisements of ship-chandlers
called Mohamed Ayoob & Co. of Singapore, Ernesto Stein of Buenos Aires,
Caesar Marquand Nflg, of Hamburg, and Ant. G. Antoniadis of Piraeus.
The whole world opens on opening the book. Cordial invitations are ten-
dered on practically every page. "When in Bombay, be sure to come and
see us, Yours faithfully, E. M. Butterfly." No sailor need be at a loss in
Alexandria; all he has to do is to remember the address, "11, Sharia Al-
Boursa Al-Kadima" where fatherly Messrs. Al-Helal are waiting for him
open-armed. Should he feel lonely in Halifax, there is Davy & Co., Flag,
Banner and Bunting Manufacturers, or Mr. R. Dubois for a dignified
funeral.

Apart from the strictly ephemeral information about the sun, Aries,
Venus, Mars, the moon, Jupiter and Saturn as they move majestically
along the arc of time, there are tables to convert practically anything into
something else. The body of them have been contributed by officers of the
Merchant Navy. There are time, speed and distance conversion tables,
spheroidal tables, tables to find distances off with the sextant, diagrams to
convert radio great circle bearings to Mercatorial bearings, and fancy tid-
bits like tables to determine the average weight of common sailors below
the age of forty in relation to the death rate.

The general articles, in almanacs called "abridged," are most useful to
those who have passed examinations in celestial navigation and global
meteorology and are still haunted by the doubt that they haven't quite yet
mastered the subject. In Brown's *Nautical*, for instance, there is a yearly

article, unchanged since the beginning of the Greenwich Hour Angle Method, called "Explanation of the Astronomical Ephemeris" which contains in one page all the young sailor will need for the remainder of his navigational existence. The chapter on marine meteorology is slightly longer (fourteen pages) but half of those are taken up by advertisements for whisky, bunker fuel in Fayal and model-ship builders who will reproduce your vessel exactly to scale and perfect down to the last detail (portholes open).

In the ship's life, the matter-of-fact section of the *Almanac* is indispensable and the young sailor will thumb through the days ahead, relishing notes like "Venus too close to the sun for observation" and curse his luck that he isn't sailing in the last week of October when practically everything is too close to the sun for observation.

The best advice I can give him is to take an out-of-date copy of the *Almanac* home on his first leave, and explain it to his girl-friend. I know of no nicer way to start an evening.

CELESTIAL OBSERVATION

NOTHING GIVES THE BUDDING NAVIGATOR A GREATER SENSE OF TRIUMPH AND exhilaration than the taking of a celestial observation that comes off. Nothing is as wrought with misery and humiliation as to have the senior officer point out that one has situated the ship at fifteen thousand feet above sea level, on the Andes.

To fix the ship's position on the globe with an accuracy of one mile true is an operation that never fails to bring home to the sailor man's victory over the unknown. Yet all that is needed is a variation on two sticks and an arc, a watch, and a couple of navigational tables prepared by scientists ashore who, in the sailor's mind, have beards. On the cover of one of the oldest tables in history, a man is shown peering along the topmost of two sticks, a dotted line connects it with a smiling sun, and the motto reads, "Man Is Not Lost."

Stripped of its scientific perfections like parallax, dip, height of eye and refraction, the making of a celestial observation is still the same simple matter it was in the days of the two sticks and the arc. All that is measured is the angle the celestial body makes with the horizon from the point of view of the observer at a given moment. One opens the table and looks up where on earth that particular celestial body would make that particular angle with the horizon at that particular hour. The young sailor should remember the essential simplicity of the operation before "entering the tables," as navigational jargon puts it. At first, one always gets lost in refraction and parallax, and the worry about the split second makes the apprentice see more stars than the one he is aiming at.

To fix the true angle at the true moment is the secret. So, to start with, only the sextant and the chronometer are needed. Concentrate on these and worry about the bewildering corrections only in due course, on "entering the tables." There are ships where the shooting of the sun is a religious ritual consisting of mumbled charms, esoteric gestures at the sky and the swinging of prayer-mills. The taking of a celestial observation on an admiral's bridge is like High Mass celebrated by an archbishop: junior officers peer through their sextants, ratings chant bearings and numbers, bells are struck and books of logarithms consulted, while the officer of the watch intones the first lesson from the almanac. Under those circumstances, I always placed the ship at fifteen thousand feet above sea level.

The thing to do, if you want to master the art at your ease, is to take as many observations as you feel like during night watches on the bridge, in private. First choose a star (Arcturus is a good one in the Northern Hemisphere because it is easily spotted and difficult to lose), then deal with the time problem. Go to the chart-room, look at the chronometer with a stop-watch in your hand, and press the watch's button when the chronometer jumps to the full minute. Then put the stop-watch in your pocket and forget about it until the actual moment of observation. Take your sextant to the bridge, fix it at zero and sight the star through the telescope. If you see two stars, adjust the error of the instrument by making them merge, and read off the index correction. This you note. Then, with the index correction applied, you sight the star again and, while keeping it in sight, bring up the handle to catch the horizon. Don't start on the horizon and sweep the skies with your telescope looking for Arcturus, for more likely than not, you will shoot Betelgeuse. So, supposing you have Arcturus and the horizon nicely in line, swing the sextant to see where the star bounces, so as to make sure that your angle is true, then press the button of your stop-watch. Note the angle indicated by your sextant, go back to the chart-room and add the number of minutes and seconds on your stop-watch to the time the chronometer indicated when you pressed the button the first time. So you have the exact moment of your observation without anybody's help and, what is more, without anybody being the wiser.

Now make your calculation. Then make it again.

HUMAN PROGRESS IS NOWHERE SO APPARENT AT SEA AS AT NIGHT WHEN approaching the coast, or sailing along it. Everywhere on the horizon the beacons flash rhythmic pinpoints of light in the darkness and, further still, the reflections of more distant ones twitch on the clouds. Of all the aids to navigation, the lighthouses are the most important, for if a ship is sound, and her crew is able, she runs little danger as long as she keeps to the open. It is when approaching the coast that disaster begins to lurk.

Nowadays, when young officers prefer the night watches because the lights make better cross-bearings than the easily mistaken landmarks during the day-time, it is difficult to recapture the sense of danger that beset the sailors of the past when approaching land after nightfall. Yet I have a notion of this, because of the war.

Just as my keenest realisation of war came when the lighthouses fell dark, so their friendly winks in the darkness give me a profound sense of peace. It is one of the rare fields of human endeavour in which our divided world still cooperates. The sailor knows little of Bulgaria, Rumania and Southern Russia; shore-leave is rarely granted in the ports of the Black Sea. Sighting the hills of the Crimea on a blue summer's day is sighting the border of an enigma. Even before making a landfall, one senses secrecy, silence and suspicion; the Black Sea is the only sea where one is actually conscious of crossing the three-mile limit. The first messenger from the land of silence is the pilot, and his behavior differs from that of his colleagues elsewhere. A pilot is essentially a jolly individual; to see his beaming head appear over the rail with its silly sou'wester, much too small, that seems to be the uniform of pilots all over the world, is to sight an old friend. He shakes everybody warmly by the hand, looks round with the innocent gaze that produces a drink, then he pats his stomach, remembers there is work to be done, climbs to the bridge and says, "Okay, captain, two hundred and seventy true, half speed please."

The Black Sea pilot is different. He climbs on board like an inspecting staff-officer and goes straight to the captain's cabin where the ship's papers are checked, to make sure that the landfall has been officially acknowledged and approved before the ship set out from her home port. There is no conversation, no back-slapping, and drinks are politely refused. He is the first man with a secret.

Yet, nothing could be more chatty and open-hearted than the Russian list of lights. Were one to ask the pilot the name of the village nesting in yonder hills, he would answer with reluctance, if at all. Yet Kamysh-

Burun lighthouse—so the Admiralty list of lights tells us—was built in 1873, last altered in 1929, is situated on the edge of the cliff near the village, is a white rectangular stone tower with house, the lights appear as a single fixed light, they bear 247° true, are five miles apart, intensified on the leading line, and lead along the axis of the third Yenikale reach of the dredged channel. The Kamysh-Burun approach channel shows a white rectangular slatted shield, black stripe, diamond top mark; it bears 276° true and is shown only on request. It is the last thing shown on request on entering the harbour. Until the pilot comes on board, even the Russian waters are part of the brotherhood of the sea.

The lighthouses and light vessels are a great boon to the young sailor, yet these friends can easily turn into fiends when sailing crowded waters unprepared. The panic of the apprentice when faced with the flashing string of diamonds that is the Channel coastline at night is an example. Hundreds of lights flash on the horizon and, during the summer, there are neon lights, dance-halls, fun-fairs and luminous crosses on churches to bewilder him even more. To find among these fireworks Le Touquet light, Group Flash 2, Ten seconds, placed on the platform of the belfry of the townhall, is not an easy matter. The best solution is to make, before one's watch begins, a list of the lights one is likely to sight during the coming four hours. Their visibility, candle power and guessed bearing should be noted on a piece of paper before the ordeal begins. In this fashion, the young officer knows what light to look for, and where, and he will be spared the trying business of stop-watches in the dark and bearings that won't come true.

PILOTS

IF I WERE TO BE MAROONED ON A DESERT ISLAND, AND COULD CHOOSE A SET of books, I would include a complete set of *Admiralty Pilots*. I could build a hut with them, and spend my lazy afternoons reading and reminiscing my way through the building from doorstep via sideboard to chimney, and have the wonderful feeling that I would never be short of exciting reading matter if I lived to be a hundred. If my hammock were slung in a shady spot, and the murmur of the gentle surf invited me to dream, I would pick a roof-tile called *Mediterranean Pilot,* Volume I, comprising the Southern and Eastern Coasts of Spain from Gibraltar to Cape Cerbère; Islas Baleares; Sardinia; the Northern Coast of Africa from Ceuta to Ras Ajdir; Isola di Pantelleria and Isole Pelagie; the Maltese Islands; Isole Egadi;

Sicily and Isole Eòlie. If my mood were poetic, I would pick Isole Eòlie; if I felt manly and adventurous, the Northern Coast of Africa from Ceuta to Ras Ajdir.

My greatest joy before even starting to read would be to glare at the pink leaf opposite the title page which says, in fat black letters underscored, "This volume should not be used without reference to the latest supplement and annual summary of notices to mariners affecting it." I would give it a raspberry, in revenge for untold suffering in my youth.

The young sailor who is ordered to copy the latest issue of notices to mariners into the *Pilots* should comfort himself with this vision of the future, or he will eventually burst into tears. Never in his life, except when being detained after school to write a hundred times "I shall not be disrespectful to my over-harassed instructors," has he faced such a chore; and "over-harassed instructors" is nothing compared to "Canal des Kerkennah" or "Monte dei Sette Fratelli from east-south-eastward." Yet he will be asked by the second mate in an irritated tone, "What? Haven't you finished your scribbling yet?" after spending three hours with his tongue between his teeth, and trying to write with his fingers sticky with glue.

By this treatment the young sailor is deprived of a great enjoyment. The *Admiralty Pilots* change from the excitement-packed volumes they are into the acme of messy boredom. Yet, open any *Pilot* at random and it will be like a glimpse beyond the horizon. "Fondeadero de Nerja.—The town of Nerja stands on level ground near the coast, and is surrounded by hills of moderate elevation covered with vineyards and hamlets. In front of the town, amidst the ruins of a castle, and about 2 cables westward of a coastguard hut, is a promenade, which can be identified from a short distance, by day, by its palm trees, and, at night, by its lights." Everything is there, the chirping crickets, the heady wine, the smell of wood-fires and *tortillas* in alleys festooned with washing, the ruins of the old castle with its cawing jackdaws, and the motionless hawk hovering in the deep blue sky.

I know of no better Christmas present for a young boy dreaming of going to sea than a redundant *Admiralty Pilot* and a set of lifeboat charts as described in the chapter on lifeboats. The charts and their red buckram envelope with basic instruments will teach him the principles of navigation, and the opening chapters of each pilot will teach him the rest. General meteorology, buoys, lights, tidal streams, observations for errors of the compass, mirage and abnormal reflection, aurora and magnetic storms. Any boy of fourteen who turns into Rodin's "Thinker" over his French grammar will be experimentally murmuring "liquid sounds" as used in "Trengganu Yanggang-a"; and when told to go to bed, he'll sneak a torch under the blankets to read on, "On the slopes of the little wooded island are the ruins of a temple that, in the day-time, can be spotted from afar by its dazzling white pillars silhouetted against the sky from the south-westward. At night, although no light is shown, the approach can be heard by the myriads of cicadas chirping in the woods. The bay offers good holding ground and shelter for short visits; water may be obtained from the local guardian, usually an ex-convict, who will prove helpful if greeted with politeness and given small presents (safety razor, puzzle-box with little ball, whistle). Spirits may be requested by him, but should not be given."

So, when the cats are on the prowl and the sparrows rustle underneath the roof-tiles, a child will sail into the great unknown, to dream about cicadas and an old man whistling in the wilderness.

Part II CREWS

THE FIRST MAN SAILING THE FIRST HOLLOWED-OUT TREE-TRUNK ALONE WAS a sailor. The first man who had a boy with him was a captain. Captains have not changed since; their vessel is still as flimsy, the sea as perilous and the boy as hopeless.

Only if the young sailor keeps this elementary state of affairs in mind will he be able to see his captain clearly. This is important, for living as he does among officers who are not yet captains but feel that they should have been long ago, the apprentice may easily be influenced by their talk at the messroom-table. It may not even be talk, just raised eyebrows, upcast looks and shrugs of the shoulders. The young sailor will be led to believe that the ship is sailed virtually by the mate, for that is the way the mate sees it.

It is difficult on a long, long ladder that reaches into the sky to see further than the next rung; it is impossible for the apprentice to identify himself with the captain. The only comfort I can offer is that the captain, despite appearances, can identify himself to an astonishing degree with the apprentice if he should be called upon to do so. It is advisable, however, to postpone this call as long as possible, for captains don't like it. They seem to be quite content with their hermit's existence, remote and godlike in their double cabin, and there will be many days when only a chesty cough or a sneeze from below reminds the apprentice on the bridge of his captain's existence.

In practice, every captain looks like an old fool and never is. His very presence determines the nature of the community that sails the ship. He is the best argument against atheism I can think of, for every quarrel, every tension, even the grimmest conflict among the members of his crew is entered into with the underlying knowledge that, if the worst comes to the worst, there always is somebody to give the final verdict. In the case of a conflict, the mate will say, "Take care the captain doesn't notice," and the chief engineer, "You'd better watch out or I'll take it up with the captain." Chief engineers refer to the captain like self-confident clergymen refer to their private deity.

Should the apprentice be driven to the point of suicide about some personal problem (and apprentices' problems always are personal), he may go and ask the captain for advice, as it is less final. He must realise, however, that by doing so he is inviting mortification. The captain will be quite kind, but the apprentice's problem will take on a puny stature in his eyes on crossing the threshold. The sight of the Old Man writing at his desk with the calm concentration of a silversmith engraving a spoon will so impress the young sailor that the captain hardly need open his mouth. It may be a humane thing to tell the apprentice that the captain is usually writing nonsense at those moments.

Probably, occasions will be rare on which the apprentice will see his captain in his true light. It may be a gale, but then it takes a fairly long time before captains are convinced that there is a gale on. Usually they only show their heads at bridge level, scowling at the officer of the watch as if they suspected him of rocking the boat. Before turning round and vanishing back into their cosy den, they will mutter, "I presume you have looked after hatch number three, Mr. Er," which strikes the junior officer like lightning from Olympus. Captains are rarely noticed checking up on hatch number three beforehand.

There is little else I can tell the young sailor about captains, until he is about to be promoted to one himself. For the time being, two basic rules will do: bad captains do not exist, and even the youngest masters are old. On board ship, it is one's sea-days that count, not the years of one's life.

MATES

MATES ARE BASICALLY THE UNHAPPIEST PEOPLE AT SEA, BECAUSE THEY ARE busy becoming captains. As everyone who has been an adolescent knows, not to be something yet is a depressing situation. What's more, every mate is convinced that he is better than his captain, for his captain only tells him what to do, rarely does it himself. The happy mate, quite satisfied with his situation, is for some reason unsatisfactory. A man who wants to remain a mate is a bad mate and a man who is a mate and wants to become a captain is frustrated, so one can easily see that a mate's lot is a hard one.

It is indeed like adolescence. Many secretly long for the happy, simple world of childhood; no man in his senses has any nostalgia for the horrible years in which he was neither child nor man but an awkward, clumsy creature between the two. This is why a mate's philosophy resembles that of the adolescent: nobody understands him, other people are always happier, girls are either too bad or too pure, and he can never do anything right, from shutting a door to packing a bag. The adolescent is supposed to wash up cheerfully, to hum a happy song while mowing the lawn or washing the car, to hop up and down clapping his hands, crying "Goody goody," when he is ordered to take Junior to the zoo. All these situations, like nightmares from the past, repeat themselves hauntingly once the junior officer becomes a mate. To be an ordinary seaman becomes the lost land of childhood; to become a captain feels like climbing a glacier in gumboots.

Mates soon give up hope of ever becoming captains because their own superiors lose no opportunity of assuring them that, if they carry on in this fashion, they will be a hundred before promotion comes their way. To hear a father talk about his sixteen-year-old son is to hear a captain about his mate: lazy, stupid, unclean, sulky, without interest or sense of duty, as deaf as a mole and as blind as a bat.

Yet I should like to see the ship that sails itself, without a mate shivering and grumbling on the bridge. There is only one hope for heavenly justice as far as the mate is concerned: that the second mate may break a leg and the captain be forced to take over his watch. It is as good as an adolescent's night at the opera when the prima donna loses her bloomers in the high C. I don't know why captains are so often unlucky when taking over a watch in an emergency; perhaps it is a proof of the power of prayer.

But this situation is as rare as a white whale. In the ordinary run of things, the mate does everything. He is the ship's housewife, psychoanalyst, handyman, housepainter, plumber, vermin expert and removal man. If rust shows its bubbles underneath the paint, it is the mate's fault. If the cargo starts to shift after a fortnight of gales in the Atlantic, the mate has done it. If the crew is rebellious, the cook sulking, the bridge slippery and the captain's grog cold, the mate is told he will be a pensioner before he is promoted. On board bigger ships, the mate eats with the second-class passengers and it is hard to describe what this does to a man who has five thousand other things to look after. For whoever is unable to evince a fascinated interest in Mr. Proudfoot's operation during the sweetbreads, and at the same time work out in his mind what error Snark the apprentice can have made in his calculations to put the ship back eighty miles on the chart, will provoke a sour little mouth in the owner's drawing-room when the captain is asked what he thinks of his assistant over a glass of sherry.

There is a poem running into sixteen couplets that describes the fate of a mate, but it is unprintable. The young sailor will soon come to know it by heart, and cherish it until the day he lays his hand on the engine-room telegraph for the first time, three centuries from now.

THEY ARE THE HAPPIEST ADDITION TO THE SHIP'S STAFF SINCE THE ADVENT of steam. The officers of the glorious age of sail may never have felt there was something lacking; who sails on a windjammer now, after having travelled on steam, misses not the engine, but the engineers.

Engineers have one idiosyncrasy: they think about everything in terms of engines. They know the ship is sailed by the deck-officers and that sailors and a captain are necessary, but they consider them as people who profit by the engines. The ship's fate is in their hands.

Engineers are calm in times of gale, soothing in times of stress, and irksome only when the sea is dead calm and a tropical sun turns their dungeon into purgatory. The young sailor will soon be struck by the circumstance that whatever engineers are doing or talking about, they always listen to their engine. In the messroom the Chief, while regaling himself with untidy forkfuls of spaghetti, will hold forth about the advantage of having cabins painted in psychological colours. In the middle of the conversation, with his fork halfway to his mouth, the Chief will freeze. Should anyone ask what is the matter, he will reply, "Sh!" The others will strain their ears, and hear nothing. Motionless silence will reign for seconds, during which the spaghetti dangling from the Chief's fork swings slightly with the swell. Then the Chief will say, "Damn it! That young ass hasn't tightened the nut on the bilge-pump yet." After that he will continue eating, but the subject of his monologue will have changed from psychological colours to modern apprentices.

Engineers have one supreme quality: patience. It is caused by their secret preoccupation with engines, which makes all other problems seem secondary; also by the professional perseverance of the man who is often called upon to lie on his back in an oil-bath, fiddling with a spanner the size of a toothpick, while a piston strong enough to crush a rock hisses up and down, a quarter of an inch away from his nose. The inner peace they radiate, which goes with a well-oiled and smoothly-running soul, reflects the perfection of their engines. I know of no better cure for inner turmoil, worry and general nervousness than a visit to the engine-room. There they are, in their greasy overalls, their caps on the backs of their heads, wads of cotton waste protruding from their pockets. On the wall are their tools, neatly lined up according to size; on the work-bench some object is clamped in a vise, and with it they are quietly pottering. The colossal racket of their engine makes conversation impossible, so each man just thinks, while his eyes rove around his, to him, completely comprehensible universe. To sit down on a three-legged stool, to look at this vast complicated mystery of whizzing, ticking, spinning and sliding parts, all of them polished like watches, is soothing. For here you are, facing the riddle of your existence and, next to you, stands another man with his back to it, filing away at the work-bench, secure in the knowledge that he understands everything.

What a boon it was that with the mechanical monster that mauled the *Flying Cloud* came so charming and patient a kornak. To those who don't speak whatever language it is, the word means: the boy who rides the elephant.

WIRELESS-OPERATORS

THEY ARE THE MOST RECENT ADDITION TO THE SHIP'S CREW, AND SHOW THE characteristics of the youngest member of the family. They don't quite yet fit into the community to which they have been added, and that is perhaps why they are still suspected of not pulling their weight.

Of course, the wireless-operator, or, as he should officially be called, radio officer, is one of the most important members of the crew as he establishes the link between the ship and the rest of the world. He is very conscious of the rest of the world and consequently feels a bit of an outsider. He also feels, and this is where the trouble lies, slightly superior.

All you need do to get an inkling of the mentality of wireless-operators is to listen in to their conversation among themselves on the transmitter or, better still, between them and the girl operators of the big shore stations. For some reason, jokes and platitudes that sound fatuous ashore take on a halo of wit and originality when droned into a microphone. No man of some experience will call a girl "Beautiful" when she is in sight; wireless-operators are very fond of the word and so, it seems, are their lady colleagues.

As wireless-operators do not keep watches but lead an independent existence in a private little cubicle on the boatdeck, they appear in effeminate garments at infuriating hours. The young sailor will find the stiffening of his jaw muscles to be a conditioned reflex at the sight of the wireless-operator in a dressing-gown, carrying towel, toothbrush, razor and a bottle of talcum-powder, strolling to the bathroom in Arab mules at nine o'clock in the morning. This reaction will find an echo at the dinner table when the wireless-operator says that life at sea is fit for fools only, and talks about putting more bite into trade unions. The same conditioned reflex is provoked by the sound of music or roars of laughter at inaudible comedians, emanating from the radio hut when the apprentice is trudging on the bridge in the drizzle. Enquiries will bring forth the reply that the wireless-operator is testing. As the only person able to judge whether a wireless-operator is testing or resting is another wireless-operator, there goes another grain, added to the secret store of animosity piling up within the apprentice's chest for the debonair intellectual, who is always so smart and witty at table and whose hair is always fit for an advertisement, even in a gale. The only wireless-operators to break through this invisible barrier are those on sinking ships, and on ocean-going tugboats during a salvage operation.

There are, of course, charming wireless-operators. Yet, however pleasant they may be, they have a hard time making the sun of their charm break through the clouds caused by their profession. They will, for instance, insist on explaining the inexplicable in simple terms. "It's quite simple, you see: radio waves are like concentric waves created on a still water surface by a stone dropped into it. Now it is not quite like a stone, you see, but like a potato-masher pulled up and down with constant frequency in the water. So the waves . . ." At this moment, he will be struck by a look of unconcealed loathing from the second mate or the messroom-boy. Without knowing it, he has assumed the same tone of talking to halfwits that Junior uses when explaining the principles of spaceship propulsion to his family.

The humour of wireless-operators is as peculiar to them as campus-jokes are to sophomores. An operator I knew was assigned to instruct some Chinese Allies in his trade during the war. As they had difficulty in pronouncing the "r," he made them chant to one another through the ether, "The frantic feathered phantom tucking frivolous foreign flags into its fly." He justified the word "fly" by saying that he put it in to make them feel at ease at the end of the message. You may think this funny or nauseating—chances are that you don't quite know which. And there you have the feeling of the messroom about its wireless-operator.

SHIPS' DOCTORS

WHATEVER THE SHIP'S DOCTOR MAY BE, A PROFESSIONAL SAILOR OR A SHORE physician taking a holiday, he will labour under the old conception of his rank, which inspired the East India Company to advertise only seventy years ago: "Ship 'Water-Sprite' leaves for Colombo on the 18th March. Fast, safe, full comfort, carries milk-giving cow and doctor."

Times may have changed, but the ship's doctor still comes after the milk-giving cow; at least in his own estimate. Doctors ashore are only seen when needed, and this has bolstered their egos. On board ship, they are waiting for someone to have a boil, fall out of the mast or notice the first pangs of a belly-ache. The one customer he can rely on is the cook; he takes the place of the traditional hypochondriacal spinster every physician suffers from. So, after the ship's doctor has told himself for a week with declining conviction how much he is enjoying himself, the day dawns when he has to explain childbirth to the chief engineer by drawing its blueprint on the table-cloth. As they have little else to do, ships' doctors bring about their own unhappiness by taking to photography or diary-writing. In the first instance, they are faced by squints, snooks, and obscene gestures; in the second, they surprise the messroom-boy reading their diary as they come back to add one more final touch to a descriptive passage.

The most depressing side of the existence of a ship's doctor is that everyone knows he has got nothing to do, and the crew will tell him so at every opportunity. Underlying the crew's tolerance of his inactivity is the uneasy notion that he is waiting for someone to get acute appendicitis, so that he may operate during a gale on the messroom table with the chief engineer giving the anaesthetic and the wireless-operator signalling his name to the papers.

The ship's doctor's worst blow will come when the first patient feels poorly and does not come to him, but goes to the captain. The captain's pharmacy consists of twenty-four numbered bottles with an explanatory list; either the numbers have become illegible over the years or the list is lost, so patient and captain kneel by the side of the case, take off their caps, the captain says, "God bless our choice," takes a bottle with his eyes shut and tells the sufferer, "One tablespoon after each meal." At least, this is the ship's doctor's version of the consultation. He cannot accept that a sailor prefers the busy captain's aspirin to the idle doctor's knife.

When there are passengers, the doctor may have a little more to do, but the major complaints will be heartburn, constipation and hangover. A fruity peritonitis or a broken neck rarely comes his way; so he remains delivered into the hands of the cook and the chief engineer.

But don't let this discourage the physician who considers making a trip as a ship's doctor for a sea-change. After the initial feeling of redundancy, he will discover that his presence gives everyone a feeling of security, in the same way a fire-extinguisher does. He will have to convince the crew by his cheerful contentment that, like the fire-extinguisher, he is not waiting for a conflagration but quietly enjoying himself, and happy to be instructed by the bosun in the use of verbena, tar and castor-oil.

SEA-CHAPLAINS

I CAME ACROSS A YOUNG PRIEST OF THE ANGLICAN CHURCH AFTER THE WAR who would have made a good sea-chaplain. He came on board in a harbour in Italy, attracted by the Dutch flag, and he left a lady's bicycle leaning incongruously against a bollard. He was on a one-man pilgrimage to the Holy Land and wanted to know whether we knew anything about Turkey. All he knew was that over there a bicycle is called "adamlik," which means "lifeless horse."

He was given tea and a biscuit and he filled our messroom, which usually was a raucous place, with a kind of tranquillity. Yet he was unhappy; he had undertaken the pilgrimage because of what he called "a divided heart." He loved the church and his work, and he believed in God, of course; although he had felt His presence only once, and that for a fleeting moment. But an old Flemish mystic had written, when he was eighty-three, that if one had been conscious of God's Presence for as much as five minutes during one's lifetime, one should consider oneself fortunate. It was those five minutes one had to live on, and the chaplain was trying to do that, although so far he had only one minute to call his own. It was this minute that troubled him.

During the war, he had been parachuted into the jungle to serve with the guerrillas in Burma. He had carried a little suitcase with holy wafers, a Communion vessel and some holy wine, but as he fell sprawling in the branches of a big tree, he had dropped the suitcase into the sea of foliage below. The guerrillas had freed him, attracted by his thin high cries, and taken him to their camp. Everyone whispered, because the Japanese were near in the jungle; the camp was choked with fear. Before setting out on an operation, the guerrillas asked him to celebrate Holy Communion with them; and then his minute came. It came as he administered the Sacrament in a whisper, with bread and ale out of a cracked cup.

The minute had been so overpowering, and the whispered Communion out of the cracked cup had so convinced him of the eternal life of the church, that he had written to his bishop. He was sure that the church would want everyone at home to know about it. The bishop had answered that in no circumstances should Holy Communion be administered in any other than the appropriately consecrated vessel. So now he was on his way to the Holy Sepulchre; he didn't quite know why; but he hoped it would help him to see things clearly.

We didn't know what to say after his story. The chief engineer, who had never betrayed any interest in his soul but was a kind-hearted man, said, after an awkward silence, that he wished he had been in the jungle. It cheered the chaplain; he was even more cheered by the food we gave him and the copious description the cook furnished of Turkey, which we intercepted too late.

We waved to him as he rode away on his bicycle, standing on the pedals because of the sloping road. The cook said, "That was a cultured man, but if you ask me . . ." The Chief said, "Shut up."

That night, in the messroom, the memory of him was still about; it induced us to discuss religion. The debate lasted for hours; the Chief wound it up. "To me," he said, "religion is like this: there is God, and here am I, and between us I want nobody. But if there must be somebody, I wouldn't mind that little man on the bicycle."

APPRENTICES

TO BE AN APPRENTICE IS AN UNEASY STATE OF AFFAIRS. ONE IS NEITHER A member of the crew nor an officer; one is a lonely youngster wandering about in an alien world, branded by one's very name with the fact that one doesn't know anything yet. Reflections on the superfluousness of examinations are induced by orders to wash the lavatory.

An apprentice is expected to be eager, polite, willing, cheerful and unobtrusive, whereas an apprentice would like to be interesting, witty, casual and manly. His authority is nil, even with the messroom-boy, to say nothing of the ship's dog. If the messroom-boy is at all aware of him, it is of the bills in his pocket, like the ship's dog is of the lumps of sugar. So the apprentice should see to it that he can provide both. The only one interested in him will be the cook, but apprentices should know that the cook's interest is in gossip and in an audience. Cooks love warning apprentices about imaginary dangers from people, the weather and foreign parts. The cook's information should be listened to as a matter of politeness, but with reservation. The worst storm of the season is not brewing and if it were so, the cook would be the last person to know about it; Colombo is not synonymous with cholera, and the chief engineer can be shaken by the hand without getting leprosy, for the white marks on his arms and chest are scars of an old burn received when he tried to repair in a singlet something that should have been approached in an asbestos suit.

Among the officers, the apprentice will find that the wireless-operator is the most sympathetic. The explanation is that he is not worried by the gangling youth, whereas the deck-officers are. The wireless-operator, like the cook, likes an audience. Here the same need for caution applies: he will ask the apprentice, aghast, what in God's name made him go to sea, considering it's a life not fit for a dog, and mysterious illnesses will be hinted at with heavy winks. The apprentice should, again, listen with polite interest but remember that life at sea is a sane profession as long as one is not a wireless-operator, and that he will be in no need of penicillin injections when he goes ashore in Bahia Blanca to buy a present for his mother.

Apprenticeship is a necessary period in one's life as a sailor. There will be moments of elation when the future presents itself in all its boundless glory, while gazing at the stars; there will be moments of dark dejection in which one thinks of suicide. The rest of the time one will mainly feel hungry.

My advice is: make friends with the dog and keep a diary. Soon another junior apprentice will take your place, and then the moment has come to re-read one's catechism. For the junior apprentice's worst enemy is the senior apprentice; what a life the two could lead if only Jesus had not died in vain.

COOKS

IT IS IMPOSSIBLE TO TALK ABOUT SHIPS, CREWS, CARGOES, FOREIGN PARTS or the mystery of the weather without bringing in cooks.

By the time the young sailor has read through the present volume, he may be struck by the thought that I seem to have come across many cooks who were almost identical. It is possible that another sailor will have come across quite a different type of cook, but if he gives the subject some thought, he will come to the conclusion that almost all the cooks he has known were practically identical too. This has led me to believe that cooks are like sunsets. Every man has a mood associated with them that changes little during his lifetime.

As in the case of sunsets, I know people who are depressed by cooks and judge them to be the most unpleasant member of the crew. Other people have the same kind of allergy towards wireless-operators. Personally, I find cooks delightful, fascinating and very tricky to get on with.

One could call them the mothers of the ship or the housewives; whatever allegory one hits upon, the feminine element will be dominant. It isn't only the messing around with pots and pans, the talking about menus while tossing back imaginary curls, it is the gossip and the superstition that give every sea-cook this touch of femininity. After some time, the young sailor may even come to the conclusion that his cook is a pansy. This is rarely the case. It is just that the job has left its indelible imprint on the man. No cook can identify himself wholeheartedly with his function without turning at least partially into a squaw. The complaint, familiar to every captain, of the cook the day before leaving, "What on earth am I going to give them to eat this trip?" was heard frequently in our nomad past when whole villages were forever on the move and womankind was harassed by menus that only varied with the seasons. In the North, pea-soup and cottage-pie are the staple diet on board ship; in the tropics it is nassi-goreng, a rice dish with a fried egg on top. By the time the eggs go bad, they are replaced by fancies like stewed onions or canned peaches which the cook has hit upon because of their resemblance to fried eggs. As sea-cooks' cooking is visual, each complaint will be met with the question, "What's the matter with it? It looks all right, doesn't it?" On the captain's birthday, cooks beat an egg-white and crown the day's dish with a wisp of white meringue, suitable or not. The same thing happens when any of the officers becomes a father.

Until he is a captain, the young sailor need not worry about the cook. All he need worry about is to be on good terms with him. To achieve this, there is only one advice I can give: treat him as if he were a beautiful rich young widow.

BOSUNS

THE BOSUN IS THE PETTY OFFICER IN CHARGE OF THE FOC'SLE AND HIS personality determines the mood of the seamen. If the bosun is happy in his job, there is a fair chance that the seamen will be too. If he is not, there is sure to be trouble during the trip. Life in the foc'sle is like life anywhere: either enjoyed or borne like a cross. A narrow bunk on board an old-fashioned ship can be either wonderfully snug or a coffin with one side missing—it depends on the mood of the man who lies in it. And that man's mood depends on the bosun's.

Bosuns who are aiming for the bridge are fairly rare. Their job needs such experience, weight of authority and knowledge of human nature that to become a bosun is enough for one man's life. Whenever a bosun is out to make the grade and studies in his free hours for his examination as a deck-officer, the foc'sle will be unhappy, for it upsets his superiority, not towards them but towards the bridge. A bosun who is eager to learn from his captain, instead of thinking that it should be the other way round, is no good at his job. The best bosuns are firmly and sincerely convinced that the ship would sink like a stone but for their benevolent vigilance over the fox-hunters on the bridge. In moments of stress or on entering a harbour, the bosun holds the wheel and he holds it like an old mechanic trying out a fussy customer's car. The bosun is the one man who really knows how to handle the ship, and if he comes across a captain who will handle her as well as he does, he will not be impressed but saddened. He'll mutter, "A body can want to know too much," and ask for a transfer at the end of the trip.

The young sailor, if he comes across the right kind of bosun, should watch him carefully and listen to what he has to say. All the solid, relaxed craftsmanship of sailing a ship is there under his very eyes, unassuming and given to big hairy yawns. A bosun who yawns a lot is all right; one who, while holding the wheel, breaks wind, shakes his head and says, "God, I'm overweight," is even better. The bosun a captain needs always knows where everything is, buys penny notebooks to write the captain's orders in but never has a pencil, smiles when the foc'sle roars with laughter, is feared but loved unreasonably by the ship's dog and writes a letter to his wife or his mother every week consisting of "Dear Ma," followed by an extract from the log and the meteorological bulletin, signed, "Your affectionate son, Herbert" or "Dad." There is usually, after long scratching of the scalp with the pen, futile cleaning of nails and chewing of matches, a P.S. that runs, "Don't worry" or "Chin up."

A good bosun is as important to a ship as a good captain, if not more so. For the captain is the mind of the ship, and it is commonly known that the mind is a feeble thing of fairly recent date. Bosuns will give advice on anything, if asked or forced by circumstances. Their advice, which comes out after an impressive prelude of chin-rubbing and nose-pulling, usually runs, "Sleep on it," if the problem is personal, and "I'll show you," if it is practical.

If a captain asks a bosun for advice, the answer will start with the phrase: "It's not my place to tell you." The captain can ask for advice without prejudicing his authority as skipper next to God, for the bosun has known all the time that he is a bungler, whatever God may think of him. He will respect the Old Man for making a clean breast of it.

Bosuns traditionally leave sinking ships together with the captains but, in contrast with the latter, they rarely drown. Owing to their intimate knowledge of the order in the chaos of the ship's insides they always get hold of something suitable that will float. The young sailor will probably come across the story of the bosun who, while treading water after a shipwreck, was invited to climb into an already overcrowded lifeboat and answered, "No thank you. I'll wait for the doghouse to come up." He was the only one washed ashore alive.

If there is a life hereafter remotely like ship life, be it heaven or hell, I hope I'll be met at the gangway by a bosun.

SHIPS' CARPENTERS

OLD JOSEPH WAS A CARPENTER AND SOME OF HIS BEWILDERMENT STILL marks those who followed him in the profession at sea. Joseph, although he is dealt with summarily in the Bible, is a fascinating character once one comes to consider his position. Plumbers whose sons become film stars have an easy time compared to what Joseph had to put up with within himself, to say nothing of his neighbours. As far as we can glean from the fleeting seconds he is mentioned in the Gospels, he pottered on with his job as best he could and tried to forget it all by concentrating on a chair, a hand-cart or a new handle to Mrs. Bathsheba's scullery door.

Ships' carpenters are still like that: kind, helpful and perplexed. They always team up with the one other befuddled member of the crew, the ship's dog. Carpenters, wherever they go, are followed closely by whatever mongrel the ship may call Spotty or Sultan, and the dog listens to the captain's instructions with exactly the same expression as the carpenter. After leaving the master's presence they trot to some secluded place where they both sit pondering for a while. Then the carpenter gets up, with one hand on his hip, the dog rises to his feet expectantly, and they go to the workshop where the carpenter collects his tools and gives the dog something to carry.

Carpenters know a lot about dogs, and are convinced that what dogs need to make them really happy would be just a little more intelligence so that they could do simple little jobs with a dog's hammer and a dog's saw. But, well, evolution has not got that far yet, though it will surely come to pass. So both the carpenter and the dog potter on in the quiet certainty of their faith, comforted by the hope beyond the horizon.

The reason for the ship's carpenter's bewilderment is mainly that on board a ship nothing is straight. Everything is rounded, unsymmetrical and even the simplest objects, like a door, go off at imperceptible untrue angles. The result is that no carpenter ashore creates as many wood shavings in the execution of his duty as a ship's carpenter, and this may well be the reason why the dog loves him. For the simplest operation, like easing the wash-stand lid that jams, turns the cabin into a circus-ring full of sawdust and wood shavings in which the dog rolls, kicks and jumps, hunting imaginary game, so that, once the wash-stand lid jams no more, wood shavings can be found on the top shelf above the bunk. Apart from jobs that are crooked, rounded, out of true or inaccessible, the carpenter is ordered to make things that none of his predecessors have ever seen in their wildest dreams: cradles for cows, a spiral staircase for a hen-house, a packing-case for a six-armed Brahma idol or a coffin for a whale's foetus kept in gin.

Ship's carpenters have no enemies because they are not that kind of people. They are philosophers, who know short moments of satisfaction when interviewed by lady journalists, as these give them the chance to say to a human being what so far they have only said to a dog. Yet there is a slight touchiness in ships' carpenters towards chief engineers, for the captain has a magic formula which makes the carpenter perform the impossible. The formula is "All right; if you can't, I'll ask the Chief to do it."

After that, both dog and carpenter go and make a collapsible pig-sty that won't.

SAILMAKERS

IN MOMENTS OF DEPRESSION, I CAN STILL BRIGHTEN WITH THE THOUGHT that I shall never set eyes on the dear old sailmaker again, stitching away in the hold by the light of a swinging lantern. Perhaps I have been unlucky, but all the sailmakers I have known were illiterate poison-pens who, every time they pricked their fingers, hissed like snakes and stabbed somebody's reputation. I remember clearly the dear old soul who sewed the Christian sails of a hospital-church-ship on which I sailed as a boy. He sang solos during the Divine Service in a high falsetto, screwing up his eyes, and while the ship's parson, swallowing, wrung out his sermon, fighting a losing battle with seasickness, the sailmaker encouraged him with nods.

Perhaps I have been allergic to sailmakers ever since the stormy night when a bosun's mate lay dying in his bunk, surrounded by a cowed little group of sailors. The sailmaker came to see him, commiserating like a nurse, but while bending over the dying man he secretly measured him for the death-sack.

It is possible that I have occupied myself insufficiently with the sailmakers' problems in the past. It is unlikely that every single one should have been spawned, like Alraune, by a toadstool underneath the gallows. They must have had mothers to coax them into toothless grins and cute little noises; they must have toddled over the cobbles, led by father's big warm hand.

The reason why I never identified myself with the hardships of the sailmakers' life in the days of my youth was that they never talked about anything else. They were like complaining spinsters locked up in little rooms facing blank walls, with nasty lap-dogs snoring on the sofa, and Philo the canary applying the dentist's drill. Yet, in retrospect, it must have been a poor life to sit locked up in a dungeon in the stench of the bilgewater sloshing under the planks, trying to sew a seam or stitch an eyelet with the world rolling and pitching about one, and an oil-lamp going berserk on the ceiling. The windjammers of my youth were about to be laid up forever, so new canvas was rare. My most vivid picture of human rage, in all its vindictive futility, was the sailmaker of that hospital-church-ship who had just finished mending a tear in the jib under impossible conditions when, from above, there came the loud tearing noise of another sail rending, followed by the thin cheering of sailors. He jumped to his feet, shook his fists at the ceiling, and prayed to his tribal god with a scream to do something to them that was staggeringly obscene, before the swinging lamp knocked him cold.

Perhaps it was small wonder that sailmakers were unsentimental about sewing a death-sack, after all.

STOKERS

THEY CAME WITH STEAM AND THEY WENT WITH OIL AND DURING THEIR short existence they were called the Black Choir.

The Black Choir was a world apart, impenetrable, dirty and full of esoteric quarrels about fire-doors, ashlifts and "you forgot to fill the hanging dog." They were led by a subterranean bosun called donkeyman and they were divided into trammers and stokers proper. The trammers were forever tunnelling in the dark caves of the coal bunkers, filling little trolleys or steel wheelbarrows with coal and pushing them to the stoke-hold, like miners at sea.

The sailors looked down on the stokers, calling them moles or bats; the stokers sneered at the sailors, calling them kulaks or drones. For the Black Choir hardly ever realized that they were at sea and brought with them, into the dark insides of the ship, the miner's class-consciousness and the heated political debates of the pit-lift. Bad weather, in stokers' language, was "those kulaks are at it again," for whenever the ship rolled it was the fault of the bridge, and if the huge ventilators that funnelled fresh air into the depths spewed water below, the donkeyman held the bosun responsible.

They were a quarrelsome crowd and whenever there was trouble on board ship, it could usually be traced to the stokers' foc'sle. Yet I think of them with a certain nostalgia. There was something about their constant complaints, their acid suspicion, the hurt looks from white sockets in pitch-black faces that in my memory stands for human dignity. To be a stoker was a hellish job in the literal sense of the word. The stoke-hold of an old-fashioned steamship in the Red Sea was such a blast-furnace that it seemed incredible that men could live and even work there. Yet they never complained about the hardship of their work. They complained about the food, about the ventilation, about shore-leave, about the lack of fresh water, the lack of showers, the lack of women, the lack of God.

A gale in the Indian Ocean was the last word in inferno below. Fire-doors would slam open, white-hot coal would pour on to the plate hissing poisonous fumes, the mountain of coal in the bunkers would cave in over the trammers' trolleys with the terrifying tremor of an earthquake that could be felt on the bridge, and there would be wounded. Yet those wounded were kept hidden; the stokers dealt with them themselves. Their world was closed and they would never show anything to those outside but scorn.

Praise for the stokers was never heard at the messroom table. The tension between the engine-room and the stoke-hold ran too high for that. All one ever heard was "the lazy bastards didn't come up to pressure again" or "if I were the Queen, I'd have them shot."

I remember a kind word, after all. It was said to a trammer who lay on the rail on a plank after a gale; a pathetic bundle of sailcloth covered with an old Dutch flag. The captain read the service for the dead and the

Chief, a dour man from Groningen who never smiled, said, "Good-bye boy, rest in peace."

They are gone now and I suppose everyone feels the better for it. They were a hostile community to which I never was admitted. Good-bye boys, rest in peace.

OILMEN

OILMEN ARE PLEASANT PEOPLE, LIKE FUEL STATION ATTENDANTS. AS EVERY one of them has replaced six stokers and trammers within the memory of most sailors alive, they still take an extraordinary pride in their job which, when all is said and done, consists of the opening and shutting of taps.

Of course, there is more to it than that. There is also a matter of reading gauges, writing numbers on a slate and making tea for the engineer of the watch on the steam-pipe, or if the ship has a motor instead of a steam-engine, on an old electric fire with dangling coils that is put on its back for the purpose.

Oilmen, being new to the sea as a species, and seeing little of it in the course of their duty, have a mentality that during elections is called "the civil-servant spirit" by the opposition. They are cheerful, talkative, know the latest and insist on telling it to you. They are the most guileless and light-hearted members of the crew of a modern ship, except in wartime, when they show a tendency to brood on their little stools in the narrow alley between the reservoirs of high-explosive.

When there is trouble in the foc'sle, oilmen are very rarely involved. If they are, they are usually in the right, though irritatingly so. For I find oilmen difficult to get on with, despite their politeness, good cheer and remarkable cleanliness. I have pondered upon this instinctive antipathy and have come to the conclusion that I am too old to get used to them. Also, liking an oilman seems disloyal to the stokers they replaced. No one oilman, even if he were voted the most popular boy at college, can replace six stokers in my heart.

Seeing them go ashore in their neat uniforms, clean-shaven, their caps at a slightly rakish angle, I once had a strange premonition. If ever life at sea should become state-controlled and bureaucrats were to be posted on ships that roam the ocean, the oilmen are naturals for the job. They have little to do, write a clear hand, and their lonely hours, spent on a stool in an alley as clean as a hospital corridor, inspire the kind of involved phraseology that goes with letters to a faceless committee. They also make a very good pot of tea.

But all this, so I tell myself, is just the sentimental reaction to the loss of the grimy, noisy, skinny staggerers that stumbled over the crane-rails in the darkness on their way to the swindlers, the brazen whores, the smoky poolrooms and the goosestepping Wurlitzer organs that were the stokers' paradise ashore.

Thus, from prejudice, injustice is born.

CABIN-BOYS

THE SMALLER THE SHIP, THE SMALLER THE URCHIN. CARGOES THAT RUN into thousands of tons have messroom-boys, coasters have boys, and everything from a trawler down has a child who picks his nose, touches his lips with the result, wipes it on the seat of his pants, puts his dirty thumb in the soup-tureen, washes up by wiping, sings lurid songs in a choirboy's voice, and occasionally has his scalp inspected by the captain, after which a liquid called Macnamara's Hunting Water, for sale in harbour drug-stores, is applied.

The young sailor will not come across a cabin-boy unless he starts as the mate of a fishing-smack or a pint-sized coaster owned by its captain. Once cleaned, combed and taught to leave their noses alone, cabin-boys are fascinating. Their one worry is to seem grown-up. They will smoke, smell of gin, whistle from the foredeck at the sight of a woman, swear until smacked and do anything for a pair of long trousers. They give it all away, however, when they are asleep, for then they look about three years old.

Cabin-boys, contrary to what anxious mothers and scoutmasters might assume, run no risk of being perverted in the foc'sle. The presence of a child turns any crew into a Fathers' Union. Men who can hardly write themselves insist on dictating clumsy nonsense to the child to keep up on his education, and quarrels break out among the tutors over a matter of spelling, which make the pupil flee to his bunk. Every week they are stood, stark-naked, in a bucket on the foc'sle table, where they look much thinner than one had assumed, and are scrubbed until they wince. They are taken to see the sights in foreign harbours, and when their elders go to a bordello, they take the cabin-boy with them, to wait for their return in the downstairs parlour, under the care of the fattest of the ladies, dressed like a circus-horse, who feeds him pralines and encourages him to talk about his travels. They are taken to bazaars where they are told to pick a present for their mother, and if they have no mother, for their aunt, and if they have no aunt, for the person that surely must exist somewhere worthy of a filial token of fondness and esteem. Difference of opinion about the suitability of the present may cause the crew to go and look elsewhere under pressure from the manager. Somehow, the quest for the cabinboy's present always ends up with a red glass vase.

The luckiest cabin-boys are those who have run away to sea and stowed away on board a small freighter. The captain will telephone the owners at his next port of call; the owners will telephone the parents; the father, angry with relief, will say, "Keep him on board, sir, I'll pay anything you ask if you can see to it that he will never want to see the sea again when he comes home."

The owner instructs the captain to lead the boy the hard life; the captain will pass the order on to his officers and wash his hands of the matter; the officers will look stern; the foc'sle will rise as one man behind the persecuted infant, and the fortunate cabin-boy will find himself surrounded and protected by eleven uncles. Whether he later goes back to sea or not, one thing he will never doubt as long as he lives, and that is the essential goodness of man.

MESSROOM-BOYS

MESSROOM-BOYS ARE THE MOST IMPORTANT MEMBERS OF THE CREW TO the young sailor. They wait on the officers at table, clean their cabins and their number-one uniforms and make their beds. They also read everything they can lay hands on.

I have found after experience that it is impossible to guard a secret from a messroom-boy. They read letters and diaries, peer through curtains, listen at doors and are more attentive to a reclining sleeper's mumblings than a psychoanalyst who is paid for it. If the young sailor has put a private document or object in a safe place and cannot for the life of him remember where, his only hope of finding it is to ask the messroom-boy.

If ever a husband was allergic to washing-up, it is the man who once upon a time was a messroom-boy. He has washed up thousands upon thousands of dirty plates, soup-tureens, knives and forks and glasses, and of all this avalanche of crockery he will remember only one thing clearly: that he lived for the last meal of the trip, after which he would stack the plates dirty so as to force his successor to prize them apart with a chisel.

Another striking recollection will be of the total amount of urine produced by a ship's staff during their leisure hours. The messroom-boy's revenge for the humiliation of emptying other people's pots, bottles and other incongruous vessels is to say, "Do you know that I think you've got sugar, sir?" Although the result will usually be either a blood-curdling curse or a badly-aimed shoe, there are few officers who won't drink their coffee bitter for at least a week afterwards.

The messroom-boy, so the young sailor must realise, either has no future or a discouragingly distant one. He may have dreams of becoming a head-waiter ashore or a self-made deck-officer; one thing is certain: he cannot do anything to bring it about as long as he is a messroom-boy. Messroom-boys cannot walk from A to B empty-handed without being considered idle, so the young sailor will always see them carrying something. If the apprentice is appointed to inspect the messroom-boy's work, he should ascertain first of all whether the messroom-boy is new to his job, in which case he should say on entering any cabin: "You'll have to do this again." Not only is this always true, but he will find dust on the top of the lamp-shade or the top edge of the panelling to prove it. If the messroom-boy has already made a trip in his present function, don't check the lamp-shade or the edge of the panelling for dust, because you won't find it there. You will find it everywhere else.

Tips to messroom-boys are necessary both before and after the trip. They should be given in money and not in kind. If you possess something the messroom-boy has his eye on, it will be gone by the end of the trip, so anything you might feel like giving him will be something he doesn't want.

One more warning: don't try to find a way to the messroom-boy's heart, for there isn't any. The best you can do to make him centre his professional contempt on someone else is to lock your cabin-door and put the key in your pocket, in which case he can read your letters without feeling obliged to dust or make your bed. For the only profession for which a messroom-boy's job provides a training is that of lock-picker.

LAMP-TRIMMERS

THEIR LITTLE LANTERNS HAVE NEARLY VANISHED IN THE NIGHT OF THE past, as they were too feeble to keep up with the brass band of progress. Of all the old crew-members lost, I mourn them most.

In my young days, the lamp-trimmer was as familiar and comforting a figure at dusk as the lamp-lighter in the streets of an old city. Their task was to fill, trim, clean and light the hundreds of oil-lamps on board ship, which was a full-time job. The wicks had to be sand-papered, the glasses cleaned, the brass convex mirrors behind them polished and, at nightfall, it took so long to light them all that the old lamp-trimmer used to start his round at tea-time. Like the oil-light itself, he was feeble, smelly and maddening; now he is gone one realises the warmth that went with him.

Lamp-trimmers were always old men with big tired feet; I remember making a note in some diary, "the lamp-trimmer trembling in his downtrodden shoes." Despite the alliteration of youth, to me it still conjures up the image of the old man, shy as a doe at sunset, startled by every unexpected noise like sneezes or the curse of the first engineer who dropped a collar-stud. Lamp-trimmers laboured under a bad conscience that no one ever quite understood. If anything went wrong on board, they expected darkly to be blamed for it. It must be said that they sometimes dropped kerosene on pillows while filling the cabin lamps, that they occasionally forgot to check whether the wicks were smoking and that they smelled of old age. For some reason, there is nothing more irritating on board ship than that particular smell, so officers would be snappier towards lamp-trimmers than their small sins warranted.

The secret of the lamp-trimmer's charm and maddening effect on others was that he lived in his own world. To tell a lamp-trimmer to change the wick in one's lamp meant a conversation about wicks that had to run its course before one could repeat the request and be noticed. To tell them to get off the ship because it was about to be fumigated was useless. They had to be escorted ashore and held down until the gas had dispersed. But if one felt lost at twilight and in need of human comfort, the lamp-trimmer was the man to look for in the long dark corridor. There would be a faint flush of light at the far end, then the glow-worm of a lantern would float from a doorway. One would call, "Trimmer!" with an echo. He would turn round, startled, worrying what he had done wrong, and have fled if his feet hadn't been so big. At one's approach, he would lift the lantern like the old porter of a monastery, peer through his sooty spectacles, and say, "Sir?" ready to apologise. If one then asked, "How are the lamps today?" a smile of relief would dawn on his face. "Ah," he would say, "you'll see that Lisbon is a very nice town. There are white marble steps going down to the river, and when you go in for a shave, the barber sprays your face with free perfume if you are a sailor." Somehow, crazy as it sounded, this was the very thing you wanted to hear. You had been depressed at the thought of what the hell you were going to do in Lisbon. All right, you could go and have your face sprayed with free perfume.

To talk about images of foreign lands with the lamp-trimmer, sitting on the edge of somebody's bunk, is an experience that is lost forever. But its memory has outshone his feebleness, and his tendency to die unnoticed among the junk in his lair.

CHINESE CREWS

IF EVER A MAN WAS MADE TO FEEL LIKE A FOOL, IT WAS THE FIRST MATE of a ship on which I sailed in the Far East when it got a Chinese crew. He changed overnight from a self-confident, breezy hustler into a hypochondriac given to slinking along walls, taking his temperature and looking at the white of his eyes by pulling the lids down in front of his mirror. From his cabin, whence so far had sounded his boisterous song while shaving and the irritating sound of an emptying bath as he gargled, now moaned the long breathy lowing of a cow as he stuck out his tongue, saying, "Aah."

The mate in question was undermined by the fact that every time he came on to the bridge, the Chinese sailor at the wheel giggled behind his hand, and every time he went down into the foc'sle to give an order, his exit was followed by swimming-pool sounds of suppressed laughter. It got him down in the end, and I should like to see the white man whom it wouldn't. There is something about us that is irresistibly humorous to the Chinese and, worse, infinitely endearing. For their mirth is tinged with indulgence; the only man they take moderately seriously is the captain. Yet even he, although treated with utter politeness and total submission, gets unsure of himself in the end, for with the arrival of the Chinese crew he has lost his ship. He is no longer skipper next to God, but next to a totally unknown Deity with whom it is impossible to come to terms as He never seems to be at home.

A heart-to-heart talk with a Chinese bosun about his crew is impossible. The crew may cut one another's throats, smoke opium or commit sodomy, the bosun will always emerge from the den of vice with a radiant smile and visit his captain as a travelling missionary visits a Zulu chieftain in a top hat, seated on a kettledrum.

After long experience, the Far East sailor will come to the conclusion that Chinese crews are ideal in almost every respect except respect. They are clean, industrious and cheerful. They know what they are working for, and this is not, as legend wills it, an ornate coffin and a single fare to their ancestors' tomb. It is a little shop in Malaya or Indonesia where, smiling genially, they will exploit all other races' credulity. No Chinese sailor on board a white man's ship intends to remain at sea, so all pride in his work is feigned. The young officer will do well to remember this: to them, the love of a ship is quaint and amusing, and a sailor's honour baffling, though advantageous to exploit.

Let him never make the mistake of thinking that there will be a real friendship between him and his Chinese bosun or even his junior mate. It is not that they are hypocrites; they are opportunists in the same sense as the young sailor when he goes down on his knees in the privacy of his cabin.

LASCAR CREWS

THE THING ABOUT LASCAR CREWS IS THAT NO ONE KNOWS EXACTLY WHERE they come from; and after they have left, no one knows where they go. They are Indians, one supposes; in any case they are brown-skinned, lithe, small and secretive.

To help the young sailor out: there is no such race as "Lascars." It is the name for all Oriental and especially Indian sailors which has been adopted into the Merchant Shipping Acts, without any definition. "Lashkar" was first applied by the Portuguese to an inferior class of sailors in the seventeenth century.

Although few men know where the word "lascar" comes from and what it means, it still has a slight tinge of inferiority. Chinese crews are the most human in the eyes of the Western sailor, the lascars are the least so.

When I was a child, and didn't yet know anything about superiority or inferiority, I sailed as a cabin-boy on an old dilapidated steamship on which the stokers were lascars. I was warned by the bosun not to mingle with them, and they looked indeed frightening, brown as they were, when they rose silently and catlike from below, blown with coal-dust. After some weeks, however, when I had been thoroughly spoilt by the white sailors and was looking for more succulent fields, I hesitantly hovered in the doorway to the forbidden world of the lascars, my head on one side, showing my most ingratiating grin. To my surprise and faint alarm, I was answered by sixteen flashing grins of white teeth in the darkness, and a hand like a woman's stretched out towards me, proffering a small glittering toy. It was a little idol made of brass and highly polished, squatting on a pyramid of brass cushions and holding up its arms with a grace that I had never seen before. Behind the little idol, a face appeared which, even now, still embodies to me the mystery of the Orient. I knew at that moment in a flash, and yet darkly, all the things I know now about the Far East, but that have taken me a long time to formulate. There was in that face all the childish innocence, the dormant cruelty, the preponderance of dreams, and the dark blue stare of a tropical sea when first sighted through a porthole. There was also the smell that, in the end, one comes to like, although in the beginning it is slightly repulsive. But, above all, there was a notion that whatever I might see and feel, we would always be talking to one another through a plate-glass window.

I came to like the lascars very much. In the beginning, because they gave me sweets which were like Turkish delight; later, because I could watch them singing, praying, ciphering and gambling with that wonderful sensation of being unnoticed, a fly on the wall. There they were, a tropical bazaar with all its strife, suspicion, twittering rows and inexplicable gaiety, and there was I, as familiar and as alien to them as the little Dutch boy on the tin of sugared condensed milk they drank from, held like a coconut.

What was clear to me then, I discovered again later. Lascars are never part of the ship. To them, it is all part of a pilgrimage to an unknown goal. They are only happy when the ship moves, for that seems to satisfy some deep religious craving inside them, like Tibetans swinging a prayer-mill. We shall never understand why Tibetans think that to swing a prayer-mill while haggling over a quart of llama's milk will do any good to their souls; we shall never understand why lascars think the same about being on the move.

There they are and there they will be, and as long as shore-leaves are carefully supervised and as long as there are no half-witted megalomaniacs among the white sailors, they will be as placid, kind and totally unapproachable as turtles in a Northern pond.

MALAYAN CREWS

THE GREAT THING TO REMEMBER WHEN DEALING WITH MALAYAN CREWS is that to them every white man's ship is still the East India Company. When the first clumsy craft manned with prisoners and adventurers was sighted from the shores of Malaya and the islands of the archipelago, a chapter of Christian history started that some people are still unable to forget. It was a case of an old culture being invaded by barbarians. To the Malayan we are and always will be the conquerors who blew up the Parthenon.

The only possible way of dealing with them without nightmares of the slow finger drawing the slow circle on the hot deck, which precedes the scream and the flashing kriss of amok, is politeness. On that basis a relationship is possible, which is more intimate than with any of the other Oriental crews. Once the sailor from the West has convinced the Malayan that there is no question of brutal force or blatant authority or—and this is the main thing—contempt, he may forget about money. The value of human dignity is greater to the Malayan than the price at which his labour is bought. He will be unbelievably lazy at times, but it will not be a white man's laziness. It has to do with the lassitude of ancient culture, with periods of nostalgic dreams that make all physical effort look like emptying the ocean with a spoon. At those moments, when the face becomes a mask hiding the empty soul and the hands hang limp in the lap, nothing can be done to call them back to what we call reality. A Malayan bosun may spend a day oiling a yard of chain, or paint the entire lower bridge in a morning. One can always console oneself with the thought that, in the end, the sum total of his work equals a white bosun's steady conscientious pottering.

Another thing to remember about the Malayan is that every physical contact is repulsive to him. Even the friendliest of gestures like a hand on the shoulder or a pat on the back provokes an echo of the sins of our fathers.

PASSENGERS

THE BEST DEFINITION OF PASSENGERS ON BOARD A BIG SHIP IS: A CROWD OF normal individuals who, when setting foot on a gangway, go quite out of their minds. It may be the accumulated lore of the sea, lying as an age-old residue in the darkness of their subconscious, that causes havoc when disturbed.

Passengers will do things on board a liner they would never dream of doing ashore. Vegetarians eat beef, teetotallers start gazing with squinting wonder at the whole of Halmaheira upside down in a glass of white wine; they will play games that would make a child of ten sulk with boredom; they overeat, oversleep, overgossip, and at the captain's dinner at the end of the voyage they put on paper hats, blow squeakers, explode balloons in the shape of pigs and teddy-bears with their lighted cigars, bellowing with laughter at their wit. Judges, cabinet ministers, dowagers and dentists— no one escapes the frenzy of the sea. They feel free of the chains of home and duty, and after the days of seasickness are over, they all share the unspoken wish that the world they left behind may be blown sky-high in their absence.

The strangest effect of the sea on passengers is that it acts as an aphrodisiac. A dignified French company that wanted to publicise its summer cruises had a member of the French Academy compose a propaganda booklet; the booklet was given to a French woman-translator who turned it into poetic English, and her slip was discovered only after fifty thousand of the expensive booklets had been printed. "The boat decks," so she had translated the poet laureate's rapturous French, "are spacious and romantic, admirably suited for sexual intercourse." The edition had to be pulped, but truth will out. To all practical purposes, the booklet could have stood as it was. Quite recently, two new items have been added to their already admirable service by the transatlantic companies: a small jeweller's shop where engagement rings can be bought, and a resident psychologist. There has been some extemporising in messrooms as to the latter gentleman's uniform and distinctives, but the fact remains that he must have filled a long-felt want.

There is, so it is said, no more cynical person in this world than an old head-waiter. I would say that the captain and the purser of a big passenger ship are close runners-up. There are captains who are good with passengers; there are captains who turn into moody porcupines on taking their seat at the head of the first-class table. If I were ever to be a passenger, I would choose a small cargo vessel with passenger accommodation. There the passengers are guests, and the ship's crew a crushing majority. They will get an inkling of the truth about life at sea while eating with the officers, listening to their stories and having their personal problems solved by the chief engineer. They will like the food and make a life-long friend of the cook by asking him for a recipe. All will be well as long as they lose the recipe before getting home, for, like sea-flowers that rise pink and turquoise from the depths to turn into putrid bits of colourless muck the moment they reach the deck, the cook's recipes are the shortest way to heartburn (and in the case of "sausages à la king" to blindness and idiocy) if concocted ashore.

Each man, deep down in his soul, hankers to go back to the sea out of which our ancestors crawled. Let him soothe this archaic nostalgia and wordless terror in silence and peace, instead of dancing with the delirious crowd in the plague-ridden town, of which the modern liner seems an image, caught in the convex mirror of the ocean.

WOMEN AND CHILDREN

IF THE YOUNG SAILOR'S SHIP IS A FREIGHTER WITH PASSENGER ACCOMMODA-tion, he will have to deal with women and children at sea.

The men are easy. The moment they have got used to their blazers, their tennis trousers, their peaked caps bought for the trip, and given up pipe-smoking because it burns the tongue, they soon achieve the state of contented somnolence which leads to poker. Once the men have started poker, they will be no trouble for the rest of the trip, except for late-night sessions in the smoke-room during which they stake their wives. Those sessions usually end noisily, but as they fill in the Middle Watch, they are a diversion for the officer on the bridge.

Women are a different matter, for to them a trip at sea means a much greater change. A woman's routine is more established at home and, although she may have been talking for years about the relish of breaking it, she will miss it once it is upset. It will give her a feeling of being lost, which expresses itself first in fussing about deck-chairs. Deck-chairs, by the way, are complicated instruments, especially designed for pinching women's fingers. If there are several women they will sit close together in a row to gossip; the quest for sunlight determines the row's movements. Apprentices on passenger-carrying freighters will soon come to associate women passengers with carrying rows of deck-chairs from one side of the ship to the other and answering questions about where the sun and the wind will be three hours from now. It takes women longer to settle into their new routine than it does men who just relax. Until the new routine is established, they will be tricky.

Children, at first noisy little beasts, will soon become delightful. For although children are even more routine-bound than housewives, it takes them little time to establish a new one. As soon as they feel secure within the daily round, they brighten life on board ship with their consistent cheerfulness. The only dangers, if they have a cabin of their own, are pillow-fights in the twilight and their discovery that, on board ship, there are always people awake during the night. The apprentice will be amazed at the amount of water children can consume during one night; he should realise that their plaintive cries are cries of loneliness and not of thirst. The less water he gives them the better, for what goes in must come out.

An important step is to reassure mothers that the foc'sle is not a den of vice. Children are attracted by foc'sles. At first by the small entrance, and later by the shocking way in which they are spoilt inside. Any little boy that is a nuisance on deck or on the bridge will vanish without trace into the foc'sle for hours on end. Little girls are happiest in the galley. Let the ship's carpenter make a miniature stove and ask the bosun for empty paint-pots in varying sizes; both the little girls and the cook will have a wonderful time.

The ship's dog may be as fierce as a wolf; towards children, he will be infinitely patient. There is absolutely no danger there; dogs treat their puppies with much more tolerance than human beings do, and are unaware of the difference in the species.

DOGS

IF A DOG'S INSTINCTIVE ACTIVITIES ARE LIMITED TO HUNTING, TRACING AND copulation, the ship's dog should be the unhappiest animal afloat. The ship is a cage in the zoo on a large scale; the only company he has are the men that sail her and the bitches in his dreams. Yet I know of no better-adjusted canine than an old ship's dog. Even young ones feel better; they don't bite the furniture, are rapidly house-trained and don't beg at table.

I think the main reason why ship's dogs are happy is that there is always somebody in need of company, even at dead of night. Another feature, comforting to the dog, is that nobody ever leaves but is always to be found somewhere, though momentarily inaccessible.

Dog psychologists tell us that the animal chooses its master when it is five months old. A ship's dog lets this moment pass unnoticed; it never makes up its mind. The cook would seem to be the most likely choice, yet this is rarely the case. The carpenter is his playmate rather than his master; the bosun is his bogey; the captain God.

Ship's dogs should be mongrels and preferably the kind of cross-breed that, on entering a door, hesitates to show its hind-quarters. Pure-bred dogs may thrive at the seaside, they are definitely landbound. The mongrel pup feels like a stowaway who escaped from a police state. His future would have been the vivisection-table or a budget fur-coat, but for the instinct that made him follow the bosun. Sea-pups, like their masters, are often brought on board drunk. One day there is no dog, the next day there is, and some hammy acting tries to hide the feeling of guilt at hearing the captain thunder at the first puddle.

The young sailor, anxious to know what kind of ship he has boarded for his first voyage, should find out whether there is a dog on board. If there is, and the animal slinks towards him wagging its tail, the ship will be all right but too well run for comfort. If a scruffy monster sits on a hatch and eyes him with disdain, he may call himself lucky. The more independent and stand-offish the dog, the more the crew have spoilt him. On a ship where the dog is spoilt, the apprentice will soon feel at home.

CATS

THE CAT HAS NEVER BECOME DOMESTICATED, BUT STILL REMAINS A WILD animal making its lair in some house. Only on this basis does the unhappiness of cats at sea become understandable.

They are really unhappy, although regally so. They will probably get off at the next harbour, where the cook will stand whistling, kissing and calling "Meeow" for a quarter of an hour at the vast steel jungle ashore. At the next port of call he will bring on another one, for kittens are irresistible to cooks. So the young sailor will find a series of kittens rather than one permanent cat.

The kittens are indeed adorable. They follow the cook with their tails in the air, ask plaintively to be lifted onto bunks, and purr at everyone with equal tenderness. Even the captain will fall under the spell of the fluffy little toy and appear on the bridge with his nose scratched. When the kitten gets to the mangy state of adolescence, its days on board are numbered. The sign for its transition is the first time it is referred to as "that cat."

The resident old tomcat is much more interesting and much rarer. It usually has no tail or a very short one, is covered with tar and paint, and has a broken ear. It does, all on its own, the things ashore that the sailors say they'll do together. A good ship's cat is an animal of stern independence and amazing strength, capable of flooring a dog, and (if one feels inclined to close an eye to the cook's petty sins) capable of opening a tin of frankfurters. "Eaten by the cat" is the most traditional of galley excuses. One thing is true: old ships' cats do indeed like rum or spirits when laced with milk. It should be given to them when they come in half their size after being drenched by a wave.

The passing of the seasons shows itself mysteriously in the fact that the tomcat on the high seas will caterwaul at an old collision-mat, a wad of cotton-waste or anything faintly resembling its mate in the darkness during the months of March and September. The apprentice on the bridge will be ordered to stop the racket at dead of night by the captain's voice, and he had better send the man at the wheel to do it. For buckets of water thrown at ships' cats in the darkness end up in the bunk of the bosun or the chief engineer, and if the sailor on cat service comes back with only a black eye or a lump as a result of stumbling, he is lucky.

Old ships' cats have favourite spots from which to watch the sea: it may be the rail of the bridge, the anchor-winch or the loop of the direction finder. In this last case, the apprentice had better check before entering its bearings in the log.

MONKEYS

EVEN THOSE WHO KNOW SO LITTLE ABOUT SHIPS AND THE SEA THAT THEY think the *Marie Celeste* is an organ stop will tell you that sailors keep monkeys. This is rarely true, and if the young apprentice should come across a sailor with a monkey, he is in for surprises from both parties. The sailor will be a lot more stupid than he looks, and the monkey a lot more intelligent. There can be no doubt that, although monkeys may be less clever than Einstein, they are more cunning than the craftiest messroom-boy afloat. They are born actors, have a cruel sense of humour and are interested in mischief only. If a monkey sits quietly in a corner minding its own business, it is either ill or waiting for the effect of some elaborate practical joke.

As if these reasons were not enough for not taking one as a pet, or refusing to admit a monkey-fancier into a community as close as a ship's, they have the supreme drawback that they stink to high heaven. They will also, if they are males, greet every woman coming on board with gestures. My earliest memory of monkeys is of being taken to the zoo with a miniature crowd of kindergarten pupils by the teacher, who was as flat as an ironing-board, wore buttoned shoes, a dress with a high collar and a boater. An enormous male gorilla, brooding in his cage, opened one eye at her appearance, leapt to life, expressed his frenzied intentions by gestures and made her flee screaming. I have since witnessed the same scene several times with different actors. Woe to the sailor who keeps a male monkey and whose captain shows his wife around the ship before leaving. I cannot think of a crazier hobby on board ship, except that of flying a kite.

So, as long as the young sailor makes the firm decision never to keep a monkey himself, he may be in for some entertainment if somebody else does. It is astonishing what monkeys will think of in the way of pranks. Messroom-fans are pelted with eggs; the captain who snores with his mouth open is awakened by a banana; the apprentice who is writing out corrections in the *Pilot* will, after a short absence, find its pages painted black with ink. Monkeys have soft gentle hands and love looking for fleas on others, as many a screaming sailor falling out of his bunk can testify. One of their favourite positions is on top of the hatch leading down to the foc'sle, where they sit waiting for the steaming mammoth canteen to be carried in. They will throw in anything they have got hold of during the last couple of hours; and if the canteen is not steaming but filled with something like apple sauce or tepid mashed potatoes, they'll jump in bodily, like children into a sandheap. Apart from food thus spoilt, this opens a series of events. The bosun will bellow "Gertcha!" the monkey will jump out covered with mashed potatoes and weave through the foc'sle from bunk to bunk, so that mashed potatoes can be spotted in the hair of the man at the wheel three watches later. They also love oil-cans, which they squirt down ventilators. Ventilators, by the way, are their favourite means of access to cabins and even engine-rooms, where they may drop from the sky onto the work-bench at any moment, preferably when the Chief is mending his wrist-watch.

RATS

RATS ARE REPUTED TO LEAVE A SHIP ABOUT TO SAIL FOR ITS DOOM. THE ONLY rat I ever saw leave a ship about to sail was called Minnie. She belonged to the cook, slept under the kitchen stove in a whisky-crate filled with cotton-waste, and could dance to "Abide with Me," blown by her master on a mouth-organ, muted in his cupped hands.

Minnie's fame among crews, apart from her dancing, was due to the terror she sowed in the hearts of newcomers who were unaware of her domesticity. Just before the ship left, she would scurry along one of the hawsers under the horrified eyes of the newcomer, whose attention would be drawn to the omen by the cook. The cook would gasp "Look!" drop a basin and stumble to the midships, crying, "Captain, Captain, let me off!" The secret was simple: an accomplice would hold on to the rat near the ship's bollard onto which the hawser was belayed, and let her go the moment the newcomer was sighted. Then she would make a bee-line for a lump of cheese hidden behind the bollard ashore.

It is undeniable that there are rats on board most ships, if not all of them. The putting up of tin barricades on the hawsers is of little use, for rats are as obstinate and persevering in their wish to stow away as little boys of twelve. Being smaller, and infinitely more cunning, they usually succeed, whereas little boys are dragged out of lavatories by their ears. The ship's dog is supposed to deal with rats, but there must be some silent understanding between them, for I have never known a ship's dog ordered to hunt out a rat who didn't lie down out of sight and go to sleep.

If rats get too numerous or are harmful to the cargo, or if some harbour doctor has a bee in his bonnet about them, the ship is fumigated by a bevy of rat-catchers, or, as they prefer to be called, rodent exterminators. They look clean, well-fed and determined; perhaps it is their faint air of complacency that makes them lack appeal to the sailor. They come on board with suitcases full of bombs and behave as if they were going to save the crew from the plague. A crew considers itself lucky if the rodent exterminators—or whatever they are called—after gassing the rats, haven't gassed the lamp-trimmer as well, who has gone on pottering about in the dungeons below like the ghost of the opera, oblivious of the fact that everybody else has fled.

STOWAWAYS

STOWAWAYS ARE AS OLD AS NAVIGATION, AND WILL PROBABLY BE WITH US until the arrival of the giant cargo-planes that will turn the sea into a place for relaxation; and whoever smirks over there in the corner has not been keeping up on his literature.

A stowaway, so the dictionary tells us, is "a person who hides in a ship in order to escape payment of passage money or to get to sea unobserved." It is good to have this impartial formula handy, because to anyone who has come across them, stowaways come in two sizes. The first is young boys who crawl, sobbing, out of the axle tunnel, clutching a shopping basket with the shell of the world of childhood inside it: greaseproof paper in which their school-lunch was wrapped, a couple of exercise books and an empty milk-bottle. The second size stowaway is an individual in need of a shave who calls "Pst!" sticking his head either round the door of the pantry, in which case he has bribed the cook, or from under the tarpaulin of a lifeboat, in which case one of the sailors has a warm future waiting for him in front of the captain's table.

Stowaways hold the key to universal popularity in their hands, and always throw it straight over the side. The sailor loves them because they provide welcome excitement and gossip, and because they are hunted, be it by the police, the income-tax inspector or a nagging wife. A third reason, subconscious, is that the stowaway chooses of his free will a means of conveyance that is not fit for a dog. Sailors take a gloomy view of their profession by nature and tradition; anyone forcing his way onto a ship is greeted with startled surprise, like a Gentile who wants to be converted to a Jew. The irrevocable fate of the stowaway of going to face the captain solicits the same admiration for his pluck as voluntary circumcision at an age when the convert is fully conscious of the operation.

Personally, I would rather face the captain as a thief than as a stowaway. His initial wrath may be more impressive, but after the punishment due to me had been meted out, all would be forgotten. The stowaway, on the contrary, is greeted with baffled grimness which will grow during the rest of the trip into an unnerving umbrage. Whereas thieves need only be entered into the record if their punishment is a fine, stowaways entail an immense amount of paper-work, and worries about whether the captain will ever be able to get rid of them. There are alarming stories in circulation about stowaways who, unable to gain admission into any country including the one they came from, became permanent fixtures on board a ship, throwing the captain into an incoherent rage every time he set eyes on them.

Stowaways could have a very agreeable existence in the foc'sle if they didn't complain about everything, and with an accent. Their complaining nature must have been the original reason why they stowed away at all, and they are unable to shake it off once they are on board. After long, involved stories about their past plight, they will change their complaints from past to present. Soon they hang underneath the low ceiling of the foc'sle like a depression over Iceland, and spread gloom and embarrassment. They usually have a profession for which no use can be found on board, even by the boldest stretch of the imagination, like taxidermists or water-diviners, so they are ordered to polish the brass or help the cook. In the first case, they will distress the lamp-trimmer, who will spend sleepless nights in the certainty that all this is a plot to make him redundant; in the second case, the galley will turn from a pleasant village square into hell's kitchen. Cooks are allergic to stowaways because they eat, and no amount of dishwashing, curtseying and gay bursts of song will change this. The captain may expect the cook any time in front of his table, tossing back his oily curls, shrilling, "Either he goes, or I do," undaunted by the obvious reply "Where?"

Once the stowaway is gone, he leaves a question which is usually put by an elderly sailor after long musing: "What do you think was the real reason why that man ran away?" There will be some speculation about murdered widows, butchered babies and raped nuns, after which the bosun, darning a sock over a tea-mug, will wind up the debate with, "Live and let live, that's my motto."

Of course the cook has known the stowaway's secret all the time: he was a hex-doctor.

SHIP-OWNERS

EVER SINCE PEOPLE BEGAN TO OWN SHIPS WHICH THEY DID NOT SAIL THEM-selves, the owner and the sailor have been antagonists. This will always be so, whether the owner be an individual, a board of share-holders or the State. It is the old conflict between the farmer and the absentee landlord.

If anything goes wrong with a ship, the owners blame the sailors, the sailors blame the owners and, in most cases, both are right. I have sailed on ships in which the drain-pipes of the first-class lavatories ran through the bunks of the sailors and on ships in which the foc'sle looked like an exclusive club. On both ships, the owners remained rapacious in the sailors' eyes, and the sailors ungrateful in the eyes of the owners.

Keeping in mind that never the twain shall meet, nor even, as a poetic engineer of my acquaintance quoted, "at God's big Judgment feet," the re-lationship between the owners and their sailors can be pleasant. This, I am inclined to say, is entirely in the hands of the owners. True, some crews are easier than others, but they need little to make them happy. The main thing is personal contact. The owner who never sets foot on his ship unless accompanied by his wife, who has ideas for curtains and disap-proves of cuspidors, will have more ungrateful sailors than the one who climbs on board alone when the ship is in dry-dock or bunkering. He should climb on board in an old suit, wear the type of battered hat in which dredger-captains specialise, and he should drink tea without worry-ing about the scientific revelation that cracked cups spread diseases. He should go to the foc'sle, sit down at the table with the startling carvings, and have himself complained at. It is unlikely that he will ever be re-quested to open his mouth, because the moment one complains, another will start telling him that he is complaining about the wrong thing. After a good time of soul-washing has been had by all, the owner will leave an atmosphere of warmth and friendliness behind when his frayed trouser cuffs disappear up the stairs, and someone will say, "Now there's a man who knows what's what."

In the messroom, so the owner will find, things are different but not basically so. If the key-word for the foc'sle is silence, in the messroom he should talk his head off. He should make his officers share his worries by reciting an incomprehensible page from the Stock Exchange Bulletin. He must remind himself that he is like a visiting physician, who will delight a patient by telling him that he has a slight inflammation of the mucous membrane of the sinus and depress him when he tells him he has the common cold. The best owner I have known was a man who looked like a prime minister and dressed like a vegetarian on his rounds. On entering the messroom, he would start by saying, "Gentlemen, I want you to tell me exactly how you feel, what your problems are and what I can do to help you," after which, during the next half-hour, nobody could get a word in.

To put it simply, the owner should be the foc'sle's confidant and make the messroom his. If he can manage to bring in a human note about women, the day is won. The officers will go on sleeping on flattened mattresses, bending down to shave in fly-specked mirrors and drink tepid water out of a broken glass. Among one another, no one will confess to doubts as to the value of the owner's visit.

Whatever he does he should not bring along his wife; he should also avoid the captain who can be talked at separately, in the parlour. In that case, the owner's wife should be there, for no captain can voice a protest holding a tea-cup poised with his little finger in the air, while being gazed at admiringly.

SHIP-CHANDLERS

OF ALL THE PEOPLE LIVING IN THE AMPHIBIOUS WORLD BETWEEN SHIP AND shore, the ship-chandlers are the most charming, persuasive, helpful and lethal to the innocent young sailor. The traditional travelling salesman, selling vacuum cleaners to old ladies who have no electricity, is a babe in arms compared to the paternal gentleman who enters the apprentice's cabin, shakes him warmly by the hand as if they were related, and then manages to sell him a crate of whisky, two crates of gin, twenty-four bottles of the ship-chandler's bargain which is either Noilly Prat or medicinal port, and achieves all this somehow by enquiring after the young sailor's health and that of his parents, and by describing the amiable character of the local inspector of customs who happens to be his best friend.

Ship-chandlers make the young sailor feel extremely fortunate that he can have spirits, tobacco, firearms and surgical appliances without tax or duty, and coax him into buying so many cheap wares that the final bill would floor a bull. My father once fell for a ship-chandler in the person of a pedlar, who sold him a thousand packs of razor blades and five hundred cubes of hard wax to prevent the edges of his high collars cutting his throat. After seven years I inherited seven hundred and thirty packs of razor blades, which would fit only into a razor that had been a fly-by-night and was now extinct, and three hundred and eleven cubes of hard wax that were useless, as high collars had gone out of fashion even during my father's lifetime. If the young sailor is not careful, he will find himself giving away gift-wrapped bottles of whisky to longshoremen who would have been satisfied with a cigarette, only to get rid of the mess in his cabin. For, although a crate of bourbon at half-price sounds irresistible, even to a teetotaller, one never visualises its size before it arrives. A ship-chandler who is worth his salt will crowd the inexperienced apprentice out of his cabin with one order.

There are stories about ship-chandlers who doctor their wares: sacks of potatoes filled with stones, barrels of beef that contained nothing but bones, and kerosene for the lamps that blew up bosuns. These stories, although perhaps true in the past, are exaggerated. Nowadays, if a cook comes to tell a captain with the conviction of Eleonora Duse that half the crate of apples he received from the ship-chandler proved to be potatoes, the captain smiles. This smile turns the potatoes back into apples.

Apart from their professional adroitness, ship-chandlers are amazingly helpful people. After ruining the young sailor and turning his cabin into a warehouse, they will go to unexpected lengths of helpfulness and hospitality. I have been shown around many towns by ship-chandlers in my youth, and I was not allowed to pay for drinks or street-car tickets. On looking back, I am inclined to say that the inside views of normally closed worlds the ship-chandlers gave me have been worth the price. It all depends on whether the young sailor has decided to become a Conrad or a commodore.

Part III SHIPS

MAIDEN VOYAGES

THE FIRST VOYAGE OF A NEW SHIP IS LIKE A HONEYMOON. THE DREAMS, THE expectations, the apprehension that have preceded it burden a maiden voyage with more than it can bear. So it usually ends in the crew being disillusioned and homesick for their wheezy old steamer, now on the scrapyard.

To start with, no one knows where anything is. The bosun who for years has found every tool, every nail and every sailor he wanted, like a blind man at home, now finds himself in a new world which he hates because it is different. The cook who has prated for so long about the wonderful new stove, the stainless pans and the pressure cooker for the foc'sle will end up by throwing stainless ladles at the enamelled walls and taking to his bed with a migraine. The engineers who during the last voyages of the old ship, were obsessed by their new toy promised for Christmas will turn up morosely with crosses of sticking plaster on their foreheads and bandaged thumbs. The new echo-sounder will throw the mate into a panic as it indicates three fathoms at high sea; the new automatic log will make the ship's speed vary between a dog-cart and a dive-bomber; and the captain, at first so self-assured in his futuristic apartment, will often stroll into the messroom on some pretext or other, in search of human comfort. For the plastic walls of his penthouse don't take nails, so he has stuck up his daughter and grandchildren with sticking plaster, and they have crashed down at dead of night. His bathroom has a bidet with an automatic douche which doused his face when he tried the taps; and he is sleeping with his face towards the wrong wall.

The main trouble always stems from the engine-room. The engines are new, the Chief is haunted by nightmares of over-heating, loose nuts and lack of oil pressure, and some apprentice down below is certain to turn on the automatic fire-extinguishers concealed in the ceilings instead of Generator Number Two. If the young sailor new to the sea should make his first voyage on a new ship, he will find that he escapes the worst, which is his initiation. For the whole ship will be full of apprentices; everybody is being initiated by some playful genie that has to be exorcised with bell, book and candle. It is usually the bosun who does the exorcising. Bosuns on maiden voyages talk to the ship when holding the wheel, like a buggy-driver to his new mare.

The first step in chasing out the genie is the first nail driven into a virgin wall. Nobody but the bosun has the courage to do this; but once he has led the way, everyone will follow suit. The captain's daughter is hammered home; the Chief at last dares to hang his razor strop; all over the ship, the magic images of witchcraft go up in the form of wives, sweethearts, and pin-ups. The ship's carpenter starts to live again, for a maiden voyage makes him feel like a lamplighter in the streets of a modern city. The last to come round will be the cook; his cry of triumph, "It's cracked!" as he shows a fireproof glass dish, means that the genie is losing its slippery hold. It flies overboard with the broken halves, flashing in the sunlight.

That night, the messroom will have cottage pie again, which the cook swore he would never serve any more once he had his new galley. It is a festive meal, celebrating his return to his old true self, in his new old galley, on board good old *Lady Godiva*. This is the secret: marriage begins when she is called "old" as an endearment for the first time.

WINDJAMMERS

ONE OF THE MOST MAGNIFICENT SIGHTS TO BE ENCOUNTERED AT SEA IS A windjammer. To see the slender tower of sunlit canvas rise slowly out of the horizon, to pass the gigantic humming-bird and feel the coolness of her shadow as she glides by are unforgettable experiences. Her bell will toll with the swell, her lines will be like a gull's, and when she slowly sinks beyond the other sky-line, the young sailor will dream about the glorious days of sail and the romance that vanished with them.

The glory of the square-rigged ship has been immortalised by poets writing sonnets about long tricks at the wheel, and artists with beards singing sea-chanties in a jersey, accompanying themselves on the Spanish guitar. The advent of steam is considered to have been the advent of grime, trade unions, and class hatred between the bridge and the foc'sle. It has corrupted the salts of yore from iron men on wooden ships into wireless-operators in flowered dressing-gowns, idly fingering the keys, while their floating hotel sails itself by means of gyro compasses, console and radar. On the ships of the future, all the chief engineer has left to worry about are his atomic piles.

I sailed under canvas as a boy and in my memory the stalwart salts with the hearts of oak were moronic bipeds dangling in the branches of artificial trees in constant peril of their lives. The sea-chanties were ditties they were forced to sing by foreheadless bosuns, brandishing marline-spikes to mark time while pulling the ropes. I never heard it sung that my mother had a mermaid's tail, nor did I hear anybody wonder what to do with the drunken sailor. The chanties I heard were either descriptions of the cook's anatomy, or based on the fact that old captains have young wives.

So, though the memory of the extinct windjammer is one of the most precious of the sea, I should not advise the young sailor to try to turn it back into reality. It was a hard life, a dangerous life, and it lacked the redeeming presence of the engineers.

Nowadays, the place for romance is the scruffy freighter, where the young sailor will find the comradeship of the sea, the battle with the elements and the harmonica on the foredeck at twilight. All he will find lacking is Burl Ives.

LINERS

SOME POET SAID, "THE LINER, SHE'S A LADY," ANOTHER POET: "THE LADY IS A tramp." One of the two was Kipling.

The trouble with poets is that they make one remember their lines and forget their names. Looking at their lines with the level eye of, say, a tugboat captain, one will find that they are bewildering. I have, for instance, known several ladies who could be compared to liners, rarely the other way round. But perhaps he meant it that way.

A modern liner is an example of the beauty that, surprisingly, came with the era of industrialization. A liner's design is functional, and yet as impressive as a cathedral. I defy anyone to set eyes on a big liner and not somehow feel proud. That is why I think old sailors' regrets for the silhouette of the square-rigged ship are tinged with the widower's sorrow, who was married to a saint in retrospect.

To the sailor, a liner inspires other feelings than pride. To be the captain of a liner becomes a dehumanising situation, unless one manages to remember that she is a ship, although awfully big. This may be the reason why tiny captains are dearly loved by liners' crews. To sail a vessel the size of a Mid-Western town is a preposterous undertaking, whichever way one looks at it; crews feel safer with someone who can barely peep over the rail of the bridge than with a portly commodore who leans backwards as if perpetually sitting for his portrait. It is the one occasion I can think of on which a captain not only may but must transmit to his crew the fact that he is intimidated by his craft, and that each sunset is the end of a lucky day.

I do not covet the dream of being the captain of a liner. Among other things, it means sailing the same route ad nauseam, like a street-car. The crew is numbered by hundreds, which makes human contact difficult. The loneliest man at sea is not the keeper of the Eddystone lighthouse but the captain of a transatlantic liner. He will rarely become conscious of his loneliness, because it is a busy life, like that of a mayor. The social worries are such that there is hardly any time left for sailing which, consequently, is done by the chief mate or extra master. Liners' captains I have talked to always seemed to be frustrated, because they hardly ever were allowed to handle their ships. The moment they show their noses at a harbour's entrance, scores of tugboats take over and they are berthed like a patient carried in on a stretcher. That is why every captain of a liner, if he was born a sailor and not an ambassador, dreams of tugboat strikes during which he will at last be able to berth his ship unaided. Another dream is that of coming to the rescue of other vessels on the high seas. To have a liner the size of Waterville, Maine, sail to the assistance of the freighter *Nancy* is an exhilarating experience, which dispels the feeling of being a fraud by which most liner captains appear to be so curiously beset.

Like all things of beauty, liners should be looked at from afar. The moment they are owned or commanded, they become indeed like ladies.

FREIGHTERS

FREIGHTERS ARE THE OLDEST TYPE OF CRAFT IN THE WORLD. THEY STARTED with the first prehistoric man who piled his perilous coracle full of hides and set out towards the distant shore to barter them for brides. The carrying of freight has become the sailor's most solid excuse to his fiancée. "You say that we are just playing around, but do you realise that the skirt you are wearing has been woven of cotton, which . . ." The fiancée's answer is always beside the point. *Navigare necesse est* is a useful and impressive line (Latin) which every young sailor should bring out at such moments to finish the argument.

Freighters are always handsome in the eyes of their crews and uninspiring in the eyes of others. In this respect they are, although referred to as "she," much less like wives than like faithful dogs of indistinct extraction. Owners of mongrels talk about the beauty of their animals much more often than those who paid a small fortune for a walking hearth-rug or a bloodhound which has got nothing to trace. I love freighters and think they are beautiful, and the young sailor, if it is his good fortune to sail on one, will soon share my affection.

They range from square-stemmed breathy steamers with perpendicular funnels and buckled hulls to the sleek lilac ghosts that ply the indigo waves of the South Atlantic on their way to and fro between Southampton and South Africa. Both are equally beautiful, though personally I prefer the former. A freighter who still runs on steam and carries the ranks of her officers in italics on enamelled nameplates on her cabin doors is the best setting to a young sailor's ascendancy. For some reason a ship, like a tweed jacket, becomes comfortable only when fondly referred to as "old." As soon as the young sailor hears a chief engineer say, "If this were my ship, I'd put in oil burners," he'll know that he is home. No one will put in oil burners, for the ship isn't worth it; all she is doing is paying for her own funeral. All the Chief wants to do is to postpone this.

Another reason why the young sailor will feel most at ease on board a ship he can refer to as "old" is that she gives a tremendous feeling of security. She has survived more hurricanes than anyone on board. She has been everywhere, done everything and radiates the kind of peace and placidity that spell happiness to any living being.

Whatever his future, the young sailor will always feel a pang of nostalgia on seeing, from his liner's bridge, an old freighter plunging her straight nose into the waves. And the sudden bursts of smoke that are still occasionally spotted on the horizon will take him back to those good old days, when the officer of the watch cursed the stokers, and the stokers cursed back.

I envy the sailor to whom the ungainliest freighter trails clouds of glory.

CATTLE SHIPS

CATTLE SHIPS WERE NEVER BUILT AS SUCH, WITH THE EXCEPTION OF NOAH'S Ark. I don't know how Noah solved the problems that face the harassed sailor suddenly turned farmer. All I know is that I pity the crew of a ship setting sail with a bellowing herd.

My worst memories of life at sea have to do with cattle. Two things no sailor will ever forget after such an experience are the pity and the smell. For cattle belong at sea as little as man does, and they have no infinite row of generations behind them to give them the erroneous feeling that the ocean is their element. To start with, cattle get seasick, and the rolling of the ship terrifies the wits out of them. A seasick monkey or pup may be amusing and easy to deal with, but five hundred head of cattle in the throes of seasickness are a nightmare. This feeling of nightmare will never cease, not even after the animals' seasickness has passed, not even if the beasts are accompanied by bow-legged creatures in garters with gnarled sticks to look after them. I don't know quite what it is, it must be the dumb terror of the animals pervading the ship. For the seasickness may pass, but the terror will remain until they are back ashore.

And then the smell. Those rustic perfumes one revels in on shore-leave, while nesting in the hay with one's beloved or lying on one's back in a sun-baked meadow, chewing a stalk and gazing at the lazy clouds, become an obsession at sea. Everything smells of sweat, excrement, hay and the nauseating porridge cooked with fodder bricks in the huge pots stinking and smoking on deck. I have known captains, who rarely showed their noses on the bridge under normal conditions, to sit in deck-chairs in the lee of the wheelhouse for days on end in the best weather, because of cattle on board. The lowing, mooing, whinnying and bleating that only calm down at dead of night are more worrying than the shrieking of the wind in the rigging. And when both are combined, hell is at hand.

Any sailor who has weathered a storm on board a cattle ship will know what I am talking about. If the animals are not firmly secured, they will get into a panic in the holds or on deck, and it is surprising how flimsy even the most solid partition is to a stampeding cow. I have never met a bosun who didn't flee from a cow rising on its hind-legs in the twilight of the holds. Stampede, by the way, is the thing to watch out for when loading and unloading. I have seen a crew in full flight on a quay in Hamburg, pursued by a herd of what seemed to be buffaloes but were miniature sheep. Any animals will frighten the life out of you when stampeding, as long as there are enough of them. I would climb a bare telegraph pole on sighting a stampeding herd of mice.

Another interesting aspect of transporting cattle is that it turns one into a vegetarian. Cooks are bad-tempered on cattle ships because the cattle upset the crew's preference for steak. The crew will ask for vegetables, bread and fruit, and the captain, sulking in his cabin smelling like a stable, beset by moos, shrieks and mating-calls, will have to cope with a screaming cook as well.

After the cattle have at least been put ashore without casualties, which is rare, certainly if it is a cargo of horses, the next voyage will still be faintly upsetting, even if the new cargo is perfume. Once one lets one cow stay on board for a fortnight, its memory lingers for a month. I have made one trip on a freighter that had transported cattle on its previous voyage, and all the way we were accompanied by a ghostly herd. It did one thing to me for which I suppose I should now be grateful: it killed the daydreams of the little cottage among the willows at eventide. It also killed my application for a trip to the Argentine.

A farmer is a farmer and a sailor a sailor, and God help you when the twain shall meet.

TUGBOATS

THE YOUNG SAILOR WHO FINDS HIMSELF POSTED ON AN OCEAN-GOING TUG-boat will be an exception. Yet, if he should, he'll do some of the finest sailing possible and get a taste of the sea that many experienced officers never had.

A tugboat, like a lifeboat, has been built for bad weather and it is surprising what a difference this makes to those who sail them. In any other ship, there is always the secret feeling that one is sailing the sea in an unsuitable contraption filled with incongruous junk. Normally, every arrival has an element of luck in it. On board an ocean-going tugboat, however, bad weather is eagerly awaited as it brings in the customers. For a change, it is an exhilarating experience to fret when the barometer stays steady and the placid white clouds sail sedately from the silver to the gold.

There are, of course, disadvantages, the main ones being lack of space and lack of sleep. As an ocean-going tugboat is a tremendously overpowered machine filled to the brim with fuel, her officers' cabins look as if they had been designed by a sardine-canner. Because the ship normally carries only two deck-officers, the captain and a mate, watches are four hours on and four hours off, which only a young man can take, or else a very old one who has arrived at that ideal state of seamanship in which he keeps watch like a crocodile, peacefully asleep with his eyes open.

Ocean-going tugboats are built for two purposes: to tow huge inanimate objects across the ocean at a snail's pace or to slam ahead at full speed into the teeth of a gale to come to the assistance of a vessel in distress. Of the two, it is hard to say which is the most exciting. Personally, I found the long slow trips towing a dry-dock, a dredger or even a whole factory in the shape of a tin-dredger a more exacting experience than the salvage business. For, during the long trips, the officer of the watch develops a tendency to gaze astern instead of ahead, which he will find a difficult habit to lose. When, later, he is on watch on any other ship's bridge, pacing up and down at the comfortable walking speed that is the secret of relaxation, he will often experience a sinking feeling in the pit of his stomach on seeing the empty wake. And what is worse, he will forget about the speed of his ship and find himself on top of yonder trawler at nightmarish velocity.

To come to the rescue of a vessel in distress is a most gratifying experience. The furious sea holds no menace, because it serves a purpose instead of being pointlessly hostile, and the only danger one runs is the competition from other tugboats. This feeling of rivalry is completely unique to the sailor who, normally, feels benevolent and full of comradeship towards his fellow mariners. The lengths to which ocean-going tugboats will go to get at a prize before the other man has made fast are incredible, and the personal hostility towards those crooked French, snooty British, pompous Germans or double-crossing fellow countrymen is pathological, one might as well be ashore. Once the towing starts, the bedside-manner comes into play and a tugboat captain can send more reassuring messages to his towee than a heart-specialist to his patient. If he is worthy of his job, he can let the ship he is towing sink slowly and make her captain like it, rather than call in a second tugboat. The direct opposite of the bedside-manner, but coming from the same source, is the sowing of terror into the towee's heart so that he may be lured into abandoning his ship together with his crew. In that case the tugboatmen get half the ship's value as prize money. To achieve this, however, the tugmaster must be a genius and the towee a Greek.

If ever an offer to sail on an ocean-going tugboat should come the young sailor's way, he should jump at it. Not only will it make him a better sailor by experience, but he will find himself at the very source of ship life as a community. The crew of thirteen lives like a family presided over by a fascinating demi-god, who unites within his breasted chest all the qualities of life on earth from dog to man. A tugboat captain's opinion on anything under the sun is so over-simplified that the young sailor will gain a feeling of comfort as regards life in general, and of self-confidence as regards the handling of men in the future. The one thing he should not try to imitate his captain in is shaving with an old-fashioned cut-throat.

MOST LIFEBOATS ARE PUT IN POSITION ON THE BOAT DECK WHEN THE FINAL touches are made to the newborn ship, and never leave it until she is broken up. They are like fire-extinguishers in the home and have the same tendency to become useless after a surprisingly short time, unless properly looked after.

Apart from their intended use, which is to save those in peril on the sea when the ship goes down, a series of unexpected and unintended uses have become connected with them. Stowaways hide in lifeboats, where they consume their stale sandwiches with high-beating heart and end by trying the emergency rations which, if the ship has been fitted out before the war, consist of biscuits that can only be used as lethal instruments, or a curious concoction known as Brimstoned Groats. Considering that even rats leave Brimstoned Groats alone, it will be readily understood why, soon afterwards, the stowaway emerges from his hideout and kneels in front of the captain, speaking Polish. The only humans known to have actually eaten Brimstoned Groats are elderly deck-officers who, long ago, were pupils at the Amsterdam Naval College where Brimstoned Groats were served for breakfast.

Another item to keep stowaways busy during the long lonely hours of twilight is a parcel found underneath the lifeboat's back seat. It is wrapped in oilskin with the red imprint "Charts for Ships' Boats." Inside, the explorer will find a red buckram envelope containing paper, pencil, rubber and protractor, a table of sunrise bearings, and six charts covering all the oceans of the world, printed on waterproof paper with, on the reverse side, the shortest course in navigation, seamanship, winds and weather and the management of boats known to man. It is a good thing that these invaluable instructions are so carefully hidden, for they would put naval colleges out of business if young sailors ever laid hands on them. Everything that it takes three solid years of study and six years of examinations to master can be read in ten minutes in "Charts for Ships' Boats." Definitions of *leeway* and *current*, how to plot a position, how to take off a course, what to do about magnetic variation, points of the compass, distance, and how to plot a bearing—all this is covered in about fifty lines of kindergarten print. Even a spinster from a Shakespearian hamlet tucked away in the rolling downs of England will know enough to become a pirate's moll with an eye to taking over command, after applying to any agent for the sale of Admiralty charts and paying (complete) $2.50. She'll know how to board a ship in a rough sea, how to use a sea-anchor and how to land in a surf. She will even be a better prophet than the meteorological office after reading the chapter "Winds and Weather" which manages to cover all the prevailing winds of the globe, from the South-West monsoon via the Trades to Local winds, in eight paragraphs. Yachtsmen wanting to master the art of navigation should start and end with the instructions on the back of the lifeboat charts. Apart from how to chew a quid and hit a cuspidor cleanly at a range of nine feet, they'll be better at the job than the local salts and unmask them for the hams they are. They will never need anything else for plotting a course on any chart than the contents of the red buckram envelope costing seventy-five cents. The greatest boon of all is the pencil which can be sharpened by simply pulling a thread.

Other uses for the lifeboat are the storing of potatoes, smuggling, and taking illicit naps; lifeboats are also eminently suitable for occasional holidays. As lifeboats are too high off the deck to be looked into from outside, the sailor, who has managed by subtle hints and casual reminders to wangle the order from the bosun that he shall clean and paint the lifeboat's interior, may well be grateful for this windfall. In my young days, I spent hours inside lifeboats that have never since been equalled by any fortnight in the mountains. One strips to the waist, for the job depends on sunny weather; one sees to it that all the tools are out of sight, as the great boon of working inside a lifeboat is that one is forgotten; one stretches out on one's back, one's head on a bunch of frayed rope or a collision-mat brought for the purpose, and starts looking for faces in the clouds, or thinking about love, or about the withering answer one will give the bosun next time he opens his stupid big mouth.

There is one lifeboat that serves a quite different purpose from hide-out, storage cupboard, or fourposter-bed. This one is the smallest and called Workboat, Longboat or just the Boat. It is used to ferry to and fro if the ship is anchored away from the quay, and for all the odd jobs that may be going; it soon turns into a harassed wreck as it is hoisted out of its bed more frequently than a village doctor. I love workboats, for they also serve for pleasure. My best memories of distant lands are of sailing up creeks or silver lakes in the company of an engineer with a gun and the ship's carpenter, who brings the dog to retrieve wild ducks. Those hours spent in the paintless, splintered, leaking little craft with its clumsy sail and its even clumsier oars are expeditions into the lost land of boyhood. In those hours one admits how good it is to be a sailor, what splendid fellows one is sailing with, and how expertly one handles a yacht.

The last use for lifeboats comes after the ship is broken up. They are sold by auction and bought by retired sailors who then turn them into pleasure craft. As we will see later, this is the best way for a seaman to spend his last precious years. He will design a superstructure when the inevitable compromise has been reached, after his wife says that she doesn't want to know it is a boat when she is inside, and he says he doesn't want to know it is a bungalow when he is outside. The result will be the kind of monstrosity frequently seen in small ports and on inland waterways: as square as a boot, top-heavy, big windows and muslin curtains with tassels. As anyone knows who owns one, a ship like that is the nearest thing to paradise two staggering old people can ever hope to get.

Once even this last use is spent, and they are rotted beyond repair, young boys buy them, and they turn into some future sailor's first ship.

DOCKING

TO SEE THE SHIP ONE HAS SAILED ON SO SAFELY LYING HIGH AND DRY IN the steel canyon of a floating dock is a strange experience. It is impressive and alarming at the same time.

The sheer wall one has to climb before getting onto the deck is dizzying; the drop down to the rusty puddles below makes one feel queasy when peering over the rail; yet the whole thing has a hint of flimsiness. Here she is, all of her, disturbingly like the toy boat one once used to lift out of the bath with one hand and hold upside down to let the water run out. Memories of blowing a gale towards the toy boat with one's lips on the surface of the water come back, and the drama of the shipwreck on one's toe stirs in the shadows of the past. Once back on board and lost in the intricate maze of the steel beehive, one forgets the dock, except that the lavatories carry a handwritten notice on the seat: "Out of Use" and that there are a lot of strangers on board in rusty overalls splotched with tar, who bellow incomprehensible communications at one another like "Woof!" and "OK, Doc, garrot the ricket!" One has the impression of being invaded by a bigger crowd of removal men than one has ever visualised. It will be stronger in foreign harbours, when one is docked to mend a screw or the rudder. The dock-hands there are an unknown race of men, who have nothing to do with the picturesque foreigners ashore.

The young sailor who feels disturbed by the impression of flimsiness should accompany the chief engineer when he goes to look at the screw. It may seem unlikely that your chief engineer should ever look small, after his stature has grown so impressively during the philosophical debates in the messroom. Yet, to see him beside that enormous bronze monster, tapping on it with a puny hammer and pointing at hub-caps large enough to house a family of Eskimos, will comfort the apprentice beset by lack of confidence in his ship.

The main thing about docking is its noise, when the riveting starts. The messroom of a ship in dry-dock while the steam-hammers are sounding off is the ideal place to impress a bore with the futility of his conversation. Long after the ship is back at sea, the young sailor will be haunted by the rattle, its echo and the echo of its echo during that day of near-madness, when the first mate presiding at table covered his ears and screamed, "For Chrissake!" It may make him realise for the first time the great blessing of life at sea: silence.

LAST VOYAGES

LAST VOYAGES ARE A MIXTURE OF SADNESS AND ANTICIPATION, LIKE NEW Year's Eve. I am not talking about the last voyages I knew during the years of the Great Depression in the early thirties, when only the sadness was felt, as in those days brand-new ships were either sold to Balkan countries or laid up indefinitely and every member of the crew knew that once the trip was over, he would be on the dole.

The kind of last voyage I am referring to is when an old ship is sailed home for the last time to be broken up, and the next trip will be on a new ship. Those last voyages have a peculiar atmosphere that goes to show the relativity of things. For the ship is old, both the deck-officers and the engineers have cursed her for years, and for the last two or three trips the new ship has been the main topic at the messroom table. Everyone has said in turn, and in a tone as if it were the first time this opinion was heard over the coffee, that he won't know himself once he is on board the new ship. Think of it, boys: every officer his own cabin, with shower attached, intercom from bridge to bunk, and as to the Old Man: I've seen the plans. A penthouse. What a pity he's going to turn it into an old vet's waiting room with all those snapshots of dogs and the kitten in the boot his wife painted. Yes, everyone has been dreaming of the wonderful new existence that will make all the difference to his life. And then it happens. The last trip.

At first, no one says anything; only there is less talk about the new ship at table. Then the little symptoms show. The first mate on day-watch looks at the rail of the bridge musingly and touches it; the messroom-boy coming up with the tea has to speak to him twice. The bosun is heard to roar on the foredeck, "Who the hell told you not to oil that winch any more? You youngsters are nothing but wreckers, the lot of you!" The chief engineer, while rolling his after-dinner cigarette, says: "Wonderful invention, those Diesel engines, but the thing about steam is that it's very quiet, you know." Nobody is surprised that he should suddenly contradict himself, after extolling the praise of Diesels and damning steam during three voyages. The wireless-operator will say, "When you look at it, this teak table is beautifully worked. They don't do it that way any more today. All plastic and plywood." Nobody reminds him that he has bored them all beyond expression for weeks by explaining why plastic doesn't mark. Yet, after these hesitant feelers, they all retire once more into the security of general conversation. The only one who is uncomplicated enough to show his grief is the ship's carpenter. He comes in with a worried look, cap in hand, bringing the dog as a witness. "Is it true, skipper, that you don't want that door fixed?" he asks. "I can do it in a jiffy." The captain says, "That's true, carp, forget it."

"But you said last time . . ."

"This is not last time, carp. This is the last time."

And then the carpenter says, "Oh, I see. Sorry," and goes away with the dog, leaving a silence.

And then the captain calls the steward and tells him to bring out his special bottle and eight glasses. And when the glasses are filled, he says, "All right, gentlemen, here she goes. God bless her."

They drink, yet they don't talk about her, although everyone realises that he must talk now or forever hold his peace. But it is difficult, for there are too many things involved. Like New Year's Eve, it is a good-bye to a year of their lives, slowly ticking towards its end. The briefness of man, the fragility of pride, the hopes turned to ashes, the love grown cold; youth has run through their fingers like sand. To all of them the day will come that someone will raise a glass, bless them, drink, smack his lips and say, "That's the stuff," like the Chief.

When the packing is done for the last leave-taking, everyone takes a little souvenir that is soon lost: an ash-tray, a chipped glass, an old-fashioned nameplate saying "Master," and then they leave.

The last one to go, when the wreckers are climbing on board, is the carpenter who has secretly fixed that door. He goes with the dog to the Café de la Marine, where he tells the fat newspaper woman in the big laceless boots all about Hawaii.

Part IV THE SEA

HOWEVER BEWILDERED, HOMESICK OR SEASICK THE YOUNG SAILOR MAY BE, he will forget himself for a few moments when he watches his first sunrise at sea.

There is something about a ship emerging from the night that cannot be equalled by any dawn ashore. Night at sea is closer to the origin of the earth than it is on land. There are few dangers that can be called real; the coast and its rocks are far away; other ships are well lit and easily spotted; the night itself hides no burglars, ghosts or cats on the prowl to tinge the darkness with terror. There is nothing but the darkness, in which an occasional wave swishes past, or a burst of spray shimmers green on starboard, red on the port side.

Dawn at sea breaks high in the sky: a faint flush on the highest peaks of the clouds. Then the miracle starts that never fails to make man humble: the momentous occurrence of the earth's creation. One moment, darkness is upon the face of the deep and the spirit of God moves upon the waters; the next moment, there is light. The young sailor will see the light and feel, more than he understands, why God called the light Day and the darkness Night, and rested.

Dawn at sea is short. Within a matter of minutes, after the first cloud's peak's being touched by the light, the new-born day starts to foretell the weather, or to reveal the lookout asleep; within a quarter of an hour, Paradise has been created and lost, Man has fallen and the gates of Paradise have closed behind him until tomorrow's dawn.

If the young sailor can keep alive within himself that moment's awe for the miracle of Creation, he will fall asleep after his first watch with the certainty that he'll be all right.

NORTH SEA

WHEN I WAS YOUNG, THE NORTH SEA WAS THE BIGGEST SEA I KNEW, AND terrifying in its might. To the youngsters of the east coast of England, the North Sea is a friend; to the ones on its opposite shores, it is wrought with menace, a never-relenting enemy. Young English boys potter around lustily with little boats and rickety old yachts in the shelter of their island; on the eastern shores of the North Sea, it is another matter.

For the prevailing winds in the North Sea are westerly, and gales are frequent and sudden. Furthermore, the eastern shores are sown with banks and shifting shoals so, apart from courage, the young yachtsman needs a solid knowledge of navigation to go playing around in the great grey open.

The North Sea, more than any other sea I know, belongs to the fishermen, a great many of whom are Dutch. They are among the toughest and most antique of their kind. Some of them still wear their local costumes and pray to tribal gods. I sailed with them as a boy; so to me the North Sea stood for seasickness, cold, wet clothes, sore hands, homesickness, and the icy wrath of Jahveh. I shall never be able to give an objective description of the North Sea for that reason. There I have known my first fears and joys; my earliest dreams of love and adventure have been circled over by mewing seagulls in a pale-blue sky, and my first anticipations of eternal damnation have been shivered out in the peak of a rusty trawler as the relentless hordes of the horses of the Apocalypse came thundering by from horizon to horizon.

To the young sailor who passes through the North Sea on his way elsewhere, it will come as a surprise. The waves are steep, short and aggressive; the currents are strong and navigation becomes tricky because of the shoals of fishermen and the intense traffic, which turns the Channel into a village main street on Fair Day. The fishermen are worse in their disdain for intruders than anywhere else. If they show lights at all at night, they show the wrong ones; and as a lot of fishing is done in pairs (two drifting luggers dragging a net between them) one should take great care not to pass between the two. For trouble on the North Sea is about the worst to be got anywhere.

On summer days, the North Sea can give a wonderful somnolent feeling of security that is dangerous. Lighthouses and lightships swing their transparent scythes through the stars, garlands of coloured lights festoon the distant shores, and the faint glow of towns lights up the haze afar. Yet those visions of a better world and eternal peace should be considered as highly suspect. Somewhere a gale is brewing, waiting to pounce with all the shrieks of hell, and there is little leeway to the east.

My most poignant memory of the North Sea in later years was a Christmas Eve over the Dogger Bank. I sat with the wireless-operator in his cubicle on the boat-deck and we listened in to the Divine Services of all the countries around the shores. There came a moment when they blended: prayers from Denmark, songs from Germany, bells from Holland, carols from England, sermons from Scotland and a faint icy tinkling of handbells, shaken by children in the snow outside some Norwegian village church. I have never felt nearer to God and His benevolent bewilderment than at that moment.

If the Mediterranean is the cradle of man's culture, the Atlantic the backdrop to his daring, and the Pacific his lonely road through space, the North Sea is the mirror of Christianity's young struggle and melodious hope.

MEDITERRANEAN

THIS IS A MAGNIFICENT SEA. IT COMBINES EVERYTHING ONE DREAMED OF as a boy: the deep blue water, the crystalline depths, the hot sun, the white clouds over distant mountains. Every shore bears the trace of antiquity: in the south, the Dark Ages loom from the forbidding hill-tops, and on deserted beaches the ant-like silhouettes of a man and a donkey trudge wearily along the surf. In the north, the orange and dark green of fir-grown cliffs and the skyline of snow-capped mountains give the sailor lost in this dream a feeling of being offered all the riches of the earth at once, like Jesus.

The keynote to the Mediterranean shores is ripeness. The fruit is bigger; the flowers, heavy with scent, bloom forever; enormous crickets rattle like dice and prehistoric fish rise gaping and monstrous within sight as in an aquarium. The people are ripe too; the centuries of strife are past; now they sit or loiter, amongst the cosy rubble of discarded cultures, and play games with giant iron marbles. They rarely sing, always quarrel, never fight; their life is punctuated by the slow swinging clatter of the wooden bead-curtains that keep out the flies; and they exert a tremendous tidal pull towards their careless, lazy existence.

The off-shore dangers, apart from the reefs and rocks, are sudden violent winds that have romantic names like *mistral, sirocco* and *tramontane*. They come literally like bolts from the blue and, in the case of the mistral, its violence is never quite realised because of the bright blue sky and the dazzling visibility. The waves are short and steep, and there are some regions marked in red on the pilot charts where crosscurrents and confused swell can sink ships without a trace. The dangers at sea are the reflection of the dangers ashore; the little islands set gem-like in the evening sky are, like the happy ripeness of life on land, offered as a temptation. To be young and a sailor in the Mediterranean is to feel like a god on Olympus. On going ashore, one feels like shedding one's cloak of immortality and turning into a swan. When Ulysses had himself tied to the mast after blocking the ears of his crew to the sirens' song, he wrote a most important addition to the Notices to Mariners, Mediterranean.

ATLANTIC

THERE IS A SOUTH ATLANTIC AND THERE IS A NORTH ATLANTIC, BUT ONLY the northern one is unique. The South Atlantic is a watered-down version of the Pacific and the Indian Ocean. It is neither the sea on which every point of the compass holds a different promise like the Indian Ocean, nor man's nearest experience to eternity like the Pacific. It is like the big square in a provincial town, smaller than others and bigger than some. It looks and feels as if it were a substitute for something; apart from the trade winds and the doldrums, the South Atlantic is just any sea until one reaches the Roaring Forties.

The trades, so the young sailor will find, make him uneasy, they just cannot be true. For the same wind to blow at the same strength from the same direction forever is, strangely enough, the very reverse of relaxing. The doldrums, important in the days of sail, have now lost their menace, except to lifeboats.

It is only in the North Atlantic that man is forever faced by Oceanus in his might. Not one day is the same: gales of incredible violence, days of supernatural glassy calm, red skies, green skies, blue skies and the fantastic Northern Lights make the sailor realise he is fighting an alien element.

It is not for nothing that, of all the great explorers, Columbus is the most famous, for ever since antiquity the Atlantic has been the threshold to the edge of the world. All fantastic stories, from sea-serpents to the Aldebaran and Atlantis, have come from the Atlantic, and no one who has not sailed that incredible sea knows what it means to be a sailor. All other oceans have their schedule: the Indian Ocean has a bad period and a good one; the Pacific gives ample warning of its mood; even the Mediterranean harbours few surprises to the experienced navigator. Only the Atlantic is completely and utterly unpredictable, despite all the solemn studies written about her character that try to make sense of her streaks of madness and her incomparable moments of majesty. All the adjectives used to describe the sea since the beginning of man's consciousness can be applied to the Atlantic. The only way to predict her aspect for to-night is to write all those adjectives on separate bits of paper, roll them into little balls, put them in a tin, shake them and let the cabin-boy draw.

It may be "azure" and it may be "fickle"; it may be "terrifying" and it may be "pewter"; the only safe ones are "deep" and "wet."

To those reared on the North Atlantic, every sea change will be a holiday.

PACIFIC

YEARS AGO I DESCRIBED IN MY FIRST NOVEL A SAILOR'S IMPRESSION ON rounding the Horn and facing the Pacific for the first time in his life. I said that the waves were different, for behind them surged twenty-five thousand miles of loneliness, and that every crew emerging into the waste of the silent ocean had a difficult time overcoming the archaic terror of man's futility in the universe. After reading the book, several old sailors wrote to me saying that for the first time they had found the Pacific truthfully described.

Yet I had never been there. All I had done was to look at a sixpenny globe atlas and realise how big it was. I have been there since and found that I was right; there is indeed something about the Pacific that makes it different from any other ocean on our planet. The description I provided as a young man was not a flash of genius; every sailor facing a waste of water which he knows to be the Pacific falls under the spell of the sixpenny globe of his childhood.

There are things man is unable to forget. To look at a photograph of a sphinx may make it look like one of a set of iron log-supports; once one sets eyes on the real thing one is assailed by the concentrated awe of hundreds of generations of spectators. The same goes for the Taj Mahal, Napoleon's tomb and Washington's spectacles. It is the magic of the countless that does its eerie work; and the Pacific, biggest ocean of the world, is the most tinged with mankind's imagination. It is a place where vessels vanish and are perhaps still sailing between water and wind. It is a desert full of ghosts, and on its trailless plain more dreams and memories course than there are shooting stars in an August night. For beyond the silver horizon lies modern man's new paradise; the islands.

People who have actually been there rarely dream about living on a Pacific island. They are not fragments of paradise; they are outsize cradles. If modern man thinks of a return to the satin and the faint smell of powder of babyhood as bliss, the Pacific islands are indeed the answer. To lie on his back, pint-sized, facing the lazy choice between his toes and the dangling rattle, is the real image of man in the South Pacific paradise. For the guitar-strumming beauties in their grass skirts are oddly sexless once one sets eyes on them, and the eternal song of the surf underneath the tropical sky has the disadvantage that it is eternal. On these conditions bliss is the best working description of hell I can think of.

The ocean itself, however, will give the young sailor an unforgettable experience. By its sheer size, it brings home to him the tempo of life at sea. To sail for weeks upon weeks without anything in sight but the water, the sky and the snub nose of his vessel slowly rising and falling will set him musing in his diary about things he has so far ignored because of his eager expectancy of land to be sighted at dawn. He will write, "I wonder whether perhaps I am idealising Maggie," which is the first step on the road that took the great philosophers of mankind out of sight of the foot-slogging army.

When at last land is sighted, and the pilot or the harbour-master climbs on board, he will have the strangest experience of all: he will feel an inexpressible mixture of relief and regret.

INDIAN OCEAN

THERE ARE TWO INDIAN OCEANS: ONE BETWEEN NOVEMBER AND APRIL, and one between May and October. The two are so different that the Indian Ocean frequently becomes the cause of heated quarrels in foc'sles and messrooms, when those who know it contradict one another with the violence of conviction. In the Arabian Sea, for instance, winds are mainly south-west from June to August, reaching gale force on eight to ten days a month. From November to April, light to moderate north-easterly winds prevail. Between Suvadiva, south of the Maldive Islands, and the west coast of Sumatra, light to moderate winds between west and north-west cradle the sailor on a sea of turquoise between November and April, whereas from May to October, he is buffeted and maddened by squalls and calms from the south. This goes for the whole of the Indian Ocean in varying degrees, and the contrasts are so strong as to be hard to believe. There are months in which one might as well be sailing the North Atlantic, snarling and grey, with low ragged clouds, and there are months of such unearthly beauty that it has taken Conrad a lifetime to describe it.

The young sailor entering the Indian Ocean in the good period will realise that he has never known there were so many brilliant stars in the sky. The whole night-dome, of dark blue velvet, seems to have turned into one colossal Milky Way, and the Milky Way itself is a dazzling furrow ploughed through the universe. The sea has an oily quality that is not encountered anywhere else on earth. It breathes slowly like a sleeper with a long cradling swell, and the ship's wake mirrors the Milky Way. Strange, luminous shapes glide silently underneath the glassy surface, squids rise like fiery rockets from the depths, and occasionally, in very still nights, the young sailor will feel as if touched by a magic wand and turn into Sindbad, when in the darkness a whale roars or a dolphin splashes.

The Indian Ocean in the calm season is a sea of dreams. To stand on the bridge at night and watch the world makes the sailor feel young and immortal. His future is brilliant, his past fortunate, his sweetheart the greatest stroke of luck any man ever had, and they say that women show their breasts in Bali. He will think of leading the life of a planter; he will look forward to all his boyhood books of adventure coming true; above all, he will be happy to be himself.

Then, when the land of promise is first discerned by a strange nutty smell, he will head for those waiting for him with a completely guileless mind. The magic will last until he either sails home in the gale season, or sights the white miracle of Aden. Until then, the rug he bought will be Persian, the brass idol gold, the Javanese rice-picker sculptured in teak a work of art and the ear-rings of conscience will be jade. Seldom will a man have brought home more junk, and a better notion of the richness of life.

I C E

ON THE PILOT CHARTS OF THE OCEANS IS FOUND A RED LINE, ALONG WHICH is printed: "Extreme limit of drifting ice." Further north, or south as the case may be, there is a second red line: "Extreme limit of Polar pack ice." Between these two lines lies a ghostly region.

No one who has not sailed these regions can quite imagine what they are like, for not only is the sea totally different from anywhere else, the sky changes also. It may run through all the colours, from rose to dark orange with a greenish hue, like the copper chimney of an old-fashioned ship's stove when it is heated.

There are many sailors who talk about the sea as if it had a personality and were subject to moods, like the early God of the Old Testament. I defy anyone sailing in the ghostly region of icebergs and floes to endow the sea with any manlike emotion. The sailor moving slowly among the icebergs, his little ship and its little noise lost in stark eternity, will, after a few days, feel creep over him the awe of the dawn of creation. For even the word "day" doesn't apply here any more. He will move either in a perpetual variation of misty dawn and hazy dusk or in an eternal night; and when Aurora Borealis raises its world-large frayed standard of victory, older than the sea itself, the sailor can truly say that he has seen, if not the edge of his world, at least its Bethlehem.

The Arctic regions are not interesting; for no man can call their effect on him "interesting." It is crushing, it is evaporating, it plays havoc with the ego and makes the ties of love and comradeship seem as flimsy as gossamer threads, at the mercy of the evening breeze. One impression is supreme: man has no business there, and in the great white silence a lesson is put to him which he is unable to grasp. The young sailor may come across some older officer or seaman who seems different from those around him. Calmer perhaps, less emotional about big things, and overshadowed by a faint sadness that yet is not dark. Chances are that his companion has sailed the Arctic route during the war. For to have witnessed man hunting man in the Arctic changes the survivor for life.

At college, the pupil is taught rules about icebergs and how to avoid them, but not until he has felt their cold radiation and heard his voice echoed by the first substance of the earth will he know what lies in store for him, when the cry goes up from the mast: "Ice!"

FISH

THE SEA, TO THE SAILOR, IS A SURFACE, AND HE HATES EVERYTHING THAT reminds him that there is anything more to it. So fish and sailors don't get on well together. Unless he is a fisherman and takes a commercial interest in the denizens of the deep, he acknowledges their existence, if pressed, and leaves it at that. Unlike birds, fish are no harbingers: they are reminders.

The reason why Miss Carson's admirable book *The Sea Around Us* is not as popular with sailors as the ladies who compose the reading bags for the Merchant Navy seem to suppose is that, in a way, Miss Carson's book is a printed fish. Next time you go on a sea voyage, take it with you and read it in your bunk. Ten to one that by the end of the first chapter, your hair will stand on end and you will be unable to fall asleep, even with the light on; for Miss Carson has contrived to make you aware of the unechoing depths underneath your mattress.

Yet fish are very interesting creatures and extremely intelligent. Any underwater hunter, who stalks his prey with aqua-lungs, frog-feet and a portable harpoon, will tell you how intelligent they are, for they usually get away. There is many a tale in the lore of the sea about intelligent fish. There was a white dolphin off the coast of Australia that used to follow the ships in, and became so popular with the sailors that a law was passed to protect it. It met its end by being cut in half by the propeller of a Turk and everyone who had ever been welcomed by its playful leaps mourned its passing.

Dolphins are magnificent fish. Anyone who has ever seen them leap and play around the ship has stared at them in wonder. Shelley wrote a poem about them; I had my ears boxed for them by Bosun Jongman of the *Loppersum* when I was look-out on duty. Apart from the dolphin, there are hundreds of thousands of different fish in the seas of the world, but the less said about them the better. Every man will see for himself. There are two kinds of fish, however, that must be talked about because they rank high in the sailor's imagination.

First, the whale which, ever since Jonah, is supposed to have a little apartment inside, complete with pot-bellied stove, cuckoo-clock and Lutheran prints. Every cabin-boy is told the story of the famous Finn who dropped overboard, was swallowed by a whale and spat out again on the beach of Monte Carlo. Some say he was green when he came out, others say red; in any case he was raving mad and an obvious liar anyhow, as the whale's gullet is not made for man. The foc'sle fantasies about whales, however extravagant they may be, are always friendly. Even the fact that a whale, when maddened by torture, will attack a boat does not change the sailor's opinion of the mammal. The people in those boats only got what they asked for. Whalers, for that reason, are not popular at sea.

The shark, on the contrary, embodies all that is evil. Scientists, divers, and big-game fishermen all assure us that sharks only very rarely eat human flesh, because they don't like the taste. "Very rarely," however, will do for the sailor. The scientists may disagree; the sailor is convinced that sharks do eat sailors and everything else that drops overboard: bottles, caps, and the scraps of discarded love-letters. When a shark is caught and hoisted on board ship, as occasionally happens on long voyages, the aft-deck turns into a slaughter-house. The men go berserk in a prehistoric orgy of fury and blood and rip out the animal's stomach to see what is inside. At those moments, the jolly old tars are not lovable. When the orgy is over, there is a bewildered sense of shame and they pretend that the slaughter has had a purpose. They will cut out the spine to turn it into a walking stick for a father-in-law; I have seen a grim, fat bosun struggle for weeks with a bit of corrugated iron skin, trying to make a handbag.

There are fish, no bigger than a finger, who come in shoals and strip a man who falls overboard down to his skeleton within five minutes. There are fish . . .

Well, there are fish.

ON SEEING

YOU MAY HAVE BEEN AT SEA FOR YEARS WITHOUT EVER REALLY LOOKING AT it. Many a landsman would be surprised to know that, after one cruise of a fortnight, he has a better picture in his mind of the sea than many a sailor; for he has been a passenger, and the sailor on the bridge or on the look-out is on duty. When a sailor scans the sea, he is looking for something or at something, rarely at the sea itself.

I had this brought home to me when I sailed as a junior seaman on a Dutch fishing-smack, out for herrings on the North Sea. The ship was buckled and rusty; the captain a stolid man given to long prayers before the meals, which consisted of fish, with stewed pears on Sundays. It was the first trip of the season.

In Holland, a reward and much publicity awaits the fisherman who brings home the first herring of spring. Life on board our fishing-smack, ordinarily hustling enough, was a frenzy this time. On all the trawlers and luggers of the herring fleet men were driven to exhaustion by their skippers, eager to catch the reward. It was before the invention of the shoal-detector, and no aircraft circled over the fishing-grounds to guide our fleet. Fishing was still in the stage it had been in on the Sea of Galilee, when Jesus spoke to the crowds from a boat.

Despite the race for the prize, the trip was a normal commercial proposition. No captain would dream of turning for home without his holds being full; so the ship that caught most in the shortest time, and was nearest home, was the winner. An impartial observer could have told us before we set out that we hadn't a hope. The ship was slow, with a blunt bow which it pushed into the waves like a cow its muzzle into the hay. If the engine turned at more than half its maximum revolutions, the whole ship shook and rivets snapped in the hull. Yet we were full of hope and the captain was full of certainty according to his prayers. At every meal-time, after we had slumped down on the wooden benches in the poky foc'sle, covered with the scales of fish, our hands clumsy things unable to move, the captain addressed God as if He were in his service. He was not downright critical, yet he made it plain that if he was not going to catch the first herring this spring, he would have to think again on the matter of religion. We listened to his prayers, dazed with the singing in the ears that exhaustion brings.

Then the morning came when the boy in the masthead yelled, "Over starboard, skipper! Two points above the beam, starboard!" We all looked. There went the lucky trawler, a white moustache in front of her bows, heading for home, flying a flag from her mast as big as a house, blowing her hooter with a white plume followed by a triumphant shriek.

The captain scowled at the winner, and we waited for him to speak, but he said nothing. He only set his jaw, and we knew that God had it coming. That meal-time, at noon, he said, "Silence." After a long, motionless silence, in which we stared at him with our hands folded, he said, "Amen."

During the days that followed, it dawned on us as we hauled in the meagre catch that the skipper believed in God no longer. Never since have I seen a man so steeped in damnation. He was not an intelligent man; his rebellion had nothing to do with reason. He stalked the bridge and the deck, his hands clasped behind his back, his head jutting out, as Adam must have stalked in Paradise after it turned into a hostile jungle. None of us understood why he should have finished with God this time, considering that he had never caught the first herring in spring. There was no reason. He had been stricken by the moment of darkness that awaits every man in his time.

The effect on the ship of his brooding, depressing at first, grew frightening. Men started to grumble, the cook burned the meals and snarled when anyone dared to remark on it. The engineer, who had concentrated on pistons and tappets so far, and to whom the catch meant little, stopped singing while oiling the engine and no longer tried to cheer the morning-table with his jokes. In the end, the captain's silence spread over the ship like a shadow. The only human sound to be heard was the mate's Gregorian chant at the hauling in of the nets.

The sun was shining all the time, it was a lovely spring. Yet I have never known a trip to last so long. When, finally, the holds were full, every man had secretly decided not to sail with the captain again. The last catch was hauled in during the evening; we turned for home and sailed into the night.

The next morning, at sunrise, most of us were still on deck packing the last herrings of the trip into the barrels. The sun rose out of a misty horizon, the sea was calm, the eastern sky opened like a flower. The morning

424

star still sparkled coldly on the edge of the darkness, but from the sea rose the promise of spring. The first man who looked at it did not look away. In the end we all looked, knife in hand. When the sun came out, our scale-covered oilskins glistened like armour. Then the captain came out into the dawn, stood still, and gazed.

The ship plodded on in the slow swell. As the colours faded in the sky, we washed, took off our oilskins and sat down in the foc'sle for the morning meal. The captain folded his hands, and said, "For what we are about to receive, O Lord, make us truly thankful." Then he took his fork and speared a fish.

"Stop me if you know this one," said the engineer.

Part V LIFE AT SEA *(Homeward Bound)*

LANDFALLS

SHORE-LEAVES ARE AMONG THE THINGS MOST EAGERLY LOOKED FORWARD TO by sailors of all ranks, and they usually fall flat. The young sailor may notice that his senior officers rarely go ashore in foreign ports on the excuse that they are too busy. If they are honest, they will say, "I have been here before," and this should be taken in its fullest sense. If they have actually been in that particular harbour before, all they will do if they eventually go ashore is drink a glass of beer in a bar they know, or go to a cinema, preferably if it shows a film they have already seen. For the sailor abroad looks for familiar things in the belief that he is looking for adventure.

The preparations for shore-leave are always the same. Sailors and stokers enquire, "How long, Mate?" when the officer of the watch comes down from the bridge, and if the answer is "Tonight," a great washing, shaving and trimming of moustaches starts. The cook is bad-tempered just before arrival as there is a heavy drain on his hot water and great talk in the galley about Somebody who is going to have the time of her life. The essential difference between the sailor and the soldier is that, whereas the soldier thinks of glorified rape as the aim of his leave, the sailor thinks of himself as the world's best lover. There are women who prefer the first conception, but all of them, when asked, say they prefer the second. So, although sailors are more loved than soldiers, they do not seem quite as satisfied with the results. The disadvantage of the sailor's consideration for the gentler sex is that he takes her out in an effort to make her mellow and assure her of his good intentions, and drinks too much. The partner he tries this on can usually drink a regiment under the table without feeling any the worse for it, so the sailor is left with two glasses, staring dejectedly at his own reflection in a puddle of flat champagne.

There are many attractions to shore-leave, apart from giving someone the best time of her life; but they are considered secondary and enjoyed less than they deserve. Shopping for presents, sightseeing, eating foreign meals and going to a concert are pleasures, on condition that they are not the result of frustration. They always are.

So there is no point, I suppose, in telling the young sailor that he can have a most satisfactory leave on condition that he forgets about his Parsifal, and buys his mother a present instead. It is a consolation that his mother will profit by his frustration in the end, as her present will be

426

bigger. He should realise, however, that his first shore-leave will show up a basic misconception about life at sea.

Every young boy who becomes a sailor does so because he wants to see the world; his first shore-leave will bring home to him that the ship has become his world, and that he'll never see foreign lands, strange peoples and ancient cultures without the commentary of the bosun or the chief engineer. Java and Tahiti, New York and Reykjavik—all they will ever be are backdrops to a bulky friend.

He needs a first leave to make the ship his home.

THE MESSROOM

THE MESSROOM IS THE DINING-ROOM, CLUB-ROOM, LECTURE-ROOM AND writing-room of the ship, and I prefer the old ones: chafed leather seats, solid teak table with a centre of oilcloth, brass pendulum oil-lamps on the walls, tiny buffet and the captain's armchair in which no one can sit down without tilting unexpectedly backwards.

If the foc'sle is the forum for story-tellers, the messroom is the Athenaeum of the ship. Once a new staff of officers unknown to one another, have waded through the off-colour jokes, the platitudes about womanhood and the lengthy discussions of the weather, which take the place of mutual sniffing in dogs, the real messroom atmosphere begins to establish itself. Soon the conversation will plane on dizzying intellectual heights.

Ashore, one reads the papers, listens to the radio and has conversations with street-car conductors, with the result that one precedes any utterance that is likely to be contradicted with the words, "I don't know anything about it, but . . ." or, "You may be right." None of this in a messroom debate. As there is no choice in the speakers, one is forced to take them seriously, and they have ample time to drive their theories home in installments. The president of the messroom debating club is the chief engineer. For some reason, his profession opens all the secrets of the universe to him. The universe, of course, is purely mechanical; any chief engineer who is not convinced that every problem under the stars can ultimately be solved with a spanner, a screwdriver and some slimming is no good at his job. So the general trend of a messroom debate is Victorian. The existence of good and evil are accepted, for every chief engineer knows there is a right and a wrong way of tightening a nut. In my young days, the universe, extra-galactic nebulae included, sounded somehow steam-driven; whereas later, as human intelligence marched on, it was shown to revolve on the principles of the Diesel engine. On board the old *Groenlo* for instance, where, as a messroom-boy, I received my philosophical training by eavesdropping, the great thing about the universe was expansion, whereas on board later ships the great thing was vibration.

If the chief engineer is the president who finally imposes his conception of the world by sheer weight and doggedness, the first mate is his most tenacious heckler. He imposes the view of what is known as "the common man" and represents tired, bewildered, yet resigned humanity. His maxim is "So what?" followed by riders like, "It doesn't change my wife's kidneys" or "What difference does that make to a child driven over by a tram?" It is interesting to hear the chief engineer's answer, most of which Plato would have gladly claimed as his own. The first mate knows all about every-day life, whereas the chief engineer knows very little, apart from its Meaning. The apprentice in need of brotherly advice in connection with shore-leave, customs, ship-chandlers and personal hygiene will turn to the mate; if he is bothered by the contradictions between morality and instinct or his baby brother's place in the expanding universe, the Chief will help him out.

A captain, if he eats in the mess and not in his own quarters, rarely takes part in the debate except to finish it, when the formula is, "Gentlemen . . ." The captain suggests omniscience by his silence, which Huxley defined as "As full of wisdom as an unhewn piece of marble is full of masterpieces." Because the captain is assumed to know the ultimate answer to everything, he is never drawn into the debate. For the point of a messroom debate is not that it shall arrive at a conclusion, but that it shall last throughout the trip.

This might be difficult without the intervention of the wireless-operator. Wireless-operators know everything, the way youth knows everything. Their arguments are dogmas, their debating weapon the sneer. The chief engineer's digestion, usually tricky, is improved by the wireless-operator making his blood circulate. Phrases like "This is the typical platitude of all obese people" and "Occasionally one wishes that people would not insist on thinking beyond their powers" are typical. The wireless-operator, although constantly brushed off as being supercilious and irritating, yet has Marconi, Roentgen and Freud hovering behind his chair, whereas the Chief only has Stephenson, Professor Diesel and, if he is angry, God. The Chief is incapable of dealing in things invisible unless one can get a shock from them like electricity; the wireless-operator works with the twentieth-century magic: radiation.

The apprentice will do well to follow the example of the junior officers and say nothing. He should be at pains to keep his mouth shut, except to agree with the first mate if he belongs to the deck and with the chief engineer if he belongs to the engine-room. He will find that, after some time, this will come naturally and that he does indeed agree.

THE FOC'SLE

AH, FOR THE DAYS I LOATHED THE FOC'SLE! THE NOISE, THE CONSTANT TRAFfic, the smells, the lack of privacy, the conversations that were always the same and the passions that were always different! If someone had told me at the time that I would one day wish myself back at the foc'sle table, thumb in my ears, scowling at a text book, I would not have believed him.

And yet it is so. Much as I like the messroom, its interesting conversation and its graciously served food, even at the height of my enjoyment I feel a small nostalgia for that sunlit square of lost boyhood: the foc'sle. This feeling is not sentimental and inherent to my age; in that case, I might just as well be longing for the parlour in Aunt Minna's farm or Mrs. Ral's sweetshop. Yet, tender as their images may be, they provoke no nostalgia.

When I left the foc'sle, at the age of eighteen, I left something behind that, at that moment, I did not recognise as a loss. In the foc'sle, man can never be alone; I hadn't yet reached the age in which man feels alone in the messroom. The very lack of privacy and seclusion that I once cursed now seems to me an enviable state. The whole atmosphere of the foc'sle stems from this fact: man is not, and cannot, be alone. So its philosophy says that he shall not. Prophets of doom, known as pessimists in the messroom, are called "sea-lawyers" in the foc'sle where they are countered with the retort: don't be gloomy. *Ape and Essence, 1984* and other modern pictures of mankind's future could never have been written in a foc'sle; come to think of it nothing could. That is why the best story-tellers afloat, always found before the mast, never write their tales down, in contrast with their less talented superiors who frequently take to the pen in the privacy of their cabins. In the foc'sle, a man cannot even write a letter to his mother, and as to love-letters, they are written jointly by the crew. In my young days, I toyed with the idea of premature matrimony and the girl of my choice must have received a somewhat vague picture of my personality from my correspondence, though she cannot have been in any doubt about my ardour. It was at that stage forcibly brought home to me that lovemaking, often considered to be man's most private expression of his most intimate personality, runs more true to type than other common functions, like eating. To those who might consider this a sweeping statement, I advise a conversation with an officer who has been a censor to the Navy during the war. I know one, once quite a letter-writer himself, who has since not committed himself to his wife with as much as a single line, as he could not for the life of him think of a phrase he had not come across in the course of his duty. The only phrases that showed a certain originality were the frank ones.

Just as it is impossible to be in love in the foc'sle without one's correspondence being ghosted by half a dozen co-lovers, so is it equally impossible to suffer at one's ease. If one feels silent or morose for longer than half an hour, somebody is sure to fork in on the privacy of your gloom by asking, "What's eatin' yer?" or "What's the puss for?" At the time, I resented this bitterly, as I considered my inner suffering much too refined for a stoker to push around on his plate. Later, in the messroom, I looked at my colleagues with a spaniel-like gaze, hoping someone would help me get rid of the horrible feeling of being marooned on a desert island. I looked in vain.

The foc'sle is a place one likes to get out of when young and back to when old. All I can do to enlighten the young sailor is to give him this useless information. I could tell him about old stories, lost faces, the haunting complaint of a badly played harmonica, and the breath-taking beauty of the square-rigged ship Jones the stoker did in a bottle. I could tell him about soulless pin-ups, crumpled mothers and resentful wives I found on the walls of bunks, difficult to remove as they had been glued on to the wainscoting with the passion for permanence every sailor betrays. I could tell him about the smell of the oil-lamp and the bosun's curses when it was found smoking, about the dreams that were dreamt aloud with half a dozen faces listening in the lamplight, and how twenty years later the very memory revealed itself as the most valuable part of the dream. I could tell him . . .

Well, I suppose I have.

THE GALLEY

THE GALLEY COMES INTO ITS OWN ONLY IN THE TEMPERATE ZONES. THAT IS the great disadvantage of the tropics. For to go in and have a chat with the cook while snatching an extra mug of tea or tasting tonight's soup is one of the great joys of ship-life.

For one thing, one is never alone with the cook. There is always somebody hanging around, listening to his gossip or tales of woe, while comfortably seated on the little bench against the warm wall opposite the stove, feet on the rail, cheeks aglow. The footrail provides the clue: the galley is the ship's village-square, and the cook and his stove the hotdog stand. It is the only place where officers and men meet on a footing of complete equality, as the young sailor will soon find out if he enters with a junior prefect's air. Short of calling him "Dear" or "Bud," the cook will put him in his place, which is beside Hank the oilman on the little bench. Only senior officers, bosuns and donkeymen have the right to lean in the doorway and thus cut off the draught to the stove. Wireless-operators never come; they stamp on the floor of their cabin above and get their coffee sent up. What happens to their reputation between the stamping and the carrying out of the steaming mug would change any wireless-operator's habits.

The young sailor will come across the legend that captains have microphones hidden on the bridge, in the messroom and in the foc'sle, or that they climb on top of their tables to eavesdrop through the sky-light. This is nonsense, but I know of one captain at least who has been toying with the idea of eavesdropping on the galley. For there the mood of the ship is made, and it is not the cook who does it. The cook is too busy, and he has never sailed on a ship like this anyhow. To the cook there is only one craft that sailed the ocean worth extolling: the Aldebaran, on which Jesus embarked with his apostles and anchored in the midst of the ocean to escape from the sinners ashore, and whose barnacles and weeds created the Sargasso Sea. Before coming to a conclusion, however, I should like to have a word with the cook of the Aldebaran.

There is an old rule that in the galley every man can speak his mind with impunity, as at Hyde Park Corner in London. An officer who holds anything spoken in the galley against a man the moment he steps outside would soon find himself sabotaged off the ship or sent to Coventry. It is quite usual to hear a sailor remark, "I must say, the Old Man is a rum bird. Fancy him having a leather frame with three nudes in it on his sideboard to pray to." The cook will ask, "Who told you that?" as if he had known all along. The officer present will say, "You are the stupidest lot of horses' asses I have ever come across. I know that wallet—it's his wife and his daughter at the seaside, in flesh-coloured swimsuits. And if anybody has seen him kneel in front of it, he was looking for a collar stud."

The cook will say, "Oh, hoity-toity," or something equally effeminate, and the sailor will say, "Well, there was something in it after all, and nobody has ever called me a horse's ass to my face without getting into trouble."

At which the cook will say, "Shoosh" or "Can it, boys," and dole out a taste of his soup.

Without this free exchange in the galley, the ship becomes riddled with undercurrents. Everybody agrees that, in the tropics, the tension mounts and crews become more difficult to handle. Some attribute this to the heat, others know that it is the loss of the age-old safety valve: the galley.

LIARS

THE WORD "LIAR" AT SEA HAS A DIFFERENT MEANING THAN IT HAS ASHORE. On land, a liar is a man who tells an untruth to achieve something, or out of cowardice. There are also those who lie because they can't help themselves, and they are called mythomaniacs. They dress up in the uniform of the Royal Air Force, cover their chest with ribbons and drive a sports car into cheering little villages which they have led to believe that there is a rally on, of which they are the winners. Some sour policeman notices that their D.F.C. is upside down, and that they spell "rally" with one "l"; so they are run in, and a magistrate in robes sitting on a woolsack, his head covered with a wig, condemns them to three weeks of solitary confinement for imposture.

At sea, the word "liar" has a better reputation, for it carries on the memory of the great minstrels, who told stories during long cold watches, firing the imagination and warming the heart. Also, because every single sailor is a liar, to condemn the telling of an untruth at sea would amount to suicide after a wholesale massacre.

Liars are indispensable on board a ship as long as their lies conform to one of two conditions: either they should be such brazen lies that it is obvious from the beginning that they have nothing to do with reality, or one should unconditionally believe them. Bunglers who tell unlikely stories are not liars, but bores.

The greatest liar I knew as a boy was a bosun, a fat, unassuming man with big hands and hair everywhere except where it was supposed to be. His head was bald but for a silver fringe round the dome, but hair grew out of his ears, his nose, round his eyes and all the way down his body; when he stripped, he still wore a jersey. An unknown artist, obviously slighted by him in the execution of his duty, had drawn a picture of him on the wall of the lavatory with his head wedged in a jar of honey. He was a bad bosun, for he had no authority whatever except when he started to tell a story in the foc'sle.

In later years, I have come to recognise that the way he started his stories was very cunning and proved a complete mastery of the art. He would always be busy doing something when he started: either darning his socks, a pair of steel-rimmed spectacles on the tip of his nose, or doing slow sums in his household book, or whittling a toothpick. The rest of the crew would also be busy, either quarrelling or washing or undressing or writing letters or looking for blackheads in a piece of mirror stood up against the ashtin in the lamplight. When the bosun started, in a conversational tone, barely audible, he would always begin by saying, "Last time I got lost in the Borneo jungle" or "That trip we were washed ashore on the Falkland Islands" or, after a chuckle, "Yes, she was a funny woman." The words had hardly left his mouth, when everybody would fall silent, drop whatever he was doing and listen to his tale, like snakes to a charmer's flute. His stories were either like episodes from the *Arabian Nights,* or so human, wise and moving that nobody for a second doubted their truth; yet everyone knew that he had never been to Borneo, and that the only shore he was ever washed up on was the bank of the Tyne River when he fell off the gangplank in Newcastle. I can still remember the stories he told when I was there: listening breathlessly behind the green baize curtains of my bunk, peeping through the crack, for I was supposed to be asleep. If he hadn't been a sailor, he might have had his stories printed and become famous. As it was, he just came and went, like the flossy seed of a dandelion blown on to the bridge of a ship on the high seas.

He gave me the liar's secret. After three weeks of listening to his marvellous tales, I became so jealous that I thought up one of my own. It was a wonderful story about a cat and a dog who were housebreakers and I couldn't see how anyone could fail to be fascinated by it. I chose my moment well, waited until the foc'sle fell silent—which was rare—and started in a self-assured voice, "Last time I was in Haarlem, a funny thing happened to me . . ." A sailor said, "Anyone seen my penknife?" Another said, "*Your* penknife? I like that!" The first sailor said, "What d'you mean, you big ape?"

The only one who had heard me was the bosun, although he didn't then betray the fact. The next morning, when I brought him his tea at the beginning of the watch, he took the mug from my hand, looked at me in a musing fashion, a way in which he had never looked at me before, and said, "When you've got a story to tell, lad, don't try it that way. Go to the galley when there is no one there but the cook, and tell it to him. After you've told him, go and wait outside. If the cook tells your story to the next man in, you can go ahead. If he doesn't, forget it."

I have been doing so until this day.

POETS

SEA-POETS CARRY ON THE TRADITION OF PURE POETRY, BEFORE ITS DETERIOration by metre and rhyme.

They are a different type of artist from the liars. However fantastic a liar's story may be, it isn't poetry, it is a story. Ship's poets never tell a story because it doesn't interest them. What they note is the beauty of something: a girl, a beach, the faint scent of flowers from the shore in a summer's night, a wisp of music blown across the water from afar.

Whereas liars have to be careful not to carry on too long with their stories in one session, one can easily spend a whole anchor-watch listening to a poet, and still ask for more. For he carries within him the image of things you'll never see, even though you may look at them in the course of time. I heard a carpenter describe a lake in Finland when I was quite young; I wanted to go there ever since, to discover eventually that the Finnish lakes were like any lake in the North. Yet they were different, and it took me some time to discover that the difference was the poet's description, still aglow in my memory after all those years.

The way to recognise a poet, as opposed to a story-teller, is that the poet always talks about small things, whereas the story-teller cannot help exaggerating. When you hear a man say, "I once saw a shell in a shop-window in Reykjavik that must have come from far away," you'll know he is a poet if he leaves it at that. If he goes on to say, "I felt in my bones that there was something inside, went in, bought it, smashed it, and look! five pellets of pure gold came out," he is a liar. If he says instead, "I smashed it, and found nothing," he is still a liar, but on the wing for another world.

Nowadays I find that I prefer the sea-poet's world to the real one, for there is something about it that makes me feel inexpressibly hopeful. I can listen to liars for hours, and if they are good they never fail to fascinate me; but when I come across that rare gnome from the sea, the poet, I want to lie down on the warm sand of a beach at sunset, and watch the evening star rise, while Man, ageless, dreams aloud by my side.

MUSIC AT SEA, IF ONLY HUMMED ON A COMB, TURNS ANY SHIP INTO A HOME.

There are musicians on every ship: they play the harmonica, the guitar, the accordion or the ocarina, and they play them very well. An occasional fanatic lugs a trombone on board, or another of those instruments on which one has to rehearse for days in order to play for five minutes; the disadvantage of trombones, tubas and trumpets at sea is that they enforce a silence which they fail to fill. Guitars sound wonderful but are fragile in a foc'sle. Accordions are bulky and quickly mildewed. So the favourite instruments are the harmonica and the ocarina. But as the high warbling of the ocarina at nightfall starts the ship's dog howling and sets the captain's teeth on edge, the harmonica is not only the most popular but also the most sensible of the sailor's musical instruments.

It is a pity that accomplished harmonica-players are only satisfied if they make their instruments sound like anything but a harmonica. They will do tricks with them like imitating dive bombers, ukuleles, street-cars rounding a corner and typewriters. It is rare that they can be made to use them the way they were created. The best concert I ever heard was given by two harmonicas, a pan with chopsticks and five paper-covered combs. It went on for hours on a very hot night, and whatever instruments Magellan's crew had with them, they must have sounded the same. There was an atmosphere on board of listening crowds in the cave of the night, and even the captain could be seen silhouetted black on dark blue among the stars over the bridge.

Like most things of the sea, ships' music is a disappointment ashore. But then, shore music sounds ludicrous on board ship, as every sailor who has sailed on a liner will know. A ladies' band blaring away in a saloon or gipsies trying to remain upright while fiddling over the diners' shoulders sound completely out of place and slightly crazy. Shore musicians executing their duty at sea are Neptune's favourite stooges; I once spent half an hour with three men trying to rope a 'cellist who had gone adrift while practising in the deserted ballroom during bad weather. He tobogganed from one wall to the other on a little gilt chair, screaming, arms and legs round his instrument to protect it from the on-rushing walls. The young sailor on a passenger-ship is sure to come across similar incidents, but the real fun starts when the grand-piano breaks loose.

The only piano I knew that did not look out of place on board ship belonged to a captain's wife, who accompanied her husband on his voyages.

It was shortened to fit between the door and the washstand, so five per cent of "The Blue Danube" was played in thin air. It sounded charming, but then she was a charming woman.

GRAMOPHONES

I AM ALL FOR TECHNICAL IMPROVEMENTS, FROM RAZORS TO JOCKSTRAPS, BUT of one thing I am certain: nothing, however cunning, can replace the old portable hand-wound gramophone.

Every elderly senior officer has one with records to match from *The Dance of the Dervishes* to an album with Schubert's *Unfinished Symphony*, carrying a contralto warbling "To the Beautiful Miller's Wife" on the back of the last record. The senior officer will prove to the young sailor that the back of any record is better than its front, "front" being the side one originally bought it for.

This is one of the great mysteries of life at sea. One discovers that almost any inanimate object has two uses, an obvious one and a hidden one, and it is always the second use that makes it valuable. Shelley's poems steady the table; the face-cloth Mother hemstitched is the ideal lampshade for reading at night; and the vase bought for Aunt Emma who so sadly died before the ship came home is the perfect receptacle for the hair of autumn plucked out of the comb.

The gramophone bought for private moments of cultured entertainment and soul-building beauty turns into the ship's local brass-band. It is brought out on cheerful occasions to quack its tinny tunes in the tropical night; and it will get stuck in the final groove of Sousa's "Be Kind to Your Web-Footed Friends," brightening the second engineer's birthday in the mess-room.

My old portable, which by now is as hoarse as a retired regimental sergeant-major, has given me hours of delight undreamt of when I bought it. Three kinds of needles went with it in the tiniest tin boxes known to man, graded soft, medium and loud. In later years, refinements were suggested in the form of bamboo needles that needed a special sharpener, and African thorns that called for an even more complicated instrument, something between a lawn-dwarf's grindstone and a dentist's polisher. These innovations were not improvements. I found the hidden uses for both instruments in due course, but they did not justify the initial cost. Sharpening a tooth-pick or cutting thin slices off feathers to use the ensuing microscopic rings as washers for a leaking fountain pen was ingenious, but

436

not worth the money and certainly not worth the nightmarish caterwauling into which they turned "Song of Songs."

In the present days of long-playing records, it is hard to believe that to have a symphony cut into fingers as mother used to do with our sandwiches is a good thing. After having turned Dvořák's *New World Symphony* in eight instalments for over a month, I came to like it much better that way than when some colleagues and I heard it in New York. It was conducted by Toscanini in the flesh, and we had looked forward to it a great deal; only to find that the five of us made a move to rise as one man at the end of chords that we had come to recognise as final. Back on board we played it again and agreed that nothing could replace the gramophone.

My gramophone has brought me nothing but joy, except on one occasion when a stoker's wife sent him a record made in a store of his baby daughter's first babblings. He brought it into my cabin, followed by a small crowd, and I put it on for him. The noises the child made as rendered by my instrument and a needle sentimentally chosen as "soft" were so hair-raising that the stoker remained convinced that she was an idiot until he got home and discovered she took after him. Since then my answer to anyone coming up with a personal record sent from home has been to lock away the heavy sound-box among my socks and to go without the food of love for the rest of the voyage.

GHOST-STORIES

THE BEST STORIES OF SHIVER-HUNGRY MANKIND ARE TOLD ON BOARD SHIPS. The ideal setting is a stormy night, lashed with rain, riding at anchor in the lee of some headland.

The gale will shriek in the rigging, the anchor chain will grind and squeak in the hawse-hole, the oil-lamp will flap its bat wings of shadows, and from time to time a swishing wave will hiss past outside. The suitable atmosphere is created by trying to make a stool turn, as the table is bolted to the floor. The advantage of a stool is that the sitters can join fingers on a shorter circumference, so that the stool will turn quite satisfactorily with as few as three mediums. The first question should be, "Ghost, art thou with us?" after which the bosun's belch should be ignored. The spirit should then be asked to agree to the following signals: one tap for yes, two taps for no, and a rapid succession of taps for "delete the foregoing." Letters of the alphabet are indicated by numbers.

437

Turning stools, under circumstances as described above, always succeeds. Interesting information about one's family can be collected this way, until the moment comes in which the spirits succumb to the temptation of jocularity. Then the time has come for stories.

The young sailor will be surprised, and lose a considerable amount of sleep, once he has been helped to a generous dose of ghost-stories of the sea. Phantom vessels, dead captains coming back, vampire rats, and deserted windjammers sailing a steady course are the traditional subjects. What is more, they might indeed have happened; there is something about the sea that favours the development of man's sixth sense. I have never sailed on a ship where there was not at least one genuine medium on board, or so brilliant an imitation of the real thing that detection became niggardly. Cooks have frequent dreams of prediction, many of which come true. How much of this is supernatural or sheer insight into human nature is impossible to make out; the result is impressive.

As to ghost-stories proper: ships' carpenters and, in the old days, sailmakers are the experts. Any ship's carpenter will, if sufficiently pandered to, come out with a collection of horror tales that will beat anything printed on the subject. After a good session of ghost-stories, the young sailor may start seeing vague shapes in shadowy corners, and the thought may occur to him that the ship is haunted. He need not fear; ships rarely are. Even poltergeists fear water; spirits that manifest themselves by the disappearance of small objects are the messroom-boy.

ENTERTAINING

OCCASIONALLY, IN LONELY FAR-AWAY PORTS, TWO SHIPS OF THE SAME COMpany or of the same nationality may meet. If the port is small enough, and far away enough, just two ships will do. The result is one of the most pleasant experiences in store for the young sailor: his opposite number of the other ship will come to visit him, and he will return the courtesy.

It starts with the captains. Out of the mothballs come number-one uniform, shore cap and boiled shirt, and the messroom-boy spits on the patent-leather pumps. If the ships are anchored out, the workboat, suddenly called the captain's gig, is lowered and after the Master has gone down the rope ladder, cursing, he is rowed across by solemn-looking sailors to the other ship. He carries a present, usually a bottle of whisky, a jar of tobacco or some fire-water from foreign shores. The sailors who stay behind watch the diminishing workboat with fond amusement, waiting for the captain to lose his cap or Abel the dope to lose an oar. Those in the workboat will be struck by the difference in the way the captain came down his own ladder and climbs the other one. The curses have changed to smiles and, rusty as the other's hull may be, the visitor looks at it admiringly while climbing. At the rail, he is welcomed by his host, looking just as uncomfortably spruce. Hands are shaken and shoulders are slapped while, in the background, a motley guard of honour looks on, to break out into grins when the first head of the gig's crew looms over the rail. Contrary to the Navy, the crew of the captain's gig doesn't stay below but follows on his heels, so every visit of one Master Mariner of the Merchant Navy to another ends by the visiting captain muttering at the rail, "Where the devil have they got to?" At his angry shepherd's shout the crew will scurry forth from foc'sle, galley and engine-room, wiping their mouths with the backs of their hands; they go down to the rope-ladder, chewing; and the captain who arrived in state is rowed back as if abducted by pirates. Because of frequent waving, the voyage home to the mother ship follows an erratic course.

After this first official visit, the treat starts. The crews of the two ships are rarely on board their own craft when looked for. The sailors exchange stories, gin, tobacco and letters from home; there are so many snapshots of babies and self-conscious women on the foc'sle table that it is difficult to sort them out. The officers start meeting in the messroom, after which each in turn takes his opposite number to his cabin where long heart-to-heart talks take place, in the position of members of the front bench in the English House of Parliament. The apprentice will show his opposite number round the ship with pride, even if he has never before realised his affection for his vessel. He will say things about her that are in flagrant contradiction with what is usually said at the messroom table; after this show of affection for the ship, the photograph of his girl-friend will come out. As she is usually pinned up inside his bunk, his colleague will lean forward in the dusk and whistle. Then the same thing happens with regard to his girl-friend as what happened with regard to the ship: he will confess that she is the perfect sailor's bride, witty, patient, affectionate and wise. "Just listen to this letter," and so he finally gets to the point the sailors in the foc'sle arrived at within five minutes.

The highlight of the encounter of the two ships will be the two dinners. Both cooks will be unbearable for twenty-four hours beforehand, and both will say afterwards, when the praise has sounded, "Now you needn't think that you'll get this every day." The last visit is exchanged between the captains, and this time number-one uniform has been put back where it belongs to give way to saggy trousers, open-necked shirt and the cap that has seen so much.

The young sailor will find that lifelong friendships are made only in one's boyhood, or in lonely bays along the shores of the sea.

DEATH

A DEATH ON BOARD WILL STRIKE THE YOUNG SAILOR WITH MUCH MORE impact than he can possibly foresee.

When it occurs in a harbour, it is like the death of an acquaintance ashore. When it occurs at sea, its effect is harrowing.

To start with, it separates the ship. If the deceased is a sailor, the officers will not feel like part of the family, but like neighbours towards the foc'sle. If an officer dies, the foc'sle stands aside.

The young apprentice may not have liked the officer, or even have known him only casually if he was an engineer of the other watch. Yet his death will affect him deeply, more so than his illness will have done. An unknown officer of the opposite watch who is ill is always a vaguely irritating element; the conversation at table is over-shadowed by the concern of his colleagues, and silence has to be observed in the corridors and the cabins, which is irksome to the young. Then, suddenly, he is dying. The captain goes to see him, and may even administer Communion, which gives him the magic status of the sole authority at sea. No captain, however pernickety or apparently senile, will ever be the same in the young sailor's eyes after someone has died on board; and it is amazing how the captain's presence eases the mind of the dying. There is a much closer contact between him and the Almighty in those moments than any clergyman ashore can ever hope to suggest. In the sailor's last hours his captain really is Skipper next to God.

The presence of a dead body on board profoundly affects the ship. Everything is changed. The bells are struck with a muffled sound; silence reigns at table in both the messroom and the foc'sle; and to the officer on the bridge the sea seems vaster, and the ship very lonely; the unspoken thoughts of the crew surround it with an invisible pall.

Then the moment comes that the ship is stopped, and the captain and the crew assemble at the rail. The service for the burial of the dead is read over the bier covered with the flag. "Man that is born of woman hath but a short time to live and is full of misery; he cometh up and is cut down like a flower; he fleeth as if he were a shadow, and never continueth in one stay." Then comes the most moving moment, when the bier is poised and the burial service is changed from the book. Instead of saying, "We therefore commit his body to the ground, earth to earth, ashes to ashes, dust to dust," the captain will read, "For as much as it hath pleased the Almighty God in His great Mercy to take unto Himself the soul of our dear brother here departed: we therefore commit his body to the deep. One—two—three, in God's name."

The plank is lifted, and the brother slides overboard with a rushing sound that will never be forgotten by those who hear it. After that, the flag goes up once more, the engine-room telegraph rings, and the ship continues her voyage across the unchanged sea.

HOMECOMING

THERE IS NOTHING LIKE COMING HOME FROM THE SEA IN ONE'S YOUTH. THE moment the ship has turned round for home on leaving the last port of call, the transition starts. The young sailor is no longer just sailing, he is going home.

He will find that this makes a great difference to his life on board. It changes enemies into friends and jolly fellows into bores. The reason is that the enemies have so far been thinking of their home with worry, and resented the youngster, clumsily eager to please. The jolly fellows are the ones who are happy at sea, and now resent everybody who has a home to go back to. Stories the young sailor has eagerly and admiringly listened to while outward bound now have the tendency to be a bit long, and towards their obvious ending he will find himself thinking of home.

To go home is better than home itself; so the young sailor should not make the mistake of suppressing his daydreams of home because they are childish. If he lets the daydreams gather like a summer haze on the horizon, he stores happiness for the future like a growing apple stores sunlight. His girl will be gayer and infinitely more understanding if he has given himself the chance to surround her in his mind with the halo of coming home; his father will be a wonderful old chap whose irritating habits will be endearing; after the dreams of his homeward voyage, the young sailor cannot wait to hear his father say, "Don't be rash" every time he announces he'll have a bath; he also will no longer be irritated when his mother calls him "pet" in the presence of others. During the voyage home he will unwrap and re-wrap their presents several times, until it almost seems a pity to give them away; he will write bright thoughts in his diary instead of solemn ones, and he will come to care for the chief engineer who has always advocated a home for the sailor because it is "solid."

The watches will be shorter, the chores lighter, and the book he reads before falling asleep less fascinating. He will also toy with the innocuous seed of what is to grow into a dangerous plant later: the playful and, of course, nonsensical idea that his girl might be on to an eternal truth in her last letter where she wrote that a home of one's own to which one returns every night is a joy that lasts forever. On his next voyage, the seed will be a spry little plant, green and touchingly tender; in the first big port of his second voyage, he'll stop in front of furnisher's shop-windows and look at curtains, musingly. But all this is still far ahead; during the first year or so, to come home will be the best time of his life.

Early in the last morning, land will be sighted after an hour of doubt as to whether perhaps it is a cloud, or a faint light will twitch that might be summer lightning; until the spark of the lighthouse flashes above the horizon.

The next hours will not be pleasant. His work will be bad, his seniors touchy, the cook's breakfast burnt and he won't get a chance to do his packing. The envy of the homeless will turn into resentment, and the young sailor will be struck by the unexpected hope that next trip they won't be on board. It is those very same men he will think of a week later in the same fashion as he is now thinking of his girl.

But for the moment he is waiting for the pilot. He'll have the silly hope that his girl or his father will be on board the pilot's cutter; he'll know that it is preposterous until he recognises his mother leaning over the rail in the midships on the approaching vessel, waving; after rapid dry sobs and a delighted answering wave he will discover that it is the cutter's cook and try to make his waving look like an elaborate scratching of the head. The pilot, when he climbs the ladder and swings his fat leg over the edge, will turn out to be the nicest pilot he has ever seen, so jolly, so typically a fellow-countryman; he will shake the pilot's hand and hold his own out like a child expecting a sweet when the pilot fumbles in his pocket to take out the letter or the telegram that will prove to be a dirty handkerchief. Everything that happens from now on is part of a conspiracy by the gods to make him look silly. It just isn't one of his lucky days.

And then: there are the pierheads; the ships going out force them to slow down, and tugboats are never in a hurry when one is incoming.

And then: the quayside, with the wavers whose handkerchiefs mingle with the gulls.

442

And then we leave him alone, for there are moments when no man should be taken at face value.

SWEETHEARTS

THE PERSON THE YOUNG SAILOR WILL BE MOST EAGER TO MEET ON COMING home is his girl-friend, so it is probably pointless to tell him that he should meet her last. The reunion with his beloved should be postponed until he has been welcomed by his family, for she is the one person to whom he is linked by the future rather than the past. The thing is to settle down comfortably in one's family's unchanged past before hazarding out into the future. It may seem more realistic to talk about the present, but girl-friends don't see it that way.

During his first home leave, the young sailor will get a fair idea as to whether she is his future wife or not. Girls are forever torn between two conceptions of love: romance and security; those who instinctively prefer the latter will make good sailors' wives at home, the others make ideal sailors' wives at sea, but this opportunity rarely arises.

There can be no doubt that the best father, husband and life's companion is the one who is rarely there; what you want is a girl who instinctively knows this. She cannot possibly know it consciously, and you should not state this fact thus baldly. Just tell the truth, as gently as you like, which is that life at sea is the life you want to live, and if it doesn't suit her, there is obviously no point in assuming that you will love her forever for making you live a life you don't like. This is for her sake as much as yours. Now is the time to decide upon these basic things, and time is short; tomorrow you will sail again and the issues will get lost in the paradise of your correspondence. One mistake you must not make: to tell her that your sea-going phase is a passing one. Even if, in your heart of hearts, you suspect it might be, don't say it. You may change your mind next week, when you are a tenderfoot no longer but a man of experience, explaining how to wash oneself to the new junior apprentice.

As to the rest of the highs and lows of emotion you will go through with your girl-friend, no one can help you. Love at this stage is a swooping ride on the giant switchback, whether you are a sailor or not. Only, you will have to go through emotional contrasts that normally take months in a few weeks or even days. You will be delighted by her tenderness, depressed by her moods; touched by her girlishness and impressed by her common sense; she will take you at your word and believe the opposite; she will call you angel and selfish beast, admire your frankness and hiss at your subterfuge, melt in your embrace and ask you when you last shaved. In short, you two will be in love.

This is the road each man has to go alone. There are no pilots, no charts, no reassurances, except one: if this situation did not eventually resolve itself, you would not be here.

MOTHERS

MOTHERS FEEL EVERYTHING, UNDERSTAND EVERYTHING, FORGIVE EVERY-thing and know nothing. Your father may worry about your soul, your mother will worry about your wet feet. Even if you come home a captain who has discovered a new continent in the southern Arctic, your mother will tell you to put on your scarf when you go out. She will mother you, and you should let her. To be mothered has nothing to do with being back in your own bed in your own room; it has to do with her reaction to your problems. If you should tell her, whispering in the darkness, about other beds, she will, if she suggests anything at all, suggest a bath. Fathers let you down in the ultimate moment by suggesting that you should talk this over with the doctor, the vicar or old Captain Podmore next door; your mother will never suggest you talk anything over with someone else, for she doesn't want to hear it herself. You may, one of these days, be amazed at the way things solve themselves once they are left alone, whether it be in your soul or in your correspondence.

Your father, during the last decade, has been waiting for you to grow up; your mother has been thinking of you as Peter Pan. You will find that her conception of you suits you best; for on going to sea you have hoped that the home you left behind would not change during your absence. The only one who hopes the same, and who has not changed herself during your absence, is your mother.

So, shut your eyes, lean back in your chair, stretch out your legs and give that long, relaxed sigh at last; you are home, as soon as she has said, "Well, now, after all this excitement, what about a nice cup of tea?"

FATHERS

IT IS DIFFICULT TO EXPLAIN HIS FATHER TO THE YOUNG SAILOR, AS HE WON'T be able to understand him until he is a father himself. Yet a few simple

444

observations may help him to make his homecoming easier for both generations.

The secret about fathers is their bewilderment. No man ever gets over his wonder that one night of love has resulted in a man going to sea with a pipe. To your father, the only way out of this predicament is pride; only by feeling that his son is living the life he once wanted to live himself can he balance his elementary bewilderment.

So the young sailor must be prepared on coming home to meet a man gruffer than a captain and more easily intimidated than a lamp-trimmer. On the one hand, the man will say, "Aha, home from seas, I see. What about doing the lawn?" On the other hand, "Have another of these cookies, son, they are wonderful." The young sailor should meet the contrasts in his father's behaviour with equanimity, and wait for the moment of crisis. This moment comes at night, when they are alone together; his father, after sucking in vain at his new pipe, will break a suddenly embarrassing silence by saying, "Well, I suppose you are grown up now."

On the son's reaction at this moment depends their happiness for the next fortnight. On the one hand, the father wants the assurance that the son is indeed grown up and can be talked to on a basis of equality, on the other hand the assurance that he will always be fourteen. All I can do to help the young sailor weather this decisive moment is to point out the essential difference between them: the young sailor thinks of himself as immortal, whereas his father is induced by the sight of the one gold ring on his son's sleeve to think that he himself will die tomorrow.

So the best answer to "I suppose you are grown up now" is to smile and say, "Dad, you look wonderfully fit. Been fishing lately?"

You will hear he has; he will tell you all about it, happy and relieved. He will tell you all about the fish, that is, nothing about his thoughts while fishing, alone, in the chilly dawn.

BROTHERS AND SISTERS

ON COMING HOME, THE YOUNG SAILOR WILL FIND THAT HIS BROTHERS HAVE become nicer during his absence and his sisters worse.

The reason for this is that ship-life has given the young sailor a new feeling of comradeship with his own sex, and a different approach towards the other. So he will discover with a feeling of comfort that his brothers are men, and with discomfort that his sister is a woman. Until he left, neither of them had a sex, they had personalities.

The difficulty is that whereas his brothers will induce the young sailor to behave in a more manly fashion than is quite warranted, his sister will do everything she can to put him back into the place he came from, and which is now too small for him. Remarks like, "I suppose you're too grand for that now" and "It's your turn for the bathroom, or are you not going to profit?" will irritate the young sailor, as they will make him suspect that his sister sees through the sham of manliness his brothers have induced him to display.

This is not the case. It's his own conscience that worries him, not his sister's perspicacity. Secretly, she is more impressed than his brothers are, and irritated with him because of it. This is why a present for a sister should be on the lavish side and chosen with care. She should be taken to a dance as quickly as possible; the young sailor should wear his best uniform when escorting her. On coming home from the dance, late, and after everybody else has gone to bed, the young sailor should offer to make a cup of tea and allow her to do it herself. Then, sitting alone in the lamplight with the steaming cups, the young sailor should ask her how girls feel about something, for instance close dancing. It's not her answer that is important, but the question. The next day his sister will have become an asset instead of a liability, and she will remain so for the rest of his stay. He will make his next homecoming easier by having another private session with her on the eve of his departure.

Brothers, on the contrary, rather tend to turn from assets into liabilities if one is not careful. The first flush of comradeship easily turns into boredom and estrangement, unless the young sailor shows a real interest in their affairs. His sister wants to be admitted into his existence, his brothers want him to enter into theirs. So if Junior is making a model ship that looks like a sausage, don't say so, but make a flag for it out of the lid of a cigarette tin, or give him an anchor from an old cap to attach to it. If Senior goes in for jitterbugging, go with him and let yourself be impressed by the display. Don't forget that brothers are inclined to overdrink and oversmoke in your presence; the ensuing feeling of malaise will be attributed to you. So, if you can, take them separately out for a sail or a walk in the open. Under those circumstances, your advice will be asked on some surprisingly adult problem if he is your junior, and some surprisingly childish one if he is your senior. Again, your answer doesn't matter much; their questions do. Look at them before you answer, and you will be overcome by an emotion which you have rarely felt in their presence before. For the first time, you will realise that you are brothers; and from that realisation your answer will come as relaxedly as a twig floating by with the current.

446

On the whole, if you manage it well, your first shore-leave may bring home to you the first notion of how lucky you are to belong to a family.

BACK TO THE SEA

HIS GRANDPARENTS WILL PROBABLY BE THE LAST RELATIVES THE YOUNG sailor will go to see, as he expects the visit to be a chore: Granddad sniggering with old men's mysterious mirth; Grannie serving rock cakes; the smelly cat, the complaints about Mrs. Brown's little daughter and her piano; the shepherd and shepherdess, coy and discoloured on the mantelpiece; the silvery clock, chiming away the slow half-hours of youth enduring senility.

He will be in for a surprise. Old Granddad is the only one who completely understands him, and Grannie's rock cakes are a treat. The reason is that Granddad, after climbing the rock of ages, has accumulated some of a captain's detachment, and that Grannie cooks the way he has come to care for on board ship.

Because he goes to see them last, their relationship as a couple will come as a mirage of relief to him. Granddad will ask, "Where did you put the thingummy?" Grannie will answer, "In the whatsisname." Granddad will go to the cupboard and find the evening paper with the day's groceries.

The young sailor will think of his girl-friend, who is a total stranger; of his father, who is a moody friend; of his mother, who is a dear soul; of his brothers and sisters, who are all right, and his dog who is sweet but stupid. He will spend a sentimental hour, regretting the way he has neglected his grandparents and fearing that, by the next time he comes back, they may be dead. On his way home through the twilit streets, he will be depressed by the mystery of life eternal carried on by the generations of mankind. By the time he reaches home, he'll be eager to get back to the simplicity of ship-life.

So, he should follow his instincts and go to see them as late as possible; for they are a signpost, pointing back to the sea.

Part VI THE FUTURE

SKIPPER NEXT TO GOD

SO NOW YOU ARE A CAPTAIN, AND YOU ARE TERRIFIED. ANYONE WHO SAYS he isn't is either a bad captain, or like everybody else.

For years this has been your goal. You couldn't wait for it to materialise; at every opportunity you have made it discreetly known to the company that your appointment was overdue. And now you sit in the double cabin, as lonely as sin, wishing you had never gone to sea.

Even before the ship moves, the loneliness begins. You haven't given a single order yet, and here you are: this is the end of the messroom days, of the watches, the outings, and, most sorely missed of all, the wonderful stimulant of cursing the captain. You suddenly realise that you are the most common brand of sailor: a born mate. Your wife's delight will depress and irritate you; your colleagues, who are colleagues no longer but subordinates, have vanished behind an invisible barrier of politeness. Well: you have asked for it; here it comes.

Your first voyage starts, and instantly everybody comes to see you about something. You had never realised that when you went to see the Old Man about something in the past, you were a member of an endless procession; now, at last, you understand why he received you occasionally with a marked lack of enthusiasm. The nature of the errands will severely tax you in the beginning, and you may be tempted to drink more than is good for you. For nobody comes to ask your advice; they come for final decisions ranging from "Shall I take those stewed pears or shan't I, Captain?" to "Must I take Williams off watch because of the boil on his neck or mustn't I?" You will feel like asking both enquirers what their own opinion in the matter is, as they know more about the stewed pears and Williams' boil than you do. But the first rule to observe is: don't ever revert the responsibility to those who come in asking to be relieved of it. It doesn't matter whether the stewed pears are taken, or whether Williams can act as a look-out with a boil on his neck. The first question should be answered "No," and the second, "Yes," for it is a good practice to give those questions serial numbers and answer "Yes" to the even ones and "No" to the odd ones. By the time they get to you, their pros and cons have been weighed in the enquirer's mind to such an extent that he can no longer decide on merit; he wants someone to choose for him from two equally valid decisions. You should never betray your ignorance about either the pears or the boil, even if you feel like an impostor. In due course, you will know about those things somehow; it is only a matter of time. And it is the captain's business to wait for his own maturity as a master, not his crew's.

To help you to give orders or to lay down the law in disputed questions, there is another rule: when you arrive at a decision, stick to it. There is nothing more unnerving than a captain who has said "No," coming back five minutes later to say, "By the way, I've thought it over and I think you are right." Even if the other person were right, it should be a lesson to you, and not to him.

In good time, you will settle down, and your life will start. For this is certain: there is no fuller existence for a man than to be the captain of a ship, as soon as he has found his self-confidence. As for this self-confidence, the important thing to remember is that it will never be yours entirely. The sea is the sea, the ship is a ship, and they will never be at peace. You will find your feet quickest if you immediately start by impersonating the favourite captain of your memory. If he happened to be calm and placid, be calm and placid too, even if the sweat prickles under your hatband. If he was wiry and nervy, be wiry and nervy. For, in both cases, you will have admired him because he complemented a lack of those characteristics in yourself.

This above all: remember that the way to be a good captain is not decided between you and the crew, nor you and the ship, but between you and your empty desk.

ON GOING GREY

THE DIFFERENCE BETWEEN GROWING FAT AND GOING GREY IS THAT THE LATter is unavoidable. Slimness as a substitute for youth is within your reach; the first grey hairs in front of your ears are the beginning of a relentless process that you'll have to accept with grace, or gloom will be your lot.

On growing fat, you can tell yourself that it is overeating; on going grey you'll have to face it: you are getting older. For a while, it will seem to you that to grow old is worse than anything that has ever happened to you. You will suddenly notice other signs, like instinctively reading the death announcements in your local newspaper before the wedding ones, the faint fatigue you feel when getting on in a promising fashion with a girl met ashore, or the fact that apprentices get younger.

Instead of scowling at your first grey hair, you should welcome it as a sunrise, for that is what it is. To start with, you aren't as old as all that; the worry about growing old is a young man's worry. A lot of things that have been bewildering you so far are about to sort themselves out. Man's life is an evolutionary process; before your birth you have gone through all the stages of life on this planet, from amoeba via fish and tadpole to little mammal, until you were finally born as a monkey. To think that your humanity started when you gave your first yell is a misconception.

You have, at last, covered the ground of the evolution of life that resulted in man, now you must start reliving mankind's own evolution. Since the dawn of his consciousness, man has explored life, his soul, and the universe around him. This exploration is by no means finished, but it has gone further than the kindergarten of philosophy in which you have lived up to your first grey hair. Antiquity, the Roman Empire, Christianity, the Renaissance, the Reformation; all of them have to be gone through once more within every man's individual soul. When you look at yourself in your mirror sideways, searching your temples, the Renaissance is on the wing.

You'll realise that the cards are dealt now, and that you have to play the hand you have got. This means to stop thinking about other jobs, other homes and other wives. Once you have realised that what you have is all you are ever likely to have, you will heave a sigh of relief. For the middle-aged man who tries to go on living in the succulent fields of youth is like that harassed merchant, the manufacturer of Christmas cards. Every year, year after year, he has to think of other cottages, other robins, other logs, until, in the end, he will find himself caught on the devil's fork that pronged the printer who turned "Happy New Year" into "For the New Annum: delectable reappraisement."

So, let the grey hairs grow, and enjoy yourself for the first time since you started to write in your diary, "I don't know what is the matter with me . . ." Happy New Year; for now you know.

CHILDREN

A SEA-CAPTAIN'S CHILDREN ARE NOT IN NEED OF CARE, WON'T GO WILD, marry dizzy blondes or Portuguese conjurers because they see so little of their fathers. If your wife is a true sailor's wife, she will be quite capable of managing them alone for the length of your trips. She will probably use your name in moments of stress like old-fashioned parents used the Turk, the policeman, or God. You won't notice this when you come home, for despite mothers' warnings, you are the man who brings them presents, who is on their side all the time during your stay, and who goes away just when your being around might become cumbersome.

You may think that not to see them grow up from day to day, nor hear their pattering feet get firmer, will be a loss. Any father will tell you that the joy of one's offspring growing is darkened by the fact that they grow out of things; and as to the pattering feet, they lack attraction when Father lies on the sofa with a newspaper over his face to have a snooze before going back to the office.

There is another thing to consider. It is amazing how little most parents remember of the various stages of their children's development. A few snapshots, a bronzed bootee now used as an ashtray, and an occasional postcard left over from the children's Stone Age, showing a cave drawing with a pointing arrow and the word "Botom." A sailor, however, has a complete record from the first outline of a baby's hand at the bottom of a letter to "Hallo dady how are you, I am very well thank you I have a boat too goodby." Then humanity begins, with warm interested questions about your health, and how exciting it must be to be at sea, and mother says you are still going to be away a long time, how sad; F. is painting the gate, not very well, but then he is still a baby; all this leading up to the P.S. "I enclose my school report," which will make you hit the ceiling. There will be snapshots, many more than you would have taken ashore, and the fact that they have a father is more brought home to your children by their mother than if you were there.

When you are on leave, you'll live the daydream all fathers have. All fathers want to go fishing with their sons and have nature rambles with their daughters; but there is always the office, a job about the house, the lawn to be done, or the accounts. You will be on holiday; so you can do all the things others have been dreaming of. By now your wife is used to not having a man about the house; the job has been done by a craftsman; the lawn has been mown by old Mr. Snooker and the accounts settled by her. If you do go fishing with your son, he can talk to you about his mother freely, for it is obvious that you get on very well with her; your daughter, during the nature ramble, will take you seriously, something daughters of landsmen rarely do.

The main advantage, so you'll discover, is that in the eyes of your children you will remain a member of your sex. To most landsmen's children, their parents are neuters with whom the Subject can never be discussed, as they obviously don't know what it's all about. Sailors' children talk much more freely to their fathers than to any land-bound parent; it may be that to be a sailor still has the halo of Don Juan. In any case, you should not destroy their illusion in either way: neither by being gentlemanly distant towards your wife in their presence, nor by being bewildered or shocked by confessions that would make you laugh in the messroom. Behave towards them the way you would towards your apprentice: as a man of the world.

On those conditions, I think you have a much better chance of being a good father than if you stayed home bending pokers, tearing telephone guides in half, and turning yourself into a neuter by saying, "When I was your age . . ." For the secret will be that you still are.

DEBTS

IT IS USELESS TO FIDDLE DEBTS AROUND ON PIECES OF PAPER, ADDING AND subtracting, until they are debts no longer. I saw these optimistic budgets strewn about many a captain's cabin when I was still a messroom-boy. The amount of correspondence and private notes a messroom-boy comes across while dusting is amazing.

To me, at the time, those budgets read like code-language. "Household Expenditure: cook, nurse, charwoman, gardener, milk, dairy produce, fishmonger, drinks, minerals, cleaning materials, etc. Insurances: personal, life, national health for four women, pier tolls, car hire, cigars, food, sundries, clothes, personal requirements, rates including water." On the next page, "Allowance for income tax: doctors? dentists? medicines? drinks?"

These cryptograms were followed by the same number in two different columns, after which the writer seemed to have given up. He did not seem to have reached any definite conclusion, for a few days later there would be the same budget, not quite as long, with piglets and manikins taking the place of the two equal numbers.

Still later, the budget would be reduced to a single amount, and then drafts for letters started to be hidden under the blotter. "Sir, I am sure you remember me after our pleasant meeting last August in the bowling alley of our dear home town." That was crossed out and replaced by, "Sir, I come to you with a request that may seem unusual, and I want to start by assuring you that I should never have written this letter if . . ." "If" usually turned into another piglet. So it would go on, step after step, towards the final draft, a couple of days before arriving in harbour. "Sir, I find myself faced with the urgent need of five thousand guilders. You may ask yourself why I address this letter to you. I should like to remind you of our pleasant meeting bowling. I can offer you my house, only partly mortgaged, and my wife's jewels as a security, amounting to a total value of fifteen thousand guilders. I can offer you a rate of interest of 5 per cent. Yours cordially, Master Mariner." The last step in the drafted correspondence would be the crossing out of "my wife's jewels," and the changing of "fifteen thousand guilders" into "ten thousand guilders," "5 per cent" into "6 per cent," and "Master Mariner" into "Captain." Among the cipherings an unfinished letter to "Darling" would get lost, starting "I have sad news for you. We cannot go on living at this rate. I have made many calculations . . ." Piglet. Finally there would be an unfinished letter addressed to a school for journalism. "Sirs, In answer to your advertisement in which you ask for true-to-life stories of drama and adventure . . ."

As a messroom-boy I found these letters funny. I have discovered since that borrowing is a bad solution, as it means continuing a train of life that is too expensive by making it more expensive. I have also discovered that a Master Mariner is always poorer than he thinks and richer than he knows. What I haven't discovered yet is how to stop fiddling debts around on pieces of paper, adding and subtracting until they are debts no longer.

ON DREAMS

ONE OF THE SURPRISING THINGS ABOUT GETTING OLDER AT SEA IS THAT THE dreams come back.

We all dreamed as children with frequent nightmares, after which we called for help and lay wailing in the darkness, waiting for the soft light of the opening door. Then came adolescence, in which dreams were rare and of a disturbing nature. Manhood is dreamless; but when summer's green riot of vitality brightens to the gold of fall, a new land of dreams is entered, where grey shapes graze placidly on pewter fields. The dreams of autumn are atmospheric rather than anecdotal. One dreams of a windjammer, rising silently out of the horizon into a tower that chills one with its shadow on passing, and all one hears is the solemn sound of a bell swung by the swell. On waking up, the windjammer has passed, its tower has sunk beyond the other horizon; yet the sea of the morning is still haunted by her memory. Children's dreams vanish to nothing on awakening; in late manhood the mood of the night will tinge the new day like a sunrise the clouds of dawn.

Of course, you have a wizard on board who will tell you exactly what

453

your dream means. A dark woman means an angry letter, a pig means money, a sleeping cat a slight illness to do with the throat, and a seagull joy connected with your children. There is a deeper meaning to your dreams, however, that only you yourself can interpret.

Dreams are thoughts waiting to be thought. When you get to your bridge and warm your hands around a mug of tea and stare across its brim at the sea, it is a good moment to reflect what thought it was that you have not allowed admission. The windjammer rising and sinking may have a meaning beyond the grasp of the cook's dreambook. Dreams are rarely hints of joys to come or disasters lurking; they are joys waiting within you, and disasters being built. The dreams of the sailor who is homeward bound on his life's voyage are the first birds that herald the shore. The best time of his life is yet to come, for he is approaching the shores of full humanity. Though his experiences in the future may be less strident and spectacular, they will be better than any he ever had.

As a boy, you may have seen the windjammer rise out of the horizon and been chilled by her shadow as she passed silently by; at that age, there was nothing but the momentary beauty. Now she passes you once more and guides your thoughts to the land towards which you are inexorably sailing. Her message is that if you can carry the peace and the marvel of the sea in your dreams, you will be able to carry it ashore.

Your dog too has dreams; when, later, you sit by the fireside and he lies asleep at your feet, he will run and yap and wag his tail in fields imaginary; but when he wakes up, he has nothing to tell. He may have been to China, the Levant, or Iceland's mystic shores; all he has been dreaming of is other dogs. You have been sailing in much the same way, until the windjammer rose for the second time within your soul.

So make the best of the years you have still to go, until your hand pulls the engine-room telegraph for the last time on "Finished with engines."

RETIREMENT

A GRIM EX-SEA-CAPTAIN ONCE DEFINED RETIREMENT AS "A JUG OF WINE, a loaf of bread, and thou knitting beside me in the wilderness."

Retirement may indeed turn into the reverse side of Omar Khayyám's moon, if its meaning is only negative. One has stopped working and so, there one sits, waiting, with an old love grown cold prating by one's side.

Retirement when looked at objectively is a sensible thing. To sail a ship one needs good eyes, a keen sense of hearing, an immense patience with other people's follies and a sharp eye for one's own. These faculties fade away with the years, and although the younger man is not necessarily better, he will certainly think he is. The time to retire is when one loses self-confidence to the extent that other people become indispensable. It is a safe bet that, when you are about to retire, you have found during the last few years a favourite bosun or an excellent young mate. They are the angels at the head of your bed who once stood at its foot.

Retirement, if taken as a reward for a lifetime of hard work and necessary privation, is attractive. For to stand there with a chilly feeling in the hollow of one's throat because of the wind, eyebrows puckered to aid one's hearing and ears drawn back to see more clearly, is not a healthy state of affairs. Your perfect bosun has no business to be that perfect, and it is high time the brilliant young mate became a captain himself. If sailing is necessary to mankind, as you once so proudly said to your fiancée, now is the time to prove it.

So, up anchor for the last time, get the funeral voyage over with, which, to your surprise, will move your staff and crew much more than it does yourself, then go down the gangway waving back from its far end as you once expected your good passengers to do.

Well, there she is. So far, she has only been a pen-pal, who almost got her babies by a correspondence course. The children have come and gone, and life is curiously reversed: yours is no longer a union blessed with issue, but with the departure of its issue. You and she are at last what you have always wanted to be, ever since you trod on her toes in the ballroom for the first time and had to take her to the wall for conversation. You are alone. During your whole life together so far, you have never been alone, even if there was no one else in the bedroom. Now you are, and surely you have something better to offer her than a jug of wine, a loaf of bread, and boredom born from silence. For you should realise one thing clearly: when, after you have waved your farewell to the sea, you go down the gangway to meet her, you are going down the aisle.

THE LITTLE HOME

WHEN ALL IS SAID AND DONE, THE HOME YOU COME BACK TO TO LIVE IN FOR the rest of your life is not yours but your wife's. It is the one price the sailor has to pay for his lifelong absence.

During the first month or so, you'll feel caged or lost, this depends on the season. At first, you will think how lovely it is to be there and share the joy of a house that has been the setting for so many of your dreams. Then you will discover that you are a guest in somebody else's.

You'll discover it in small things. Wiping your feet, for instance. You have rarely wiped your feet on board, because it wasn't necessary and because there was a steward. You'll sorely feel the lack of your steward, whose presence became so much a part of your existence that you forgot what he did for you. During your shore-leaves, you may not have wiped your feet either, but your wife never mentioned it because you were going away again soon. Now you'll have to change your little habits, for this is a home, not a ship.

You will come to realise, with hurt amazement, that your wife has a much lower opinion of ships than she has so far led you to believe. There is an element of victory in her disdain of ships, which, if you think about it, is quite justified. So, in my opinion, the best solution is to take her for a holiday as soon as you arrive.

Take her as far away as you can, even if you have been dreaming of sinking into your armchair, stretching out your slippered feet and not moving for the next year. Your home-coming-for-keeps is a difficult period to get through, and your only salvation lies in postponing it until your wife and you come home together. Take her to a place where neither of you have ever been, like the mountains. You should, on no account, take her to the seaside. A small bungalow on the shores of a little lake will do, as long as the lake is little and fills you with a faint repulsion. To her, it will be the sea, and your lack of interest in it will do her more good than an expensive present.

On coming back to the little home, together with her, you will find that you will become interested in it. You will do jobs about the house, which never are the jobs she wants you to do. This is just a natural state of things which can easily be arranged by taking care of the jobs she indicates as well, however impractical they may be. You may think of major improvements to the home, but I must advise you strongly against them. For, although they may be improvements, they will also be changes which, in your wife's eyes, are sad. This goes for the most unlikely things, like black paint in an ill-lit room that you want to change to white. On board ship, you have come to believe in white hard gloss, whereas it will make your wife think of a hospital. Women consider rooms cosy in direct proportion to their darkness. That is why they like to turn out the lights the moment the fire in the grate produces a flame. You must realise that this is a result of her job, much as your preference for glaring white is a result of yours.

456

Rooms in which jobs are done by others must be light, whereas the blessing of darkness is that one doesn't feel guilty when idle.

Evenings by the fireside are wonderful on your wife's conditions. She will talk and be happy, and you can close your eyes and look contented, whereas with the lights on you'll look disinterested.

Then the spring will come and, looking for something to do, you will think about growing roses.

AGAINST ROSES

THE MOMENT YOU FIND YOURSELF THINKING ABOUT ROSES, TAKE HEED, FOR anything to do with roses in connection with a retired sailor is nonsense. You have never grown a rose in your life and there is no point in starting to do so now. Your sailor's existence, which has taken the major part of your life's span, has prepared you in no way whatever to become a rose-grower. Your wife will undoubtedly mention roses. She will tempt you with catalogues, showing dream-flowers, with such legends as "Lady D'Arcy-Smith, late blooming, fares better in a pot than against the wall."

Well, if she feels like growing roses, let her. But be a spectator yourself, a slow delighted ambler past the fragrant bushes full of lice, blight, caterpillars, mildew, cancer and the bends. (I don't know what the disease is called that manages to make rosebuds look like the insides of walnuts.) As you bend over one of the more healthy blooms, behave as if you were smelling something nice, make the sound that you use to reassure her that a steak is well done, but let each rose you sniff at whisper, "Remember you are a sailor."

This is the important point. Although you will never sail the sea again, you are a sailor and you will remain one as long as you live. In other words, if your wife does not have any visions of the back patch as a bower of roses in which you'll be condemned to gossip and drink tea until your ultimate sob, turn the back patch into a shipyard. In the chapter about lifeboats, I have mentioned how a redundant sloop bought at an auction can mean the difference to you between senility and the spiritual renaissance which turns old age back into childhood without its disadvantages. If you can lay hands on a clumsy craft like that, construct inside and atop the old lifeboat the little bower your wife has been dreaming of. The ship should contain a little cockpit to sit in when the sun shines; the superstructure should have big windows, where your wife can hang lace curtains, and little shelves for geraniums on the window-sills. There should be a settee on either side and a folding table between. Out front, a lavatory and a little kitchen.

A boat like this is cheaper than even the most measly rose-garden in the long run, and will enable you to explore the forgotten world of the inland waterways, their silence, their peace, their reflections of clouds, little islands and placid barges. You will also do your wife the enormous service of giving her the chance to play with a really big doll's house, a thing she has been secretly longing to do ever since her third Christmas. Everything on board, so you'll find once she has furnished it, will be a miniature: doll's table, doll's tea-set, doll's stove; and if you are a handyman, fix her a spring-driven cuckoo-clock. Cuckoo-clocks with pendulums will stop when the boat rocks.

Christen the boat with both your names, or abbreviations of them, so if she is called Ivy and you are called John, make it *Ivyjohn*. Care should be taken that her name or its abbreviation come first, or you'll be wondering for days what on earth is the matter with her this time.

You now have the ideal means to turn your old age as a couple into something young and promising. I must give one warning though that is all important, or the promise will come to naught: you must under no circumstance or provocation bully her because you are a sailor, for you'll make her feel that she is only your cook. The word "sea-cook" lies only just below the threshold of a woman's consciousness, and will pop out in a scathing sense at the oddest moments. If, for instance, she fastens the aft hawser to a tree with a bow and you should say, to use its gentlest form, "No, no, not that way," the word "sea-cook" is sure to flash like forked lightning out of the clouds of her ensuing depression. Leave the bow as it is; if you can reach the stage of hypocrisy in which a man says, "Splendid" while wincing, so much the better. Also do not get irritated if, even after months of sedate cruising, she does not know one end of the boat from the other. Women will talk about "out front" when they mean "aft" for the simple reason that to them the entrance to the cabin is the front door. Don't try to correct this, you'll only make her bewildered and unhappy. Let her potter around inside to her heart's content; enjoy the rain with her, for women adore the sound of pattering drops on the roof as long as it doesn't leak, and they are really happiest if the windows are steamed over. Then you will be submitted to that endless stream of talk that cartoonists have tried to make you consider as irritating, but which is more peaceful than the babbling of the wavelets against your bow, or the tapping of the rope against the flagstaff. When the tea-kettle starts to sing and you become conscious of the relentless ticking of the cuckoo-clock, pecking

458

at the rock of time, you'll know what happiness is, and realise that you owe it all to her.

Even if you don't, say it, and you'll hear something soon that you haven't heard since your honeymoon: a woman's voice singing in the kitchen, while chopping parsley for your favourite dish.

Any fool can grow roses.

LIFE IN A LAND-BOUND COMMUNITY

THE FIRST THING THAT WILL STRIKE YOU ABOUT LIVING IN A LAND-BOUND community is that gales are much more frequent. A breeze that has delighted you as a tailwind and caused trouble only with the ventilators of the stoke-hold is ashore described as a storm. People accost you in the streets, holding their coats together at their throats, and ask you if you have ever known anything like it at sea. The grocer's wife, jolly and rotund behind the counter, will say, "Shut the door, dear," when you come in for a bottle of salad-oil and a pack of matches; and as she worms a new cork into the bottle with a rabbit-like squeak, she will say, "Now aren't you lucky not to be at sea any longer? Listen to the chimney."

Breezes called gales are the symbols of life in a land-bound community. If you say to those who accost you, "Don't be silly" or "You make me sick," as you may feel inclined to do, realise that this will support the landsman's conviction that old sea-captains are "grumpy." I know an ex-sea-captain in the Isle of Wight, who became grumpy and ostracised because he burst into laughter on reading a banner-headline in the Isle of Wight County Press: "Water-spout Ploughs across the Island; Canary Dies of Fright." The right way to react to the meteorological comments of those around you is to say, "Isn't it?" or "You said it" or "This is nothing to what is about to come." This last phrase, though not to be used regularly, will raise your popularity, for land-bound communities adore prophecies of storms, floods and disasters. If these do not come, you will be treated like the rain-maker in African tribes: any disaster not materialising has been averted by you.

Jumble-sales are another thing to be approached with care. When the vicar turns up rubbing his hands, inhales deeply through the nose and says: "Commodore, you are the very man I have been waiting for," brace yourself. He will ask you for quaint souvenirs or little objects of foreign art, to be sold at the Garden Fête next spring, weather permitting. Give him something from the attic, but go carefully here. I once witnessed one of these meetings, in which the ex-sailor produced a Papuan male adornment with a red plume on top from a cupboard. The vicar looked at it with round eyes, asked what it was, and while the blushing sailor stammered something about "trusses," the vicar's face brightened. He cried, "Of course! I played one as a student," pulled out the plume and blew the object like a hunting horn. It produced a sound which nearly brought the flabbergasted sailor to his knees.

When the Garden Fête eventually occurs, you will be asked to take charge of either the fortune-telling tent or the treasure hunt. You should keep clear of both assignments. You will not be able to resist the temptation of hinting at what everybody knows when you tell fortunes, and the treasure hunt under your direction will turn into a punitive drill.

Remain a stroller and a buyer, and if a lady advances on you crying, "Aren't you Squire Hammond of Little Nook?" don't answer, "Quite the reverse." Answer: "I am afraid not. But I know whom you mean. Isn't he a charming person?"

In short, when you come home to live among them, treat all your neighbours as if they were passengers. This will make them treat you as a captain, which is what you want.

LECTURING TO NAVAL PUPILS

IF YOU ARE ASKED TO GIVE A LECTURE TO THE PUPILS OF YOUR OLD NAVAL college, accept the invitation. Not only will it be a welcome change to both the pupils and yourself, you will find the experience gratifying. For here is the dear old school, where once you were so desperately bored, and whose officers were examples of authority and knowledge that you have never been able to equal. You'll relish seeing it all again: the ivy on the house of the commander whose wife was called Electric Lisa; the training ship in the courtyard with its female figurehead which only the bosun was allowed to scrub; the fencing-hall surrounded by the row of little lockers with numbers on them, and the fan-shaped display of foreign swords over the doors.

You will be surprised how little has changed. Only, everything will seem much smaller, including the new commander's wife who will now be called something else. The commander himself, to say nothing of the officers, will be a mere youngster whose rotundity inspires dietetic thoughts rather than awe. The training ship, whose masts once soared to dizzying heights, will look as bare and as stumpy as a playing-tree in a monkey's pen in the zoo. You will also be surprised by the youth of the pupils. In your memory, you were a man; once you stand facing yourself multiplied three hundred times in the fencing-hall, you will feel like hugging them all. Now comes your lecture.

The commander will have introduced you with some flatulence and made you frown by his clumsy hints at the Ancient Mariner. Remember, if you listen to him at all, that the only old man in the room is he. Your lecture itself should not start with what you have written down. It should start by an expression of your feelings. Remember your own evenings of being lectured at in the past, and you will recall that the secret is a conversational tone and no paper. The moment someone brought out notes and spectacles, boredom had settled before he opened his mouth. Say, "In my time, she was called Electric Lisa." Then turn to the young woman with the matronly bosom by the commander's side with your radiant smile and say, "Sorry, madam." If you make them laugh within the first minute, you are home and can start enjoying yourself. If you have not actually smuggled chocolate in your time, or put embarrassing questions during catechism, invent them. Among the three hundred facing you and sizing you up, there are two hundred and fifty who have. For once, you can let yourself go with your stories; the commander cannot interrupt you, as he has sawn off his own legs in his introduction, and you are not here to please the commander but the pupils and yourself, which amounts to the same thing.

If you have films or lantern-slides to show, take care not to fall off the rostrum as you step backwards explaining them with your face to the screen. Show them the Boro Budur and the Taj Mahal with your wife climbing up the ancient steps, wearing a topi. They will love it and their laughter is benevolent. If you have films in which aboriginal ladies lack certain garments, they will love them too. In short, have a high old time in which you do everything except lecturing them.

LETTERS TO THE EDITOR

AS A CAPTAIN, YOU HAD TIME TO READ THE PAPERS, AND YOU WILL OCCASIONally have felt the urge to write to the editor. The subjects may have varied, but they had always to do with ships and the sea. It is unlikely that you have actually written those letters, for on board ship one doesn't take letters to the editor as seriously as one does ashore.

Take, for instance, the matter of whether the wireless-operator shall be called "Wireless-Operator" or "Radio Officer." On board ship, he is "Wireless-Operator" and the hell with him; but ashore, you will be filled with indignation at reading the word "Wireless-Operator" and feel like writing to the editor that he should be called "Radio Officer."

I advise you to write this letter, and to feel no regrets that you haven't done so before. Had you written this letter while still afloat, your relationship with the wireless-operator would have deteriorated, owing to the false presumption on the latter's part that you were interested in him. Now that you are safely separated from him by an unknown number of nautical miles his image will have become rosy with distance, and both you and the wireless-operators of the world will be the better for your intervention.

You will find ample cause for letter-writing in your daily paper the moment the land-lubbers start writing about the sea. No editor knows the difference between "to heave to" and "to lie to." Neither do they know whether a vessel is a boat or a ship, or whether a lifeboat is a row-boat, a rowing-boat, a launch, a sloop, or a dinghy. Tell them the difference in an amusing fashion, and sign your letter, "Extra-master." For some reason, this reads better to the housewives and invalids who are your readers than "Master mariner" or "Captain, Retd."

If your cat has had fourteen kittens, ask your editor if this is a record. If you don't think the weather is influenced by the atomic bomb, state it, and if it is your opinion that church-bells should keep silent until a reasonable hour on Sunday mornings, tell him; but always do so in your quality of "Extra-master" and not just as any quarrelsome old gent. It is surprising what respect your opinion will evoke if you reveal your sailorly past, whether the subject be dogs fouling the sidewalk or how to fry crisp bacon.

Once you have seen the first of your letters in print, you will wait eagerly for another occasion. This will present itself in due course, and the only rule to observe is that a letter written at first impulse should be kept for a couple of nights in a drawer, then written again, and re-written. It will get shorter in the process; a fair portion of the letters will get so short that they are no longer worth sending. This does not matter, for the importance lies in the writing itself. Whether you are printed or not will become immaterial to you in the end; and that is the point to aim at.

Because at your age, many subjects will reveal themselves as being unsuspectedly related, your writing of a letter to the editor on the phases of Venus may well be the beginning of a little volume called *An Old Sailor's Reflections*, which is the way some of our finest literature started, even if it was never finished on this side of the great unknown.

THOUGHTS ON IMMORTALITY

NO MAN EVER FEELS COMPLETELY ADJUSTED. HE MAY FEEL AT EASE, YET there is always the small gnawing doubt that he may be living in a fool's paradise. If you meet someone who, with a contented sigh and a radiant look around his cabin, parlour or potato-field, says, "God, I'm happy," all he wants is your confirmation.

After your retirement, and once you are firmly rooted in dotage, there is a sure way of knowing if you are indeed well adjusted for the first time in your life. You are so the moment the thought occurs to you that immortality is unimportant.

You will not believe it if you read these lines too early, and you shouldn't, for it is a discovery one makes only at the end of the road. There are, at first, the young man's thoughts on immortality, when he will think that it is unimportant as well. He will think so like a child drawing the same modern picture as Picasso does. There is a difference of a lifetime between the two similar conceptions.

With the bald patch, the reading-spectacles and the early morning lassitude, come the series of conceptions of immortality that mankind has gone through over the ages. Plato's immortality in one's children, Christianity's immortality of the soul, Voltaire's immortality of the garden and the book. Only when the world has come to consider you as useless will you find that the hour of your final adjustment to life is at hand.

You will think on simpler lines and with more lucidity than before. You are at last rid of ambitions, tensions and unimportant worries; you will at last live in a house you do not want to change, and perhaps sail a little boat that you do not want to improve. So life will at last be the present, instead of being only the unfulfilled future. The notion will dawn on you that everything is part of everything else, that man is part of mankind as the sailor is part of a crew. So you will approach the conception of immortality shared by the great mystics of history. Your inner peace and fondness for mankind will make you consider immortality as unimportant.

For who are you, to think that no ship will sail any more after you are gone? Yet there is something in the thought that, however slightly, it is due to you that they are still sailing. So, to achieve that happy state of complete fulfilment, go to the cliffs, sit down and watch them go; for there goes your immortality.

AFTER YOU HAVE LECTURED, SHOWN YOUR FILMS, TOLD YOUR ANECDOTES, written to the editor of your newspaper, and thought your thoughts on immortality, the moment will come when the last question will rise from the wintry mist: "Dear God, what is the meaning of it all?"

Much depends on where the question occurs to you. If it is on board your converted lifeboat moored to the willows in the reeds, and you sit smoking your pipe while waiting for a fish silly enough to bite, the chances are that you need only look at the horizon to know the answer, or, at least, to let the question sail overhead like a cloud. If it strikes you on a rainy day, when you are looking out of the window at the wet street and Mrs. Morrison hurrying past with her umbrella, you will be tempted to answer the question with "Nothing."

These two situations suggest that the question is an old one, asked by every living soul who watched the dusk gather and the leaves fall, and that your answer will be influenced by your mood of the moment. If you can carry the mood of the reeds and the lake within you until you sit behind the steamed window, gazing morosely at tripping Mrs. Morrison, you will have got as far as you are ever likely to get.

Some people find comfort in the hope that, once their souls have set sail like the ancient explorers, they may alight on a distant shore, where old friends and animals they loved are waiting for their arrival. It is a comforting thought, but you may come to doubt it at moments, and it is those moments you must be prepared for.

Give up the hope of ever reaching land, and remember the joy of being alone at sea. You are fortunate among mortals; for, alone on your bridge on the ocean of the past, you have known happiness. You may find the same happiness on the longest voyage of all.

If this is your hope, and not the land beyond the horizon, you will brighten the darkness of human despair with a spark of the light of the sea.

HOW TO PAINT A SUNSET

THE TIME WILL COME WHEN YOU WILL BE ALONE, EXCEPT FOR A DOG. THAT IS the time to paint a sunset.

When you were even a little younger, you would not have believed that a sunset is not only worth looking at from beginning to end, but invites the relaxed observer to catch the secret of its glory on a piece of three-ply with a child's box of paints.

To paint a sunset on the sea's horizon is a joy. For one thing, it is easy. A sunset over a forest will get you into trouble with the trees, and lots of people have done it before without conveying anything but a sunset over a forest. Sunset over the sea is different, for the sea is yours and the sunset is yours also.

Don't go in for fancy colours. Just draw a horizontal line across the paper, fill the top half with the sunset and the bottom half with the sea. If you use enough water on the former, the latter will, of its own accord, produce the reflection. Part of the joy of all this is, so you will find, that you don't care a fig what anybody thinks of your sunset.

When the picture is finished, which it will be once it is too dark to see, and you sit waiting for it to dry, you will wonder what gives you the feeling that something is lacking. Don't try any other colours; not only will they spoil the picture, they'll look different in the daylight. Take your finest brush, don't make it too wet, dip it lightly in the black, and paint, inside the yolk of your creation, two masts, a funnel and the thin black line of a ship that has almost sailed out of sight.

JAN DE HARTOG

Jan de Hartog was born in Haarlem, Holland, in 1914, and ran off to sea at an early age. In 1940, just after the Germans occupied Holland, his novel *Holland's Glory* was published, a rollicking story of the Dutch ocean-going tugboats on which he had served. Although it mentioned neither the war nor the Germans, it became a symbol of Dutch defiance and was banned by the Nazis, but not until 300,000 copies had been sold. The author escaped to England, by "the long trail": via Belgium, France and Spain, a journey of six months during which he was imprisoned five times, crashed with a plane and was wounded by rifle bullets as he crossed the Spanish border.

Since then, Mr. de Hartog has sailed many miles and has written a goodly number of books. In addition to the three collected in this volume, they are *The Little Ark, The Spiral Road, The Inspector, Waters of the New World, The Artist* and *The Hospital*. *The Hospital* told the true story of a difficult but ultimately successful attempt by the author and a small group of fellow Quakers to change conditions of squalor and neglect in a large American charity hospital.

Mr. de Hartog's name has also become a familiar one through the great popularity of his plays, *The Fourposter* and *Skipper Next to God*. Three of his novels have also been made into films: *The Distant Shore* as *The Key, The Inspector* as *Lisa,* and *The Spiral Road*.